THE AURELIAN'S FIRESIDE COMPANION

An Entomological Anthology

Paphia Publishing Ltd
2005

'BRETHREN OF THE NET'
Albert Harry Hamm M.A., F.L.S., F.R.E.S. (1861-1951)

Albert Hamm left school at the age of twelve to help his father, who was a
printer. Natural history was a lifelong interest and most of his early pocket
money was spent on store boxes and collecting equipment. Although he was
almost totally self-educated, he was said to show 'powers of observation
which rivalled the great masters of the past'. In 1942 Oxford University
recognized his achievements by making him an honorary M.A.

THE AURELIAN'S
FIRESIDE COMPANION

AN ENTOMOLOGICAL ANTHOLOGY

Michael A. Salmon, F.R.E.S.

&

Peter J. Edwards, F.R.E.S.

Additional research and material by

Alec S. Harmer

Original illustrations by

Tim Bernhard

Paphia Publishing Ltd
2005

Published by 🦋 Paphia Publishing Ltd
Covertside, Sway Road, Lymington, Hampshire SO41 8NN, England

The Aurelian's Fireside Companion: An Entomological Anthology
Original text © Michael A. Salmon and Peter J. Edwards, 2005

Edited by Alec S. Harmer
Designed by Paphia Publishing Ltd

Original illustrations and dustjacket by Tim Bernhard
and copyright of Paphia Publishing Ltd

© 2005 Paphia Publishing Ltd

Text set in Baskerville Classico
by Printwise of Lymington, Hampshire, England
Colour reproduction by Printwise of Lymington
Printed and bound by Butler & Tanner, Somerset, England

British Library Cataloguing-in-Publication Data
A catalogue record for this book is available from the British Library

ISBN 0 9537236 1 5

This anthology is dedicated to the memory of our fellow
'brethren of the net' — Edward Newman, Henry T. Stainton
and James W. Tutt — and to those other lepidopterists
whose ardour has not yet evaporated.

This is number 553 of 1000 copies printed in April 2005

During the last fifty years, the mildly eccentric web of entomologists has shown us that international co-operation, worldwide, is not only possible and friendly, but agreeable and productive. Between us there are stoutly held views, but no wars, suicide bombers, bayonets or strikes and unfeeling cruelties, only convictions on matters such as the classification of butterflies or on our affinity with chimpanzees.

Miriam Rothschild, D.B.E., F.R.S.
Ashton Wold (2004)

Some years ago I played the part of a dentist, who also collected butterflies, in the popular television comedy — 'Butterflies'. My father, as a boy, had been a keen collector and I grew up admiring his beautiful mahogany butterfly cabinet and can see his Swallowtails and Purple Emperors even now. Although shamefully ignorant, I have always had an interest in the subject and was fortunate to be in Mexico with the BBC Natural History Unit when they filmed the migration of the Monarch butterfly — a quite wonderful experience.

Geoffrey Palmer, O.B.E.
Buckinghamshire (2004)

Scarcely is this boxed, when a gorgeous butterfly rushes out of the gloom into the shade, and in a moment is seen to be a novelty; then comes the excitement of pursuit; the disappointment of seeing it dance over a thicket out of sight; the joy of finding it reappear; the tantalizing trial of watching the lovely wings flapping just out of reach; the patient waiting for it to descend; the tiptoe approach as we see it settle on a flower; the breathless eagerness with which the net is poised; and the triumphant flush with which we gaze on its loveliness when held in the trembling fingers.

Philip Henry Gosse
The Romance of Natural History (1860)

TABLE OF CONTENTS

LIST OF ILLUSTRATIONS

COLOUR PLATES

TEXT FIGURES

TEXT ILLUSTRATIONS

All illustrations are by Tim Bernhard except for the engravings reproduced from *An Illustrated Natural History of British Butterflies and Moths* by Edward Newman. The Latin names are those used in the articles illustrated; those currently employed are listed in the Appendix.

FOREWORD

What is it about butterflies that creates such a strong sense of nostalgia — that irresistible combination of sweetness and pain? Maybe their association with childhood nature rambles in those summer days of long ago, or perhaps because vast swarms of butterflies are now so rarely seen and we all regret it. Vladimir Nabokov, that great exponent of sensuous writing, had a more original theory: collecting and chasing butterflies was a spine-tingling pleasure, comparable only with creative writing. 'The spine knows best,' he wrote. We may see with our eyes and read with our brains, 'but the seat of artistic delight is between the shoulder blades'. That 'little shiver behind' is the truest form of emotion; we all recognize it, and we all remember it: the spine has a long memory.

If we follow Nabokov in considering that literature and collecting butterflies are the twin peaks of human experience, then what can we say about the literarture of butterfly collecting? Perhaps an obvious starting point is the poetry of the names of butterflies and moths. The great Aurelians of eighteenth-century London, among the first in the world to study butterflies scientifically, clearly had a natural affinity with words. Classically educated, they lent their hitherto un-named butterflies the names of sprites, nymphs and shepherds — *arion, galathea, lucina* and the rest — with exactly the light, airy quality of their diaphanous subjects. They showed the same sureness of touch with the English names. We may have forgotten what 'admiral' and 'fritillary' meant, or what colour or shade was meant by 'high brown', but no-one has seriously suggested changing them. When we behold the unimaginative, if not plain ugly, names given to less fortunate insects by their modern successors, I think we should be grateful to those distant, poetical naturalists in their satin coats and wigs. *Floreat Aureliana*!

But for all the emotion that Nabokov and others have recognized in the pursuit of butterflies, real butterfly literature is sparse and elusive. Of course, there are lots of books about butterflies — never more than today when nearly every English county has its own field guide. If anyone wants to look something up there are plenty of places to go to find out times of appearance, or where to see a rare species, or to marvel at the skill of butterfly artists like Richard Lewington or Donald Russwurm. But this is not literature in the Nabokovian sense (it is closer to his sense of 'pure science'), for it leaves out the space from which literature is formed — in the happy meeting place, or hunting ground, between people and butterflies. Encounters with butterflies deserve quite as much attention as the details of the spots on a wing, or the botanical preference of a particular caterpillar, as our authors Michael Salmon and Peter Edwards make clear. In this book you will find a gallimaufry of spine-tingling moments garnered from old journals and other reminiscences. For anyone who loves butterflies and moths (herein treated as honorary butterflies) there is much here to browse and dip into, ideally in a comfortable armchair by the fireside in winter. It is sure to delight and entertain the Aurelian in all of us, but will also remind us tinglingly of pleasant days gone by and, one hopes, pleasant encounters to come.

It is as well that the journals of the nineteenth century were less exclusive of anecdotes and stories than their super-scientific successors. Entomology seems to teem with good stories that never get written down. Salmon and Edwards have a good eye for the quaint, the bizarre, and the amusing; the things that make butterfly collectors stand out a little from the common crowd. And part of the fun is that most of them had no idea that their behaviour was at all unusual. For instance, there is the one about the wealthy collector who drank a toast to every specimen he caught and was eventually taken home snoring in the back of the Rolls by his long-suffering chauffeur. Or the man who fed all the 'dull brown and grey' moths to the chickens, assuming his friend would only care for the pretty ones. We are vouchsafed glimpses of personalities like the immortal Baron de Worms emerging bedraggled from the swamp roaring, 'I've got *pallustris*! I've got *pallustris*!' Or the clown Grimaldi, presenting 'Dartford Blues' to the no doubt delighted mistress of the king. And we hear from the man who caught 800 Pale Clouded Yellows: he explains that there were in fact three collectors and it took them three weeks to amass the said number, though that is still far more than the total number to visit Britain in the past fifty years! I for one will never look at the Meadow Brown in the same light again since learning that the profile of a famous Victorian statesman appears on some specimens — what a collection that would be: a portrait gallery revealed in the wings of a butterfly!

There are snapshots of collectors having the usual adventures — falling into fen lodes, arrested as spies or lunatics, and so on. We can gauge the truth of Nabokov's saying that entomologists are the gentlest of people until roused by some taxonomic problem or doubtful record, when they dip their pens in the acid bottle. We learn that over-collecting was a matter of some controversy as early as 1875: not so much because individual collectors did much harm but because the sport was getting too popular. As the wife of Commander Harper noted, among the fraternity were senior servicemen, doctors, clergymen (there's a butterfly-collecting canon in *Barchester Towers*) 'and even an occasional Prime Minister'. Above all, we are reminded of those sometimes exhilarating — sometimes exhausting or disappointing — times, chasing over the downs after Clouded Yellows, peering at palings in the cold morning light for Rannoch Sprawlers (something I once did amongst new-fallen snow while learning to ski), and getting a crick in the neck scanning the tree-tops for Purple Emperors.

Some people, Nabokov realized, are oblivious to butterflies. Perhaps there are fewer people than before who are likely to be brought into sympathetic communication by a drawer of dead insects. But for those of us who did feel the spark, be it ever so many years ago, I am sure this book of 'strange facts and strange adventures' will strike a chord.

My own memories of collecting butterflies as a child are oddly intense. I remember those books of bad advice, like slipping dead insects into paper triangles — and trying to relax them afterwards. I recall the seeming impossibility of setting Brimstones without snapping the costal vein, or of coaxing a small moth to look right without making a hole in the wing. But most of all I remember the living butterflies: the velvet-winged Camberwell Beauties gliding through the glade on our spring holiday in the Alpes Maritimes; the Orange-tips fluttering along the village lanes; the stunning lustrous blue of the Adonis Blues on the downs where the Channel terminus now stands; and that Small Blue without the smallest spot on its underside that I saw plainly but could not catch, and would dismiss as a dream now had I not the diary record to prove it. I remember the first time I really noticed butterflies on a family holiday in North Wales. We chased the Peacocks and caught the browns and whites in our cupped hands. And I remember my father (my companion and guide on all those early collecting trips) haring off down a lane as though a Monarch or Camberwell Beauty had descended on us from butterfly heaven. 'What was it?' we cried, as he returned from his quarter-mile sprint. 'Was it a Purple Emperor?' 'Well no,' he replied, 'it was only another Peacock . . . but one of exceptional size and speed!' he added, defiantly.

A long time has passed since one chased after Peacocks. But I'm forever grateful to the butterflies for awakening a passion for nature and wildlife, and carrying it into the future. The ways in which we bring butterflies into our lives may have changed over the years, but their presence has always been a blessing.

This fascinating book not only brings a lost world to our attention, it is a reminder that entomology is more than science. It is an intensely human world with its own customs, ideals, language and folklore. To understand why butterflies matter we should look not only out-of-doors but inwards to our own firesides.

Peter Marren,
Ramsbury, Wiltshire. 2005

PREFACE

The year 1937 was a good one for Clouded Yellows — not an '*edusa* year',* it is true, but a year when many of the clover fields in southern England seemed to come alive with these dancing yellow butterflies. It was during that year that Dr Philip Bertram Murray Allan first endeared himself to British lepidopterists by publishing *A Moth-Hunter's Gossip*, the forerunner of his quartet of best-selling and heart-warming volumes. During the dark war years scores of butterfly hunters were able to read and re-read this book, many snatching odd minutes to delve into it, between meals, between air-raids, or while helping the nation to fight the foe. Some regarded the book and its wartime successor, *Talking of Moths* (1943), as bedtime reading at its very best. Two post-war volumes were to follow: *Moths and Memories* (1948) and the posthumous *Leaves from a Moth-Hunter's Notebook* (1980). Overnight, P. B. M. Allan became established as one of the butterfly hunter's best-loved authors. However, with the publication of these last two volumes, the series came to an end. When Allan died in 1973, it effectively marked the end of an era. Now that he had passed on to that 'great relaxing-tin in the sky', as he so charmingly would have put it, a veritable chasm had opened up. Butterfly hunters were left without any prospect of a sequel to the Allan quartet; indeed, during the past quarter of a century nothing remotely similar in context to these four books has been published. So, it is with this in mind, and without attempting in any way to copy the Allan style, that we have assembled this anthology. We feel sure that the spirit of P. B. M. A. would approve of its contents, and that many of the quotations used would have amused him or certainly stimulated his legendary powers of critical analysis.

William Fox Talbot, one of the earliest pioneers of photography, once wrote: 'The book of nature is always open winter and summer and is always within reach, and the print is legible if we have eyes to read it. But most persons are too preoccupied to have their attention arrested by it.' Although not aimed directly at any one group of persons, these words effectively introduce a very remarkable group of individuals — the entomologists — whose attention has rarely been so preoccupied, and within whose ranks are the butterfly hunters and collectors. What were they really like? Their articles and letters tell us that they were anything but dull. Some were splendidly eccentric and others dilettante. Most of them were incredibly hardworking and totally committed to the study of their beloved butterflies and moths.

We have spent many leisure hours reading through back numbers of the various British entomological journals, back as far as the first issue of *The Entomological Magazine* in 1833. While reading these it became immediately apparent that there were literally hundreds of articles, notes and letters that by virtue of their eccentricity, wit or curiosity begged inclusion in an anthology such as this. The problem was — which ones should we include? The choice was never going to be easy, but after due consideration we selected two hundred articles — and then added a handful more for good measure. Each of these merited inclusion because of its special interest. Some made us smile, or perhaps raise an eyebrow; some told us of new discoveries, while others claimed to have debunked ancient theories or established practice. We soon got to know a number of butterfly hunters rather well and came to regard them as

---

**edusa year: a year in which spectacular numbers of the Clouded Yellow butterfly migrate to our shores. Such years occur about once in a decade. The old Latin name for this butterfly was *Colias edusa* Fab.

particular friends; their articles turned up repeatedly. We had no hesitation in making room for articles by such well-known lepidopterists as J. W. Douglas, Henry Stainton, and J. W. Tutt from the nineteenth century; and Margaret Fountaine, Henry Rowland-Brown, F. W. Frohawk, E. B. Purefoy and P. B. M. Allan himself from the modern era.

There are a number of articles on entomology in the trenches during both the Great and Second World Wars. We found it remarkable that men subdued by the stress of warfare should have been not only able to note the butterflies and moths around them, but also to actually sit down and record their observations at a later date. We especially remembered Major-General 'Kit' Lipscomb: even in the midst of intense artillery bombardment he was still able to admire the freshness and beauty of the Black Hairstreak that alighted in the trench where he was sheltering.

Our chosen butterfly hunters are an eclectic bunch. Some have hidden behind a soubriquet such as '*Omega*', '*An Old Moth-Hunter*', '*Two Old Hands*', or just '*D.T.B.*'. Others have added titles, honours, degrees and the letters of various learned societies to their names. Among their ranks are numerous clergymen, high-ranking soldiers and medical men; most, however, were less exalted. One thing soon became apparent: whatever their calling or mode of address, butterfly hunters all seem to speak with the same enthusiastic voice, and we came to the immediate conclusion that these individuals spent much of their working day and doubtless most of their sleeping hours dreaming of the 'delightful pastime'. Indeed, some would clearly have sacrificed everything to spend most of each day roaming the countryside with net and killing bottle. We were humbled by the sheer dedication and stamina some of these Aurelians exhibited in the pursuit of their hobby. How many of us, nowadays, would be prepared to walk eighty miles home after a successful collecting trip, as indeed did H. J. Harding in his quest for the Swallowtail at Whittlesea Mere in the early decades of the nineteenth century? Or, perhaps, the between performance excursions made by the nineteenth-century clown Grimaldi on foot from Sadler's Wells down into Kent in the early morning hours for the 'Dartford Blue' — a round trip of thirty miles — on three consecutive nights?

Other than having taken the opportunity to correct some of the more obvious typographical errors and to standardize the odd journal reference here and there, we have as far as possible stayed faithful to the articles as originally published. For the purposes of this book, however, some of them have been adapted to make them more reader friendly. To have included lengthy lists of Latin names, of captures made or species found, would have been against the spirit of this anthology, and because of this we had no hesitation in removing them. Similarly, the authors of the Latin names have been omitted except where originally included. The contemporary Latin names that appeared in the original articles have been retained, but to assist the reader the common English name has usually been included. Again, with the reader in mind and for the purpose of clarification, we have adopted the slightly unconventional approach of using bold print to help identify our contribution from those of the authors of the original articles and quotations.

Since the Second World War, attitudes towards the collecting of butterflies have hardened. Conservation issues directed towards saving the countryside and its fauna from urbanization have given the collector a bad name. Consequently, the number of active lepidopterists in this country has dropped to an all-time low. Back in the mid-Victorian era, Henry Stainton, editor of the *Entomologist's Annual*, published directories of collectors whose numbers at that time ran into thousands. Today there are just a few hundred.

Stainton once imagined a conversation between two moths when he wrote: 'Why should he catch us? Does he live on moths?' Reflecting on this, he went on to say: 'We have ourselves more than once been posed by a somewhat similar inquiry, when surrounded by the small fry which prevail in Charlton sand-pit and other localities, "What do you catch 'em for? Are they good to eat?"' A simple answer that will satisfy all seems strangely remote. Nevertheless, the pursuit of butterflies and moths had an enormous appeal during the nineteenth and the first half of the twentieth centuries.

Today, however, butterfly collecting takes on a different perspective. Should we collect or not? — that is the question. There are, of course, two sides to every argument and we are acutely aware that the morality of butterfly collecting worries an increasing number of people. Now that this pursuit is on the wane, those pleasant memories of yester-year — the heyday of butterfly hunting — ask to be revived, and it is for just that reason that we have put together this little collection of articles, letters and editors' notes. We have attempted to recapture some of the fun and inspiration that once persuaded men and women from all walks of life to collect butterflies and moths. The present-day argument that asks whether or not we should collect butterflies reminded us of the old stage-coachman's remark as to the difference between a railway accident and a stagecoach upset. 'Why,' says he, 'if the train comes to a smash, and you get thrown off the line, where are you? But, if the *coach* overturns into a hedge or ditch, *there you are!*'

When P. B. M. Allan wrote *A Moth-Hunter's Gossip*, in 1937, he advised that, 'as its title implies, this book is not a serious, still less a scientific, treatise on entomology, but merely tittle-tattle about certain moths which happen to interest me'. *The Aurelian's Fireside Companion* is similar. It is not a scientific treatise, but tittle-tattle and gossip about a number of butterflies and moths and the habits of their collectors which have not only interested us but apparently the individual contributors themselves.

Michael A. Salmon, New Forest, Hampshire.
Peter J. Edwards, Dinton, Buckinghamshire.
2004.

ACKNOWLEDGEMENTS

When it was first suggested that we might compile this anthology a number of lepidopterists begged us to include articles that particularly appealed to them; indeed, there were so many that if we had included them all the present work might have appeared in several volumes. To all those who suggested articles we give our grateful thanks, and we ask forgiveness from those whose choices were not included.

We have been greatly encouraged by a number of good friends and we extend our hearty thanks both to them and to the new acquaintances we have made during the preparation of this book: David Allen, Rupert Barrington, Carol and John Bartlett, Deborah-Jayne Cassey, John Chance, June Chatfield, Eric Classey, Mark Colvin, Bernard D'Abrera, John D'Arcy, Anthony Day, Colin Drage, David Dunbar, Nina Ford, Robin Ford, Brian Gardiner, Barry Goater, Deb Goodenough, Gwen Gulliver, Pat Hall, Revd Anthony Harbottle, Basil and Annette Harley, Julie Harvey, Graham Howarth, Tom Inch, Dr Tony Irving, Geoff Martin, Andy Mason, Muriel Mason, Dr Leonard McLeod, Mark Middleton, Charlie Newman, John Ounsted, Christopher Palmer, Geoffrey Palmer, John Phillips, Revd Steve Pittis, John Scott, Edward Sadler, Edward Sibbick, Bernard Skinner, David Smith, Christine Taylor, David Wilson and Graham Wilson.

We would also like to acknowledge the help of those who sadly are no longer with us: Viscountess Bolingbroke (Valezina Frohawk), Michael Chalmers-Hunt, Sir Cyril Clarke, Stella Lucas, Humphrey Mackworth-Praed, Dr Ernest Neal, L. Hugh Newman and Dame Miriam Rothschild.

Malcolm Simpson requires special mention. Not only has he supported the writing of this book from the start but his great knowledge of the history of British entomology has directed our searches in many fruitful ways. He has willingly loaned equipment and other material from his famous collection of entomological memorabilia for which we are extremely grateful.

Our thanks go to Richard Weaver, whose photographic skills, so evident in *The Aurelian Legacy*, are once again clearly apparent. Many of the photographs included here were taken by him or copied from Victorian and early twentieth-century prints, many of which were terribly faded and silver-coloured. His skill in transforming some of the early pictures has been truly amazing.

We wish to thank Berit Pedersen, Librarian to the Royal Entomological Society, and her staff for their unfailing courtesy in searching for obscure references and for photocopying dozens of articles; they always found time to help us. We also would like to thank the staff of the Entomology Library, Natural History Museum, English Heritage and the Royal Archives.

We thank Alec Harmer and Tony Pickles of Paphia Publishing Ltd, whose faith in our enterprise and in our selection of articles never wavered. Their enthusiasm has ensured publication. At the same time we would also like to record our thanks to Printwise — in particular to John Playle and Steve Hayes, who has worked wonders with the text and illustrations we supplied. Their contribution to this project is greatly appreciated. Last but by no means least we extend our grateful thanks to Susie and Jane, who have 'lived' with the production of this work day and night for the past three years. They have never ceased to support us wholeheartedly.

M. A. S. & P. J. E.

PICTURE AND TEXT CREDITS

PICTURE CREDITS

The illustrations in this book are reproduced with the kind permission of the following institutions and individuals in whom the copyright is vested or who supplied photographs from material out of copyright. Others have been reproduced from material generously lent by private collectors.

Colour Plates are reproduced courtesy of the following:
Plate 1: Rupert Barrington (a), Aaron Jones (b), Richard Weaver (c, d, e, g, h & i), Alec Harmer (f); Plate 2: T. Graham Howarth; Plate 3: © The Natural History Museum, London; Plate 4: the late Gordon Beningfield; Plate 5: the late Dame Miriam Rothschild (a), Michael Salmon (b); Plate 6: Julian Nieman; Plate 7: John Scott (a), Alec Harmer (b), Matthew Austin (c); Plate 8: David Wilson (a), Julian Nieman (b).

Black and white illustrations are reproduced courtesy of the following:
Royal Entomological Society of London: frontispiece, portrait of Philip Henry Gosse, Figs 2, 4, 5, 6, 8, 11, 13, 24–26, 29, 30, 38, 39, 44, 46, 47, 72, 74, 77, 80, 84, 90, 92, 99, 101, 102, 112–114, 116–118, 124–130 & 133; the late Dame Miriam Rothschild: portrait of herself, Figs 28, 49 & 51; Sally Palmer: portrait of Geoffrey Palmer; John Webb: Figs 1 & 75; Dr Paul Hillyard: Fig. 7; *The Entomologist's Record and Journal of Variation*: Figs 10, 16, 31, 35(a and b), 45, 58, 87, 91, 104, 106, 115, 119 & 131; John Scott: Fig. 12; The Dorset Natural History & Archaeological Society: Figs 14 & 15; Edie Powles: Fig. 17; Joyce Cowern: Fig. 18; John Chance: Fig. 19; the late Stella Lucas: Fig. 20; June Chatfield: Figs 22 & 27; Alec Harmer: Figs 23, 36 & 123; Robin Ford: Figs 32, 33, 61 & 94; Malcolm Simpson: Figs 34, 35(c), 64 & 137; David Allen: Fig. 37; the Housemaster of Sergeant's, Winchester College: Fig. 41; Jenni Tubbs and Mrs Robert Coles: Fig. 42; Gwen Gulliver: Fig. 43; Dr James O'Connor: Fig. 50; Graham Howarth: Figs 52, 53, 96 & 97; Anthony Day: Figs 54, 56, 57 & 59; Cambridge Evening News and Basil Harley: Fig. 55; Keith C. Lewis: Figs 62 & 107; John D'Arcy: Fig. 63; Rupert Barrington: Figs 65, 68–70 & 103; Brian Gardiner: Figs 66 & 67; the late Gordon Beningfield: Fig. 71; Revd Anthony Harbottle: Figs 73 & 138; *Entomologist's Monthly Magazine*: Fig. 74; Eric Classey: Figs 75 & 76; Suffolk Naturalists' Society: Fig. 78; the late Dr Ernest Neal: Fig. 79; John Phillips: Fig. 81; the late Humphrey Mackworth-Praed: Fig. 82; Dr Leonard McLeod: Fig. 83; Michael Salmon: Figs 85 & 86; Dr Tony Irving and Norfolk Museums Service: Fig. 88; Somerset Military Museum: Fig. 93; Susan Salmon: Fig. 98; David Wilson: Figs 100 & 134; the late L. Hugh Newman: Figs 105, 135 & 136; Peter and Pat Gardner: Fig. 108; Richard Revels: Fig. 109; Laurence Pollinger Ltd: Fig. 110; Printwise: Fig. 120; National Portrait Gallery: Fig. 121; Entomology Library, Natural History Museum: Fig. 122; Dust jacket: Andrew Wakeham-Dawson (Michael Salmon); Jane Edwards (Peter Edwards); Jonathan Pointer (Tim Bernhard).

TEXT CREDITS

A book of this kind certainly would not have been possible without the generous cooperation of the entomological journal editors who kindly granted us permission to draw so liberally from the literary treasures contained within their collective volumes. We are especially indebted to: the Editor of the *Bulletin of the Amateur Entomologists' Society*; the proprietors of Gem Publishing Co. (*Entomologist's Gazette* and *Entomologist's Monthly Magazine*); the Editor of *The Entomologist's Record and Journal of Variation*; and the Editor of *The Journal of the British Entomological and Natural History Society*. In addition, we would also like to express our sincerest thanks to the following institutions and individuals for their assistance: The Royal Entomological Society for permission to use extracts from several of its publications; E. W. Classey for permission to use extracts from P. B. M. Allan's *Talking of moths*; The British Broadcasting Corporation for permission to use extract from the Sir Compton Mackenzie and Moray McLaren broadcast; Daily Sketch for permission to use 'Day off from war'; Health Services Library; A. P. Watt Ltd on behalf of the Literary Executors of the Estate of H. G. Wells for permission to use 'The Moth'; Dame Miriam Rothschild for permission to use extracts from *Dear Lord Rothschild* and *Nathaniel Charles Rothschild 1877–1923*; the Editor of the National Trust Magazine for permission to use extract from the summer 1987 issue; and Mark Isaak for permission to use 'The Modern Entomologist'.

While all reasonable attempts have been made by the authors to trace the owners of copyright material, we unreservedly apologize to any who inadvertently may have been omitted. If notified, we will endeavour to rectify any errors or omissions at the earliest opportunity.

PROLOGUE

In 1869 Dr Henry Guard Knaggs of Camden Town published his *Lepidopterist's Guide*, a slim volume primarily intended for the young and inexperienced collector of butterflies and moths. It is full of good advice based on the good doctor's many years of experience. At the conclusion of his text is a thoughtful homily in which the conduct of entomology is discussed. Although this was written more than 130 years ago, at a time when collecting was enthusiastically pursued by thousands of schoolboys and adults, it makes interesting reading today.

OBJECTS FOR WHICH MEN BECOME ENTOMOLOGISTS

Science ought to hold the chief place, but science is a very much abused word, and therefore requires to be explained to the beginner. The individual who sits in his library all the year round up to his eyes in entomological dry specimens and drier literature, writing elaborate Latin diagnoses of probable new species, or turning out descriptions of improbable ones, at the rate of so many per hour, is apt to imagine that *his* occupation constitutes Entomology; and, as a consequence, he too often looks down upon the poor fly-catcher with something like contempt; but for all that, the despised collector often, of the two, does the more for science, by which is here meant the acquisition and diffusion of sound knowledge, and not the art of piling up a synonymy for the bewilderment of future generations.

The observer, on the other hand, when his observations are conducted with caution and carefully recorded, is the most scientific; or, in other words, does more than the other two put together to acquire and diffuse knowledge. The true scientific Lepidopterist should combine all these three in one, and should, moreover, be an anatomist and physiologist.

Pursuit of truth, with a love of nature, and a laudable desire to investigate the histories of the wonderful organisms which God has, in his wisdom, created.

Healthful occupation for those who have spare time to devote to a pursuit which leads them, with an object constantly in view, to green fields, country lanes, sunny banks, shady groves, noble parks, and makes them familiar with beautiful scenery.

Emulation — a desire to excel, an ambition to possess the finest collection, to be considered the best collector, to be known as a most accurate observer, or to be handed down to posterity as a great nomenclator.

Acquisitiveness, the feeling which actuates the school-boy to hoard up marbles, buttons, "bacon," birds' eggs, and postage stamps. It is, at any rate, better to gratify this propensity (when we are unfortunate enough to possess it) by collecting, than it is to become a wretched miser.

The good effects of Entomology are numerous; patience, perseverance, and punctuality, are essential for successful collecting; memory, discrimination, and logical reasoning are necessarily cultivated; early rising is encouraged; the mind and body of youth find occupation; temptation to immoral pursuits loses its effect; and liberality with a desire to assist brother collectors is generally engendered, sometimes because it is pleasant, at others because it pays better than greediness. On the other hand, it must be confessed, late hours have to be kept; important duties sometimes go the wall, and with certain covetous folk, barter, lying, deceit, and greed gain uncontrolled sway over their contemptible little minds; nor is this the worst, for some who ought to have known better, have not stopped even here, but led on by sordid *amor habendi*, or the ridiculous prices attached to curious varieties and rare British species, have resorted to fraud, forgery, and theft, to enrich their cabinets or replenish their purses.

[Knaggs, H. G. 1869. *The Lepidopterist's Guide*. London, Van Voorst].

CHAPTER ONE

THE CURIOUS CASE OF ALBIN'S 'HAMPSTEAD EYE'

'Happy the Cicadas' lives
Since they all have voiceless wives.'

Xenarchus, Rhodes. (44 BC)

IMAGINE IF YOU WILL a magnificent stretch of flowery turf thinly dotted with heath and furze where the distant lowing of cattle and the incessant song of skylarks are the only sounds to reach the ears of a curious listener. It is the early eighteenth century and this open patch of countryside, later to be named Hampstead Heath, is little more than an exaggerated clearing to the north of London. From high ground near the Spaniard's Inn, one might on the finest days obtain a distant view of old London — but that was all — for the heath then was still a considerable way off. According to legend it was here, on what turned out to be a memorable day that a wanderer might have witnessed the animated figure of Eleazar Albin striking out at a butterfly with his two-handed clap-net. Albin (fl. 1690–1742) was an artist and illustrator — some say the finest of his time — who not only collected butterflies and other 'natural objects' but painted them as well. On this particular occasion he had a heart-stopping experience. He captured a butterfly that was not only quite unknown to him but, for that matter, to all the leading experts of the day. But more anon!

Developing their interest in the late sixteenth and seventeenth centuries, the earliest collectors, or *Aurelians** as they were known, were men of learning who, when not out collecting, met regularly in fashionable coffee houses and taverns. It was at such meetings that they would discuss their findings, show off their captures and welcome new members to the established circle of friends. Such was their enthusiasm that within a comparatively short period of time they had identified most of the British butterflies and even worked out the details of many life histories. By 1740 they had founded the first learned society to be devoted to the study of butterflies and moths, named, appropriately enough, the Aurelian Society. And it was from that moment that 'the delightful pastime' as it was known became more scientific. This first chapter introduces the reader to some interesting characters and one or two very rare butterflies.

THE GREAT CORNHILL FIRE AND THE DEMISE
OF THE FIRST AURELIAN SOCIETY

Dr Ronald S. Wilkinson, New York. (1977)

One of the most familiar accounts in the history of British entomology is that of the demise of the "first" Aurelian Society, apparently the earliest organised entomological society in England (although prior groups of naturalists had pursued entomology as part of their total activities). The precise cause of the dissolution is stated by Moses Harris in *The Aurelian* (London [1758]–66). He was introduced to the study of insects by his uncle, also named Moses Harris, a member of the Society, which held its meetings "at the *Swan Tavern*,

---

*From the Latin, *aureolus*, which refers to the metallic golden markings of certain chrysalides.

1

in *Change-Alley*", London. However, the nephew was not of sufficient age for admission to the Aurelian Society, and was "deprived of that Pleasure" by a subsequent calamity:

"... not long after the great Fire happened in *Cornhill*, in which the *Swan Tavern* was burnt down, together with the Society's valuable Collection of Insects, Books, *&c.* and all their Regalia: The Society was then sitting, yet so sudden and rapid was the impetuous Course of the Fire, that the Flames beat against the Windows, before they could well get out of the Room, many of them leaving their Hats and Canes; their Loss so disheartened them, that altho' they several Times met for that Purpose, they never could collect so many together, as would be sufficient to form a Society."

Research into contemporary sources has revealed more information about the great Cornhill fire and the Aurelian tragedy. A typical account of the disaster is that given in the London *Daily Advertiser* of 26th March, 1748:

"Yesterday Morning, about One O'Clock [i.e., 1 AM, 25 March], a Fire broke out at Mr. Eldridge's, a Peruke-Maker, in Exchange-Alley, which consum'd several houses in the said Alley, Birchin-Lane, and Cornhill; but the Wind being South-South-West, all the Bankers Houses in Lombard-Street, and their Effects, are safe. No publick Office has been burnt, except the London-Assurance ... Garraway's, the Jerusalem and Jonathan's Coffee-Houses, the Swan Tavern, with the rest of the Houses in Change-Alley, are destroyed, except Baker's and Sam's Coffee-Houses, which are greatly damaged. The Flames extended themselves into Cornhill ... It's said, by People well acquainted in the Neighbourhood, that upwards of 160 Houses were burnt down."

The sources agree that the fire began well after midnight, in the early morning of 25th March, at a distance in Exchange-Alley from the Swan Tavern. Despite the wind and the ferocity of the blaze, it would have been a little while before the "Flames beat against the Windows". Why, then, were the members of the Aurelian Society "sitting" in the tavern at such an hour? The answer would seem to lie in the eccentricities of the eighteenth-century calendar.

In 1748 the official year in Great Britain began on 25th March, not 1st January. Due to reform in the sixteenth century, the old Julian calendar was gradually supplanted in Europe by the Gregorian, which meant beginning the new year in January rather than March. Because Protestant countries considered the Gregorian calendar a "Popish innovation" and only slowly accepted it, there was considerable confusion in dating. This was heightened by the Gregorian correction to solar time, so that, for example, 28th December, 1651 in London would be 7th January, 1652 in Paris. Dates between 1st January and the new year were often written with both "old" and "new" style years to avoid confusion (e.g., 12th March 1720/1), but not until 1752 were eleven days omitted from that year to begin "new" style dating in the British Isles. In custom, there were two "new years" in England; for some time various celebrations had been held for the January date (Brand, 1853), but the "old" style was commemorated as well in 1748; as the sources of the time demonstrate, the eighteenth-century Englishman took what opportunity he could to raise his glass.

When the flames reached the Swan Tavern in the early hours of New Year's morning, the Aurelian Society was still in attendance, and it is only reasonable to suppose that it's members were there because they were still toasting 1748. (Lest some entomologists become dismayed, we should recall those bibulous meetings of Edward Newman and his friends at that popular watering-place for insect-hunters, the Bull Inn, Birch Wood Corner, so celebrated in the nineteenth-century *Entomological Magazine*.) The Swan was burned down before dawn, and in the following weeks the London press did not fail to notice the results of the disaster; it was, as one would say today, a "lead-story". In the *Daily Advertiser*, an appeal was made for funds to aid the victims of the great Cornhill fire, and such notices ran for several months. The ruins of the Swan Tavern were eventually sold as real estate, and it would be some years before the younger Moses Harris and his fellow enthusiasts would found the "second" Aurelian Society.

[Wilkinson, R. S. 1977. The great Cornhill fire and the demise of the first Aurelian Society. *The Entomologist's Record and Journal of Variation* **89**: 250–251].

It is tempting to compare more recent entomological meetings with that of the ill-fated Aurelian Society in 1748. One such meeting – a conversazione held by the Entomological Society of London – was reported in *The Entomologist* for 1908.

CONVERSAZIONE

Henry Rowland-Brown, M.A., F. E. S., Cavendish Square, London, W. (1908)

What we believe to be the first reception of its kind by the Entomological Society of London was held in the rooms of the Civil Service Commission – formerly the London University Buildings – on the evening of Friday, May 15th. The somewhat chilly atmosphere of officialism which pervades the great examination schools had, however, been dispelled by the joint efforts of furnisher and exhibitors, and Fellows who only know the great hall, the vestibule, and the western wing generally under its customary aspect were agreeably surprised at the transformation effected. The former was reserved as a refreshment and conversation room, Miss Rosabel Watson's Ladies' Æolian Band performing selections of pleasant music during the evening, especial care being taken that the sounds should not penetrate to the theatre in which the several addresses kindly given by Mr. [H.] Donisthorpe, Colonel D. Bruce, C.B., F.R.S. and Professor E. B. Poulton, F.R.S. were to be delivered. The guests who numbered about two hundred and fifty were received by the President, Mr. C. O. Waterhouse, Miss Waterhouse, Prof. Poulton, and one of the Secretaries, and it is only to be regretted that many more had not accepted the invitation of the Society, it being a matter of some congratulation, however, to those who did, that there was no undue overcrowding, either at the exhibition stands, or at the tables where the microscopes were installed . . .

[Rowland-Brown, H. 1908. Entomological Society of London – Conversazione. *The Entomologist* **41**: 154–156].

ELEAZAR ALBIN AND HIS REMARKABLE 'FIND'

James Petiver F.R.S. (1663–1718) was known to eighteenth-century entomologists as the 'father of British butterflies'. He was a good naturalist and a keen observer who recorded his findings in some detail, but as an apothecary in charge of a physic garden at Aldersgate in the City of London he was said to have sold quack cures as well. Petiver liked to record lists each year of his newly acquired natural history specimens, including butterflies, and the second volume of his *Gazophylacium* (1702–06) contains reference to an extraordinary butterfly, the history and identity of which was to intrigue naturalists for the next two hundred years: '*Papilio oculatus Hampstediensis ex aureo fuscus* – Albin's Hampstead Eye.

Where it was caught by this Curious Person, and is the only one I have yet seen.'

Eleazar Albin, the 'Curious Person' of James Petiver's *Gazophylacium*, lived near the Dog and Duck Tavern in Tottenham Court Road. This locality, then on the outskirts of London, was described as a 'good place for snipe shooting' (Saunders, 1949). His book *The Natural History of English Insects* (1720) was the first to include coloured plates of British butterflies.

Fig. 1. Albin's Hampstead Eye – *Junonia villida* (Fabricius, 1787). From James Petiver's engraved plate of 'British Eye-wing'd Butterflies'. Petiver (1663–1718) is credited as being the first to bestow our butterflies with English names.

It was some time after Albin had told his friends how he had caught this unusual butterfly that the specimen came into Petiver's hands and later still, was acquired by Sir Hans Sloane, whose collections formed the nucleus around which much of the British Museum was built. Although no other specimens were found, 'The Hampstead Eye' achieved considerable fame and was illustrated in most butterfly books (usually in black and white, but later in colour) for the next one hundred years or so. Adrian Hardy Haworth (1767–1833), of Chelsea Village, the distinguished lepidopterist who founded the third Aurelian Society, included it in his *Lepidoptera Britannica* (1803). Intrigued by the mystery surrounding it, he suggested that it was probably a 'lost species' – indeed, he wrote it was 'entirely new to me and all my entomological friends'. Some four decades later, Noel Humphreys and John Obadiah Westwood published *British Butterflies and their Transformations* (1841) and this included Albin's 'Hampstead Eye' – for the first time in colour.

The Revd Francis Orpen Morris (1810–1893), known to naturalists and public alike as 'the Gilbert White of the North', was next on the scene. He included the 'Hampstead Eye' in his *A History of British Butterflies* (1853). A best-seller from the start, this book informed readers that although some experts considered the 'Eye' to be a foreign species, others argued that it was 'the product of two different species'. Morris went on to say: 'The specimen is no longer in existence, and cannot speak for itself; no "*ecce signum*" can now testify to the truthfulness of the Entomologist who shall pretend more accurately to describe it, than in the stereotyped form in which it has come down to the present day.' Both Morris and Humphreys copied Petiver's original woodcut. In fact, their two illustrations are exactly the same size as Petiver's and each is a facsimile of the other. There is little doubt that they used Haworth's excellent description of the original specimen to enable them to depict the coloration as accurately as possible. This was an extraordinary achievement as there is no evidence that either ever saw the original specimen.

As to the fate of the 'Hampstead Eye' we must look to the answers given by Charles Koenig (1774–1851), Keeper of the Department of Natural History, to the Parliamentary Select Sub-Committee investigating conditions at the British Museum. When, in 1835, he was asked: 'How does it happen that the collection has been lost?', Koenig replied: 'When I came to the Museum most of these objects were in an advanced state of decomposition, and they were buried or committed to the flames one after another . . .' When asked if there was a single insect remaining of the original collection of 5,439 specimens, Koenig replied:

'I should think not.' In spite of this and the fact that the Revd Morris had stated 'the specimen is no longer in existence', both men were wrong. Years of neglect and cremations of damaged specimens at the British Museum meant that most of Sir Hans Sloane's collections had been consigned to history. Few remained, but amongst these were some specimens from James Petiver's original collection, including the 'Hampstead Eye' of Eleazar Albin.

Today, Albin's 'Hampstead Eye' is recognized as *Junonia villida* (Fab.), a common butterfly of the Far East. Why he thought that he had caught his specimen flying across Hampstead Heath at the beginning of the eighteenth century is open to question. Any suggestion that it had arrived on a ship from the Far East is surely wrong; journeys at that time took far too long. Although the East India Company commenced trading with countries in the Orient long before Albin's time, any ovum, larva or pupa inadvertently carried amongst potted plants in the cargo of an East Indiaman would have probably undergone metamorphosis to produce an adult butterfly long before the ship reached Tilbury. Could Albin have confused his specimen with another species? We don't know. Did he wittingly set out to achieve fame by fraudulently producing the specimen as something new to Britain? We will probably never know. But if the 'Hampstead Eye' was an attempt to hoodwink other Aurelians, Eleazar Albin must surely be the forerunner of the infamous nineteenth-century 'Kentish Buccaneers' — entomological dealers who thought nothing of importing living 'rarities' from the Continent, which they released under the noses of naïve British collectors for a substantial fee (see p. 293).

JOSEPH GRIMALDI AND THE DARTFORD BLUE

Joseph Grimaldi (1778–1837) was England's greatest clown. He also collected butterflies and bred pigeons. His particular fascination was the 'Dartford Blue', so named because of the frequency with which it had been found in North Kent. This butterfly was in fact the Adonis Blue (*Lysandra bellargus*). In Charles Dickens' *Memoirs of Joseph Grimaldi*, edited by 'Boz' (1838), there is an excellent account of Grimaldi's entomological adventures. Dickens suggests that 'his love of entomology, or exercise, was not the only inducement in the case of the Dartford Blues'. He had, he says, another strong motive, and that was that he had promised a little collection of insects to 'one of the most charming women of her age'. The lady in question was Dorothy Jordan (1761–1816), an actress who was also the mistress of William IV and mother of ten royal children. Mrs Jordan was delighted to accept Grimaldi's gift. 'She took the frames away in her carriage; and she warmed his heart by telling him that his Royal Highness considered the flies equal, if not superior, to any of the kind he had ever seen.'

GRIMALDI THE LEPIDOPTERIST

Charles Dickens. (1838)

. . . Grimaldi contrived to find moments of amusement besides, which were devoted to the breeding of pigeons and collecting of insects. This latter amusement he pursued with such success as to form a cabinet containing no fewer than 4,000 specimens of butterflies, 'collected,' he says, 'at the expense of a great deal of time, a great deal of money, and a great deal of vast and actual labour' — for all of which, no doubt, the entomologist will deem him sufficiently rewarded. He appears in old age to have entertained a peculiar relish for the recollection of these pursuits, and calls to mind a part of Surrey where there was a famous fly; one of these was called the Camberwell Beauty (which he adds was very ugly), and another the Dartford Blue, by which he seems to have set great store; and which were pursued and caught in the manner following, in June 1794, when they regularly make their first appearance of the season.

Fig. 2. Charles Dickens (1812–1870). He used the pen-name 'Boz' when 'observing everyday life and everyday people'.

Being engaged nightly at Sadler's Wells, Grimaldi was obliged to wait till he had finished his business upon the stage: then he returned home, had supper, and shortly after midnight started off to walk to Dartford, fifteen miles from town. Here he arrived about five o'clock in the morning, and calling upon a friend of the name of Brooks, who lived in the neighbourhood and who was already stirring, he rested, breakfasted, and sallied forth into the fields. His search was not very profitable, however, for after some hours he only succeeded in bagging, or bottling, one Dartford Blue, with which he returned to his friend perfectly satisfied. At one o'clock he bade Brooks goodbye, walked back to town, reached London by five, washed, took tea, and hurried to Sadler's Wells. No time was to be lost — the fact of the appearance of the Dartford Blues having been thoroughly established — in securing more specimens; so on the same night, directly the pantomime was over and supper over, too, off he walked to Dartford again, and resumed his search. Meeting with better sport, and capturing no fewer than four dozen Dartford Blues, he hurried back to his friend's: set them — an important process, which consists in placing the insects in the position in which their natural beauty can be best displayed — started off with the Blues in his pocket for London once more, reached home by four o'clock in the afternoon, washed, took a hasty meal, and then went to the theatre for the evening's performance.

As not half the necessary number of Blues had been taken, Grimaldi had decided upon another visit to Dartford that same night, and was consequently much pleased to find that, from some unforeseen circumstance, the pantomime was to be played first. By this means he was enabled to leave London at nine o'clock, to reach Dartford at one, to find a bed and supper ready, to meet a kind reception from his friend, and finally to turn into bed, a little tired of two days' exertions.

Fig. 3. Joseph Grimaldi, who once presented the mistress of William IV with a case of butterflies.

The next day was Sunday, so that he could indulge himself without being obliged to return to town, and in the morning he caught more flies than he wanted; so the rest of the day was devoted to quiet sociality. He went to bed at ten o'clock, rose early next morning, walked comfortably to town, and at noon was perfect in his part at the rehearsal.

Grimaldi's only companion on these trips, besides his Dartford friend, was Robert Gomery, or 'friend Bob' as he was called by his intimates, at that time an actor at Sadler's Wells, and for many years a public favourite.

'Bob,' said Grimaldi, 'I am very hungry.'

'So am I,' said Bob.

'There is a public house,' said Grimaldi.

'It is just the very thing,' observed the other.

It was a very neat public house and would have answered the purpose admirably, but Grimaldi having no money, and very much doubting whether his friend either, did not respond to the sentiment quite so cordially as he might have done.

'We had better go in,' said Bob. 'It is getting late — *you* pay.'

'No, no, you!'

'I would in a minute,' said Joe's friend, 'but I have not got any money.'

Grimaldi thrust his hand into his right pocket with one of his queerest faces, then into his left, then into his coat's pockets, then into his waistcoat, and finally took off his hat and looked into that; but there was no money anywhere. They still walked on towards the public house, meditating with rueful countenances, when Grimaldi, spying something lying at the foot of a tree, picked it up, and suddenly exclaimed, with a variety of winks and nods, 'Here's a sixpence.'

The hungry friend's eyes brightened, but they quickly resumed their gloomy expression as he rejoined, 'It's a piece of tin.'

Grimaldi winked again, rubbed the sixpence or the piece of tin very hard, and declared, putting it between his teeth by way of test, that it was as good a sixpence as he would wish to see.

'I don't think it,' said Bob, shaking his head.

'I'll tell you what,' said Grimaldi, 'we'll go to the public house, and ask the landlord whether it's a good one, or not. They always know.'

To this Bob assented, and they hurried on, disputing all the way whether it was really a sixpence or not; a discovery which could not be made at that time, when the currency was defaced and worn nearly plain, with the ease with which it could be made at present.

The publican, a fat jolly fellow, was standing at his door, talking to a friend, and the house looked so uncommonly comfortable, that Gomery whispered as they approached, that perhaps it might be best to have some bread and cheese first, and ask about the sixpence afterwards. Grimaldi nodded his entire assent, and they went in and ordered some bread and cheese and beer. Having taken the edge off their hunger, they tossed up a farthing which Grimaldi happened to find in a corner of some theretofore undiscovered pocket, to determine who should present the 'sixpence'. The chance falling on himself, he walked up to the bar, and with a very lofty air, and laying the questionable metal down with a dignity quite his own, requested the landlord to take the bill out of that.

'Just right, sir,' said the landlord, looking at the strange face that his customer assumed, and not at the sixpence.

'It's right, sir, is it?' asked Grimaldi, sternly.

'Quite,' answered the landlord. 'Thank ye, gentlemen.' And with this he slipped the — whatever it was — into his pocket. Gomery looked at Grimaldi; and Grimaldi, with a look and air which baffled all description, walked out of the house, followed by his friend.

'I never knew anything so lucky,' Grimaldi said, as they walked home to supper. 'It was quite a Providence — that sixpence.'

'A piece of tin, you mean,' said Gomery.

Which of the two it was, is uncertain, but Grimaldi often patronized the same house afterwards, and as he never heard anything more about the matter, he felt quite convinced that it was a real good sixpence. . . .

Unfortunately, Grimaldi's interest in butterflies and moths did not last long. About 1800, as he attended a rehearsal at Sadler's Wells, thieves broke into his house:

The thieves, whoever they were, were very wanton fellows, and added outrage to plunder, for with the most heartless cruelty, and an absence of all taste for scientific pursuits which would stigmatise them at once as occupying a very low grade in their profession, had broken open a closet in Grimaldi's room, containing his chosen cabinet of insects, including Dartford Blues, which, either because it was not portable, or because they thought it of no value, attaching no importance to flies, they most recklessly and barbarously destroyed. With the exception of one small box, they utterly annihilated the whole collection, including even his models, drawings, and colours: it would have taken years to replace them, if the collector had been most indefatiguable; and it would have cost at least £200 to have replaced them by purchase. This unforeseen calamity put a total stop to the fly-catching; so, collecting together his nets and cases, and the only box which was not destroyed, Grimaldi gave them all away next day to an acquaintance who had a taste for such things, and never more employed himself in a similar manner.

[Dickens, C. 1838. *Memoirs of Joseph Grimaldi*, edited by 'Boz'. London].

Although Emmet and Heath (1989) attribute the name 'Dartford Blue' to the Revd F. O. Morris, this is obviously incorrect. In *A History of British Butterflies* (1853) Morris refers to 'Grimaldi's Dartford Blues', which must imply that Grimaldi had used the name at an earlier date. In fact, Grimaldi, who was born in the eighteenth century, died nearly thirty years before Morris published his work. Earlier authors referred to the Adonis Blue as the 'Lead Argus' (Petiver, 1717) and the 'Clifden Blue' (Moses Harris, 1775).

SOME REMINISCENCES OF THE LATE PROFESSOR WESTWOOD

Rev. Octavius Pickard-Cambridge, M.A., C.M.Z.S., Bloxworth, Dorset. (1893)

Professor John Obadiah Westwood (1805–1893) was a Hope Professor of Invertebrate Zoology at the University of Oxford. He had a distinguished scientific career and was elected as President of the Entomological Society of London on no fewer than three occasions; and in 1883 was elected Honorary Life President, an honour conferred on only two other persons. He was nominated for election to The Royal Society on a number of occasions, but always declined that honour. In 1841 he collaborated with Noel Humphreys to publish *British Butterflies and their Transformations*, a work of great importance.

In an affectionate obituary (1893) the distinguished entomologist Robert McLachlan F.R.S. (1837–1904) described his close friend Westwood as follows:

> He had his eccentricities, one of which was his parsimony in the matter of stationery: one seldom received a letter from him that was not enclosed in an envelope that had already been used, and his papers, memoirs, and drawings were usually written and made on the blank side of prospectuses, circulars, &c., and so on — "waste not, want not", was his motto. In society there could be no more genial companion, full of anecdote, but with small appreciation of humour. At home there could be no more generous host.

Fig. 4. Octavius Pickard-Cambridge, Rector of Bloxworth, in Dorset, and one of the most accomplished naturalists of his day.

McLachlan continued:

> As to the accuracy of his work there can be no question, and few men have made less mistakes. There was, however, a somewhat ludicrous incident in this respect. Many years ago he exhibited at the Entomological Society what he pronounced to be a gigantic flea, found dead in a bed at Gateshead, and described it as *Pulex imperator*, but which afterwards he discovered was only the young larva of a cockroach, crushed laterally. Such a mistake might have crushed a more sensitive and less famous man; as it was the name he imposed on the supposed flea clung to him for years.

Figs 5 and 6.
The two faces of John
Obadiah Westwood,
the eccentric Oxford
Professor who was
said to lack a sense of
humour. His last visits
to the University
Museum were made
in a bath chair.

After studying these two portraits of Professor Westwood it is hard to believe that he lacked a sense of humour, a fact nevertheless confirmed here by the Revd Pickard-Cambridge:

Among the obituary notices of the late Prof. Westwood, perhaps that by Mr. McLachlan, in the February number of the 'Entomologist's Monthly Magazine,' p. 49, gives one the best idea of his versatile genius; but I have not seen anywhere any allusion to one of his most noted accomplishments, — the mending of broken insects. I have seen him with his little pot of dirty gum, a bit of an old match, two or three needles and pins, and a paper of the veriest *fragments* of an insect, and in a brief space of time the insect would appear built up in the most marvellous way, almost defying the power of an ordinary pocket-lens to discover that it had ever been otherwise. I remember once, however, finding the Professor's assistant, many years ago, carefully collecting and lightly affixing fragments of numerous insects from an entomological drawer to a sheet of paper. On enquiring what this was for, he said that by and bye the Professor would restore each bit to its proper insect in the drawer. Presently the Professor walked in, confirmed this statement, and at once set to work with his gum-pot and other implements. I ventured to hint at the chances of some insects obtaining bits to which by nature they might not have been entitled, and so tending to confuse future entomologists. He repudiated the idea with scorn, and, full of confidence in himself, proceeded with his labours. I think this was the secret of his general success in life, as well as in mending insects, — abundance of self-confidence; and, after all, though it might result, as it did, in the instance mentioned by Mr. McLachlan, in mistaking a crushed cockroach of tender age for a gigantic new flea, yet it is a quality without which very little good or original work is ever done. If future students of the Hope collection of insects should find anything queer in the structure of some of the specimens, it would hardly be inexplicable; but they must not think worse of the dear old Professor than his friends did in the matter of the flea; while if no such results of his mendings should ever reveal themselves, it will be the best possible evidence of his accurate knowledge of varied insect structure, as well as his dextrous manipulation of insect fragments.

Mr. McLachlan remarks on the Professor's lack of any *sense of humour*. I could illustrate this by several amusing stories; but I will only mention one, in which, it seems to me, that his confidence in himself is also very notable. I was visiting the Museum one summer's afternoon, many years ago, when the Professor informed me that he had a lecture on the next morning, and asked whether I would care to attend it. The subject (insects injurious to gardens) was a popular one, and he expected a good audience. Ten minutes before the hour of the lecture next day I duly appeared at the lecture-room, where I found the Professor completing his arrangements, and making a final disposition of his beautiful drawings and specimens. We remained there chatting for some little time, but no students or other audience appeared. Half an hour passed; still no arrivals. But the Professor was hopeful (was he not *Hope* Professor? but such a horrible joke could not occur to *him*): "They will come presently; they are often rather late." A gentle knock is heard at the door at last. "Come in;" but no one coming in, the Professor goes to the door. "Is this Professor Westwood's lecture-room?" asks a timid little voice. "Yes ma'am; we are all waiting." And the Professor returns, followed by a little, rather elderly, frightened-looking lady, who is duly placed in a front seat; whereupon, without moving a muscle of his countenance, the

Fig. 7. 'The lion in his den.' Revd O. Pickard-Cambridge at home in his study.

Professor begins, and goes through an excellent and interesting lecture, with this little old lady as his whole audience; for it was only by being employed in assisting him with his drawings and specimens that I could restrain myself from exploding at the absurdity of the whole thing. First and last the Professor was as serious as if the whole University was before him. If he had had even the smallest sense of humour, he must have exploded. After the lecture he merely remarked: "Oh, I daresay there is some cricket match going on to-day; some of the undergraduates do take an interest in Entomology, but there is always boating or cricket going on." I was informed later from other sources, that the Professor's lectures were not unfrequently attended (or rather *not* attended) as on the occasion mentioned.

It must not be imagined for a moment that in recording these little "items" I desire to speak lightly of the Professor. Some of the most enjoyable hours of frequent visits to Oxford, many years ago, were passed in entomological work in his rooms at the Museum, as well as in his own house; and I never experienced at his hands anything but the readiest and most abundant courtesy, hospitality and help.

He was, I fancy, about the last survivor of the older generation of entomologists. There may be abler specialists among the present generation, but none, I suspect, who will command more universal regard, either as a man or scientist, than my old and valued friend J. O. Westwood.

[Pickard-Cambridge, O. 1893. Some reminiscences of the late Prof. Westwood. *The Entomologist* **26**: 74–75].

Octavius Pickard-Cambridge (1828–1917), the Rector of Bloxworth, in Dorset, was a first-rate field naturalist. A leading authority on British spiders, he was also an outstanding lepidopterist with a particular interest in micro-moths. It was in August 1885 that he took his two sons butterfly hunting on Bloxworth Heath. The outing proved memorable — for the boys each captured specimens of the Short-tailed Blue (*Everes argiades*), a butterfly previously never seen in Britain but known for many years afterwards as the 'Bloxworth Blue'. The Rector was an athletic man who not only played cricket well into middle age but celebrated old age by achieving a long-held wish when he was carried aloft in a flying machine.

THE PRESIDENT'S COLLATION

Anon. (1856)

Victorian entomologists liked nothing better than to organize field trips for the purpose of finding and collecting rare or local species (Figs 11 & 115). These outings were gregarious affairs which often ended with a celebratory dinner at the local hostelry. The Bull Inn, Birch Wood Corner, near Darenth, Kent (see p. 15), and the White Hart at Reigate, were especially well known for their lavish hospitality. However, the range of entertainment varied considerably. While the Cotteswold Naturalists' Field Club could boast of champagne suppers, the Essex Field Club sought more modest refreshment. It is recorded that on one occasion members of the 'Essex', who had devoted an afternoon to studying earthquakes and parish church architecture, as well as entomology, concluded their field trip with an 'excellent meat tea at the Enterprise Temperance Hotel'. In the following article, published in 1856, the President of the Entomological Society of London invited members to join him for a 'cold collation' at the conclusion of their outing to the Surrey countryside.

One of the most interesting entomological events of the season was the meeting at Reigate, last Saturday, to do justice to the "cold collation" to which the members of the Entomological Society were invited by their hospitable President.

The number who sat down was, we believe, at least thirty-six; and, the appetites of most of the party being sharpened by several hours' ramble in the neighbourhood, in pursuit of specimens, there was soon a sudden diminution in the weight of the various comestibles under which the table groaned.

After the cloth had been removed sundry toasts were given; and one of the most interesting was proposed by a gentleman who, it was stated, was about to become a member of the Entomological Society. Mr Fenning complained that, whereas the company had already drunk success to Entomology and to the Entomological Society, with the healths of the President, Vice-President, &c., &c., no one had yet proposed the health of *insects*; yet without them the science of Entomology could not exist. He thought this was an unintentional slight which the meeting would be only too happy to rectify; and he would therefore propose the health of a little beetle which had made some sensation at his end of the table; and though it might be objected that, the beetle being dead, it was useless to drink its health, yet there were no doubt living representatives of the species; and therefore he had much pleasure in proposing the health of *Callistus lunaticus*. He might be in error about the name, but he believed it was either *lunaticus* or *lunatus*. The toast having been duly honoured, *Callistus lunatus* [a rare ground beetle] was called upon to return thanks; but, not responding, Mr. Janson was requested to represent the *Callistus* on this occasion. Mr. Janson regretted that the insect was so rare that he had not sufficient personal acqaintance with it to be able adequately to follow out the train of ideas which *Callistus lunatus* might be conceived to possess; but he hoped, if called upon to speak for the same insect another year, he might be better able to act as its representative.

Mr. Janson then sat down; but, had he proceeded to give a longer address to the company, he would, on the suggestion of Mr Westwood, have spoken somewhat as follows:—

"Gentlemen, — I cannot allow the present opportunity to pass without expressing my regret that so little attention is paid by the collectors of *Coleoptera* to the habits and primary states of the insects they profess to study. It is true we occasionally find recorded the discovery of some larva, or of some trait in beetle-life previously unknown; but it does not appear to me that there is that energetic, persistent attempt to work out the primary states of each species of a genus, which has been found so successful in another branch of Entomology.

"I can have no wish to undervalue the labours of my coadjutors; but it occurs to me that a Power is gifted with higher powers than those of thrashing sallows and exciting gamekeepers (so that he has to run for his life from their indignant ire); that a Wollaston has other work cut out for him than in enumerating the insects of Madeira. If Mr. Wollaston would travel on the Continent he would learn that there is another island in the Atlantic than that with which his name is honourably connected."

Perhaps, however, this portion of Mr. Janson's speech will be delivered on the next occasion.

[Anon. 1856. The President's collation. *The Entomologist's Weekly Intelligencer* 1: 102–103].

'The President's collation' was followed by a short note entitled 'Singular coincidence':

A gentleman, not yet entangled in the meshes of Entomology, who was invited by Mr. Saunders to the Reigate *réunion*, received a visit last night from a *Cimex lectularius* [Bed bug], an insect whose acquaintance he had not made for the previous twenty years. He looked on it as a reminder that he was the next day to dine with a party of bug-hunters. "Coming events cast their shadows before."

[Anon. 1856. Singular coincidence. *The Entomologist's Weekly Intelligencer* 1: 103].

Fig. 8. Edward Newman (1801–1876), founder member of the Entomological Club in 1826. He once remarked: 'In the summer if my life and health should continue, I propose wandering about the country.'

THE BIRCH WOOD DINNER

(On the 9th July, 1858, the Members of the Entomological Club and their friends, held their annual festival at the 'Bull Inn,' Birch Wood Corner, [near Darenth, Kent] Edward Newman, Esq., F.L.S., in the chair.)

Ye Muses, help me while I sing
    The Birch Wood Day once more,
The festival that still takes place
    As it took place of yore.

Ah! Days of yore, when Newport, great
    Anatomist, came out
And left his books and microscope
    To join the laugh and shout.

And genial Edward Doubleday
    Erased the stamp of care,
And of his classic episodes
    Contributed a share.

And Yarrell stern, but with a heart
    With finest fibres strung,
You liked him when you heard him speak,
    You loved him when he sung.

All these are gone, yet oh! blest shades!
    Each loved and lovely spot
You used to tread, still witness bears
    That you are not forgot.

"Breakfast at half-past nine" the card
    As usual says in vain,
Ten always strikes before the guests
    That welcome meal obtain.

The table cleared, the friends go out;
    The woods, the lanes, the fields,
The banks, the orchards, all are searched,
    And each its insects yields.

Some go a-shooting; rifle shots,
    And jokes ring through the park,
And long-bow shooters try their skill,
    And often miss their mark.

The dinner hour draws near, and each
    Lifts up his nose from far,
And smells the fragrant viands which
    Are ready at the bar.

They hasten in and take their place
    Around the festive board,
When all that's good for hungry men
    In vast profusion's stored.

The loving cup goes round, and song
    And wit succeed each other,
And every one there present feels
    That every man's his brother.

How fast and furious grew the fun,
    Those only know who there
Helped on the sport; enough to say
    That Newman filled the chair.

At length the fading light reminds
    'Tis time to go away,
And one and all regret the end
    Of one more Birch Wood Day.

                         J.W.D.

[Douglas, J. W. 1858. The Birch Wood Dinner. *The Entomologist's Weekly Intelligencer* **4**: 135–136].

In 1867 tickets for the annual dinner were priced at 16s. each.

Fig. 9. The Bull Inn, Birch Wood Corner, near Darenth, Kent.

Fig. 10. The Lancashire and Cheshire Entomological Society (1894).
C. F. Johnson. J. Watson. C. G. Barrett. R. Newstead. Revd A. W. Carter. J. W. Ellis. H. Capper. L. Greening.
I. C. Thompson.
R. Wilding. C. S. Gregson. B. H. Crabtree. S. J. Capper. G. C. Bignell. W. Johnson.
W. E. Sharp. C. H. Walker. J. Collins. H. H. Corbett. W. Webster.

Fig. 11. Visit of the Entomological Society of London to Oxford (1902).
H. Rowland-Brown. Prof. E. B. Poulton. H. St. J. Donisthorpe. Dr David Sharp.
M. Jacoby. Revd F. D. Morice. R. McLachlan. H. H. C. J. Druce.
(seated) Miss Poulton. Sir G. A. K. Marshall. A. J. Chitty.

16

A DISPUTE OVER BUTTERFLIES QUESTIONABLY BRITISH

Letter to the Editor, *The Entomological Magazine* **(1836):**

Sir, . . . At page 530, Vol. 1 of the Magazine, we see that *"Colias Europome* [Moorland Clouded Yellow] has been noticed in the meadows, near the confluence of the Avon and Severn, flying with great swiftness in August; but is a rare insect near Worcester." Also, *"C. Chrysotheme* [Lesser Clouded Yellow], rare near Worcester, in the cabinet of Mr. A. Edmonds." In your last number, Mr. Newman, (taking no notice of the reputed *Chrysotheme*), says a pair of *Europome* are in the possession of Mr. Edmonds, of Worcester. The gentleman by whom *Europome* was first recorded as above, as being known at Worcester, has since said that his authority for inserting it in his list, was, the having, in 1820, seen *"a brood"* of *them*, "flying with very great swiftness," near Tewkesbury. Of the pair now in Mr. Edmond's collection I know nothing — but I know of four or five other pairs of it, which are, or were lately, in cabinets in Warwick and Worcester shires; and which were all procured, a little more than two years ago, from a dealer who assured me that they had been taken in abundance in the neighbourhood of York. Being somewhat sceptical, I made inquiry, the result of which was that they had been seen at York, but only in the boxes of this dealer, who there asserted that they were taken at Manchester; and thus succeeded in selling a pair of them as *Hyale* [Pale Clouded Yellow].

To show the facility with which the cabinets of the credulous may be enriched by dealers, I will add that I very lately saw a box containing specimens of *Mancipium Daplidicæ* [Bath White], *Argynnis Lathonia* [Queen of Spain Fritillary], *Vanessa Antiopa* [Camberwell Beauty], *Lycæna Virgaureæ* and *Chryseis* [Scarce and Purple-edged Coppers], *Deilephila Euphorbiæ* and *Lineata* [Spurge and Striped Hawk-moths], *Catocala Fraxini* [Blue Underwing], &c. &c., some of them in considerable numbers, with tolerably respectable looking pins, and all, of course, warranted British. Ere long these will have been admitted into different cabinets, and your pages may probably have to record their occurrences in the different localities assigned to them by the dealer.

I am, Sir, yours, &c.

Birmingham, February, 1836. THOMAS MARSHALL.

With this tirade Thomas Marshall really set the cat among the pigeons. Many years before he was moved to write this letter unscrupulous dealers had preyed on naïve collectors, persuading them to accept a number of Continental species as British. The most infamous group of dealers — the so-called 'Kentish Buccaneers' — imported hundreds of Continental specimens during the Victorian era, released them in selected localities, usually somewhere in Kent, and then invited gullible collectors to 'find' them. A wire to say that 'such and such' a species had been seen at 'such and such' a place was usually sufficient to bring down the unwary at once. The collector, for an appropriate fee, would then be guided to the right locality and, with luck, would be able to return home that evening with exciting Continental butterflies that he thought were British (see p. 294). A number of senior lepidopterists were appalled by this behaviour. In the following article, published in *The Entomological Magazine* (1837), 'Inquisitor' suggested that as a result of unscrupulous dealers' doings perhaps only sixty-five species could be regarded as unquestionably British. 'Inquisitor', who was in reality Edward Newman, editor of *The Entomological Magazine*, was so disturbed by letters such as Thomas Marshall's that he took the bold step of telling his readers just what he thought was going on.

NOTE ON BUTTERFLIES QUESTIONABLY BRITISH

Inquisitor. (1837)

In the Lists of British Lepidoptera which have been published by Messrs. Stephens and Curtis, many names occur which, in our cabinets, that is, in the cabinets of those few entomologists who are scrupulous, stand, year after year, as names only; now, if there really are British insects corresponding to these names, it is very well to allow the vacancies left for them to remain, until some fortunate entomologist discovers the locality for these rarities, and supplies our cabinets; but, on the contrary, if there exist no such insects in Britain, it is surely ill-advised in us to retain the names; I suggest that it would be far better to forget that such insects have ever been recorded as British, and should they hereafter occur, I would reintroduce them as entire novelties. The following butterflies are more or less abundant in cabinets of professedly British insects, but of any authentic record of capture in this country we are wholly ignorant.

Podalirius [Scarce Swallowtail], far from uncommon.

Europome [Moorland Clouded Yellow — southern yellow form], very common, existing in thirty-one cabinets that I have inspected.

Palæno [Moorland Clouded Yellow], in catalogues only.

Chrysotheme [Lesser Clouded Yellow] (?)

Apollo [Apollo], a fine series in a cabinet in the North of England, and single specimens in several cabinets.

Mnemosyne [Clouded Apollo], *Tessellata* [The Straw May Fritillary of Petiver: a variety of the Heath Fritillary], *Maturna* [Scarce Fritillary], *Hampsteadiensis* [Albin's Hampstead Eye], *Niobe* [Niobe Fritillary], *Populi* [Poplar Admiral], *Sibilla* [in this context: Southern White Admiral], *Levana* [Map Butterfly], *Huntera* [American Painted Lady], *Maera* [Large Wall Brown], *Phaedra* [Dryad], *Alcyone* [Rock Grayling].

Ligea [Arran Brown], in the cabinet of Mr. Stephens, and lately introduced into those of Mr. B. Standish, and several of our dealers. Mr. Stephens, in his Illustrations [*], acknowledges himself ignorant of the time and place of its capture, and of the name of its captor.

Mnestra [Mnestra's Ringlet]. *Hero* [Scarce Heath], not uncommon in cabinets.

Arcanius [Pearly Heath], not uncommon in cabinets. *Spini* [Blue-spot Hairstreak].

Chryseis [Purple-edged Copper]. In every collection of any importance, either in town or country; sometimes a whole series of males, females, and undersides, being displayed; to be purchased abundantly of dealers, at a price seldom exceeding one shilling for a specimen.

Hippothoë [another name for the Purple-edged Copper]. Introduced as *dispar*?

Virgauriæ [Scarce Copper]. In every collection; I have seen nearly a thousand of this species, said to be British; fine recent specimens, said to be taken last year (1835), may be purchased abundantly, and at a very low price, of many dealers. I am not aware that a single syllable, even hinting at the capture of this insect in Britain, has ever been written.

Dorylas [Turquoise Blue], *Icarius* [Amanda's Blue], *Eros* [Eros Blue]. Those described under these names varieties of *Alexis* [Common Blue]? or intended as recording the capture in this country of the species so-named on the continent?

Titus [?Castle Eden Argus**], *Malvæ* [in this context: Mallow Skipper], *Oileus* [Tropical

---

[*] *Illustrations of British Entomology* (1827–28)

[**] J. C. Dale's (1833) reference to 'P. *Titus* or P. *Salmacis*' implies it as being the Castle Eden Argus. In Humphreys and Westwood (1849) P. *Salmacis* is The Durham Argus (Castle Eden Argus); P. *Titus* is mentioned separately as being a non-native species described by Fabricius, who was mistakenly informed that it was British.

Chequered Skipper], *Sylvius* [Northern Chequered Skipper], *Bucephalus* [The Fiery Skipper], *Vitellius* [also The Fiery Skipper]:

Can any of your correspondents oblige the writer of this article with any information on either of the above-mentioned species, or with any positive fact relative to the capture of any butterflies, with the exception of the sixty-five following:—

Machaon [Swallowtail], *Rhamni* [Brimstone], *Electra* [Clouded Yellow], *Hyale* [Pale Clouded Yellow], *Brassicæ* [Large White], *Rapæ* [Small White], *Napi* [Green-veined White], *Daplidice* [Bath White], *Cardamines* [Orange-tip], *Sinapis* [Wood White], *Cratægi* [Black-veined White], *Lucina* [Duke of Burgundy Fritillary], *Athalia* [Heath Fritillary], *Artenus* [?*artemis*, an old name for the Marsh Fritillary], *Cinxia* [Glanville Fritillary], *Dia* [Weaver's Fritillary], *Selene* [Small Pearl-bordered Fritillary], *Euphrosyne* [Pearl-bordered Fritillary], *Lathonia* [Queen of Spain Fritillary], *Adippe* [High Brown Fritillary], *Aglaia* [Dark Green Fritillary], *Paphia* [Silver-washed Fritillary], *C. album* [Comma], *Polychloros* [Large Tortoiseshell], *Urticæ* [Small Tortoiseshell], *Io* [Peacock], *Antiopa* [Camberwell Beauty], *Atalanta* [Red Admiral], *Cardui* [Painted Lady], *Iris* [Purple Emperor], *Camilla* [White Admiral], *Ægeria* [Speckled Wood], *Megæra* [Wall], *Semele* [Grayling], *Galathea* [Marbled White], *Tithonus* [Gatekeeper], *Janira* [Meadow Brown], *Blandina* [old name for Scotch Argus], *Cassiope* [Small Mountain

Ringlet], *Hyperanthus* [Ringlet], *Davus* [Large Heath], *Pamphilus* [Small Heath], *Betulæ* [Brown Hairstreak], *Pruni* [Black Hairstreak], *W. album* [White-letter Hairstreak], *Quercus* [Purple Hairstreak], *Rubi* [Green Hairstreak], *Phlæas* [Small Copper], *Dispar* [Large Copper], *Argiolus* [Holly Blue], *Alsus* [old name for Small Blue], *Acis* [old name for Mazarine Blue], *Arion* [Large Blue], *Corydon* [Chalk Hill Blue], *Adonis* [Adonis Blue], *Alexis* [an old name for the Common Blue], *Argus* [Silver-studded Blue], *Agestis* [Brown Argus], *Alveolus* [an old name for the Grizzled Skipper], *Tages* [Dingy Skipper], *Paniscus* [old name for Chequered Skipper], *Linea* [Small Skipper], *Actæon* [Lulworth Skipper], *Sylvanus* [Large Skipper] and *Comma* [Silver-spotted Skipper].

The above-named sixty-five butterflies I consider unquestionably British; and of this number, *three* have been introduced since the publication of that portion of Mr. Stephen's "Illustrations," in which they would have occurred. These are *Dia*, on the authority of Mr. Weaver; *Pruni*, on the authority of Mr. Seaman; and *Actæon*, on the authority of Mr. Dale. But it must be observed that, although specimens unquestionably British of all these sixty-five insects do exist, yet the majority of the rarer ones, as *Daplidice, Lathonia, Antiopa*, &c., although exhibited as British, are decidedly and evidently exotic: the three last-named species may be purchased for a mere song. In order that I may not offend gentlemen possessing rich series of the questionable species, I subscribe myself simply,

INQUISITOR.

[Inquisitor. 1837. Article XXI. Note on butterflies questionably British. *The Entomological Magazine* 4: 177–179].

A SIGN OF THE TIMES.
THE OVER-COLLECTING OF BRITISH BUTTERFLIES

Fig. 12. The Spirit of the Age. Cover design for a popular book on butterflies published in 1913 (see page 324).

Victorian butterfly collectors often amassed huge collections, in which a single species might be represented by a series of anything between fifty and one hundred specimens. Some unscrupulous dealers went further: collecting many hundreds of specimens, often from small or isolated colonies. Fig. 21 illustrates an advertisement placed in *The Entomologist's Weekly Intelligencer* of 1857 asking for *twenty gross* of the extremely local Northern Brown Argus (*Aricia artaxerxes*). Why the editor allowed this advertisement to be published is not known. Its appearance merely served to remind readers that the time had come to take a critical look at collecting or perhaps more accurately, 'over-collecting'. The argument about collecting and 'over-collecting' continues to this day and the following note from a clergyman is typical of the correspondence that editors of some entomological journals were prepared to publish.

WHOLESALE SLAUGHTER

Rev. Walter L. Freer, Andover, Hampshire. (1938)

For many years I have been keenly interested in entomology and in a small way a collector of British Lepidoptera. Each month I look forward to reading the *Entomologist* and the records there of other collectors, but it is frequently distressing to discover in these records the number of rare insects that are often quite needlessly destroyed. In the present number (February, 1938) one contributor, for example, mentions a friend of his in the Cotswolds who on one night took at light 35 examples of *Ptilophora plumigera* [Plumed Prominent]. How unnecessary it seems that there should be this wholesale slaughter of rare insects! It serves no useful or scientific purpose, and surely such large series are quite unnecessary for the ordinary private collection. Could not some pressure be brought to bear to curb the acquisitive instincts of these unrestrained collectors? They give all entomologists a bad name, and it is naturally concluded that we are all tarred with the same brush, so that the very sight of an entomologist with a net is repulsive to many people.

(Many plans have been discussed at different times, to my knowledge, having as their objective the restraint of the over-zealous collector, but none has ever proved practical. There is no doubt that the vast majority of entomologists strongly disapprove of reckless collecting, and this "public opinion" has already had some effect. On the other hand, it may well be that at times what appears to be needless slaughter has little if any harmful effect upon the species collected. We know too little about the causes of fluctuations in insect populations to be able to dogmatize. — Ed.).

[Freer, W. L. 1938. Wholesale slaughter. *The Entomologist* 71: 66–67].

We have considerable sympathy with this outcry from the Revd Freer. The Plumed Prominent is a very local moth that inhabits calcareous areas from Dorset to Suffolk, as well as the Cotswolds and Chilterns. It flies in the early winter months and comes readily to light. There is quite clearly a marked distinction between collecting and 'over-collecting'. When Baron J. Bouck's collection came up for sale in 1938 it was found to contain over 900 specimens of the Large Blue butterfly — a species that was officially declared extinct some forty years later. The next article reports on a meeting of the Entomological Society of London at which Fellows debated this important subject.

OVER-COLLECTING — A LEARNED DEBATE

James W. Tutt, F.E.S., Blackheath, London, S. E. (1896)

Nothing shows more the advance of scientific opinions among lepidopterists than the remarkable discussion which took place at the meeting of the Entomological Society of London, on May 6th [1896]. There can be no doubt that, in the opinion of many lepidopterists, the man who simply collects is rapidly becoming a public nuisance, and it is pretty well understood that his exterminating processes act distinctly as a check to the scientific aspirations of entomologists.

The discussion showed that it was well recognised that collecting was necessary to obtain material for study; further, that large numbers of men collect with no intention of study, but merely to make a collection, which can, at some future time, be converted into cash. This led up naturally to the assumption that the large money value of purely British insects was the real basis of the evil of over-collecting. If rare British insects had a value in agreement with that of Continental specimens of the same species, it was clear that the professional collector would become a general collector of material for scientific study, instead of the exterminator of comparatively rare or local species, to fill up gaps in collections, whilst the amateur-professional, knowing that his collection had only a general value, and that no particular species had an unreasonable intrinsic value, would cease to persecute such insects as, at present, have a high money value, to the verge of extinction.

Fig. 13. Robert McLachlan F.R.S. (1837–1904) was probably the first entomologist to suggest that the extinction of certain butterflies might be due to overzealous collecting.

Mr. McLachlan opened the discussion, and pointed out that *Chrysophanus dispar* [Large Copper] and *Nomiades semiargus* [Mazarine Blue] had already undergone extinction, whilst *Lycaena arion* [Large Blue], formerly a somewhat widely distributed species, was slowly undergoing extermination at the hands of collectors. *Papilio machaon* [Swallowtail] would undoubtedly have long ago become extinct but for the inaccessibility of some of its haunts. He considered that the damage was almost entirely committed by amateur collectors, and thought that certain species should not be collected at all for some years. He stated that one of the objects he had in view in bringing this matter forward was to see whether some plan could not be devised to protect those narrowly localized species which were apparently in danger of being exterminated by over-collecting.

Mr. Goss instanced how *Melitaea cinxia* [Glanville Fritillary] and *Lycaena arion* had largely been exterminated, the former in its Isle of Wight localities, the latter in Gloucestershire. He complained bitterly of the damage done to *L. arion*, last season, by Major Still and a North London collector. He would like to draw up a Bill to prevent all collectors capturing these species for a time. He further stated that *Papilio machaon*, although apparently doomed to extinction in its chief locality in Cambridgeshire (Wicken Fen), would probably linger on in the county in smaller fens, such as Chippenham, where the larvae had been found feeding on *Angelica sylvestris* [wild angelica]. It would certainly survive in the Norfolk Broads, both from the irreclaimable nature of the fens there, and the extensive range of the species in the district, which Mr. Goss said he had explored in 1887 in boats.

Professor Meldola knew little of British collecting, but thought that schoolboys should be led rather to make observations on the habits of the living insects, than to capture and kill them for no specific purpose whatever.

Capt. Elwes thought that legislation in this direction would be somewhat difficult. He did not think that schoolboys destroyed many species. He considered that the bad seasons, which had been so detrimental to farming, had also been injurious to insect life, and that many insects disappeared from meteorological causes.

Colonel Irby said that *L. arion* had disappeared many years ago, not only from Barnwell Wold, Northamptonshire, but from another part of the county on the estate of Lord Lilford, not accessible to the public, and that its disappearance there was no doubt caused by the destruction of the food-plant and other herbage by burning the pasture, and by the grazing of sheep.

Mr. Tutt thought that it was improbable that the average seasons were now any more injurious to insect life than they had been for the last few thousand years. The question divided itself into two parts. (1) Was there overcollecting? (2) If so, how could it best be stopped? In support of the first query he instanced *Apatura iris* [Purple Emperor] and *Melitaea athalia* [Heath Fritillary], which in the "seventies" abounded in Chattenden. He had seen as many as eight amateur and two professional collectors stationed at the top of the hill (around which every specimen of *A. iris* in the wood flew from about 11 a.m. to 3 p.m.), at a distance of about two or three yards from each other, practically fighting for each specimen as it came up. For about six or seven years, a dealer from Dartford, and another from Erith, practically lived on the ground from July 12th to August 10th, never missing a fine day during the time the insect was out, their total captures decreasing from about 250 in 1880, to an odd specimen or two in 1888, since which time the species has been practically extinct. *Melitaea athalia*, being easier to catch, had fared even worse. One man, living at Soham, was practically responsible for all the damage done to *Papilio machaon*, at Wicken, the collectors of the village being too wise to kill the goose that lays the golden eggs. The extinction of the commonest butterflies in every wood within easy reach of London bore evidence to the fact that "over-collecting" did occur.

As to a remedy, Mr. Tutt thought legislation impracticable, and considered that, as the country was well covered by natural history societies, a committee should be formed to submit any information relating to over-collecting, of which it might become possessed, direct to the local association in whose district it occurred, with a request to the officers of such association to take steps to put a stop to the injury that was being done to the local fauna. He proposed a resolution that such a committee be appointed, which, being seconded by Capt. Elwes, was carried unanimously.

[Editor. 1896. A sign of the times. The over-collecting of British butterflies. *The Entomologist's Record and Journal of Variation* 8: 81–83].

Throughout most of the twentieth century the argument that collectors and over-collecting had decimated our British butterflies and even led to the demise or extinction of various species continued to exercise the press and the public. In spite of evidence to the contrary, in 1925 *The Times* newspaper promoted this argument in a number of reports which were guaranteed to upset the entomological fraternity. Percy Bright, co-author with Henry Leeds of *A Monograph of the British Aberrations of the Chalk-Hill Blue* (1938), was one of several butterfly collectors who reacted strongly to these reports.

Percy M. Bright, J.P. (1863–1941), the owner of a chain of department stores in the south-west, was Mayor of Bournemouth and the epitome of the cheque book collector. During the collecting season he would appear at well-known localities in his Rolls-Royce and inspect the captures of any other collectors present before producing his cheque book and making an offer for those specimens that took his fancy. Much of his own collecting was done for him by his ever-present chauffeur, and he was not the only lepidopterist to adopt this practice. Lord Rothschild used to appear at Worth Matravers near Swanage during the summer and, accompanied by his chauffeur, would work the steep slopes at Winspit for Chalk Hill Blues. Mr Newman, landlord of the Square and Compass at Worth Matravers (Figs 14 and 15), remembered his father telling him that the chauffeur carried a golf bag over his shoulder which usually contained three or four butterfly nets (pers. comm.).

Bright's famous collection was initially offered to the Bournemouth Corporation, but under terms that were not acceptable to them. Because of this he bequeathed his remarkable series of the Common, Chalk Hill and Adonis Blues to the South London (now the British) Entomological and Natural History Society, while the Revd J. Marcon and S. G. Castle Russell catalogued the rest of the collection for auction at Messrs Glendining & Co., in the West End of London. As with John Marcon (see p. 126), Percy Bright was also involved in a road traffic accident. But, unlike Marcon, his accident proved fatal, a vehicle striking him as he entered a Bournemouth street after laying flowers on his wife's grave.

OVER-COLLECTING

Percy M. Bright, J.P., F.R.E.S, Bournemouth, Hampshire. (1925)

Some very misleading and mischievous paragraphs have recently been appearing in the public Press, and especially in the *Times*, on this subject. Misleading, because sufficient care has not been taken in ascertaining all the facts; mischievous, as they will tend to make the property owners more ready to refuse collecting facilities, especially to young collectors, thus tending to extinguish the desire to pursue the study of Natural History in the field, and so reducing the number of field entomologists. Now, after weighing all the facts that I have been able to gather together, it appears extremely doubtful whether so-called over-collecting has been responsible for even the scarcity of any species, much less its extermination. Superabundance of any species seems invariably to precede extreme scarcity or disappearance in any locality. At any rate the facts are all against over-collecting being the cause of the scarcity of any of the species mentioned in a paragraph that recently appeared in *The Times*.

The species mentioned were *Lycaena arion* [Large Blue], *L. bellargus* [Adonis Blue] and *L. coridon* [Chalk Hill Blue]. Of the first of these it was stated that in a certain locality eight or nine collectors last year succeeded in taking only one specimen between them, and that the locality had remained unchanged since the days of the species' abundance there. These two

Fig. 14. The Square and Compass, Worth Matravers, Dorset (*c.* 1930s) — a mecca for thirsty collectors on the Purbecks.

Fig. 15. Charlie Newman (*c.* late 1940s). Landlord of The Square and Compass from 1907 until his death in 1953, he was 'mine host' to many famous collectors of the period. June Chatfield's book *F. W. Frohawk: his life and work* shows Frohawk and his daughter Valezina in a similar pose outside the inn.

statements, if true, might cause serious anxiety as to the continuance of this species in this locality. But although it is quite true that a certain number of collectors did fail to take the species there last year, it is also equally true that other collectors in the same locality found the species in quite good numbers, and certainly in no danger of disappearing. It is well

Fig. 16.
Percy Bright, Mayor of Bournemouth and the epitome of the cheque book collector.

known to those who know this species that it varies considerably in the date of its appearance, and that its emergence stretches over a long period. Last year it was very late in putting in an appearance, so the first collectors, through being too early, failed to take it, whilst the others found it in fair abundance. The second statement, that there has been no change in the local conditions, is quite untrue. Any entomologist who has known the particular Cornish localities for the past fourteen years knows that a very vital change affecting this species has taken place, one which fully accounts for its having become scarcer. The gorse has been allowed to grow up over the whole area to a much greater extent than formerly, and especially in the neighbourhood of Millook. This has choked out the food-plant of *L. arion* in many places where it was very abundant, and has also driven away the ants that play so important a part during the larval stage of this species.

The second species mentioned, *L. bellargus*, was very scarce last year, and again this year at Folkestone, one of its chief headquarters, and as there have been a good many collectors there each year they have been blamed for bringing this about. But surely some little inquiry should have been made into other facts bearing on the situation before such hasty and unjustified conclusions were arrived at. One has only to search the records of the past to discover that periodically this species becomes exceedingly scarce. Moreover, it is not only in this well-known locality that *L. bellargus* has become much scarcer, but in most, if not all English localities where it occurs. I know of at least eight or ten other localities where usually it has been found in fair abundance, in which, although a net is hardly ever seen, it has become equally scarce.

Then as to the last of the three species, *L. coridon*, nobody who has the slightest knowledge of the range of localities and periodical abundance of this species can seriously maintain that there is the slightest possible danger of its being exterminated, or even made scarce, by any conceivable number of collectors. But here again there has been no careful collection of facts and judicial weighing of them. Just because it was very abundant in the Chilterns one year, and many collectors were attracted there by the large numbers of var. *syngrapha*, whilst the next year it was very scarce, without any further consideration, the poor collector is blamed for over-collecting *coridon*, at all events in this locality. Yet the facts are all against this conclusion. I happened to be in that particular locality for twenty-four hours quite late in the last season in which *coridon* was abundant there, and I found both males and females flying in great abundance, most of them being in a worn condition, with perhaps 15 per cent quite fresh. It is no exaggeration to say that millions of fertile eggs must have been laid that year, and yet the very next season *coridon* was extremely scarce there. It is therefore quite evident we must look for reasons other than over-collecting to account for this. Besides, how is it possible to blame collectors for this sort of thing when in the locality where this species has been most collected it has been more consistently abundant during the last ten years than in any other locality that I know — and I have personal knowledge of at least twenty?

Another species that has been mentioned in the pages of the *Entomologist* is *M. athalia* [Heath Fritillary], and I am rather surprised that *M. aurinia* [Marsh Fritillary] has not been added to the list. What are the facts concerning *M. athalia* in the Kent Woods? It is to these localities that reference has been made. At no time has the species been so well established and in so many localities as now. This year it occurred in thousands quite close to the original locality, and also in some others where it had been introduced. But the fact that has not been referred to, and which largely governs the exact spots in which this species occurs in anything like abundance, is that its food-plant grows only where the undergrowth is sufficiently low to give it air and sunshine.

In my opinion the facts that I have been able to gather together indicate that the more a locality is collected in the more certain is a species to remain abundant there. And if that is true, I assume it is probably because the varieties that entomologist so much prize are the products of weakness rather than virility in the colony, and therefore the more effectually they are weeded out the better for the species. I would even go further, and seriously doubt the wisdom of trying to provide sanctuaries for species even such as *Papilio machaon* [Swallowtail], for it is certainly true of this species that it is more abundant in other localities than it is at Wicken.

I have pleaded before, and I plead again, for the careful, unbiased and unprejudiced consideration of all the available facts that may help us to a fuller knowledge of the undoubtedly difficult and complex question of the varying abundance and scarcity of almost all our species of British butterflies in different years.

[Bright, P. M. 1925. Over-collecting. *The Entomologist* 58: 273–275].

A Monograph of the British Aberrations of the Chalk-hill Blue, **published in 1938, is an attractive volume, being embellished with a number of coloured and monochrome plates and originally bound in leather. In this work the two authors, P. M. Bright and H. A. Leeds, identify around 400 different aberrations. Inserted loose into later copies of the book was a leaflet by Leeds entitled: 'Important Announcement to Natural History Societies, Etc., and Lepidopterists', that included an order form. Dated May, 1941, it ended: 'P.S. — If any library has lost a book by enemy action, please let me know, as, if possible, it will be replaced.'**

Fig. 17. Henry Attfield Leeds, the railway clerk who devoted most of his leisure time to naming over 400 aberrations of the Chalk Hill Blue.

Henry Attfield Leeds (1873–1958) (Figs 17 and 18) was both a dedicated collector and namer of butterfly aberrations. He would visit the Chalk Hill Blue colony at Royston each year, where he would be 'on the Heath as early as eight a.m.' and could be found 'inspecting resting specimens with a bicycle lamp after dark'. On one occasion, 'he was butted from behind by a deer while he was stooped over examining moths feeding at a sugaring site' (unpublished biography by John Chance). Apart from his entomological activities Henry Leeds was a noted athlete, amassing over sixty prizes from various sprinting events. He worked in the Goods Manager's Office at King's Cross Station, and on retirement in 1933 settled in Wood Walton. An annotated page from his personal copy of the Bright and Leeds '*Monograph*' (Fig. 19) shows the neat and very distinctive handwriting he employed on his data labels.

Fig. 18. H. A. Leeds and friends at Wood Walton, Huntingdonshire (*c.* 1934). In 1942 he generously presented his long and varied series of the Meadow Brown, Gatekeeper and Small Heath to the South London Entomological and Natural History Society.

According to L. Hugh Newman (1967), Bright's collection 'was so vast, containing so many rare and unique butterflies, that its sale had to be divided into five separate sessions, spreading over a period of two years'. From this it would appear that Percy Bright was well qualified to write on the subject of 'over-collecting'. However, P. P. Graves, of London, was incensed by Bright's article. He just could not reconcile the idea of 'over-collecting' with species survival within a given habitat.

Letter from P. P. Graves to *The Entomologist*, December 1925:

Mr. Percy Bright's letter published under the above title in the *Entomologist* last month is an interesting but unconvincing attempt to uphold the theory that no species of butterfly can have been exterminated or is likely to be exterminated by over-collecting. Unconvincing, because Mr. Bright is obviously unfamiliar with the history of disappearance of certain localized species from their habitats both in this country and abroad, and because he bases his arguments on certain unproven assumptions; interesting, as revealing the danger of employing arguments which may be pushed to the most startling logical conclusions. . . .

So much for Mr. Bright's facts. They lead him to the remarkable inference that "the more a locality is collected in the more certain is a species to remain abundant there." Now collecting means killing, for I cannot think that Mr. Bright takes his *arion* [Large Blue] and *thetis* [Adonis Blue] home to decorate his garden. So, abandoning the agreeable vision of an entomologist in a blue halo of fluttering *Lycaenids* canonizing the saviour of their race, and omitting to speculate how species managed to survive their own aberrations before the kind collector came to care for them, I arrive at the following conclusion, the logical result of his premises: "The more a species frequenting a locality is killed in that locality, the more

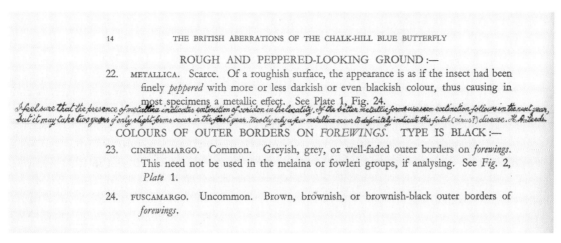

14   THE BRITISH ABERRATIONS OF THE CHALK-HILL BLUE BUTTERFLY

ROUGH AND PEPPERED-LOOKING GROUND :—

22.   METALLICA. Scarce. Of a roughish surface, the appearance is as if the insect had been finely *peppered* with more or less darkish or even blackish colour, thus causing in most specimens a metallic effect. See Plate 1, Fig. 24.

I feel sure that the presence of metallica indicates extinction of vision in the locality, of the better metallic forms are seen extinction follows in the next year, but it may take two years if only slight forms occur in the first year. Mostly only a few metallica occur to definitely indicate this fatal (virus?) disease. H. A. Leeds.

COLOURS OF OUTER BORDERS ON *FOREWINGS*.   TYPE IS BLACK :—

23.   CINEREAMARGO. Common. Greyish, grey, or well-faded outer borders on *forewings*. This need not be used in the melaina or fowleri groups, if analysing. See *Fig. 2, Plate* 1.

24.   FUSCAMARGO. Uncommon. Brown, brownish, or brownish-black outer borders of *forewings*.

Fig. 19. Annotated page from H. A. Leeds' personal copy of *A Monograph of the British Aberrations of the Chalk-Hill Blue*. His neat handwriting is a distinctive feature of his specimen labels.

certain it is to remain abundant there." Therefore it is useless to preserve or protect anything, salmon included, for the more they are collected — for cabinets or for kitchens matters not — the more they will prosper. Therefore the butcher = the benefactor. Therefore *Homo sapiens*, to benefit his own species, ought — " but, Heavens, this is the *Entomologist* and not a militarist organ. But shades of the Great Auk and the Large Copper, it *is* a remarkable theory.

[Graves, P. P. 1925. Over-collecting. *The Entomologist* 58: 297–298].

Philip Perceval Graves, F.E.S. (1876–1953) was born at Bantry, Co. Cork. Educated at Haileybury and Oriel College, Oxford, he became well known as *The Times* correspondent in the Near East. During the First World War he served with the rank of captain in military intelligence in Egypt, and one of his duties was to handle Lawrence of Arabia. He developed his interest in entomology during his many travels throughout Palestine, Bulgaria and Egypt. On retirement he made a particular study of the Irish Rhopalocera, and he described the Irish subspecies of the Meadow Brown (*Maniola jurtina* ssp. *iernes* Graves). His obituarist wrote of him as being a 'conversationalist of outstanding character'.

The argument about collecting and 'over-collecting' continued. As we have seen, the Revd Walter Freer (1938) reacted strongly to the 'wholesale slaughter', as he termed it, of the Plumed Prominent (*Ptilophora plumigera*). Fifteen years later when P. A. Desmond Lanktree purchased a copy of J. W. Tutt's *British Butterflies* (1896) he found it contained a miscellany of enclosures, including a number of newspaper cuttings. These were from *The Standard* and were probably published in 1899. The cuttings referred to a letter from the Revd Frank E. Lowe, in which he reported the discovery of large numbers of the Long-tailed Blue butterfly (*Lampides boeticus*) in Guernsey. What Mr Lowe did next clearly upset some of his readers.

Letter from the Revd Frank E. Lowe, F.E.S., St Stephen's Vicarage, Guernsey, to the Editor, *The Standard*, 13th September (?1899):

Sir, — Because it should interest others than "mere collectors" of butterflies, I venture to ask a corner in your paper to record the remarkable abundance of the "long-tailed blue" in Guernsey. Its headquarters appear to be in my own garden on the outskirts of the town. Here I have taken for myself, or friends, over eighty specimens, besides others which have been given their liberty again. On September 1 took eleven, including two females, and daily since I have taken some. On September 4, I netted thirty-three specimens in all. This species is very rare in Northern and Central Europe, though not uncommon on the Mediterranean coast and Asia, extending to Australia and the Cape. Its sudden appearance, therefore, in numbers in this little spot, in spite of its reputed tendencies for migration, is very perplexing. Messrs. Newman and Tutt, in their respective "Histories of British

Butterflies", quoting evidently the same authority, say "In 1859 the species was abundant in the Channel Islands". Perhaps this refers to Jersey, but as to Guernsey, I believe the facts are these. In 1859 Miss Renouf took eight specimens of *L. boetica*, and one more in August, 1872. The next recorded capture is one by myself in this same garden, on September 15, 1892. About two years earlier, a schoolboy is reported also to have taken a battered specimen on the sea coast.

Thus it will be seen that it is forty years since more than one specimen has been taken in the same season in this Island, and now they are to be had *ad lib.* [*]

This letter provoked a number of replies, two of which were anything but complimentary. It will be seen, however, that Mr Stephen H. Terry, the second correspondent, rather spoiled his case by engaging in an extraordinary flight of fancy.

Fig. 20. Revd Frank E. Lowe (1853-1918), Rector of St Stephen's, Guernsey. He was taken to task in the press for catching too many Long-tailed Blues.

a) Letter from T. Lloyd Davis of Gunnersbury, W. London, to the Editor, *The Standard*, 14th September (?1899):

Sir, — From a letter in *The Standard* of to-day, I gather that the Rev. Frank E. Lowe is to be congratulated on his good fortune, for his vicarage garden in Guernsey appears to be the headquarters of the "long-tailed blue", over eighty specimens of this rare but all too confiding butterfly having been netted by our energetic informant during the last few days.

In this period of complaint about diminished incomes, it is pleasing to note that someone has an opportunity for increasing his official emoluments; and the zeal for extermination with which Mr. Lowe is fired, justifies me in suggesting that both by art and nature he is eminently qualified to set up a "corner" in long-tailed blues.

b) Letter from Stephen H. Terry, Whitehall Club, Parliament Street, London, S. W., to the Editor, *The Standard*, 14th September (?1899):

Sir, — Your Correspondent, a clergyman, the Rev. F. E. Lowe, writes with great complacency of having destroyed eighty specimens of a rare butterfly. It seems to me that,

[*] Perhaps partly in response to the criticism his letter subsequently attracted, when, a few years later, the Revd Lowe wrote to *The Entomologist's Record* (1904) to report that *boetica* had again bred on the island and had appeared in some numbers in his garden, he pointedly remarked 'I captured one or two for examination, which I, however, set free again.'

instead of rushing into print on this subject and so leading others (with about an equal respect for the vital spark in created beings) to destroy the remaining specimens, he should think quietly over this wanton destruction, and be thoroughly ashamed of himself. It is actions such as his that render any beautiful specimens, whether bird, beast, or insect, extinct. What can exceed in grace and beauty a living humming-bird moth poised on the wing, or darting to fresh flowers; yet the average boy taught by Mr. Lowe would consider such an insect more beautiful in a cabinet with a pin stuck through it.

In 1865, in a boat off Sea View [Isle of Wight], I saw for a few moments, resting on the boat, the last specimen of the Apollo butterfly seen in England. I might easily have caught it. I stopped the boatman from doing so. I knew its rarity and wished it to live. This the most beautiful of all our British butterflies, now extinct, was once common in the Isle of Wight, but building operations, and cutting down of the trees and shrubs on which the caterpillars fed made it scarce, and the "bug-hunter" did the rest. How can we expect ladies to give up wearing aigrettes because of the destruction of bird life involved, when we have a clergyman boasting of having killed eighty specimens of a rare butterfly — thirty-three in one day. A novel has lately been written, called "The Lust of Hate". It seems to me what is wanted is a homily, with examples on the lust of destruction.

[Lanktree, P. A. Desmond, 1960. Some old records of Lepidoptera, and "The last Apollo seen in England" — an allegation referring to 95 years ago. *The Entomologist's Record and Journal of Variation* **72**: 120–125].

When Mr Terry suggested that the Apollo (*Parnassius apollo*) was 'once common in the Isle of Wight' he was clearly imagining things. There is but slender evidence that this species has ever been resident in the British Isles, although very occasional immigrant specimens have been recorded (e.g. Scott, 1955). It does not appear to have ever inhabited the Isle of Wight. And when Mr Terry wrote that 'building operations, and cutting down of the trees and shrubs on which the caterpillars fed made it scarce', he was on even more dangerous ground. The caterpillars of this species do not feed on 'trees and shrubs', but the low-growing stonecrop (*Sedum* spp.) and similar plants.

The above correspondence is thought to date from 1899. However, the argument about 'over-collecting' goes back a great deal further. In 1875 H. Ramsay Cox greatly upset colleagues when he dared to suggest that the 'good old free spirit of collecting' had vanished. Instead of soliciting agreement from other lepidopterists, his letter resulted in a most extraordinary reply from Arnold Lewis, F.L.S. Did anyone really catch 800 Pale Clouded Yellows?

'THE MAN WHO CAUGHT 800 PALE CLOUDED YELLOWS'

Letter from H. Ramsay Cox to *The Entomologist* 11th April 1875:

Collecting is at present carried on very differently from how it was fifteen or twenty years ago. It is now much harder work than it was then, owing to the great number there are in the field. So far so good; but (which is much to be lamented) the good old free spirit of collecting is rarely to be found. Years ago, when a few entomologists started on a day's ruralizing, what unbiassed delight was experienced and evinced by us all! We started at early morn, intent on one object, — a day's thorough and innocent enjoyment. If one of our number captured a rarity we *all* were pleased; how we congratulated him, and loved to admire his specimen! If the rest of us were unfortunate there was no grumbling, no unpleasant exhibition of the "green-eyed monster;" there were no insinuations of Mr. Dealer

So-and-so having that season imported a few gross of continental pupae, and of having placed them in the woods for development, with a view to "making" them "British."

The object was, then, principally a day's innocent pleasure, and not so much with a view to amassing a large number of specimens in the shortest possible time. We want some of that collecting spirit now, for the *pleasure* of entomological rambles is comparatively little sought after; it is, "Who has the largest collection?" And much to the disgrace to many of our time, if collectors cannot get their coveted specimens by honest exertions, they will cheat in exchanging (or "bartering," as one of our best Lepidopterists facetiously termed it); or else procure foreign specimens, and insert them as British. Shame on these collectors; their originally pure pursuit is getting more dishonest than English horse-dealing.

WANTED TO PURCHASE, about Twenty Gross of the SCOTCH ARGUS (*P. Artaxerxes*), in good condition, either alive or set. Also any quantity of good second-hand CABINETS, at reasonable prices. By James Gardner, Naturalist, 52, High Holborn, London.

N.B. Carcases with sliding trays not acceptable.

Fig. 21. Advertisement in *The Entomologist's Weekly Intelligencer* (1857).

A proof of the deterioration of the manners of most of our collectors is that they are now generally considered, by the non-entomological public, as persons of questionable character. A gentleman, maybe perhaps one of large independent property, or perhaps a "reverend divine," is staying with his family at a village; ere he exhibits his deadly weapons he is considered quite *comme il faut*, but let him once show his amusement he is immediately dubbed as "only a fly-catcher;" he is snubbed by the world in general, and looked at by all as some one to be carefully avoided. This is no mere conjecture, as I have repeatedly of late noticed it in various parts of England. . . .

Those who may chance to read these few hasty remarks will perhaps say: "What is the *use* of thus complaining?" To which I reply: "Can we not start a new clique of collectors, who, throwing aside all contamination they may have imbibed from the modern school, will follow the Science in its original and pure manner, arrange their gatherings for a day's sport, and collect or exchange in the style of the 'good old times?' "

[Cox, H. Ramsay, 1875. Collecting as it was, and as it now is. *The Entomologist* 8: 103–104].

Letter from W. Arnold Lewis, F.L.S. to *The Entomologist*, 20th May 1875:

. . . I can confirm Mr. Cox's reference to "the good old free spirit of collecting." Free enough, in all conscience, that collecting was. I have myself spoken with a gentleman who in one year captured on the south coast *eight hundred* specimens of Colias Hyale [Pale Clouded Yellow], and I recollect that he boasted roundly of the exploit! The same once informed me,  when I was in search of the second brood of Leucophasia sinapis [Wood White], that I need not expect again to see that insect in the neighbourhood, because he had that season *taken the whole spring brood.* It is possible that your correspondent has himself heard of these incidents, or others like them; and on these facts I should wish to make one or two remarks.

Anyone who captures eight hundred butterflies of one kind, when his own collection receives perhaps four-and-twenty, must have a very distinct *motive.* Mr. Cox speaks most truly when he hints that "the pleasure of entomological rambles" could have little to do with such a feat. What pleasure, in truth, could come from taking the lives of eight hundred defenceless Hyale? After the capture of, let us say, the first one hundred and fifty, sensations of "pleasure" must have begun to give way to physical fatigue. In Mr. Cox's expressive words, the object was once "principally a day's innocent pleasure, and not so much with a view to amassing a large number of specimens in the shortest possible time." But certainly in the case of the eight hundred, "amassing the large number" must have remained the motive long after pleasure, innocent or not, had left the scene. Setting out eight hundred butterflies must be a very tiresome business, and probably no other collector has experience of the labour it entails; seven hundred and seventy six Hyale, we may suppose, would be of no use to the captor, and they would remain over for distribution to Lepidopterists in want of the species. One almost envies this hard-working collector the spectacle of their "unbiassed delight." I am not perfectly informed whether this was the course taken by the captor of the eight hundred; but, if it was, he has doubtless made himself the most popular collector in the country. Far be it from me to say that this gentleman was anticipating "the modern school." I merely suggest that such a feat of the old, free spirit of collecting scarcely answers to "a day's enjoyment," but savours rather of "amassing specimens." . . .

As to collectors' demeanour towards each other, that is a subject which has caused me reflections times and oft. The mysteries made about a locality; petty dissimulations about times of appearance (to throw another off the scent); concealments of the facts of capture being made; these and other paltry and more detestable things are, I fear, common. It must be really shocking to encounter a collector with a stock-in-trade of all these arts . . . The evil has grown entirely out of the fictitious value ascribed to native specimens, and must vanish, like a breath, directly foreign specimens are admitted to have an equal worth. . . .

[Lewis, W. Arnold, 1875. Some remarks on collecting and collectors. *The Entomologist* **8**: 127–130].

Letter from Mr H. Ramsay Cox to *The Entomologist*, 14th June 1875:

When I began reading Mr. Lewis's remarks on this subject (*Entom.* 8: 127) I thought his rhetoric and clever insinuation respecting the eight hundred Colias Hyale referred to myself (by the bye, I fail to see why "defenceless" should be especially applied to that species), as I, in company with three other collectors, did capture about that number a few years ago, and, not having heard of a similar number being taken by others, I presumed he referred to me. Glad was I to find, on continuing, that it was not so; and lest some readers, who have either forgotten or did not read the circumstances under which these Hyale were caught, should be misled by Mr. Lewis's paper, and so connect me with the attempted extermination of the "gentle creature, Sinapis," I crave a few lines space. At p. 179, vol. iv., of the 'Entomologist,' it will be seen that *four* of us were collecting; and as we were more than *three weeks* getting the number, the "physical fatigue" was therefore not so very great: an average of two hundred and fifty specimens a week is surely not *very* hard work for four enthusiastic collectors! Great pleasure most certainly did come through my success, which enabled me to give some of my friends some very fine series of this insect. I also attempted a little exchanging, but soon found the greatest pleasure was to be obtained in giving them away. As to the man who took "the whole of the spring brood" of Sinapis, it is the first I have heard of it. Anyone who could attempt such a mean and selfish action (unless he were a dealer, — it would be pardonable then), should be treated with silent disdain and contempt.

[Cox, H. Ramsay, 1875. A few remarks on some collectors. *The Entomologist* 8: 179–180].

It was at this point that Edward Newman, Editor of *The Entomologist*, intervened with the comment: 'This little passage-of-arms must end here.'

> A Wigan collector called Caley
> Used to water his window-box daily,
> It was full of lucerne
> And he thirsted to learn
> Why he never caught sight of *hyale*.
>
> R. S.

[R. S. (Air Marshal Sir Robert Saundby) 1952. *Entomologist's Gazette* 3: 2].

Butterfly collecting today is in decline. Long gone are the days when south coast trains disgorged their army of weekend collectors, and hotels and boarding houses in the New Forest and other 'good spots' for butterfly collecting were booked up months ahead by the real enthusiasts. As the dangers posed by habitat loss and degradation become evermore apparent and the need to take specimens of our common butterflies has diminished, butterfly enthusiasts nowadays will more often pursue their quarry with camera and binoculars than with a net.

In the 1970s the conservation movement gained pace with the publication by the Joint Committee for the Conservation of British Insects (now called Invertebrate Link) of *A Code for Collecting Insects and Other Invertebrates*. The latest update of this code has recently been published and is widely supported by various entomological societies and invertebrate enthusiasts alike. In 1975 the Conservation of Wild Creatures and Wild Plants Act was passed; it included the legal protection of one butterfly, the Large Blue. This Act was quickly superseded by the Wildlife and Countryside Act 1981 which extended complete protection to a few of the most endangered species of butterflies and moths and protection against trading in a further list of vulnerable species. There are quinquennial reviews of the species offered protection by this Act, with an opportunity to add or delete species from the various

schedules. Many amateur entomologists enthusiastically support the work being done by the conservation bodies to increase our knowledge of insect distribution and to protect their special habitats, and find this outlet for their interest in insects to be most rewarding.

DESTRUCTION OF SWALLOWTAIL LARVAE BY CUCKOOS

F. W. Frohawk, F.E.S., M.B.O.U., Thundersley, Essex. (1922)

Frederick William Frohawk (1861–1946) was not only one of the finest entomological illustrators of the twentieth century (see Plate 5) but also a first-rate field naturalist. In this short communication he reports a previously unknown cause of mortality in Swallowtail larvae.

It is generally supposed that brightly coloured larvæ are immune from the attacks of birds owing to such ornamentation acting as a protective colouring, and as a rule certain species possessing the so-called warning colours are undoubtedly distasteful to birds — for instance, I know of no bird which feeds on the larva of *Pieris brassicae* [Large White], which although not brilliantly coloured, is nevertheless a conspicuous object. I have often watched several species of birds such as garden warblers, wrens, robins, hedge-sparrows and blue titmice, all busily engaged in searching beds of cabbages for the larvæ of *Pieris rapae* [Small White], which they manage readily to detect although their coloration harmonises perfectly with the colour of the leaves, and greedily devouring them, but I have never seen any bird attempt to eat the larva of *P. brassicae*, which are passed unnoticed by all birds, although they are among the most conspicuous larvæ in their manner of living fully exposed on both surfaces of the leaves. Whether *brassicae* larvæ are eaten by the cuckoo I have failed to determine; certainly those of which I have examined the stomachs have contained no trace of these larvæ. Unfortunately the handsome and richly ornamented larva of *Papilio machaon* [Swallowtail] is a favourite diet of the cuckoo (although it might be considered distasteful owing to its brilliant colouring, and the forked retractile tubercles emitting a strong acrid scent which are protruded when the larva is irritated) according to the facts stated by the late Mr. Fergus M. Ogilvie, who was one of the most skilled and accurate of field naturalists. I therefore think it may be of general interest to other entomologists to quote the following observations made in Norfolk and recorded by him. I omit the precise locality for obvious reasons. Mr. Ogilvie states — "One young cuckoo, obtained July 27th, contained a considerable number of the larvæ of the swallow-tailed butterfly. . . . Cuckoos are exceeding plentiful here. They are distributed in greater numbers over the Broad district than in any other locality with which I am acquainted. . . . I have little doubt that the cuckoo of the Broad lays a heavy toll on the swallow-tailed larvæ when they are in season. It may well be that the progressive diminution of this — our handsomest butterfly — is in some measure due to the quantity of cuckoos in the district and their insatiable appetites."

It might be argued that as both the cuckoo and *machaon* have been in existence for ages, these butterflies would in course of time have long since ceased to exist where cuckoos abounded, but when we know that birds sometimes gradually acquire a liking for a new diet, which naturally becomes an inherited habit, such may possibly be the cause for the now prevailing fondness of cuckoos for *machaon* larvæ, and if such is the case this fine insect may finally disappear from its British haunts.

[Frohawk, F. W. 1922. Destruction of *Papilio machaon* larvæ by cuckoos. *The Entomologist* **55**: 280–281].

Fig. 22. Frederick W. Frohawk with his daughter Valezina, whom he named after a striking form of the female Silver-washed Fritillary.

Fig. 23. Frohawk's grave at Headley, Surrey, is surmounted by a wooden cross which bears a carving of the Camberwell Beauty (2003).

June Chatfield (1987), Frohawk's biographer, recalls that 'the old man of the forest', as he became known, was closely associated with the New Forest over the best part of his lifetime. He made many annual pilgrimages there in search of butterflies and recorded his detailed memories in a journal:

> Insects of all kinds literally swarmed. Butterflies were in profusion, the Silver-washed Fritillary (*Argynnis paphia*) were in hoards in every ride and the beautiful var. *valezina* was met with at every few yards as were both the Dark Green and High Brown Fritillaries, the elegant White Admiral (*Limenitis camilla*) were sailing about in quantity everywhere. On a bank under a sallow was a large female Purple Emperor (*Apatura iris*) with its wings expanded in the sun, evidently washed out of the sallow by rain. The Large Tortoiseshell (*Nymphalis polychloros*) was a frequent occurrence and the Brimstone (*Gonepteryx rhamni*) abundant in every ride.

Frohawk died at his home near Epsom in 1946. His grave at Headley, on the Surrey Downs, bears a simple wooden cross on which is carved a Camberwell Beauty (Fig. 23). Valezina, his daughter from his second marriage, was named after the beautiful var. *valesina* of the Silver-washed Fritillary. 'With her auburn hair she was strikingly attractive', and her musical talent was such that she studied the cello under the world-famous cellist Suggia. When her father died Valezina married Lord Bolingbroke, an entomological family friend.

THE LARGE COPPER AND LARGE BLUE BUTTERFLIES

More has probably been written about these two butterflies than most others. But many of the early accounts of the Large Copper are very confusing. This confusion stems from the fact that there are three different 'Large' Coppers, viz: the English *Lycaena dispar* Haworth, and two Continental subspecies. One of these, *L. dispar batavus* (Oberthür), is confined to the Friesland area of northern Holland, while *L. dispar rutilus* Werneburg, first discovered near Berlin, can be found widely distributed throughout Europe. Many of the early authors appeared to confuse the names of these subspecies, although there is anecdotal evidence (see p. 45) that *L. dispar rutilus* may have once occurred in the Cambridgeshire Fens. Apart from the Large Copper itself, there are two other 'large' or 'largish' copper butterflies, one of which, *Lycaena virgaureae* (Linnaeus), the Scarce Copper, may have occurred in England up to the eighteenth century. The other, *L. hippothoë* (Linnaeus), the Purple-edged Copper, has probably never occurred in England. Both species are common in France, Germany and other parts of Europe. James W. Tutt, the eminent lepidopterist, wrote important articles on the British history of both the Large Copper and Large Blue butterflies and we have included abridged versions of these, as well as a number of other letters, notes and short articles.

THE LARGE COPPER BUTTERFLY (*CHRYSOPHANUS DISPAR*)

James W. Tutt, F.E.S., Blackheath, London, S. E. (1896)

The Large Copper butterfly was first noticed as being a British species by Lewin in his *Insects of Great Britain* (1793). Under the name of *hippothoë*, he figures it on Pl. 40 of that work, and states that specimens were met with by a gentleman in Huntingdonshire, on a piece of moorland. The specimens were afterwards sent to Mr. Seymer, F.L.S., of Dorsetshire, who presented them to the late Dowager-Duchess of Portland.*

At the time that Lewin's work was published, Donovan was producing (in parts) *The Natural History of British Insects*. He also figured (Plate 117) the Large Copper under the name of *hippothoë* [actually the specific name of the Purple-edged Copper], and it was not until Haworth published the *Lepidoptera Britannica* (1803), that the name *dispar* was applied to our British insect, which was described as "a new and very beautiful species." . . . Until this date all the authors who had called the British insect *hippothoë* had done so under the impression that the British insect was the *hippothoë* of Linné, which, however, is another species. Among other things, Donovan asserted that this butterfly had been taken in Scotland.

Returning to Haworth, we find that he informs us that "the butterfly in July frequents the marshes of Cambridgeshire in certain but indeterminable years," further, "that it is a new and very beautiful species, lately detected by himself and his very dear friends W. Skrimshire and F. Skrimshire, M.D., and formerly in Wales by the celebrated botanist, Hudson." He also adds that the species has not been taken in Scotland, as Donovan has affirmed from erroneous information. It would appear that the Messrs. Skrimshire first saw the butterfly near Ely, in 1797 or 1798, and that, knowing it was not a common one, they afterwards went with Haworth to capture it. . . .

---

* We wonder whether Mr. Davies can tell us whether these are included in the Catalogue of insects, sold with the Duchess of Portland's collection, that he has? Specimens of *C. virgaureae* (two pairs) are included, *vide, Ent. Record,* **5**: 126.— ED.

Before leaving Haworth's own published remarks, it may be well to quote a letter of his on the subject to the Rev. W. T. Bree, who communicated it to Loudon's [*Magazine of*] *Natural History*, 1834. In this Haworth remarks:— "Some entomologists once made an excursion into the fens for the purpose of taking the beautiful *Lycaena dispar*, or Large Copper butterfly, which, it is well-known, frequents low marshy grounds. The Coppers were captured in great abundance. It so happened that the following winter proved to be a very wet one, and the entire tract of land where the Coppers had been found was completely inundated, and actually lay under water for a considerable time. The entomologists deemed that the flood would certainly destroy the Coppers, and that the race would become extinct in that part of the country. The next summer, however, the butterflies were found again on the very same spot, as plentifully as before. Subsequently the tract of land was submitted to the action of fire, and the whole surface burnt, with a view to agricultural improvement. After this operation, the Coppers were no longer met with in that particular locality."

Kirby and Spence (1826) make reference to this species, in their *Introduction to Entomology*, in the following sentence:— "Morasses also have their peculiar insects. In this kind of district, in the Isle of Ely, has been taken that scarce and beautiful butterfly, *Lycaena virgaureae*, by a Fellow of Trinity College, Cambridge," [Mr Wolley] showing that even then the nomenclature, as in use among British lepidopterists, was somewhat mixed.

Mr C. W. Dale [1890] asserts that, after the capture of the specimens mentioned as having been taken by Haworth and the Messrs. Skrimshire, "the next specimens were taken at Whittlesea Mere, by Thomas Speechly, an old boatman in my father's employ, in July, 1819, and subsequently by my father himself and the Messrs. Standish. It appears to have occurred in great plenty, as several hundreds were taken within the next ten years by the London collectors, who visited Whittlesea and Yaxley Meres during the month of July, for the sole purpose of obtaining specimens. In 1827, Mr Haworth took fifty specimens in a single day in Bardolph Fen, Norfolk; a few also were taken at Benacre, in Suffolk."

In 1828, Stephens wrote of this species as follows:— "This splendid insect appears to be confined to the fenny counties of Cambridge and Huntingdon, with the neighbouring ones of Suffolk and Norfolk, unless the account of its capture in Wales by Hudson be admitted; but this may probably be the following species (*hippothoë*), which may, moreover, eventually prove synonymous with *L. dispar*. In the first two localities it appears to occur in great profusion, as several hundred specimens have been captured within these last ten years by the London collectors, who have visited Whittlesea and Yaxley Meres during the month of July, for the sole purpose of obtaining specimens of this insect, which is also stated to occur on the coast of Suffolk, at Benacre; but that locality may, however, belong to the next insect."

It is very dubious for which of the Coppers Stephens' *hippothoë* was meant. One would, on reading his comparison of it with *L. dispar*, be inclined to agree with him that it was an aberration of the latter, "the female of *hippothoë* differing from that of *L. dispar* in having the spots on the upper surface of the anterior wings smaller, and in having the entire disc of the posterior wings above dusky, clouded with deeper spots, and without the fulvous nervures; the under surface has fewer and smaller spots than *L. dispar*."

The general remarks that follow, however, tend to lead one to the conclusion that it was an imported Continental species . . . Of the insect described under the name of *hippothoë*, Stephens writes:— "The inferior size of the above insect, as well as the differences in the number and size of the ocellated spots on the lower surface of the wings, and the colour of the upper surface of the inferior ones of the female, combined with the circumstance that, amongst several hundreds of *L. dispar* which have been taken at Whittlesea Mere, not one specimen occurred agreeing with the above definition, seem to point out the present insect as a different species. The male which I possess was in the late Mr. Beckwith's collection, and the female is in that of Mr. Haworth, who informs me that he obtained it many years since from an old cabinet that was formed by a gentleman residing in Kent, and which contained scarcely any insect that was not the production of that county, thence called the 'Kentish Cabinet,' which renders it probable, as Mr. Haworth surmises, that the true locality of the insect is Kent." So little care was taken in those early days to separate British and Continental specimens, that one is driven to conclude that this must have been an importation. That either Stephens' or Haworth's specimen was a Kentish one, we do not for a moment believe. The description suggests that the species is indeed the *rutilus* form of *C. dispar*.

There is something to be said in favour of considering these to be really British specimens of the *rutilus* form, for Mr. G. Bethune-Baker [1892] states that this form was undoubtedly taken in Britain. He writes:— "I have known for many years that my father took both ordinary *C. dispar* and var. *rutilus* some time between 1825 and 1834. My father tells me he captured all his specimens (eight in number) himself, all of which are in my collection, *viz.*, five ♂ and three ♀. One male is typical *rutilus*, another almost typical, but with slightly larger spots, whilst a third is midway between *dispar* and *rutilus*, the remaining two are true *dispar*. Of the females, one is fairly typical *rutilus*, another is on the upper side like the darker

specimens occasionally taken on the Continent, *viz.*, with larger spots on the upper wings, but the spots beneath are decidedly larger than any of my var. *rutilus*, whilst the third is true *dispar*" (*Entomologist's mon. Mag.* **28**: 190).

But the day of extinction was not very remote, for in 1847 or 1848, the last capture of this species in Britain was made by Mr. Stretton, who took five specimens in Holme Fen. Thenceforth, all references to British *C. dispar* are in the nature of reminiscences of what the insect was.

Many of these reminiscences are interesting. One of these was recently penned by that entomological Nestor, Mr. Sam[uel] Stevens, now undoubtedly *the* father of British entomologists. He writes, "I well remember, at the meeting of the British Association at Cambridge, in the year, I think 1844 or 1845, I was introduced by Mr. Vernon Wollaston, or Rev. Hamlet Clark, to a man of the name of Rawlinson, the "Pie-man," he was called. He used to go out for gentlemen of the University, to collect for them in the Fens — plants, insects, and other objects of Natural History — in the summer time, but in the winter he sold pies. Rawlinson asked me if I wanted caterpillars of the Large Copper; I said I could do with a few. Two days afterwards he brought me a dozen; I told him six would be enough, which I purchased of him at the price he asked, sixpence each. I took them home and bred five fine and perfect specimens. At that time one could buy the butterfly, from Argent and other London dealers, at 1s. and 2s. each. If one could only have anticipated what has happened, I should certainly have taken the dozen caterpillars and laid in a large stock of butterflies, for a little fortune might be made out of them." (*Science Gossip*, 1895, p. 20).

Another reminiscence, which, written as it was by a professional collector ("old Harding," of Deal), has a pathetic interest, as it tends to do away with the pleasant fiction, in the belief of which we have all made ourselves comfortable, that collectors had no direct hand in the extermination of this beautiful species, but that the untoward result was brought about by the drainage of their haunts. . . .

Tutt goes on to quote at length from H. J. Harding's article (see pp. 169–172). And picking up on Harding's observation that although the habitat appeared unchanged, neither the butterfly nor its larvae had been seen for several years, he continued:

The facts that its food-plant existed "in plenty" long after the insect had gone and that "the larvae had been too closely hunted for," speak volumes. . . .

Stainton (1857) then quotes Mr. Bond as follows:— "You are quite right in supposing that I have had personal acquaintance with living *C. dispar*. I much fear that I shall never have that pleasure again, as I am quite sure they have disappeared from the Cambridge and Huntingdonshire fens. All I can tell you about their habits is this, that they were very active and shy, and would only fly when the sun shone; they would always settle on a thistle when they could find one in bloom, flying off to attack any insect, no matter what, that might come anywhere near them; not always returning, but generally passing on to another place. It was very little use following them if you missed your first stroke with the net, as they went away like the wind, and seldom let you get a second chance; indeed, it was difficult to follow them, as keeping your eyes on them and the boggy places was rather a difficult job."

[Edward] Newman (1871) adds a little. Among other things he says:— "Varieties of this species are not common; in those that have passed through my hands there has been a remarkable uniformity of colouring, but Mr. Dale informs me that he possesses a female almost entirely black." He then adds, "My acquaintance with the caterpillar and chrysalis was made very many years ago, in Mr. Doubleday's garden at Epping, where the very plant of *Rumex hydrolapathum* [water dock], on which the caterpillars fed, is still in existence." The present writer believes that he possesses, thanks to the great generosity of Dr. Chapman, one of the very last specimens that Mr. Doubleday bred on that plant. . . .

There is one little item in the history of *C. dispar* which we have not been able to fathom. This originates in a report of the meeting of the South London Entomological Society, held on March 9th, 1893, where we read that "a discussion rose as to the occurrence of *Polyommatus dispar*, Haw., at Camberwell, fifty years ago, and Mr. Fenn and Mr. Tugwell, both recorded probable Kentish specimens previous to 1848." (1893. *Entomologist's Record J. Var.* 4:121). I have already quoted what Stephens says of a species of large Copper, supposed to have been captured in Kent, long antecedent to the date of his work (1828), and which he described under the name of *hippothoë*. The only other references that I can find bearing on the subject is a paragraph, which is rather more detailed than Stephens' remarks, although evidently referring to the same specimens, by Mr C. W. Dale, who writes:— "It (var. *rutilus*) has been recorded as British under the name of *hippothoë*. Concerning this my father wrote in *Loudon's Magazine* for 1834: 'Mr Haworth told me that they came out of an old cabinet called the 'Kentish Cabinet,' and were said to have been taken near Faversham. I had a male and a female from the late Mr. Latham, which were from Capt. Lindegren's cabinet, whence, probably, all the supposed British specimens came.' " (*British Butterflies*, p. 46). This is all I can find relating to Kentish specimens of *Chrysophanus dispar*.

Some of the impossibilities relating to the records of the occurrence of this species may be mentioned. We have already stated that Donovan considered that specimens were taken in Scotland, whilst Haworth records it as having been taken formerly in Wales by the celebrated botanist, Hudson. Mr. J. B. Hodgkinson, of Preston, states in the *Entomologist's Weekly Intelligencer*, 4: 10 (1858), that he saw a specimen "in Cumberland," that he took "a very deliberate look at it and lost it after all." This set the ball rolling, for, in the same Mag., p.131, Mr. W. Winter, of Ranworth, says: "This species has again appeared in the fens here; I saw four yesterday, but missed them all." This was on June 19th, 1858. One is recorded (1873. *Entomologist*, 6: 221) as having been seen on Hackney Marshes. I doubt whether any one of these has a suspicion of probability in it. . . .

The latest disturbance, however, on the "Copper" horizon was started by Mr. Bethune-Baker, who asserts that he has specimens of var. *rutilus* of undoubted British origin, captured in the Fens years ago with the ordinary *dispar*. Of course, this is, from a scientific point of view, the most natural thing possible, for there is no doubt that all local forms of a species will occasionally turn up as chance aberrations in all localities where the species occurs under other variations. But it is unfortunate from the speculator's point of view, for now he cannot insist that the var. *rutilus*, which are occasionally offered for sale as British, are not in reality so. Two undoubted var. *rutilus* were offered for sale as British, in the auction rooms, and, we believe, purchased as such, on April 13th last. . . .

There are still some hundreds of British *C. dispar* in existence, but every year lessens the number. Accident, and the falling of old cabinets into a neglected condition, are the two main causes of the reduced numbers. Hence the price of *C. dispar* will always be on the up-grade. When we commenced to collect, in 1871, no dealer's list priced the finest *C. dispar* at more than 15s., and anything over a pound for a good specimen was looked upon as exorbitant. Slowly and surely as the number of specimens has decreased, and the number of buyers has increased, the price has steadily advanced. It is in my mind that only one specimen has ever produced more than £7, this was at the sale of Mr. Tugwell's collection, when a specimen went for £7 7s., but many have come near it; whilst £5 5s. for a really fine male, and £5 10s. for a really fine female, can be looked upon as ordinary market prices. . . . High as these prices are, they are nothing to what may be expected in the not very distant future, when "Coppers" may produce figures more nearly approaching the prices that have been given for Great Auk's eggs.

To anyone who can see the humorous side of things there is much to be amused at when the sale of *C. dispar* is on. There is the professional, who will give a couple of guineas for any specimen, in the poorest condition, if perfect; but who will not look at the most brilliant example if it has an antenna missing. He knows his market, and he never buys the latter. Then there is the keen amateur, who bides his time, watches the sale of the less important collections, and tells you he has a series of 10 or 12 specimens, for which he has not paid more than £2 or £3 each, and which are quite as fine and perfect as specimens which, in better known and better advertised collections, produce about £5. Then there is the wealthy collector, who must have the specimen, and simply runs all opposition off its legs. It may be urged that this is derogatory to science, and that we should not descend to these particulars. We can only reply that this is the only method left now by which one can collect British *C. dispar*.

[Tutt, J. W. 1896. The Large Copper butterfly (*Chrysophanus dispar*). *The Entomologist's Record and Journal of Variation* 8: 57–65].

Tutt's comments on the prices paid for supposedly British examples of *C. dispar* in 1896 are of great interest: today, an undoubted example of the British Large Copper might fetch between £250 and £300. The debate concerning the date that the last Large Copper was

taken in Britain continues. In 1890 C. W. Dale, son of the great J. C. Dale, Squire of Glanvilles Wooton, Dorset, wrote that the last captures – five specimens – were made by Mr Stretton in Holme Fen about 1847 or 1848, although the report by W. Winter (*vide supra*) suggests that it may have existed in small colonies for at least a further decade – a fact that Tutt refused to believe. However, amongst a series of genuine British Large Coppers owned by one of the authors are two specimens labelled 'Holme Fen, 1860'. This date is some twelve years after Mr Stretton was reported as taking his five specimens in Holme Fen – the last said to have been taken in Britain!

The Large Copper quickly became for British entomologists a status symbol and an object of national pride. Our species was larger and more brilliant than either of the Continental subspecies, and its extinction in the fens of East Anglia was an unmitigated disaster. Some authors actually refused to admit that it had gone forever, while others, as we have just read, dreamed that it had turned up in unusual, unsuitable, or very out of the way, places. A number of reported sightings appeared in the entomological journals. One collector claimed to have found it in Somerset, another in Monmouthshire, while Richard Weaver, who had already found another rarity – *Boloria dia* (Weaver's Fritillary) – outside Birmingham, made a name for himself when he suggested that a friend had found the Large Copper in Staffordshire. This claim, however, was too much for John Scott, a leading entomologist of the day, who immediately took issue with him. Unfortunately his attack failed to douse Weaver's enthusiasm and the following acrimonious correspondence was exchanged:

CHRYSOPHANUS DISPAR IN STAFFORDSHIRE

From *The Entomologist's Weekly Intelligencer* (1856):

Richard Weaver, Birmingham; 9th April 1856, p. 18:

Seeing in your "Manual," it is stated at page 11, that the Large Copper is only to be obtained in the fens, I beg to say, that a few days ago a gentleman brought to show me a male and female of that species, which he had captured last year in Staffordshire: this is a new locality to me, and I suppose is so to most entomologists: I quite expect this insect will be diligently looked after this season in this new locality.

John Scott, South Stockton; 6th May 1856, p. 51:

This sounds at present not unlike capturing it five miles from anywhere. Perhaps Mr. Weaver will be kind enough to favour us with the *part* of Staffordshire, or the place therein where it was taken, and which evidently, in his earnestness to make public this valuable discovery, he has overlooked.

Richard Weaver, Rugeley; 24th May 1856, p. 67:

A county *is* rather an extensive locality; but *the place where* the butterfly was taken my friend did not let me know, as he wished to try the place for it this season for his own cabinet, and also for that of a friend: last season he only captured two specimens. It is anything but pleasant to be criticised when I did my best to please (as I thought).

John Scott (1823–1888) ended his days a severe epileptic in an asylum. His obituary (Anon., 1888) tells us that he was a self-educated man who became a civil engineer:

He had a good knowledge of music, and the violin quartettes of classical writers, led by him at his house at Lee, were real treats. He had a wide knowledge of English literature. Yet all these availed him little in the conduct of life, for, although when in the humour, he was a genial companion, and in his time had done many good and generous acts to those requiring aid, he had a most impetuous disposition, and a vehement, unconciliating temper, of which no one was better aware or regretted more than himself. Moreover, like Yorick, he was "a fellow of infinite jest," but being oblivious at the moment that

"A jest's prosperity lies in the ear
Of him that hears it, never in the tongue
Of him that utters it,"

the acerbity of his wit and repartee too often wounded those to whom they were addressed. Thus, from one cause or another, friends were alienated, and many who might have been on friendly terms

Fig. 24. John Scott. 'This sounds at present not unlike capturing it five miles from anywhere.'

43

with him, and have done him service when he sorely required it, held aloof. "Alas, poor Yorick!" Requiescat!

Scott suffered a series of violent epileptic seizures 'attended by partial paralysis; aberration of mind ensuing, he was taken to an asylum, became imbecile and unconscious, and death finally released him.'

A LAMENT FOR THE LARGE COPPER

E. C. Jenkins, Sleaford, Lincolnshire. (1859)

To the Editor, *The Entomologist's Weekly Intelligencer*:

Sir,—In your 'Manual of British Butterflies and Moths,' which I have lately procured, and which I would have given anything for when a young man, after your description of *Chrysophanus Dispar* [Large Copper], you allude to a letter from Mr. Bond, stating "You are quite right in supposing that I have had personal acquaintance with the living *Dispar*," &c., &c. I infer from this that you have not had the pleasure yourself; I therefore proceed to give you some account of my own acquaintance with that most beautiful insect, which, some thirty years ago, was so abundant in the unreclaimed fens about Whittlesea Mere that I never expected to hear of its utter extermination. Its brilliant appearance on the wing in the sunshine I shall never forget, and to watch it sitting on the flower of the *Eupatorium cannabinum* [hemp-agrimony] and show the underside of its wings, was something ever to be remembered. I once took sixteen in about half an hour on one particular spot, where the above-mentioned plant was very plentiful; but unless the sun was very bright they were very difficult to find. In those days the larva was unknown, and I attribute the disappearance of the butterfly to the discovery of the larva, to the unceasing attacks of collectors, and to the burning of the surface-growth of the fens, which is done in dry weather when they are to be reclaimed.

Thirty years ago the fens about Whittlesea Mere were most interesting localities for the entomologist, the botanist and the ornithologist. I lived then in that neighbourhood, and those pursuits were my delight. *Papilio Machaon* [Swallowtail] might then be had to any amount; the flight of *Chrysophanus Dispar* was abundant in July; the moth *L. Dispar* [Gypsy Moth] was very plentiful; besides many other rare and beautiful insects. Now, however, everything is totally changed. The Great Northern Railroad runs through a part of the fen where, when I was a boy, one could scarcely walk: at the spot where I used to land from my boat, on the edge of the Mere, stands a farmhouse; my favourite locality for *C. Dispar* — where the bog myrtle used to grow in profusion and scent the air with its delicious perfume — was (as I myself saw last season) converted into a field of stinking cole-seed, with a flock of sheep eating it off. All the better, no doubt, for the landowners, but ruinous work for the naturalist, and as such you will sympathize with me in the destruction of what was one of the most interesting localities in the whole country for persons inclined to such pursuits, — you will understand how indignant I felt when some one irreverently told me, a few years ago, that they had "*tapped the Mere!*"

[Jenkins, E. C. F. 1859. A lament for the Large Copper. *The Entomologist's Weekly Intelligencer* **7**: 79–80].

WAS THE GERMAN SUBSPECIES OF THE LARGE COPPER EVER FOUND IN BRITAIN?

George T. Bethune-Baker, F.L.S., F.E.S., Edgbaston, Birmingham. (1892)

I was not aware, until hearing a day or two ago from my friend Mr. Barrett, that the continental form of *P. dispar* was supposed never to have been taken in this country, as I have known for many years that my father took both ordinary *dispar* and v. *rutilus* some time between 1825 and 1834. My father tells me he captured all his specimens himself (eight in number), all of which are in my collection, viz. 5 ♂ and three ♀. One male is typical *rutilus*, another almost typical, but with slightly larger spots, whilst a third is midway between *dispar* and *rutilus*, the remaining two are true *dispar*; of the females, one is fairly typical *rutilus*, another is on the upper-side like the darker specimens occasionally taken on the continent, viz., with larger spots on the upper wings, but the spots beneath are decidedly larger than any of my v. *rutilus*, whilst the third is true *dispar*. There is no doubt of these being truly endemic specimens, as my father (who, with his brothers, were keen collectors in their early years) remembers them, and he says he never bought an insect in his life. I suppose, moreover, that very few *rutilus* would find their way over here as long as sixty years ago, still less into the quite unknown collections of boys under twenty years of age. My father has never been on the continent at all.

[Two of the specimens in question are before me. They are clearly of the var. *rutilus* — the spots much smaller and the under-side less blue. Mr. Baker, Sen., recollects their capture, and as British specimens they are of extreme interest. — C. G. Barrett.]

[Bethune-Baker, G. T. 1892. *Polyommatus dispar* var. *rutilus* in England. *Entomologist's Monthly Magazine* 28: 190].

THE MYSTERY OF THE LARGE BLUE BUTTERFLY

Dr Thomas A. Chapman, M.D., F.R.S., F.E.S., Reigate, Surrey. (1914)

The Large Blue excited the interest of Victorian collectors for a number of reasons. Entomologists who attempted to breed it invariably failed. After the fourth and final instar (skin moult) the larvae would leave the wild thyme that up till then they had been feeding on, and start to wander about aimlessly. Once this happened, it was not long before they died. Clearly this did not occur in nature. What was so important about the fourth instar?

Dr Thomas Algernon Chapman (1842–1921) was a distinguished lepidopterist who described the life cycles of two European butterflies, subsequently named after him as Chapman's Blue (*Plebicula thersites*) and Chapman's Hairstreak (*Callophries avis*). In 1915 he joined Captain E. Bagwell Purefoy (1868–1960) and F. W. Frohawk in attempting to solve the mystery.

The mystery of *Lycaena arion* remains a mystery. I obtained eggs at Gavarnie this summer and reared some larvae, of which I succeeded in getting about a score to the last instar (supposed hibernating stage). Though in their fourth and last instar they are only about as large as the larvae of *Agriades coridon* [Chalk Hill Blue] or other ordinary blues when they go into hibernation. They no doubt do something, and without further moult appear (to very few people) the following June quite full grown. The mystery is, what do they do in the interval, where do they live, and what do they feed on? I hoped to get nearer this by aid of my score or so of caterpillars, but they behaved as they always had done with me previously, after not very many days they were all dead. Though I made no further discovery, by watching them more closely and considering them more seriously, I am able to advance a little nearer the enemies' trenches, but so far without the slightest confidence of being able to take them.

Fig. 25. Dr Thomas A. Chapman described the life cycle of various European butterflies, two of which are named after him.

I offered my larvae the companionship of the proper ant. Without showing enmity, neither ants nor larvae fraternised in any way. I offered the larvae various kinds of food, all the hopeful sorts of plants I could obtain, of these they seemed to sip the sap of kidney beans, but these they did not eat, nor did they increase in bulk; other things they would not look at. I had no young green peas available (the date last August), the food that Mr. Frohawk found they would deal with. I offered them mashed ant larvae, which did not even rouse their curiosity. I gave them various hibernating facilities such as have suited other Lycaenid larvae, but they would not settle down until they were exhausted and, in fact, dying.

These are all facts that have been known for some years to Mr. Frohawk, the Hon. N. C. Rothschild, and myself, and are, one may say, now known to everybody. There are, however, several other points that, in a sense, are equally well-known, and yet, so far at least as I am concerned, were not, for really practical purposes, known so as to be properly appreciated and weighed.

The central fact of these is that, when the larva enters on this last instar, when it has taken its last moult, and sets out at once on its wanderings, it does not first eat any more of the flower-heads of the thyme. It starts its wanderings, therefore, without any of the stored nutriment that larvae have when they go into hibernation. It wanders about and the real object of these journeys is no doubt to find food. As in captivity it always dies before many days, unquestionably of starvation, it follows that at large it succeeds in finding food within a similar limited period. This does not in the slightest answer the questions, where and what, but it implies that it ought not to be so difficult to somehow follow the larva at large for a few days and see what it does. The structure and small size of the head imply that the food is vegetable and not difficult of mastication. This does not negative the idea that it becomes the guest of ants, but the neutrality observed between the larvae and the ants is strongly against it, the importance to the larvae of an early supply of food would necessitate a prompt treaty between the ants and their guests, if this is how its wants are supplied.

I have had the advantage of a talk with Mr. Rothschild over my observations and some he has made this summer. I do not agree with him in regarding the ants' nest hypothesis as altogether improbable, but I think there is more to be said in favour of a vegetable diet found by the larva itself than I had previously appreciated.

[Chapman, T. A. 1914. The mystery of *Lycaena arion*. *The Entomologist's Record and Journal of Variation* **26**: 245–246].

THE LIFE HISTORY OF THE LARGE BLUE
BUTTERFLY REVEALED

Capt. Edward Bagwell Purefoy, F.R.E.S., East Farleigh, Kent. (1953)

During May of 1915 the late Dr. Chapman went to Cornwall to pursue further investigations into the life-history of the Large Blue butterfly (*Maculinea arion*). On pulling up a plant of wild thyme he disclosed a half-grown *arion* larva and damaged it in so doing. The plant was growing on or close to a nest of the ant, *Myrmica scabrinodis*, and the larva was, in fact, among the ants. As it was impossible to try and rear the larva he decided to examine its contents under the microscope and he found that it had been feeding on the small larvae of that ant. That was pretty conclusive but the information was not broadcast at the time and we did not hear about it until the following autumn. No doubt this news would have saved us much trouble, but the fact that we were without it made the undertaking, I think, much more interesting.

About this time the late Hon. C. Rothschild sent a botanist down to Cornwall to tabulate all the plants he found growing with the thyme in likely spots where the butterfly was prevalent. He sent me the list. If I remember right, there were fourteen and we were able to obtain all these, chiefly from Blue Bell Hill between Maidstone and Chatham.

We began preparing for the experiments early in the spring and the hills or sites where the thyme and other plants were to be established and the ants' nests started were placed in the sunniest part of the garden. Two hills were built up facing south and boarded up on each side. They were made to slope fairly steeply to the south. On these were planted thyme and some of the plants named in the Rothschild list, as we considered it quite possible that some succulent root was what *arion* required in the fourth instar. We then brought *Lasius flavus* nests of varying sizes from Blue Bell Hill and tried to establish several of these among the thyme. The red ant, *Myrmica laevinodis*, was common in the garden and some of these were not long in finding their way on to the hills. Before long we noticed that nests of them were starting and one in particular seemed to be very promising, being up against the side boarding. We ourselves did nothing about the red ants and left them strictly alone. The dimensions of the hills were roughly nine feet by seven.

In due course the late Mr. L. W. Newman sent us females of *M. arion* and we had no difficulty in obtaining plenty of ova. The rearing of the little larvae up to the completion of the third moult was uneventful.

It was a hot Sunday in early August when we had the first *arion* larva ready to put out. It was placed on thyme growing on a *flavus* nest. We were to take it in turns to keep it under constant observation. It soon fell off the thyme and started wandering about aimlessly. For a long time no ant came across it, but it was eventually found by a *red* ant who remained with it for a considerable time. Then it was reported to me that the ant had run away with it in its jaws, had left the hill and gone down the garden path into some weeds.

Fig. 26. Captain E. Bagwell Purefoy unravelled the complex life cycle of the Large Blue.

At that moment some friends arrived unexpectedly from London. What a moment! Thus, the result of the first day's observations left us wholly mystified.

During the next day or two other larvae were ready to be put out and the first of them was placed on the ground fairly close to the *laevinodis* nest which was up against the boarding. It was found very quickly and carried under a plant of thyme which grew on the nest.

These investigations were being carried out on behalf of the late Mr. F. W. Frohawk and it had been arranged that he should join us directly anything decisive occurred. Now was the moment to call him in, and he has described at length in his big work (1924) [*Natural History of British Butterflies*] many of the interesting events of the next few days. It was Frohawk who first spotted the fact that the larva hunched itself up as a signal to the ant that it was ready to be carried into the nest, and the sketches that are reproduced in his big work were all made at East Farleigh.

Fig. 27. F. W. Frohawk — 'the hub around which amateur lepidopterists gravitated'.

We left the hills quite undisturbed until early October when Frohawk came down again.

It was a thrilling moment when we carefully removed the board that supported the nest of *laevinodis* into which we had seen disappear several *arion* larvae. Four or five inches below the surface we came across the first larva and Frohawk made a beautiful little sketch of the discovery before we investigated any further . . . We found several more larvae in the same nest.

So it will be seen that our experiments with *L. flavus* were of no avail and that *M. laevinodis* came on the scene entirely on its own initiative and finally solved the mystery.

Frohawk has described how we subsequently experimented with *arion* larvae using the half of a large walnut shell as their home after the third moult. This method has the great advantage of making inspection quite simple without interfering much with either the ants or the larvae. It is, of course, necessary to add fresh ant brood from time to time. Two *arion* larvae can be reared under one shell.

The ant *laevinodis* should be employed in preference to *scabrinodis* as the former will accept larvae from another nest of its own species whereas the latter will not. When observed in a nest isolated by water, it carries the strange larvae to the edge of its platform or even pushes them into the moat.

Although we had been successful in rearing *arion* larvae up to the hibernating stage during the first season of the experiment, it was quite otherwise with the pupae. For one reason or another two or three seasons had to elapse before this was achieved. It was the employment of the walnut shells that brought success.

I think that it was during the summer of 1918 that we bred out a beautiful series and they were presented to the Wellington College Museum. My son was at that school at the time and was acting as curator to the Museum. As far as I know this was the first series of "home bred" *arion* that had been produced in England.

The following curious incident is worth noting. I think it was during the third year of our experiments that we had a flower box about fifteen inches square and standing on legs two and a half feet from the ground, full of wild thyme, and netted over. It stood in a cold greenhouse, the door of which was always open. Several *arion* females had been placed on this thyme during the season and either their ova or larvae removed by us. During October we were about to dismantle this box when we noticed, for the first time, that there were *M. laevinodis* about it; they had, in fact, established a nest in it, running up and down one of the legs of the box when active. On emptying the contents of the box, out fell about a dozen *arion* larvae of very small size, perhaps rather less than half the size of the ones we had brought up under walnut shells with plenty of ant brood. There was practically no ant brood left in this nest. These larvae, though so undersized, were perfectly healthy and vigorous and we distributed them among our shells and they settled down quite well. Had they been again kept on short commons after hibernation, they might well have produced very small imagines. Too many larvae may occasionally be carried into a small nest with this probable result.

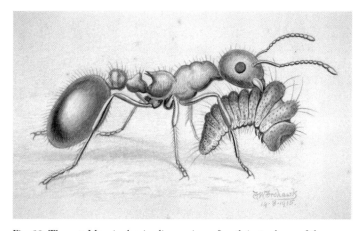

Fig. 28. The ant *Myrmica laevinodis* carrying a fourth-instar larva of the Large Blue. From the original drawing by F. W. Frohawk, 1915. It necessitated him kneeling on the ground for an hour or more, with a lens in one hand and a pencil in the other. It is included in his two volume *Natural History of British Butterflies* (1924) — the culmination of twenty-four years painstakingly breeding, observing and illustrating each life cycle.

In June, 1906, Frohawk and his friend Rayward were trying to solve the mystery and set about digging up a number of *flavus* hillocks on which they had so often seen *arion* laying its eggs. They did finally turn up several nearly full grown larvae. Now red ants not infrequently take possession of one side of a *flavus* hillock and it is absolutely certain that the larvae they found were, in fact, among red ants, and I have never been able to understand how it was that they did not spot this at once. That they did not do so is proved by the fact that they proceeded to dig up many more *flavus* hillocks and never came across another *arion* larva. I believe myself that *flavus* is quite unsuitable as a host and I have never been able to bring the two together in any way. Underfeeding in a red ant's nest might well account for the very small specimens of the perfect insect occasionally found.

Finally, to discuss briefly why this problem of *arion* proved so difficult to solve. It may be said that she drew two red herrings across the path of investigators. In the first place, she was observed to select *flavus* hillocks with great frequency and yet these nests had no secret to give up. Secondly, Frohawk found that larvae after the third moult would readily feed upon the soft interior of either green peas or runner beans. They lived on this pabulum for several weeks and doubled their size. This pointed very strongly to some succulent root being what they looked for during their last stage.

Well, it was all intensely interesting and I shall always consider that we were very lucky to have a "finger in the pie".

[Purefoy, E. B. 1953. An unpublished account of the experiments carried out at East Farleigh, Kent, in 1915 and subsequent years on the life history of *Maculinea arion*, the Large Blue butterfly. *Proceedings of the Royal Entomological Society of London* (A) **28**: 160–162].

During 1996 the authors had an opportunity to examine the entomological collections at Wellington College. These were found to be in a sadly distressed condition. Alas, there were no Large Blues and the staff were unable to say where Captain Purefoy's specimens had gone.

In 1954, E. A. Cockayne, writing in *The Entomologist's Record* (p. 89), suggested that G. B. Oliver was the first person to find the larva of the Large Blue. In a reply, Oliver (1954) stated:

> I do not think, however, that I can claim to be the first to find the larva of *arion*; the discovery of it, I believe, is due to Mr. B. G. Adams, who preceded me by roughly one month. My first find was 15 pupae and 1 larva, the last-named resulting in an imago on 10th August 1920. I still have my bred series of 15 specimens, each with its own pupa-case (the 16th case was too broken to be worth keeping).

He went on to describe digging up an ant's nest for F. W. Frohawk and packing it in a biscuit tin, which he (Frohawk) took back to London with him by train, with the intention of establishing the nest in his garden. Oliver went on to wonder 'what the reactions (and antics) of his fellow passengers were when the ants escaped and explored the train compartment! – the tin being far from "ant-proof"!' The G. B. Oliver series of Large Blues, complete with pupal cases, is in the collection of one of the authors of this anthology.

NOTES ON THE LARGE BLUE BUTTERFLY IN DEVON

Gervase Mathew, R.N., F.L.S., F.Z.S., H.M.S., "Britannia," Dartmouth, Devon. (1877)

Captain Gervase Mathew (1842–1928) was Paymaster-in-Chief to the Royal Navy. He is remembered for his discovery of a rare moth, Mathew's Wainscot (*Mythimna favicolor*), in 1895. In this article on the Large Blue he describes its traditional nineteenth-century headquarters in South Devon. This place can still be identified today. From the summit of the Bolthead, the ground, carpeted with thrift, wild thyme and heather, slopes steeply downwards towards the sea. The Green Hairstreak, Silver-studded Blue and Dark Green Fritillary are still there – and quite often abundant. But there is little doubt that the encroachment of bracken (often six foot in height), the loss of grass-cropping rabbits from myxomatosis, as well as the unfettered activities of dozens of collectors in the 1870s and 1880s, have all combined to extinguish the Large Blue. Although wild thyme is still abundant and *Myrmica scabrinodis*, an ant so willing to adopt larvae of this butterfly, is still there, a major conservation programme would be needed if the Large Blue was ever to be re-introduced to its former haunt on the Bolthead.

. . . *Lycæna Arion* – one of the largest European blues – is a butterfly which, on account of its restricted habits, but few British entomologists have had opportunities of seeing alive, so perhaps some account of my various excursions to Bolthead in quest of it may not be altogether uninteresting.

My first visit was on July 7th, 1870, and a glorious morning it was, as we left Kingsbridge by steamer at half-past nine for Salcombe. The trip down the estuary occupied about an hour: on the way several likely-looking woods were passed, while on the mud-banks stately herons stood and watched us as we steamed by, or, rising, flew in a flapping, lazy manner a short distance, and again alighted.

On reaching Salcombe I went to the King's Arms Inn, where I procured a bed-room and a sitting-room: the floor of the latter showed signs, in the shape of strips of paper, stray pins, &c., of the recent presence of an entomologist. Upon enquiry I learnt that a "fly-catching gentleman" had only vacated the room the previous day; but could not ascertain from the landlady what

Fig. 29. Captain Gervase Mathew, discoverer of Mathew's Wainscot.

he had been catching, or whether he had taken any blues: all she knew was that he had been several times out to "the Bolt." By this time it was nearly eleven o'clock, so as soon as I had unpacked my apparatus, and partaken of some slight refreshment, off I started.

The day had now become excessively hot; there was scarcely a breath of air to counterbalance the scorching rays of the sun, and in the evening, when my labours were over, I found the back of my neck was much blistered. The distance from the village to Bolthead is about two miles, the path in many places steep and rough. *Arion* occurs chiefly beyond the Bolt to the westward, where, between it and the next point, a slope sweeps down from the brow of the high land to the edge of the cliffs below, and here, at times, when the turf is dry and slippery, it is decidedly dangerous to approach too near the cliffs. The upper portion of this slope was thickly overgrown with patches of stunted furze and heather, the latter in profuse bloom; in the open spots wild thyme, *Potentilla*, and bird's-foot trefoil flourished; while, further down, thistles, mullein, and foxglove reared their flower-spikes above the bracken; here and there, behind the shelter of a dilapidated stone wall, grew dwarfed brambles; and from the turf, just above the cliffs and right down their face to the rocks below, sprung countless tufts of thrift.

Upon reaching this charming spot *Arion* was one of the first butterflies I noticed; there was no mistaking it: its size and brilliant appearance at once attracted my attention as it flew swiftly towards me, and suddenly settled on a sprig of heather quite close to my feet. For a few moments I gazed at it with rapture, for what exquisite delight one experiences in meeting for the first time in its native haunts a species one has never seen before alive, especially such a lovely insect as this; but my desire to possess it speedily overcame all my admiration; so with a sweep of my net I captured, and then boxed it. In the course of the day I secured about three dozen, and might have taken more had I desired to do so, but found many of them worn: these of course were allowed their freedom. As far as I could judge I should have been on the spot at least ten days earlier, although this species probably soon gets injured when flying among the furze, for many, otherwise in perfect condition, had small pieces chipped from their wings, showing that they must have flown, or been blown, against the prickly bushes.

The flight of this butterfly has been described by Dr. Bree (Zool. 1852, p. 3350) as resembling that of *Chortobius Pamphilus* [Small Heath] and *Satyrus Tithonus* [Gatekeeper], — both weak flyers; but, as far as my observations go, I cannot corroborate this, for I found it anything but easy to catch, and should call it decidedly swift and strong on the wing. . . .

My next visit to Salcombe was on May 22nd, 1875. I left Dartmouth at eleven o'clock, and drove to the little village called Portlemouth, situated on the east side of the harbour, just opposite Salcombe, from whence I crossed by ferry; I arrived about three p.m. Upon this occasion I put up at the Victoria Inn. After refreshing myself I walked out to the Bolthead to endeavour to find the larvæ of *Lycæna Arion*. The afternoon was wild and gloomy, with heavy, dun-coloured clouds passing rapidly overhead, treating me now and again to a brisk shower. On reaching the slopes, where *Arion* was so plentiful in July, 1870, I hardly recognised the spot. The patches of furze and heather, which were then nearly knee-deep, had disappeared; their places were occupied by young, bright green shots of the former, while the greater part of the latter seemed to have been entirely destroyed: here and there were ominous large black patches, the result of recent fire. I was vexed, and anticipated small success here; nevertheless, in certain places, which had escaped the ravages of fire, I fancied I might make a lucky hit, and stumble across this much-coveted larva. Accordingly down I went on my hands and knees, scrutinizing every plant of wild thyme I came near. The thyme grew best round the patches of furze and heather, so I commenced one side of a patch, and gradually worked my way round to the other. This went on for a long time, during which I must have crawled round some dozens of clumps, with only the uncomfortable result of making my back ache terribly. Consequently I was obliged to give up this plan in despair, and think of some other. Fancying that perhaps the larvae at this

period of their existence might be night-feeders, and secrete themselves during the day at the root of their food-plant, an idea now struck me that if I set to work and dug up a number of the plants bodily, and shook their roots vigorously over a sheet of paper, I might get them. No amount of shaking, however, produced aught but a few common *Noctuæ* larvæ. Next I tried flowers of furze, tender twigs of heather, leaves and roots of *Lotus*, various grasses, &c.; still nothing rewarded my efforts: so, after about four hours of decidedly hard work, I had to give in, and acknowledge myself fairly beaten. I must confess that when I started in the morning I felt very sanguine of success, so my bad fortune was exceedingly disappointing. No doubt it will prove, after all, an easy larva to find, when its habits are discovered by some more fortunate brother of the net and pin. . . .

I returned to Salcombe about seven, and should have gone out again after dark to have had a search for larvae by lamplight, but the wind blew so heavily and in such strong gusts no lantern would have stood it.

The next morning was much brighter; so after breakfast I walked again to Bolthead, and had another three hours' hard work in a different locality, but unfortunately with the same result. I then went back to Salcombe, when crossing the ferry I walked back to Dartmouth, reaching the ship about eleven o'clock, thoroughly tired and done up, and pretty well disgusted at my want of success.

On July 8th, 1875, I left Dartmouth by the evening coach, intending to go as far as Kingsbridge, sleep there the night, and take the steamer to Salcombe the next morning; but in the course of the journey one of my fellow-passengers observed that he was going to Salcombe that night, and had ordered a boat to be waiting for him at Frogmore, a little village between Torcross and Kingsbridge, where an arm of the estuary nearly touches the high-road. He kindly offered me a passage, which of course I gladly accepted, as it would save me some distance and expense; also giving a clear day to start with on the morrow. Accordingly on reaching Frogmore we bade farewell to the coach, jumped into the boat which was waiting, and had a pleasant pull down the creek to Salcombe, where we arrived at half-past eight. I put up at my old quarters, the Victoria Inn.

The next morning when I got up, a little before seven, hoping to have a good long day before me, I was wofully disappointed at finding it was raining heavily, with but little prospect of a change. At ten o'clock it became lighter, a slight break appeared in the clouds, and it ceased to rain; so I sallied forth towards Bolthead. However, this was but the forerunner of a more furious downpour, for I had scarcely gone half-way when the rain descended again in perfect torrents. I had to return in a soaking condition to my inn. There was no change for the remainder of the day; the rain poured without intermission. During the afternoon I came to the conclusion that whatever Salcombe might be in fair weather, it was anything but a lively place to spend a wet day in — at least by oneself.

The following morning when I awoke it was fine, but I noticed from my bed-room window broken clouds flying at a great pace across the sky. After breakfast, when I had walked beyond the shelter of the town, I discovered that the rain of the preceding day had given place to a fresh gale from the south-west. On reaching the favourite locality for *Lycæna Arion* I found the wind so strong it would have been impossible for a butterfly to face it; indeed, in some places I could barely stand, so gave up all hope of capturing any by ordinary means; but I thought by searching to the leeward of bushes and patches of high fern I might possibly find some sheltering. Several hours hard, back-aching work only produced a few *Argynnis Aglaia* [Dark Green Fritillary], *Satyrus Semele* [Grayling], and *S. Janira* [Meadow

Brown], many of which upon being disturbed were carried off by the wind at a tremendous pace. I gave it up as a bad job, and returned to Salcombe. Thus ended my second expedition of 1875, for the next day I had to return early to Dartmouth.

It will be noticed that I did not observe a single perfect insect myself that year, but this, in a great measure, was owing to the unfortunate state of the weather at the time of my second visit. A collector who visited the locality a few days later, when the weather was more favourable, took about a dozen worn specimens.

I was unable to go and have another search for larvæ of *Lycæna Arion* in the spring of 1876; but on the 14th July I left Dartmouth by coach for Kingsbridge, and from thence went on by boat to Salcombe, where I arrived about half-past three in the afternoon. The day was most lovely, the sky clear, and heat almost tropical. As soon as I had deposited my luggage at the Victoria Inn I set out for Bolthead. On getting there I saw nothing whatever of *Arion*, but was not much surprised at this, for it is a butterfly that does not fly much after mid-day, and it was nearly five o'clock before I reached its favourite habitat. *Satyrus Semele* and *S. Janira* were very abundant, as was also *Argynnis Aglaia*, but there was nothing like the assembly I witnessed here in July, 1870. Indeed, in this locality I doubt if such a thing will be seen again.

The next morning (July 15th) was most glorious, and after bathing and breakfasting I strolled out to the cliffs, and spent nearly the whole of the day there. The weather was all that could be desired for butterflies, — bright, hot, and cloudless, with scarcely a breath of air; indeed, the heat was almost too excessive for active exercise. Had there been many *Lycæna Arion* in existence surely they would have been about on a day like this, but I only saw five, — one male and four females; and those captured were all considerably worn. The species might have been out for some days, and was passing, which would probably account for me seeing so few. I hoped this was the case; but from information I gathered from persons living in the neighbourhood I fear it is becoming scarcer each season. At any rate, it will be seen from the above that since my first visit, in 1870, it has notably diminished. The question naturally arises as to the cause of this decrease. An entomologist, whom I met on the ground, gave it as his opinion that the chief cause was attributable to burning the heather and gorse in early spring; but this only occurs at intervals of several years, and takes place in patches. Moreover, this burning has perhaps been going on for ages; so I do not think this can be looked upon as the principal reason, although no doubt a considerable number on a limited area may thus perish. My belief is that the ruthless manner in which they are indiscriminately captured and destroyed, by entomologists and collectors, is the primary cause of their annual diminution. I feel convinced if they were left to themselves, and strictly preserved for four or five years, they would become as plentiful again as ever. Now, not a year passes without the place being overrun by collectors; and I was told by a coastguard man, who had been for some years stationed at Salcombe, that he has often seen five or six gentlemen together "hunting flies." I have seldom been there myself without seeing someone, although those I have been fortunate to meet would, I am certain, only take what number of specimens they actually required, and allow the ragged females to fly. All, however, I am sorry to say, would not be so scrupulous; and they, as I have before mentioned, kill worn specimens in their nets, and afterwards throw them away. That this is often done in pure thoughtlessness, I feel positive.

Should this notice meet the eyes of any entomologists who may hereafter visit Bolthead, may I implore them to spare these wasted females, for it seems a great pity that such a beautiful species should become extinct in this locality, simply for want of a little proper care.

Since I was at Salcombe in July, 1875, a bird-stuffer's shop has been opened in the town. I paid the owner a visit to enquire if he had any rarities; and after looking at his birds I asked him if he collected butterflies. He replied that he did, and showed me about two dozen *Lycæna Arion* on a board. They were nearly all females, badly set, and in wretched condition; there was not a single specimen fit for a cabinet. Mr. Nicholls, of Kingsbridge, who has long known *Arion*, — in fact, discovered it, I believe in this locality, — tells me that he is of opinion it is fast becoming exterminated.

[Mathew, G. F. 1877. Notes on *Lycaena arion. The Entomologist* **10**: 35-40; 70–73].

Throughout much of the nineteenth century the Large Blue butterfly occurred locally in Devon, Cornwall and parts of the Cotswolds. But, before 1800 it was even more widely distributed with ancient records from Folkestone, Barnwell Wold in Northamptonshire, the Marlborough Downs, Winchester, and Cliveden in Buckinghamshire. This butterfly exerted a powerful influence on the Victorian collectors who visited the West Country each year to collect it in large numbers. Unfortunately, progressive degeneration of many of the favoured localities led to a slow, continuous decline in this butterfly's fortunes. By 1885 Herbert Marsden was warning readers of the *Entomologist's Monthly Magazine* that it had now become so rare in the Cotswolds that no specimens had been seen in the Gloucestershire district for the past four years.

Ernest Neal (1994) remembered his days as biology master at Rendcomb College, in Gloucestershire:

> It was Founder's Day when parents visited the college and some celebrity was invited and speeches made . . . On this occasion, after the parents had collected for tea, Ian [Menzies] sidled up to me in a conspiratorial manner and excitedly whispered "I've discovered the Large Blue!" I knew this butterfly was supposed to occur in the Cotswolds, but it was reputed to be extinct. I knew Ian didn't make mistakes over things like that, so I quietly left the gathering. He slipped into my car, and off we went to Withington, a village not far away. He led me over a field to some rough grazing dotted with ant hills, and sure enough there were several of these butterflies flying over the patches of thyme. It was thrilling! It was not long before he discovered several other colonies in the neighbourhood and was studying them in detail.

Ian Menzies (pers. comm.) recalled that these events happened in 1946 and that small colonies of the Large Blue continued to exist, albeit precariously, in the Cotswolds until about 1950.

By 1900 the Large Blue had vanished from many of its West Country haunts. However, in 1891, Mr E. A. Waterhouse delighted the entomological fraternity by announcing the discovery of a large and apparently thriving colony at Millook in Cornwall. The inevitable result of his announcement was that even more collectors spent their summer holidays looking for Large Blues, and the newly discovered colony was almost extinguished. After the Second World War the species continued to decline until in 1979 it was officially declared extinct.

In the next article Henry Rowland-Brown (Fig. 30) recalls meeting with the Large Blue in Gloucestershire.

THE COTTESWOLD LARGE BLUE BUTTERFLY

Henry Rowland-Brown, M.A., F.E.S. (1919)

I had never seen *Lycaena arion* alive in England, and when I received instructions to transfer myself to Gloucester towards the end of June visions of the Large Blue loomed larger in imagination. Mr. G. T. Bethune-Baker, writing to me on the eve of my departure, rather mitigated the glory of my dream. "The form on the hills" at a certain place he was good enough to indicate, "is only worth going for as evidence of degeneration. . . . A Birmingham man was over there just before the war, and the form he found there was not uncommon, but reduced in size and coloration most extraordinarily; and this was not from one year's taking only. It seems to me a very unusual case, and one cannot quite account for it."

On arrival at Gloucester the weather was all that could tempt the quarry abroad. The season was backward, and this was in my favour. But I had hardly been two days in that ancient city when the weather broke: grey skies and "a rushing, mighty wind" succeeded the universal calm blue; and when I found myself at what I expected to be the appropriate locality, not an insect was flying. A few *Anthrocera trifolii* [Five-spot Burnet] clung tenaciously to the flower-heads and as many disconsolate *Coenonympha pamphilus* [Small Heath] rose from the rough grass. The ant-hills of *Myrmica scabrinodis* [later corrected to *Acanthomyops* (= *Lasius* = *Donisthorpea) flava*] were there, the heaps sparingly invested with *Thymus serpyllum* [wild-thyme]. On the way out a passing cyclist had disturbed a privet bush, from which rose several *Thecla w-album* [White-letter Hairstreak], as it seemed, and that was all. I prowled about for a couple of hours until I was fairly blown off the ground.

So much for June 26th; and the prospect of the next day was hardly more encouraging when I admitted daylight through the window of the very ancient inn which has housed pilgrims of all sorts for the past five centuries. I may add that the only conveyance available was a pre-war "push-bike," the property of the boots — a small man whose legs must have

Fig. 30. Henry Rowland-Brown (1865–1922). 'His knowledge of the butterflies of Central and Western Europe was certainly without an equal in our country.' See page 253.

been some inches shorter than mine. I am not likely to forget this "infernal machine." I did most of the pushing myself up the Cotteswolds, and even more wearisome was the labour of holding back on those downward "shoots" which land you from the heaven-kissing hills to the valley beneath — on your head if you are not cautious to exasperation. However, things went very differently on the 27th. The wind was more than a cap-full, but I had the cheerful company of Mr. C. Granville Clutterbuck as guide, philosopher, and friend, and I owe it to him entirely that I realised my dream, and achieved the felicity of observing *L. arion* in its native haunts. We should have done better if the sun had been a little more prodigal of its favours. At all events, there were intervals of brilliance; and then the several hill-sides were alive with Lepidoptera of all sizes — at least, so Mr. Clutterbuck assures me, for his activities centred upon the "micros," and judging from the rapidity with which he wielded his net he should have bagged a plenty of the "wee folk." A prolonged study of Army Forms for the past five years must have impaired my sight, for I simply couldn't spot the most obvious Tineid, or appreciate on the wing the elusive Tortrices which my companion boxed and boxed again as it were from thin air.

The Cotteswold country in which *arion* lingers closely resembles certain places, loved of old, in the Basses Alpes, places where the flora and vegetation is scanty, and the only accompanying Lycaenids are *Cupido minimus* [Small Blue] and *Nomiades semiargus* [Mazarine Blue]. Who in Gloucestershire is going to restore the "Mazarene Blue" [*sic*] to the British list from which some of us once on a time were preparing to delete *arion*?

I have so often found that I get my best captures by seating myself and taking a wide horizon that I was scarcely surprised when Mr. Clutterbuck, who was sitting beside me — on an ant-hill — suddenly cried out "there's *arion*!" The stiffness engendered by that cursed bike dissolved like magic, and in a moment I had the pleasure of taking a fine, newly emerged male in my net. It appeared to be the only occupant of this particular terrain, and as the prospect was now distinctly more encouraging we migrated to an entirely different range of hills, round whose feet the beech-woods and larches clustered temptingly, with "rides," in the distance like to green ribbons, intersecting the greater forest.

How often in the days that are no more have I carried my net to such "fresh woods" and emerged unexpectedly into the land of the entomological heart's desire. Rare orchids haunt these plots "of beechen green, and shadows numberless," the witch-like *Orobanche* [broom-rape], and the wicked looking "toothwort." From such a spray my companion had taken a remarkable *Plusia* which I will leave him to describe; *Abraxas ulmata* [*A. sylvata* — Clouded Magpie] was the sole tenant today.

Debouching from the woods, in a sheltered amphitheatre protected here by the rising slopes and there by the ring of beeches, I presently was ushered into one of the finest butterfly corners I ever met with in this country. Had the weather been less fickle I might have made a big bag. A shower descended, splashed the whole hill-side with diamonds, and then the sun shone hotly for a few minutes at a time. At once the landscape was alive with insects of all Orders. *A. trifolii* was in force, and what I take to be *A. lonicerae* [Narrow-bordered Five-spot Burnet]. Males of *Argynnis adippe* [later corrected to *cydippe* – High Brown Fritillary], fresh from the pupa, darted madly up and down the slope with occasional females. *Melanargia galatea* [Marbled White] was also coming on, and *Aphantopus hyperanthus* [Ringlet]; and presently single examples of *L. arion* put in a welcome appearance, for the most part in perfect condition, while Mr. Clutterbuck picked up one or two from the meagre thyme clumps on the ant-hills.

I can find no evidence of the deterioration in size and colour mentioned by Mr. Bethune-Baker as observable in specimens from some other Cotteswold localities. The Cotteswold *arion* is, indeed, a much less brilliant insect than the Cornish — just the difference, as it seems to me, as you find on the Continent between the *arion* of the oolite, lias, and volcanic regions and those from the limestone and calcareous formations. I have a short series from these very Cotteswolds collected by the late Herbert Goss. They are nearly all dull in colour and below normal size — one or two quite small — and I have not come across any such in the many haunts of *arion* abroad which I have visited. I find that they were collected on or very near to the ground more particularly indicated to me by Mr. Bethune-Baker, and at a considerable distance from the locality under review. The *arion* we took on June 27th are quite up to normal English size, and are no less brightly coloured than many from Digne, and comparatively low altitudes off the chalk elsewhere: slaty, but not dull. Under more favourable weather conditions I have no doubt we should have found the species not uncommon, for Mr. Clutterbuck had been on the look-out a week previous, and I saw his captures still on the setting-boards. . . .

[Rowland-Brown, H. 1919. The Cotteswold *Arion*. *The Entomologist* **52**: 174–178].

THE GRADUAL DECADENCE OF THE LARGE BLUE

James W. Tutt, F.E.S., Blackheath, London, S. E. (1896)

James W. Tutt (1858-1911), Headmaster of Snowfield's Board School, Bermondsey, South London, was one of the great characters of Victorian entomology. Red-haired, fiercely competitive, Tutt's aggressive manner — at times arrogant and dogmatic — was always likely to dominate any entomological meeting that he attended. He wrote a monumental series of volumes: *The Natural History of the British Lepidoptera*. These books included virtually everything that was then known about each species. They were so detailed that no less than four volumes containing more than 1700 pages were required just to cover the Blues and the Skippers. Tutt never lived to complete his *magnum opus*: he died of heart failure, probably the legacy of childhood rheumatic fever. The ninth volume remained unfinished at his death and was completed posthumously by the Revd George Wheeler.

Even in death Tutt proved no less controversial. Examination of his will, which, in keeping with his prodigous literary output during his relatively short lifetime, extended to eight pages of small type, showed us that after bequeathing fifty pounds to his wife he left no fewer than twenty-four properties, mainly terraced houses in the Medway Valley, to

relatives and friends — an extraordinary fact when one considers that for most of his professional life he was paid no more than the salary of a Victorian schoolmaster, notwithstanding any royalties he may have earned from writing. Tutt left his 'watch and chain and any jewellery of which I may die possessed' to his son James; while to 'my friend Ada Cochrane . . . who helped me in so many ways . . .' he bequeathed his collection of butterflies as well as 'such books as she may select from my scientific library' and the 'freehold house and premises known as 41 Wisteria Road, Lewisham in the said County of Kent'.

Fig. 31. The 'indefatigable' James W. Tutt. 'Yes, I know I am often brutal in the way I put things, but I can't help it, and you know I am right.'

Here, he describes the rise and fall of the Large Blue in England.

Some collectors tell us that our local butterflies are becoming rarer each year, because the seasons have recently been so unfavourable. Such forget that most of the species of British butterflies have been cut off from the Continent for several thousand years, that unfavourable seasons have recurred again and again, that such insects as *Chrysophanus dispar* and *Lycaena arion* were abundant sixty years ago, and that their extermination is a very recent matter, and requires explanation. We do not wish to suggest that unfavourable climatic conditions do not influence insect life, we know that they do; but we do suggest that unfavourable climatic conditions, which have allowed an insect like *Lycaena arion* to exist in tolerable abundance for many thousands of years, did not rapidly exterminate it, say at Barnwell Wold in the "fifties," at Bolt Tail in the "sixties," in certain parts of the Cotswolds in the "seventies," and leave it all this time in comparative abundance in its retired haunts in Cornwall; and we further suggest that this particular species was exterminated in its old quarters, in regular order, as its haunts became known to, and regularly visited by, collectors. The history of this species in Britain will, we doubt not, be interesting to those entomologists to whom libraries containing the works of old authors are not readily available.

Lewin (*History of British Insects*, 1795) writes:— "This species is but rarely met with in England. It is on the wing in the middle of July, on high chalky lands, in different parts of the kingdom, having been taken on Dover Cliffs, Marlborough Downs, the hills near Bath, and Clifden in Buckinghamshire." Donovan (*Natural History of British Insects*, 1796) writes:— "*Papilio arion* is a very scarce insect in this country, and it does not appear to be much more common in any other part of Europe, as Fabricius only says, 'Habitat in Europae pratis [meadows].' Mr. Lemon, a collector of eminence, some years since met with it in England." In these early days, the apparent rarity of all but the most common insects, was due to ignorance of the distribution of the various species.

Stephens (*Illustrations of British Entomology*, vol. 1., pp. 87–88, 1828) writes:— "An insect of great rarity, found on commons and in pastures in the beginning of July; it was taken by the late Dr. Abbot near Bedford, in the Mouse's Pasture, where Mr. Dale caught a single specimen in 1819; it has also been caught near the signal-house on Dover Cliffs, and on bramble blossoms, in rocky situations, in North Wales; several specimens were taken in Kent during the past season, I believe in the vicinity of Deal; it is said to have occurred near Winchester in plenty; and Lewin tells us that it is found on Marlborough Downs, Wilts, on hills near Bath, and near Clifden in Bucks."

Passing from 1828 to 1857, Stainton adds:— "Barnwell Wold, Northamptonshire," and quotes the following extract from the *Zoologist* for 1852 (p. 3350), by the Rev. Wm. Bree, of Polebrook:— "The great prize of all the butterflies of our neighbourhood, however, I hold to be *Polyommatus arion*, which, if I mistake not, was first discovered here by myself some thirteen or fourteen years since. It is confined entirely, as far as my experience goes, to Barnwell Wold and the adjoining rough fields, with the exception of a single specimen which I once met with in a rough field near Polebrook. . . . Many entomologists have, of late years, visited Barnwell Wold in search of *arion*; in short, a summer never passes without meeting in my rambles with brother entomologists from distant parts of the country. I rejoice, however, to be able to state that its annual occurrence does not appear to be diminished in consequence. Unless my memory fails me, I think Mr. Wolley, of Trinity College, Cambridge, informed me that one year he captured in a few days between fifty and sixty specimens in and about Barnwell Wold, though, in point of weather, the days were anything but favourable." Stainton adds (*Manual*, i., p. 60, 1857):— "Since the above was written the insect has apparently become less abundant," to which, under the circumstances, we would add "as well it might, if the entomologists from different parts of the country served the species as did Mr. Wolley" and Mr. Bond, who took forty-nine specimens at Barnwell Wold, remarking at the time that he reported the capture of these specimens, that the insect "is a very local one, for, although I have searched the Wold well, I have only found it in one spot, in the corner of a rough pasture under a wood; it is an easy insect to take, flying very low, and is very conspicuous, settling occasionally on wild thyme, etc." [*British Butterflies*, (Newman), p. 140]. Under the onslaughts of the Wolleys, Bonds, and those who thought that an insect restricted to "a corner of a rough pasture under a wood" could stand their continuous annual attacks without being exterminated, the insect soon became extinct in Barnwell Wold, as it had previously become in Beds, Bucks, Kent, Hunts, Hants and Wiltshire.

About the same time Mr. Quekett and others did their best to exterminate the species in Somersetshire. Of Mr. Quekett's exploits we read:— "I took about forty specimens on the 15th June, 1833, in a situation abounding with long grass and brambles at Langport, near Taunton; and on the same day, in 1834, I took about twenty specimens, and Mr Dale ten." Newman adds:— "Subsequently Mr. Quekett visited the same locality on several occasions, and always with the same success," and then, of course, *L. arion* became extinct in Somerset.

Devonshire was the next point of attack. In 1865, Mr. Bignell writes that he captured, on June 17th, thirty-six specimens near Plymouth, some of them much wasted (1865. *Entomologist*, 2: 295), whilst Mr. Gatcombe writes:— "Two years since, when with some friends, we caught several dozen of that species, and about a fortnight since many were taken in that locality (Bolt Head) by a friend of mine" (1867. *Entomologist*, 4: 301). Following this up is a communication from Mr. Bignell (1870), which is quoted by Newman as follows:— "From the Bolt Head to the Bolt Tail. One year I took it, wasted, on June 14th; but the following year it did not make its appearance until July 7th." Then comes the following information – Kingsbridge Road (by rail), Kingsbridge (by coach), Salcombe (by steamer or boat), then two miles walk to Bolt Head. This was followed by a series of visits of the fraternity who lived at a distance, two or three being located year after year at the King's Arms, Salcombe, and then, at last, appeared the inevitable note from Mr Bignell:— "I feel quite certain that the haunts of *Lycaena arion* at Bolt Head must be looked upon as a thing of the past." There is the usual reference to "the destructiveness of the elements," as if the seasons have never had their counterparts in the ten or twenty or hundred thousand years that have elapsed since our *Lycaena arion* were separated from their relatives on the other side of the Channel.

Then came Gloucestershire, when Mr. Marsden (1867. *Entomologist*, **3**: 314), Mr. Merrin (1867. *Entomologist*, **4**: 104–105), and Mr. Watkins (1868. *Entomologist*, **4**: 120–121) told the world their localities. Following on this came the usual irruption of the collector tribe — "brother entomologists from distant parts of the country" — to exterminate the local species. Aided as the immigrant collectors were by the locals, who collected the insects in the bad seasons, the process of extermination was rapidly carried on. Again, the weather was to blame, as may be seen by the following note by Mr. Herbert Marsden (1885. *Entomologist's mon. Mag.* **21**: 186–189), who writes:— "It was on June 17th, 1866, that I first saw the species alive, when, in the course of a long ramble, I captured it in a narrow valley amongst the Cotswold Hills. The early part of June, 1867, was dark and cold, and I only secured some 12 or 15 examples. The season, May and June, 1868, was hot and brilliant, and *L. arion* appeared on June 5th, which is the earliest date I ever heard of the species being out; but, although rather more plentiful than the previous year, it was still rather scarce. In 1869, another fine or partially fine season, it was more abundant, and I find from my diary that on June 19th I took 10 at rest about sunset. The year 1870, however, is the one to be marked with a white stone by the lovers of *Lycaenidae*, and *L. arion* appeared much more widely distributed than in any other year I know of, either before or since. It would, I am sure, have been possible for an active collector to have caught a thousand specimens during the season, for, in a few visits, I secured about a hundred and fifty, not netting half of those seen, and turning many loose again. During the next few years *L. arion* continued to appear, but very irregularly as regards numbers; the best seasons since 1870 being those of 1876 and 1877, the latter especially, but on no occasion has it been nearly so abundant as in 1870. Now come the dark days. The latter part of June, 1877, was damp and broken, not at all the bright warm weather which *L. arion* loves. In dark, cloudy weather, they are always still, and I believe they will only deposit their eggs when the sun is warm and bright. In 1878 the weather was worse, there being hardly a fine day in the month, and less than a dozen were seen, mostly worn and weather-beaten, for there were scarcely two consecutive fine days. In 1879 the weather was still worse, and *L. arion* was scarcer than ever, while in 1880 only two were obtained, and two or three more seen. For the four years, 1881–84, not one has been seen in the Gloucestershire district that I have been able to trace."

But six years before the above was penned, Mr Marsden had written (1879. *Entomologist*, **12**: 220–221) a note, relative to the rapid disappearance of the species in the Cotswolds, and his report was so gloomy that collectors practically ceased to go there for that species. This respite gave the butterfly another chance, for, in 1890 (1890. *Entomologist's mon. Mag.* **26**:

214), we find Mr Goss "pleased to be able to report that *L. arion* is not, as I feared, extinct on the Cotswold Hills. Yesterday (June 24th), in one of the localities, where I caught *L. arion* in 1877, I took three specimens, all males; of these one was worn, and two had apparently recently emerged from the chrysalis. On visiting a second locality, some four miles from the one last mentioned, I was disappointed at not finding a specimen. To-day I have succeeded in taking two male specimens, both fresh, in a new locality, some two or three miles distant from the former ones." Since then, the gentlemen who wish to "renew" or "enlarge" their series have given the "Blues" on the Cotswold Hills a terrible doing. How local the species is in its haunts in these hills is explained by Mr. Merrin, who says that "the spot most frequented by them was, however, partly sheltered by a stone wall. The same locality subsequently yielded as many as were taken on the first day, while all the district round about, though much of it is of the same character, was perfectly clear of them. This tends to show that the species is very local. On another spot, some miles distant, but of a similar broken character, the species was also found; the area, however, being still more contracted." So regularly have the collectors visited the Cotswolds during the last few years, that the insect has become exceedingly scarce again.

In 1893, Mr. Goss recorded (1893. *Entomologist's mon. Mag.* **29**: 190) the capture of the species in North Cornwall, and Mr. McLachlan [*idem*] purposely omitted the locality in the record of these captures. The insect is now confined to the hills and coast of Gloucestershire, Devonshire and Cornwall, and we have no doubt our collectors will pursue it there until its last south-westerly haunt has been reached. Mr. Goss, at a recent meeting of the Entomological Society of London, recounted, with some warmth, the injury done to the species last season by the late Major Still and a London collector.

At the meeting of the City of London Entomological Society, held on June 16th last, it was stated by Captain Thompson that a party of nine was visiting a village in one of the South-western counties for the purpose of aiding in the extermination of this species. Unfortunately, we had previously heard of this, and that some of these visitors were making the journey an annual institution.

The average educated man will naturally ask, what are the marvellous scientific results obtained from the expenditure of so much enthusiasm and ardour, for he will suppose that the scientific result which attracts the same men to the same locality, for the same insect, year after year, must bear some commensurate importance with the skill and energy expended; and we have to inform the average man that, in 1870, the late Mr. Newman described the egg of the species, whilst, in the same year, Mr. Porritt described the newly-hatched larva, and that the whole of the life-history of the insect, besides these two items, is a blank.

[Tutt, J. W. 1896. The gradual decadence of *Lycaena arion*. *The Entomologist's Record and Journal of Variation* **8**: 121–125].

A chap who had scores of *arion*
Found some more on the links at Polzyon,
While trying, no doubt,
To wipe the lot out,
He was clubbed on the head with an iron.

R. S.

[R. S. (Air Marshal Sir Robert Saundby) 1952. *Entomologist's Gazette* **3**: 39].

A PERSONAL PRIVATE MUSEUM

Nets, pins, killing bottles and setting-boards. Pill boxes and forceps! Although these 'weapons of the chase' enabled the collector to capture, kill and set his specimens, he still needed special equipment for their long-term display and storage. Some Victorian collectors used cork-lined store boxes that were made to resemble leather-bound books, or glass-fronted display cases which could be hung on the sitting-room wall. However, most collectors possessed a cabinet of ten, twenty, forty or even more, glass-topped drawers in various sizes.

In the next article the history of the butterfly cabinet is explored.

ENTOMOLOGICAL CABINETS

Richard L. E. Ford F.R.E.S., Yarmouth, Isle of Wight. (1979)

Richard Lawrence Edward Ford (1913–1996) was the eldest son of the distinguished lepidopterist Leonard Talman Ford M.A. (1881–1961). Educated at Hurstpierpoint, he started his entomological career at L. W. Newman's butterfly farm before moving to the Commonwealth Institute of Entomology, based at the Natural History Museum, London. From 1941 to 1969 he ran Watkins and Doncaster, the natural history suppliers. He was the author of *The Observer's Book of the Larger British Moths* (1952) and *Practical Entomology* (1963). In 1949, in partnership with Eric W. Classey, he founded the *Entomologist's Gazette*. While at Watkins and Doncaster, Ford donated nearly 27,000 entomological and palaeontological specimens to the Natural History Museum. In 1969 he retired to Yarmouth on the Isle of Wight to pursue his interest in palaeontology — in particular, the microfossils. 'He was involved in a number of dinosaur excavations, and discovered many notable fossils from the Tertiary of the island.' (Blows, 1998).

Now that the craft of making fine entomological cabinets has virtually died out and future craftsmen will be prevented from making more cabinets by the cost, it might be as well to place on record a few details of past manufacturers.

I think without doubt that the finest entomological cabinets that were ever produced were those made by Brady, father and son.

The main features which distinguish these beautiful products were: — All mahogany throughout, hidden bearer runners, lifting off frame lids with an extremely narrow frame, and these narrow frames, the thinnest made by anybody, closed down to a tongued and grooved base.

They were so airtight in fact that many think they are difficult to use, as great care is

Fig. 32. A cornucopia of cabinets. Watkins and Doncaster 110, Parkview Road, Welling, Kent (*c*. 1960).

Fig. 33. Richard L. E. Ford (1938). He purchased the naturalist suppliers Watkins & Doncaster in 1939, running the firm until he retired to the Isle of Wight in 1969. His many palaeontological achievements included the discovery of the island's first Cretaceous mammal teeth.

needed when lifting the lids. The camphor cells were concealed in the side of the drawer and closed by a small piece of the 'rail' holding the frame, sliding out. So well did these fit that they were almost invisible. I heard a remark at an auction that 'I didn't go for that cabinet, it has no camphor cells'. A fine investment opportunity lost!

The Bradys flourished around 1900. The cost was then ten shillings a drawer but you could not just go and order a cabinet, Brady worked for love as well. You had to get alongside him and remark that you had dined with a Mr. So-and-so and saw his wonderful cabinets and wished you were lucky enough to have one like it. All being well Brady might offer to make you one. When my father had one, Brady followed it up with two for birds' eggs for one of my uncles, and they are still in the family*.

Between the wars, John Jacques of that famous Sports Firm and a micro collector, made in his factory two very fine copies of a Brady cabinet, but these were in two tiers of ten. Using modern machinery they were very fine copies but just distinguishable from those made by the master. These two are now in a museum in the West Country [Overbeck House, Salcombe, Devon. (National Trust Property)].

*The Brady may be regarded as the Rolls-Royce of cabinets. However, whereas the Rolls is still being manufactured, Brady ceased production some 60 [c.1920] years ago. According to an invoice in my possession dated the 1st of June 1909, Brady was a "Shop fitter and Entomological Cabinet Maker", of 368 Lower Fore Street, Edmonton [see Fig. 34]. He appears to have begun making insect cabinets around 1870, and on the back cover of *The Entomologist* for April 1878 was advertising from 3 Bridport Cottages, Silver Street, Edmonton, London E., mahogany cabinets at 10s per drawer [see Plate 7]. For sheer perfection of workmanship, the Brady cabinet has never been equalled, nor indeed is it ever likely to be — J. M. C.-H. [Chalmers-Hunt].

Brady was closely followed by Gurney who went to the other extreme by being more robust. The frames on the drawers were very much wider, often to conceal a continuous camphor cell which ran right round the drawer. The door was generally about $1^1/_4$ inches thick and the whole cabinet very thick. While Brady cabinets were mostly of 20 drawers each, in one tier, Gurney made cabinets of 40, 20, 12 and ten drawers but the smaller ones were rarer.

Before the 1914 war thin sheets of virgin cork were used, pieces being jig-sawed together and then sanded down. Both Brady and Gurney used this method and like Bradys, the Gurney cabinets were all of solid mahogany, even the bases of the drawers.

During and just after that war, cork became difficult and for a time odd makers (not the above) used cork linoleum as a substitute. This was of course not as good. It can be distinguished by two features. The drawer feels very heavy, and when you withdraw a pin there is a very slight 'click' and a jerk as the pin is gripped by the lino (and off comes the body!).

Immediately after the war came Crockett. He introduced plywood for the bases of the drawers. He made sound and useful cabinets often in deal, sometimes with mahogany sides and doors and often using the rail principle to support the drawers instead of the concealed runners. This means the drawers looked deeper as there had to be a flange in front to conceal the rails on the insides of the cabinets. Towards the end of his career, Crockett did produce a few cabinets in mahogany. Unlike the first two makers, the drawers of Crockett's cabinets were not as well fitting and not always interchangeable with each other.

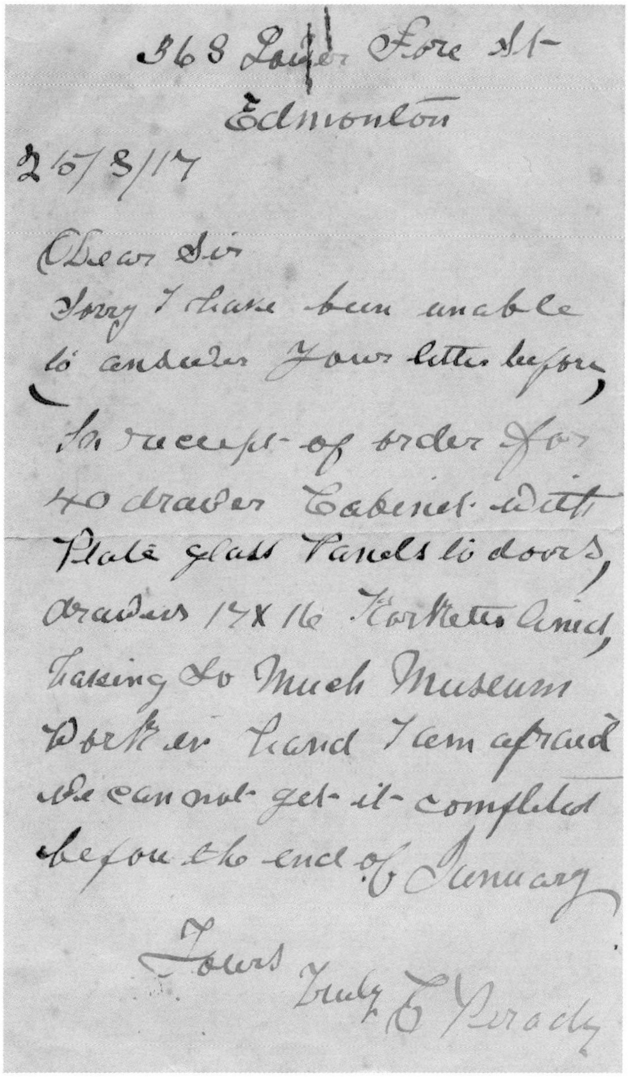

Fig. 34. Letter from Charles Brady to a customer (1917).
'The Brady may be regarded as the Rolls-Royce of cabinets.'

In the period between wars Watkins & Doncaster dominated the cabinet scene, the maker being Kendrew who, at his best produced cabinets almost as fine as any. The last one he made in the top bracket was purchased by the late John Spedan Lewis, and I think is still in his country house and preserved there.

W. & D. produced a very wide range of cabinets, from deal with a dark varnish (which scratched easily) for the schoolboy trade, to the finest mahogany cabinets. At this time they could take advantage of two items, composition cork and mahogany plywood.

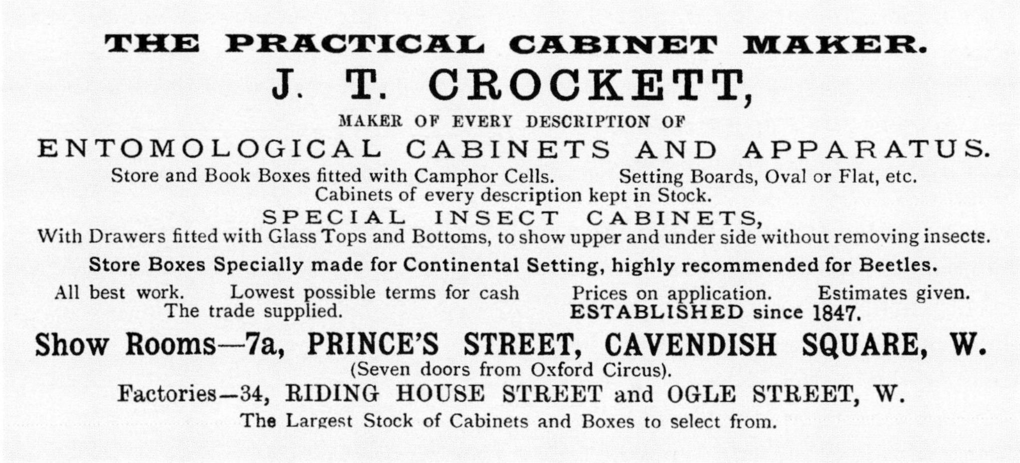

Fig. 35   Entomological cabinet makers
(a). *The Entomologist's Record and Journal of Variation* (1893).
(b). *The Entomologist's Record and Journal of Variation* (1903).
(c). The Butterfly Farm price list for British Lepidoptera (*c.* 1936).

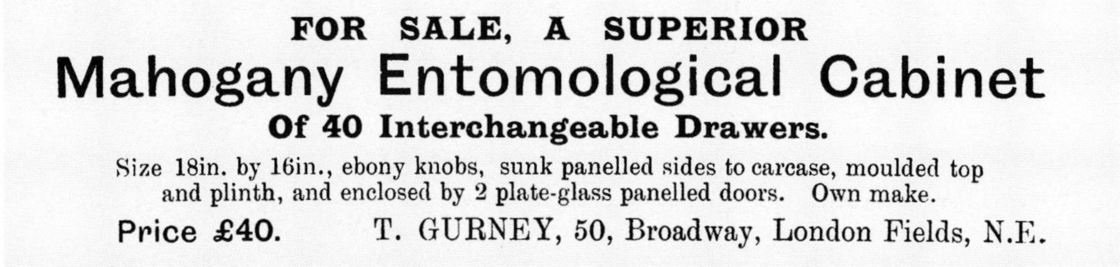

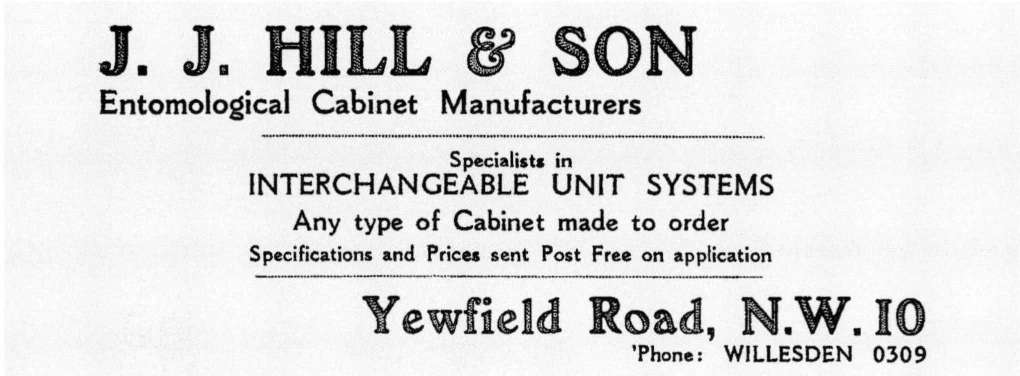

The joints of the sides of the best of Kendrew's and all those made by Brady and Gurney were dove-tailed.

Hills, father and son, introduced a new and very good system for cabinets. They produced a cabinet with a loose base and top and a unit of ten drawers so that you could stack 10, 20 or 30 drawers in a single tier. The units had a shutter to close them although later some were made with hinged doors. The reason for the shutter was that the cabinets were designed to be built into a continuous bank. They were made in oak or mahogany facings with, generally, whitewood sides to the drawers. The drawers had comb corners and a fairly generous tolerance so that they could be quite interchangeable with any unit. On the whole a good idea, but once committed to this scheme one had to continue, and when prices advanced during and after the war some collectors felt they were trapped!

I once inspected the coleoptera collection formed by the late Nathaniel Lloyd. He had what looked like a huge collection of about twenty cabinets each in two units of ten. He did not like stooping however, and the bottom units were empty without even a pin hole in the drawers, and served to support the upper deck. They went to Manchester I think, and what a windfall for them.

The main manufacturers used a different design for the edging on the tops of their cabinets, so you can sometimes distinguish them by this. But over the years various amateur makers copied styles, possibly to match a cabinet they possessed or even by accident, so that this feature does not always serve as a reliable guide to the maker.

There must have been hundreds of cabinets of all shapes and sizes produced over the years. My own father, in the earlier days, even made about three, using walnut from a tree in the grounds of his father's estate. I once bought a beautiful cabinet, made at Osborne House by the then Queen's (Victoria) carpenter for one of the ground staff. Not only was it of solid mahogany, but the bases of the drawers were made from half inch thick mahogany [Plate 7].

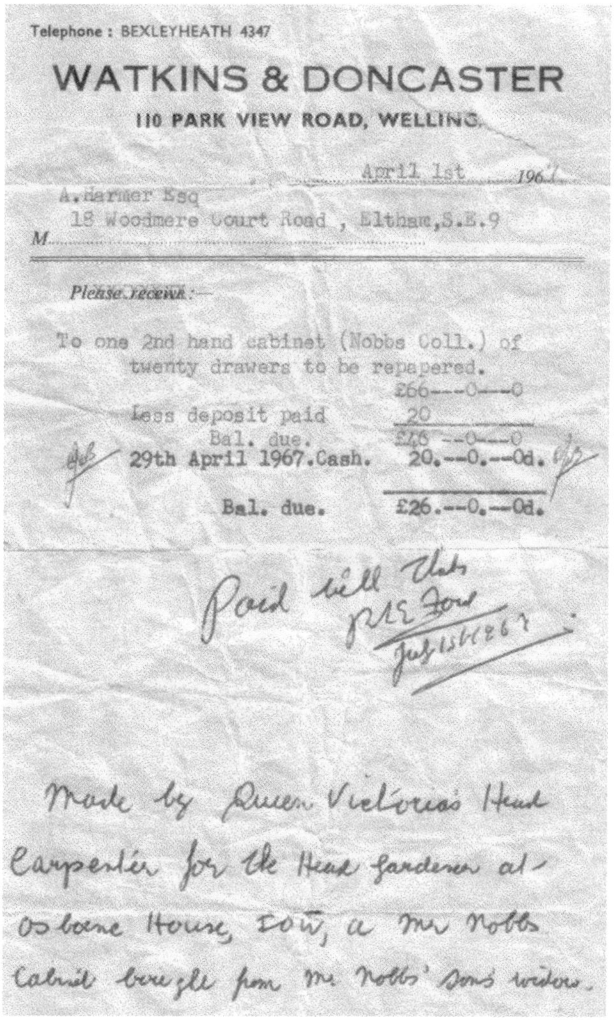
Telephone : BEXLEYHEATH 4347

WATKINS & DONCASTER

110 PARK VIEW ROAD, WELLING

April 1st 1967

M. A. Harmer Esq
18 Woodmere Court Road, Eltham, S.E.9

Please receive:—

To one 2nd hand cabinet (Nobbs Coll.) of twenty drawers to be repapered.

	£66---0---0
Less deposit paid	20
Bal. due.	£46 --0---0
29th April 1967. Cash.	20.--0.--0d.
Bal. due.	£26.--0.--0d.

Paid bill thats
RLE Ford

Made by Queen Victoria's Head Carpenter for the Head gardener at Osborne House, I.O.W., a Mr Nobbs. Cabinet bought from Mr Nobbs' Son's widow.

Fig. 36. Receipt for the Osborne House entomological cabinet.

I have even seen a cabinet with two secret drawers, one at the top and one at the bottom. So good was the top one that the owner passed on without knowing what he had. It contained blown larvae with a lot number from a sale. No doubt these were made for specimens on the 'protected list'!

[Ford, R. L. E. 1979. Entomological cabinets. *The Entomologist's Record and Journal of Variation* **91**: 308–310].

Following publication of Richard Ford's article Alec Harmer of Lymington, Hampshire, wrote to *The Entomologist's Record* to say that in 1967 he had been fortunate enough to have purchased the Osborne House cabinet mentioned.

. . . The cabinet comprises 20 drawers in a single tier behind a fully-glazed door, and is made from Spanish mahogany with stained oak lid frames. . . . and each drawer front is fitted with a brass dummy keyhole . . . According to the bill of sale [Fig. 36], it was made by Queen Victoria's head carpenter for the head gardener at Osborne House, a Mr. G. Nobbs, and contained his collection of butterflies. As might be expected *Melitaea cinxia* [Glanville Fritillary] aberrations were well represented, and I remember at least one drawer that contained about 60 little round mirrors with a small piece of cork glued to each. This drawer included many *cinxia* aberrations, and the idea was that both upper and undersides could be viewed with ease in the mirror without having to remove the insect.

[Harmer, A. S. 1980. Entomological cabinets. *Entomologist's Record and Journal of Variation* **92**: 258].

Some of the distinguishing features of Brady's fine craftmanship can be seen on Plate 7. Another characteristic feature is the usual absence of the maker's name anywhere on the cabinet! So far as is known, there is only one Brady cabinet that does carry the manufacturer's details. Equally rare too, perhaps, is the Brady display box (Plate 7) that belonged to the late Michael Chalmers-Hunt, who had purchased it from Richard Ford. Although it does not bear the maker's name, it does however have an impeccable provenence — Brady having made it for Richard Ford's father.

CHAPTER TWO

NOCTES AMBROSIANAE — LIGHT-TRAPS AND SUGAR

'The desire of the moth for the star,
Of the night for the morrow.'
P. B. Shelley (1821)

FAR TO THE WEST OF LONDON lies an area of marsh thick with alders, sallows and rosebay willowherb; an area that fifty years ago saw few people near its wild narrow waterways other than an occasional fisherman. Today this place is surrounded by sprawling houses and a commuter population which grows ever more numerous year by year. In the 1940s, however, it was the scene of youthful entomological adventures. We were young then and our first experiments with a primitive light-trap and sugaring produced epic encounters with a host of night-flying moths, most of which we knew only from illustrations in Richard South's *The Moths of the British Isles*.

There was always something special about nocturnal moth hunting. Distant memories recall nights when searchlights criss-crossed the skies in their search for enemy planes, while far below our diminutive figures might have been seen stealthily approaching the line of trees and posts that were liberally daubed with our own brand of ambrosian nectar. Earlier in the day we had been allowed into the kitchen, with strict instructions to use nothing but the oldest saucepan into which we threw lumps of coarse brown sugar and a small amount of water. This sticky mixture was then brought slowly to the boil before a cupful of stout, a few drops of jargonelle essence and a small packet of lemonade crystals were added. With this elixir we were ready for anything . . . and the results were magic!

 We remember nights when furry, large-bodied moths fought each other for places at the feast, while others, inebriated and hopeless, fell to the ground and buzzed round and round amongst the grass. One night, a large Death's-head Hawk-moth visited our sugar. But we never caught it. We also remember our endless talk and fantasies about that wondrous rarity — the Pease Blossom (*Periphanes delphinii*). This moth fascinated us from the moment that an old collector told us that it had only ever been seen five times; indeed, on one of those rare occasions no more than a wing had been found trapped in a long-deserted spider's web on the Duchess of Portland's estate at Bulstrode, Buckinghamshire. To us *this* was the stuff of dreams. Our fascination grew even stronger some years later when we learned that another extremely rare moth, the Purple Cloud (*Actinotia polyodon*), had also been found in a spider's web, this time by the Revd Hawker at Ashford in Hampshire (p. 176).

The apparent association of rare Lepidoptera and spiders' webs continued to intrigue us, and in 1955 our joy knew no bounds when we read the account by Colonel S. H. Kershaw of the last Mazarine Blue (*Cyaniris semiargus*) butterfly to be caught in Britain. Incredibly, while his brother was butterflying in a meadow near Aberystwyth, his wife pointed out a butterfly trapped in a cobweb. He immediately identified this as *C. semiargus*, and then just to rub things in he took a second specimen flying close by. Such is the luck of the earnest collector!

In Chapter Two we assemble our light-trap and boil more saucepans of brown sugar. We also discover that nocturnal moth hunting can lead one into strange places, including a Court of Law.

THE ORIGIN OF SUGARING

David E. Allen, Winchester, Hampshire. (1965)

Dr David Elliston Allen (b. 1932) is a distinguished botanist and writer on the history of various natural history subjects. He was educated at Rugby and Cambridge University, where he obtained a Ph.D. in the History of Science. At present, he is the main Careers Coordinator of the History of Medicine Programme of the Wellcome Trust and Honorary Lecturer in the History of Life Sciences at University College London. Among his numerous written works are *The Victorian Fern Craze: A History of Pteridomania* (1969) and the highly acclaimed *The Naturalist in Britain* (1976).

. . . The earliest observation of the attraction of sweets for moths and the value of this as a means of capturing nocturnal species seems to have been in September, 1831. In that month three London collectors, Walton, Bowerbank and Hoyer, noticed moths guzzling the ripe berries of yew-trees near Mickleham, in Surrey. Returning with their lanterns on the next and subsequent evenings they took a rich haul 'in the very act of feasting on the saccharine juices of the fruit' (Walton, 1835). It does not appear to have occurred to them, however, to use the berries as a bait independently of the trees.

In much the same way Dale (1833) reported that he had observed (though apparently no more than observed) that 'the bottles filled with sugar and water which are frequently hung against walls to attract wasps, and so preserve the wall fruit, will attract moths also'. Some

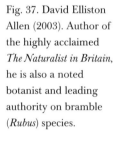

Fig. 37. David Elliston Allen (2003). Author of the highly acclaimed *The Naturalist in Britain*, he is also a noted botanist and leading authority on bramble (*Rubus*) species.

years later Stevens (1843) mentioned that a relative of his had accidentally caught a scarce moth in 1838 near Arundel 'in a bottle containing beer and sugar, that was placed against a wall to catch the wasps'; and perhaps for this reason Stevens, a Hammersmith collector, preached the virtue of mixing sugar with beer instead of water when the fashion for sugaring had caught on (Newman, 1844). Bartlett (1845) also began invariably using these same two ingredients after observing 'a year or two since' some dozen moths drowned in a bottle of sugar and beer hung in a tree to catch wasps.

Even before Dale's note, however, Edward Doubleday (1833), then aged twenty-one, in a now famous letter written in November, 1832, had secured for empty sugar hogsheads the credit for inspiring the first fermentation bait devised and used in entomology. The Doubleday brothers helped to run the family grocery business at Epping and in the course of their daily work had noticed that moths were attracted to hogsheads turned out of their warehouse. Taking the hint, they put out several that were just emptied in open places near gardens and fields, capturing by this means no fewer than 69 species, some of them distinctly uncommon. English (1882), a close friend, claimed to have noticed moths at the grocery hogsheads independently; according to him, the moths came to the bait only in small numbers, chiefly during the autumn and rainy seasons, in summer the bees in a single fine day cleaning the casks of every vestige of sugar.

It is not clear whether this discovery was made in 1832 or even earlier. Nor is it clear how long the Doubledays persisted with their undoubtedly cumbrous technique. We have it on the authority of English that Henry Doubleday never utilised sugar in any other way before 1840; and Edward (1840, pp. 214, 275) only mentions the use of light as his method of collecting Noctuae in his account of his nineteen-month collecting trip to America. It is not certain, even, that more than one other collector bothered to act on their suggestion. Dale (1833), writing only a month or two later, advised that 'if sugar barrels are heated, they will attract moths much sooner than when cold; some gauze should be so placed as to prevent the moths injuring themselves, and a person should stand near with a net ready' — but these may have been suggestions and no more.

The one other collector whom the Doubledays certainly inspired was P. J. Selby, High Sheriff for Northumberland and one of the foremost ornithologists of the day. At that time birds were still Henry Doubleday's principal interest and it is quite likely that the two were correspondents. If so, it would have been natural for the new method to be recommended when Selby first came to take up entomology seriously in 1835. In a letter quoted by Duncan (1836, p. 105 — not 1834, *Entomologia Edinensis*, as cited in error by Allan), Selby begins: 'In

The Doubleday brothers 'had noticed that moths were attracted to hogsheads turned out of their warehouse'.

the course of my entomological pursuits — for that fascinating department of Zoology has for the last year engrossed a great part of my leisure — my attention was first directed to the mode I have since adopted for the capture of nocturnal lepidoptera, by the extraordinary success that I understood had attended the exposure of a sugar-cask, recently emptied, in a favourable situation'. As sugar-casks were not readily procurable in his part of the country, he cast around for a substitute; and an empty bee-hive (locally known as a skep) generously smeared on the outside with honey, quickly showed itself the perfect answer, as was immediately apparent from the first evening's experiment, which took place in the second half of August. Selby does not specify the actual year referred to in the passage quoted by Duncan, but from the wording considered in relation to the date of publication it seems likely to have been 1835. This is supported by the fact that the first part of his Fauna of Twizell (his Northumberland estate), which included the Lepidoptera, was laid before the Berwickshire Naturalists' Club in December, 1835 . . . Although four years elapsed before the Fauna of Twizell appeared in print . . . it seems fair to assume that the published account was substantially the same as that written in 1835. If this was indeed the case, 1835 is established as the *terminus ante quem* by the fact that the paper contains a description of the bee-hive method — as well as additional comments on its potential usefulness that are identical word for word with those used in the letter quoted by Duncan in 1836. A yet further reason for dating Selby's discovery to 1835 is that this was the first summer when at long last his ten-year series, *Illustrations of British Ornithology*, had been put firmly behind him: it may be that he took up entomology as a refreshing change after a temporary surfeit of birds.

The date of Selby's discovery has been gone into in some detail, because it can now be shown that he was the first person to consider (though not, it would seem, actually to instigate) the more practicable method of sugaring that has been used ever since. This is revealed by a letter in April, 1837, to the Rev. F. O. Morris, who had written for further details after reading the account in Duncan's book. Morris considered Selby's reply of sufficient general interest to send it for publication in Neville Wood's *Naturalist* (1837, **2**: 147), where until now apparently it has lain overlooked. Terming it 'a certain trap for all the nocturnal Lepidoptera', Selby recommended that the hive be placed 'on a forked stick at the most convenient height for taking the insects with the clippers' [*]. 'I set it', he continues, 'immediately after sunset, and visit every half hour till ten or eleven o'clock, during autumn and summer . . . . The Moths are generally so engaged in sucking the honey, as to allow themselves to be easily taken if quietly approached. A candle or lamp is used, but not left standing with the hive'. In 1836, he adds, he took in this way many rare species not expected in his district . . . On a favourable night in July he had seen the whole outside of the hive covered with moths and taken eighteen to twenty different species on it at a time. 'Anointing the trunks of trees', he goes on, 'would no doubt have the same effect, but it would require a much greater consumption of honey, as wasps, bees, and other insects would devour every particle during the day. Inferior honey answers as well as the best, and I find it more attractive than sugar'.

Ten years later, however, he had changed his mind, perhaps swept along by the subsequent fashion; for we are told (Selby, 1848) that in that season at Twizell Noctuae 'resorted to the boles of trees anointed with honey or syrup of sugar'. Even if he was not the first to adopt this simpler method, it is clear that he had at any rate evolved a 'sugar-beat', paying periodic visits with a lantern, and in view of this his claim to the title 'Father of Sugar' is surely a stronger one than allowed by Allan (1937).

[*An early form of butterfly net.]

In his other accounts Selby recorded that he generally selected a sheltered situation, near to wood, for his hive. He had apparently experimented with a variety of other objects but found the local type of bee-hive best, because its larger surface and circular shape made capturing the insects easier. He stressed the potential value of the method for studying the periods of duration of various species and the varying proportions of the sexes.

It is curious that Selby's suggestion of 1837 seems to have met with no reaction from the Doubledays, even supposing that they were aware of it. For the method of sugaring with a brush was invented, apparently quite independently, a few years later by James English, who almost immediately introduced it to Henry Doubleday (English, 1882). Noticing the attraction honey-dew on some plum leaves in his Epping garden had for moths, English hit on the idea of making a kind of artificial honey-dew by dissolving sugar in water and brushing it on leaves. This at once met with immense success.

Fig. 38.
Henry Doubleday (1808–1875), the Epping Forest greengrocer who independently discovered that sugar attracted moths.

English dated his discovery to 1843, but, as Christy (1888) later demonstrated, this is certainly incorrect. It would appear, rather, to have been in the summer of 1841. For Humphreys & Westwood (1843–45), in their preface dated October, 1841, had announced that 'Mr. Doubleday has recently tried the experiment of brushing a mixture of sugar and water upon the bark of trees where moths are likely to abound, and found the plan perfectly successful, having captured immense numbers this season in that way, many of them of the most rare and beautiful species'. Furthermore, in a letter to T. C. Heysham of Carlisle in August, 1841, Henry Doubleday had written: 'I go out every night that is at all tolerable. By taking some sugar and water and brushing it on the trunks of trees or sprinkling it on the bushes, you attract an immense number of moths, . . . and with a light you may select what you want'. . . .

Some of the leading collectors had certainly copied Doubleday's method by the beginning of the season of 1842. J. W. Douglas, of London, and Robert Edlestone, of Manchester, were two of these, though the latter claimed it was useless: 'possibly', remarked Douglas (1842), 'the sugar he uses is not strong enough; treacle I find does equally well'. (This is the earliest mention of treacle as such.) From letters from other correspondents Douglas concluded that the method was not generally understood by collectors outside London, and he accordingly contributed to the *Zoologist* (Douglas, 1844) a detailed account of it. Some people, he noted, boiled the sugar and water, and more than once he had seen one collector use sugar with rum and another sugar without rum, and the former had twice as much success. A large number of collectors wrote into the *Zoologist* as a result (Newman, 1844), some warmly thanking Douglas for making such a useful method known, others still complaining of a total lack of success. It was finally left to Gregson (1844) to point out to those who remained sceptical that they were using the wrong kind of sugar: ordinary white household sugar was no good; they needed to use the very dark brown, strong-smelling sugar from the lower part of West Indies hogsheads. From that point on success seems to have been universal.

[Allen, D. E. 1965. The origin of sugaring. *The Entomologist's Record and Journal of Variation* **77**: 117–121].

SUGAR

Henry Guard Knaggs, M.D., F.L.S., Camden Town, London. (1869)

Dr Henry Guard Knaggs (1832–1908) lived in Camden Town, which during the mid-Victorian era was a scattered village on the northern outskirts of London. He trained for the medical profession at University College Hospital and practised in north London until gout forced him to retire in 1896. His hearty, generous and jovial nature made him very popular among entomologists of the day and it is recorded that after meetings of the Entomological Society, Fellows would happily repair to the doctor's residence for refreshment and conviviality. Indeed, his house during the early 'sixties' became an informal meeting centre for many of the best-known collectors of the time.

Dr Knaggs wrote his entomological best-seller *The Lepidopterist's Guide* in 1869, and this slim volume, intended for the young and relatively inexperienced collector, was full of good advice. The following notes were intended to assist the novice over the little matter of capturing moths at sugar:

Sugar, however, is the great medium employed in this country; there are few natural attractions that can vie with it, and it possesses the great superiority over flowers that the visitors to it come to us from all parts, congregating in a small space, where they are at once plainly visible. Various prescriptions have been extolled for their efficacy, but, as good a basis as any may be made by boiling up equal weights of **foots** sugar and treacle in a sufficient quantity of stale beer to bring the mixture to the requisite consistency; that is, it should not be too thick or it will not "work" well with the brush, nor too thin or it will run away to the ground too quickly, and the upper parts of the patch will dry up; lastly, a small quantity of rum should be added shortly before use — if too much be added, the moths will be too quickly intoxicated, will fall to the ground, and be lost among the herbage. Some collectors think proper to flavour their sugar with ratafia, anise-seed, essence of jargonelle pears, or the not easily procured essence of ginger-grass. Honey is preferred by some to sugar, but besides being more costly it is less efficacious.

The apparatus required for sugaring is varied; the collector must take his choice of what he considers necessary from the following:

A Sugar tin with a brush attached to the lid is sold for the purpose, but a soda water bottle, a small gallipot for the reception of a little of the mixture at a time as required, and a brush of about three-quarters of an inch diameter at the bristle end, and carried well wrapped up in brown paper, will answer all ends perfectly.

A lantern. This should be fitted at the back with a tongue which may be slipped into a belt or the waist of the trousers or the vest; or it may be suspended from one's mouth by a piece of wire bent at two right angles, the part between the two angles being encased in a tubular bit of wood of the thickness of a drawing pencil, so that it can be grasped by the teeth; or thirdly, it may be slung round the neck by means of a strap, on the ends of which are fastened two hooks which pass into two triangular rings soldered to the back of the lantern, either of these additions sets a hand at liberty. The front should be of plate glass, for a bull's-eye concentrates the light too much, and scares the flies; a darkening cover is also important. N.B. — Always look to the trimming of the lamp, &c., before starting.

A net for sugaring is best constructed by socketing two "paragon" wires into a **Y**-piece, and connecting their diverging extremities with a piece of cat-gut, which will readily adapt itself to the shape of a tree or other object against which it may be pushed. Bag, as usual, but not very deep.

A catching and pinning box is considered by many indispensable. To make this, a tube of about two inches (or three at least, for *Catocala* [Red, Crimson, or Blue Underwings]) in diameter should be sawed transversely half through at about half-an-inch from one end; in the slit thus formed, a circular valve should be made to work so as to close up the tube if required; the other end should be *firmly* covered with strong open net-work. Then a sort of piston corked at the end should be made to fit the cylinder. For use, the valve is opened, the mouth of the tube clapped over the insect, which of course flies towards the net-work, when the valve ought to be instantly closed; next insert the corked piston up to the valve, open the latter and push the insect against the net-work, pin it through one of the meshes, and then withdraw the piston with the insect stuck upon it, repin properly, and transfer to the collecting box.

Fig. 39. Dr Henry Guard Knaggs, the jovial medical practitioner who delighted in entertaining his entomological colleagues.

A fork formed by three darning needles, driven at the angles of an imaginary triangle eye foremost into a handle, is sometimes employed for impaling the very skittish *Catocalæ* on the sugared trees. With practice, a single darning needle may be used very effectively, but the readiest way of procuring them in good condition is to stun them by striking them down with a battle-dore; when netted, they quickly damage their plumage. The use of a single needle reminds me of the Scotchman, who having dreamt that he had captured a Clifton Nonpareil upon a paling by sticking it with a certain big pin, for years carried the *long* pin about with him in the expectation of meeting with the *Catocala*. At last one day sure enough he saw the Nonpareil sitting on a fence, but horror! he had forgotten his pin. Now you, my reader, would doubtless, under the circumstances, have been dreadfully excited, and have rashly made some absurd attempt to secure the prize, which would, in all probability, have got out of your clutches, with the loss of a few scales. But this was not what our Scotch friend did; he went quietly home, got his pin, returned with it to the spot, and coolly pinned the great Blue Underwing.

A pinning box, the usual complement of chip boxes, and killing bottle, will be required. And lastly, and by no means leastly, *lucifers* must not be forgotten.

Choice of locality. Sugaring may be employed in almost any locality, from the most barren and bleak to the most fertile and sheltered districts; the rides and clearings in woods are favourite places of resort. The heaths, sandhills, mountain sides, fens, under-cliffs, parks, borders of fields, are all productive. We should avoid situations where the foliage is dense. Trees which have been repeatedly sugared are always more profitable than those newly tried, and we should therefore be cautious about rushing off to a fresh spot for the reason that we have been unsuccessful. We should not give up dirty water until we are sure we can get a clean liquid.

Choice of evening. The unfavourable circumstances to be regarded are east wind, or a too boisterous wind, bright moon, unseasonably cold weather, too calm weather, ground fogs, the counteracting effect of certain blossoms and of honey dew, untried districts, abundance of ear-wigs, woodlice, slugs, &c., the condition of air *after* a thunder-storm. Favourable are warm dark nights, clouded sky but the air clear near the earth, previous hot weather, moderate wind blowing steadily in our direction, such as W., S.W., or S., thunder in the air, and even during the continuance of a thunder-storm, for in spite of pelting rain, insects will sometimes swarm at sugar. On such a night I remember counting over 150 of various kinds on two small patches — rather embarrassing! NOTE. — Though moonlight nights are *usually* unprofitable, I once saw Noctuæ swarming at sugar about 1 a.m., when the atmosphere was as clear as space, and the luminary of the harvest denomination. N.B. — Bats and night-jars are good signs.

Time for Sugaring. Sugar should be got on before dusk, but not too soon before, or its virtues and sweetness will be expended on the desert air; when the first cockchafer or "lousy-watchman" [Dor-beetle] booms past us, we should be reminded that it is at once time to lay on our sugar: Many leave their sugared trees for home at too early an hour: it should be remembered that some species fly at one hour, others at another, and that a succession of visitors arrive from dusk to dawn.

Modus operandi. We should sugar at intervals of about ten yards, choosing such trees as have the roughest bark, as oak, elm, and poplar; smooth ones, such as beech, horse-chestnut, sycamore, and lime, don't, as a rule, pay. The sugar should be put on these in a long narrow streak reaching from shoulder height down to within a foot of the ground, and should be applied on the sheltered side. When there are no trees in the locality, palings (but they ought to be open ones, or the scent of the sugar will not be wafted away) may be sugared; if these be not present, we may sugar foliage of bushes, reeds, or flowers of ragwort, umbelliferæ, knapweed, bramble, thistle stalks, &c., marking the spot in some way that we may not overlook it — pieces of white paper answer the purpose. But in some barren spots not even this class of herbage is present. On the sand hills for instance, the method is to tie tufts of *Ammophila* [marram grass] into knots and sugar these; where the grass is very short we must carry laths or boughs to the scene of operations for the application of our sweets; and if not that, we must e'en content ourselves with sugared rags (conveyed to the spot in tins), laying them out to the best advantage we can, or apply our nectar to the bare stones.

857. Finally, pill boxes, obtainable of any druggist, complete the outfit of the entomologist. There is now an excellent kind manufactured, of which the tops and bottoms never come out, owing to a little management in avoiding the usual pressure : it is important to get these. It is important also to avoid sitting on pill boxes, as it must interfere with their structure : to avoid this, the author carries them in a breast pocket.

Fig. 40. Sound advice from Edward Newman (*A Familiar Introduction to the History of Insects,* 1841).

Capturing insects off the sugar may be effected by the pinning box or fork already mentioned, but generally there is no difficulty in boxing them in the ordinary way; that is, take the bottom of the chip box between the thumb and little finger, the lid between the index and third finger, the second finger resting on the top of the lid, then apply at one point a portion of the circumference of the lid to a corresponding part of the box itself: — with a very little practice, the box can be quickly opened and shut with one hand; another way is to put the cyanide bottle under them and tap them in; if they be very skittish, they must be netted or knocked down as they fly off. In examining the sugar, we should shut off the light while approaching a tree, we should then place the triangular net underneath the patch, holding it in position by our knee, and having gently turned on the lantern, proceed to box such moths as may be considered worth taking. . . .

NOTE. — Whilst sugaring one must be on the look-out for other visitors besides *Noctuæ*, for *Bos* [a bull], attracted by our lantern, sometimes puts in an unexpected appearance; and had it not been for suddenly "dousing the glim," on the occasion of a pair of horses coming full gallop at my light, it is more than probable that the "Guide" would never have appeared.

By day, sugaring may be used to attract *Vanessæ* and other butterflies with good chances of success.

[Knaggs, H. G. 1869. *The Lepidopterist's Guide*. London, Van Voorst].

The entomological literature is full of advice for would-be sugarers and replete with various recipes for the 'perfect' sugaring mixture. Few authors, however, were as dogmatic as Brian Worthington-Smith (1951):

> The most important ingredient of the sugaring mixture is the sugar itself, for moths are pernickety and fastidious creatures where sugar is concerned. They insist on rich, dark brown 'Barbados' (Foot's) or nothing. If you cannot obtain 'Barbados' sugar it is only a waste of time and money to use any other kind. Moths won't look at it.
>
> Next obtain a 1 lb tin of cane treacle. Golden Syrup will not do. It must be black treacle. Tip the treacle into a saucepan, then add 2 lbs of 'Barbados' sugar. Then pour in half a pint of water. Stir and heat slowly to the boil . . . When the mixture is luke-warm — and not before — add one generous teaspoonful of 'Old Jamaica Rum.'

LAMENT OF A TREACLER

I've sugared in the forest, I've sugared in the glen,
I've sugared up on mountains, been successful now and then.
I've had *c-nigrum* by the thousand and *nupta* by the score,
Wainscots in the fenlands, rare migrants by the shore.
Fraxini fair evades me, *zollikoferi* as well,
But not for want of trying; perhaps it's scent or smell.
Cunning are my recipes, brewed with practised skill.
Pungent subtle odours waft from out the kitchen "still."
One day I made a Special Trip. I judged the time was ripe
For optimists like me to get the Lunar Double Stripe.
My luck was out however: I drove home in the rain.
Cold again the night was: all that way seemed vain.
Yet from underneath the bonnet when I cleaned my motor car
There came forth all the four wings of a Double Striped Lunar!

R. F.

[R. F. 1948. Lament of a Treacler. *The Entomologist* **81**: 270].

ON THE PROWL

Rev. George. M. A. Hewett, B.A., M.A., Winchester, Hampshire. (1895)

The western sky is all aflame:
The sun's red steeds their stalls are nearing:
Or if they aren't, it's all the same:
You know the sort of track I'm steering.
It's time to get the treacle pot,
And not to talk that kind of rot.

Now night unfolds her dusky wings:
A few faint stars are coyly peeping:
I wonder why one hunts the things
That haunt the woods, instead of sleeping!
We're nearly there, with hope elated,
Fetch out the spirits (methylated).

The moon her silvery orb aloft
Through spaceless depths is slowly raising;
I rather fancy I'll be scoffed
If that's the kind of night I'm praising.
Those matches, please, this way,
young man, turn;
I think it's time to light the lantern.

Red glows the light on many a gold
And pink and saffron tinted pinion.
I've got as much as I can hold,
I've filled my pill-boxes and tin one.
It's getting late by my chronometer:
Just net that little last geometer.

You see yon glimmer in the East,
That's where the day will soon be breaking.
I really think the man's a beast
Who goes to bed when moths are waking.
But I've got other work to do
To-morrow morning — haven't you?
G. M. A. H.

[Hewett, G. M. A. 1895. On The Prowl. *The Entomologist's Record and Journal of Variation* 6: 168].

Fig. 41. Revd George Hewett and Sally (1908). 'From boyhood he had been the keenest of observers and lovers of open-air nature . . . every form of open-air sport was the breath of life to him.' (*The Wykehamist*, 1927)

The Reverend George Mottram Andrews Hewett (1858–1927) was born at Nuthrop, near Banbury in Oxfordshire. Educated at Bromsgrove School, he went on to graduate from Pembroke College, Cambridge, in 1882, and for the next thirty-four years he was a master at Winchester College. His obituary in *The Wykehamist* described him as 'A giant in frame, he had a heart as big. He loved the world of Nature; to walk with him was to realise one's own blindness, as time after time he would stop to discover and to love some tiny plant or bird or butterfly, which we should never otherwise have seen . . . He loved children and was loved by them. To teach a child to make a whistle out of a willow twig, to classify and name a boy's first collection of wayside flowers, meant real joy to him.'

In addition to his entomological offerings, he wrote *The Open-Air Boy*, *The Pedagogue at Play*, and *The Autobiography of a Rat*.

SUGARING PROHIBITED IN THE NEW FOREST

Sidney. J. Bell. (1905)

During the last decades of the nineteenth century and for the first few of the next, the New Forest in Hampshire was arguably the richest and most popular collecting area in the country. Each season huge numbers of entomologists were irresistibly drawn to it like proverbial moths to a flame; nowadays, there is very little evidence of 'entomologizing' to be seen. A century ago, however, the scene was very different – the Forest then fairly hummed with activity. 'Most inns in Lyndhurst and Brockenhurst were virtually taken over during the summer months by collectors. Livestock and desirable specimens were traded on Saturday nights at certain hostelries by professional dealers and impecunious collectors seeking to make their hobby self-financing. Several of the New Forest keepers (crown foresters) ran lucrative sidelines in selling insects and acting as weekend guides.' (Oates, 1996). It was indeed big business and collectors made a very welcome and important contribution to the local economy.

Inevitably, all this intense entomological activity was bound to cause tension and conflict at times. Apart from the general rivalry prevalent amongst individual collectors, professional dealers, with their often unscrupulous practices, further exacerbated the situation – 'that "worthy" exterminator, the "dealer," whose ranks there are daily increasing, much to the dismay of the poor collector, who arrives with the idea of having good sport, and gets nothing, except the proverbial "hump"' (Lawrance, 1903). He went on to describe an instance where a particular dealer 'was netting all the White Admirals he could possibly lay his hands on, and then retailing them to schoolboys, &c., at one halfpenny each. I should not wonder if he retired this season.'

Fig. 42. Pondhead Inclosure, New Forest (1904). Warning notice to collectors.

Responding to several complaints concerning a particularly unsavoury sugaring incident, the Deputy Surveyor for the Office of Woods (responsible for the management of the New Forest at the time) decided to take firm action. Therefore, when Mr Sidney Bell came down for his summer holiday in 1905 he was in for something of a surprise. He was the Secretary of the City of London Entomological Society, which had started life in 1858 as the Haggerstone Entomological Society and whose members, it is said, 'met in a pub, smoked clay pipes and, when they could afford, bought natural history books'.

Fig. 43. New Forest 'velveteen' (c. 1920). George Blake was a Head Keeper and lived at Ashley Lodge, in the north of the Forest, until the Second World War when his home and the surrounding area were requisitioned for a bombing range; the house was later destroyed. The largest bomb ('Grand Slam' — containing nearly ten tons of explosive) ever to have been dropped on England was exploded there by the R A F in March 1945.

It will probably be news to many of your readers — as indeed it was to me when I reached Brockenhurst last July — to hear that "sugaring" in the New Forest was strictly prohibited, such prohibition applying alike to enclosures and open ground.

On receiving this information from a Brockenhurst tradesman, in response to an order for the necessary saccharine fluid, I was of course incredulous, but decided that it would be advisable not to seek further information on the point until the close of my holiday. I sugared persistently for a fortnight without interruption in sundry spots which had better remain unspecified out of consideration for the ranger in whose district they lay, and who should have ousted me therefrom; the "sugar" proved unattractive, however, not only to "velveteens,"[*] but also to the wily moth — but that is another story.

On the day of my departure I sought out the former and interrogated him, learning to my astonishment that it was an actual fact that orders had been issued to stop "sugaring." Pursuing the enquiry further, I found that, in the event of any lepidopterists proving contumacious, the ranger would produce — not the customary notebook for the purpose of recording the offender's habitat, as might be expected, but a pail filled with a mixture of clay and water, with which concoction he would plaster over the delectable patches in accordance with instructions received.

According to local report the origin of the "pother" was a complaint made to the Forest commissioner by the professional collectors of the district *re* a certain individual, a visitor, who labelled a favourite ride his very own, and defied anyone else to use it at their peril. For this I cannot vouch, but if it be true it seems a poor reason for the drastic action taken.

Now it would appear that the method to be adopted to check sugaring is so unconstitutional as to make it obvious that the prohibition cannot be legitimately enforced or maintained, and a protest from an authoritative scientific source would doubtless result

[*] A reference to the light-green shooting suit with dark green velvet collar worn by the keepers (Fig. 43).

in the curbing of the excessive anti-entomological zeal of the local authority.

I am aware that the "mere collector," as a rule, receives short shrift at your hands, but I venture to think that even this personage will receive your cordial support when he protests against the application of County Council Park Rules to this much frequented happy hunting ground of naturalists.

[Bell, S. J. 1905. Sugaring prohibited in the New Forest. *The Entomologist's Record and Journal of Variation* **17**: 261–262].

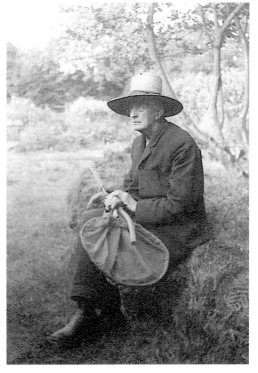

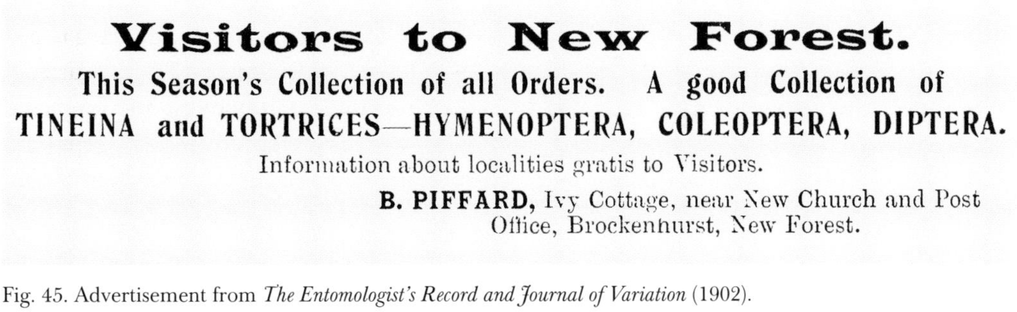

Fig. 44. Bernard Piffard (1832–1916). Resident entomologists in the more popular collecting localities often used their hobby to supplement their income.

The 'hands' referred to belonged to the editor of *The Entomologist's Record*, J. W. Tutt. He was not unsympathetic to the situation and his response included some typically British advice:

There are one or two points that want elucidating in the above. As we understand the matter all amateur visiting lepidopterists have been forbidden to sugar owing to the reputed ill-mannered behaviour of some individual 12 months ago. This prohibition appears to have been made owing to the representations of local professional collectors, to be asserted in favour of these same local collectors who one assumes are not forbidden to collect in this manner. Is this assumption correct? One supposes that no discriminating rule of this kind can be maintained. The matter, of course, needs ventilating in the *Times*, where the facts should be clearly set forth. There are many of our entomologists learned in the law who perhaps can advise Mr. Bell. At any rate one cannot, after all Mr. Goss has done for entomologists in the New Forest, imagine him taking such a rebuff to the free use of the Forest lying down. – ED.

Visitors to New Forest.

This Season's Collection of all Orders. A good Collection of TINEINA and TORTRICES—HYMENOPTERA, COLEOPTERA, DIPTERA.

Information about localities gratis to Visitors.

B. PIFFARD, Ivy Cottage, near New Church and Post Office, Brockenhurst, New Forest.

Fig. 45. Advertisement from *The Entomologist's Record and Journal of Variation* (1902).

Despite the questionable legality of the sugaring ban it obviously persisted for quite some time. In 1911 Claude Morley (p. 193) had warned readers of *The Entomologist* that there was a legend erected high on a venerable oak of Queen Bower in the New Forest which stated: "NOTICE. – Sugaring on Trees is Prohibited. By Order." He suggested that the legend was probably unique among the many warnings to wanderers throughout the world. He continued:

We remember that Herbert Goss had something to say respecting the legality of a prohibition which could relate to damage only in so far that lepidopterist sugar might be supposed to disfigure trees. However the law may run, it is certain that permission to sugar has, we are told, been categorically denied recent applicants by Mr. Lascelles [Deputy Surveyor, New Forest], and that the keepers have orders to "clay" all fresh treaclings.

Fig. 46. Claude Morley. 'A delightful personality . . . even eccentric, with a hatred of modern "progress".'

Following Morley's warning, a correspondent wrote to *The Entomologist* (1911, p. 303):

Referring to Mr. Claude Morley's note under the heading "By the Way" in the August number of the 'Entomologist,' I think the Germans have improved on the notice prohibiting sugaring on the trees in the New Forest, as in the little valley at the head of the Konigser they have put up a board to the effect that anyone convicted of catching *Parnassius apollo* [Apollo] or taking away its larvæ is liable to a fine of 150 marks [£7 10s. 0d.] or three months' imprisonment. — H. S. S.

THE SUGAR BAIT

T. W. Edwards, Ashford, Kent. (1856)

I hope you will pardon my troubling you, but as I am a *very old* entomologist, born before sugaring was known, and as I am again taking up my favourite amusement, I shall feel obliged by your giving me the plain and simple way of making this very enticing syrup. I find in Mr. Shield's work on 'Moths and Butterflies' a recipe for it, but I do not understand what some of the ingredients are intended for. He begins by recommending the following "Sugar." Now I can find *no sugar* mentioned in the body of his recipe, and I find something called "Foots." May I request the favour of your telling me what it is, and where to be obtained?

("Foots" is the name for the sugar that is saturated with molasses which drains downwards in the casks in which sugar is imported from the West Indies. The recipe of Mr. Shield is good, but we have found the mixture efficacious without the honey and essential oil of almonds — [Editor]).

[Edwards, T. W. 1856. The sugar bait. *The Substitute* No. 12: 135].

A NEW METHOD OF SUGARING

Nicholas F. Dobrée, Beverley, East Yorkshire. (1887)

Judging of others by my own experiences, probably field naturalists have been at times exercised how to lay their bait when desirous of sugaring large open places, such as the sea-shore, sand-hills, the edge of cliffs, open fields, and other similar places where no friendly trees or palings are within reasonable distance. I, therefore, extract the following from the 'Societas Entomologica' for May. Dr. R. Benteli, of Bern, writes:— "I have adopted the following plan for several seasons:— Take an old umbrella, open it, join the extremities of the ribs by string so as to keep them in position, and then cut away the silk entirely; attach to the extremity of each rib a small ring, and on this hang, by means of a piece of bent wire forming a hook, a short piece of string, to the other end of which a piece of sponge, about the size of a fist, is attached, which has been lightly dipped in any bait that may be preferred. Cut away the handle of the umbrella, so as to fix it at will into another stick of two or three feet long, provided at one end with a socket in which to fit it, and at the other end with an iron point by which to fix it firmly into the ground. I have five of such skeleton umbrellas. When closed they pack into a light box of about three feet long and a few inches square, which can be carried over the shoulder by a leather strap, and the whole weighs less than five pounds. The bait is carried in a tin box. I am thus ready to go into, or out of, action in a few minutes, and can try many places otherwise very tedious to work." The writer seems ignorant of our English plan of sugaring trees, for he joins them by a stout string provided at intervals with small rings, and to this hangs his bait, in a similar manner to that described above. Pieces of dried apple threaded on the string, or pieces of sponge dipped in apple-juice, appears his usual bait; but this may arise from the prevalent view that beet-root sugar, which alone is in general use abroad, is not attractive to insects.

[Dobrée, N. F. 1887. A new method of sugaring. *The Entomologist* 20: 164–165].

A TRAP TO CATCH A MOONBEAM

Rev. Francis O. Morris, Nafferton Vicarage, Yorkshire. (1853)

Francis Orpen Morris (1810–1893), son of Rear-Admiral Henry Morris, was a natural history polymath and litterateur. His *A History of British Butterflies* (1853) was extremely popular, and was followed in 1870 by *A History of British Moths*. Apart from these, he wrote a number of books on birds and other natural history subjects and, for years, was accorded the soubriquet − 'the Gilbert White of the North'. Although he was one of the first to use the chloroform bottle, he continued to use the old and out-dated clap-net to the end of his collecting days.

Another mode of capturing moths − 'unde a quo abi redeo' − is by means of a light − to which, in the dusk of an evening, they are attracted . . . One plan, of primitive simplicity, and which was adopted by us at school, was to place a candle near an open window; tie a long string to the handle of the frame − they were old-fashioned lattice ones − get comfortably into bed, and when a moth made his 'entree' pull the window instantly to, thus securing him within.

[Morris, F. O. 1853. *A History of British Butterflies.* London, Groombridge.].

The following poem by *Omega* owes much to 'Excelsior' by Henry Longfellow (1807–1882). *Omega* was probably the pen-name of John W. Douglas (1814–1905) (Fig. 133), a well-known lepidopterist who seized every opportunity to contribute doggerel verses to the entomological journals, most of his poems being parodies of Longfellow.

THE SUGARER

Omega. (1857)

The shades of night were falling fast,
As through a quiet village passed
A youth, who bore upon his arm
A jar that had a wondrous charm,

    A "sugar-pot!"

His brow was glad, his eye beneath
Shone like a Noctua's on a heath,
And as he went he gaily sung,
In accents of an unknown tongue,

    "Empyrea!" [*]

In cottage homes he saw the light
Of farthing "dips" gleam dimly bright;
Above, but one pale star there shone,
Yet still he altered not his tone,

    "Empyrea!"

"Doan't goo to-night," the old man said,
"The clouds be gatherin' overhead;
"The stream down yonder's deep and wide!"
He whistled gaily, and replied,

    "All right, old boy!"

"Oh, stay!" his aunt had said, "and rest;
"Go not to-night of moths in quest!"
A saucy glance was in his eye,
He answered, with a heart-drawn sigh,

    "The moths won't wait!"

"Take care, sir, of yon narrow bridge,
"Doan't 'ee goo too fast up the ridge!"
This was the peasant's last "good night:"
A voice replied far up the height,

    "Good night, my friend!"

[*] 'Empyrea'. This is *Trigonophora empyrea* (now *T. flammea*) – The Flame Brocade – a moth that readily comes to sugar and light. During the mid-nineteenth century it was found not uncommonly near Brighton and Lewes, in Sussex. Today it is confined to the Channel Islands from whence it occasionally migrates to mainland Britain.

At break of day, as in the sky,
The merry larks sang loud and high,
Utt'ring their grateful matin prayer,
A voice cried through the startled air,

    "It's time to go!"

A being, by the faithful hound,
At the green garden-gate was found,
Still grasping, empty, 'neath his arm,
That jar that had the wondrous charm —

    His "sugar-pot!"

There, in the twilight (*sans* his hat),
Drenched (but with lots of moths) he sat;
And on the servant's drowsy brain
A voice fell once — and once again —

    "My breakfast please!"

       Ω

['Omega'. 1857. The Sugarer. *The Entomologist's Weekly Intelligencer* **2**: 79–80].

'A RARE OLD PLANT IS THE IVY GREEN'

William D. Crotch, Weston-Super-Mare, Somerset. (1856)

William Duppa Crotch, M.A., F.L.S. (1832–1903) was born at Richmond in Surrey and trained initially as a doctor, but he found the studies distasteful and so did not qualify. During his early years he devoted much of his time to the study of the Lepidoptera, Coleoptera and Hemiptera, and he wrote a number of amusing and provocative articles. He later married a Swedish wife and settled in Scandinavia. It was after this that he gave up entomology to study the lemming and its migration.

As 'The Substitute' is a "Fireside Companion," by antithesis an account of "doings in the frost" may prove not altogether uninteresting. Dinner and a final glass of port having been discussed, I received sufficient moral courage to say to my brother, "Suppose we take a lantern and visit the ivy which we saw in bloom to-day." This remark was of course caught by the quick ears of the ladies, and elicited divers doubts expressed on their part as to our sanity, including belief in a sufficient stock of that quality in the moths to prevent their exposing themselves to such inclement weather. However, we sallied forth, not without inward qualms and outward wrappers. The ivy reached, a lantern was held to throw a little light on the affair, and my brother cried "I see a moth, — one, two, three." "Where? catch it then."

Fig. 47. William Duppa Crotch, author of amusing and provocative articles.

But the wind blew and out went the light, and after it every match struck to renew it. Two 'vesuvians'[*] (the initiated will understand) in succession raised a flame, and we began our search anew. The moths seen at first were *S. satellitia* [The Satellite], of which we took thirty-five; we also took *C. Vaccinii* [The Chestnut], *O. lota* [Red-line Quaker], *A. pistacina* [Beaded Chestnut] and *Xanthia ferruginea* [The Brick]: this was our first night, and was rich in promise. Noisy was our greeting on return, for we affected no success; only after a little of the renowned non-inebriating cup, we requested a loan of some steam from the tea-urn to kill our specimens, the sight of which so turned the tables in our favour that we have been ever since allowed to depart unmolested, save by a casual and harmless grin. The second night I discerned a long crumpled article motionless under an ivy flower. G. pronounced the said article to be *C. exsoleta* [Sword-grass], and recommended its speedy capture: gingerly did we set about it, for the place was difficult; how to get him into the net was a puzzle, till in despair I proposed knocking him in; the blow was struck, and the moth rolled an inert mass to the depths of his gauzy prison; neither pinching nor pinning disturbed his equanimity, and we naturally supposed him stunned, but finding the event recurrent we concluded that, having taken no pledge, ivy-intoxication was allowed among the *Noctuae* at Christmas. Henceforth we carried a small baton to tap them gently into the net. On this night, and a few following, we took fifteen *C. exsoleta*, eight *X. semibrunnea* [Tawny Pinion], some *X. Lambda* [The Nonconformist], and, "spes ultima gregis," *D. rubiginea* [Dotted

[*] *Vesuvian*: a fusee, or match specifically designed for lighting cigars.

'A rare old plant is the ivy green.'

Chestnut]; once with a rustle and a plunge a downy monster — *Atropos* [Death's-head Hawk-moth] at least — plumped into my net; pinch him; he squeaks — claws and feathers — by all that's Lepidopterous it is *Troglodytes vulgaris* [a wren]! We took 160 *Satellitia*, and of course have plenty to spare for anybody who may desire to roast their toes by the fire instead of chilling their fingers on the ivy. Sugaring in the same locality proved an utter failure, and pupa-digging scarcely less so, though the most productive last winter. I may mention, in conclusion, that *Ch. dispar* [? *Chrysophanus dispar* — Large Copper] was taken here last summer, and is in my possession; as also two *S. Convolvuli* [Convolvulus Hawk-moth] taken this autumn, *Edusa* [Clouded Yellow], *Corydon* [Chalk Hill Blue], *Adonis* [Adonis Blue], *Alsus* [Silver-studded Blue], *Argiolus* [Holly Blue], *Agestis* [Brown Argus], *Camilla* [White Admiral], *Machaon* [Swallowtail], and others which I forget, have also been recent prizes; but as they have not much connexion with frosty evenings I conclude.

[Crotch, W. D. 1856. "A rare old plant is the ivy green." *The Substitute* No. 9: 100–101].

' "The Substitute for what?" so asks some reader of our title who has not seen *The Entomologist's Weekly Intelligencer*, in which our advent was announced.' So began the editorial of a new weekly publication for entomologists in 1856 — *The Substitute*. It was conveniently subtitled: *or Entomological Exchange Facilitator, and Entomologist's Fire-side Companion*, and succeeded *The Entomologist's Weekly Intelligencer* when that journal ceased publication in 1856. *The Substitute* ran from 25th October 1856 until 7th March 1857, and provided a very chatty forum for those entomologists who, like W. D. Crotch, had something to say. We read his adventure with ivy blossom with considerable interest and noted his '*final* glass of port' taken before 'sallying forth', and wonder how much this might have coloured the content of his article. The Large Copper and Swallowtail in Somerset? Not very likely one might think, but Crotch went on to record further specimens of the Large Copper from Weston-Super-Mare and Brean Down in 1857. At the present time the jury is still out, considering their verdict as to the authenticity of these records.

'IT HAPPENED AT . . .'

In 1950 the *Entomologist's Gazette* published the first of a short series of stories entitled 'It happened at . . .' The author was Dr Edward Alfred Cockayne (1880–1956), an autocratic but brilliant and mildly eccentric physician, lepidopterist and crypto-analyst. Dr Harold W. Salmon, father of one of the authors of this volume, remembered his days as Medical Registrar to Dr Cockayne at The Middlesex Hospital. He would recount the occasion when, after the usual Saturday morning ward round, Dr Cockayne approached him and asked: 'What are you doing this afternoon?' 'Well, Sir . . . er . . . well . . . nothing very much I think.' 'In that case I would be pleased if you would drive me to Tring.' At that point, Cockayne, very much the master of a situation, handed him the car keys and Dr Salmon felt obliged to drive him out into the Hertfordshire countryside. On arrival at the Rothschild Museum, Dr Cockayne handed him five shillings with instructions to 'buy yourself lunch and report back here at 4 pm'.

Dr Cockayne (known to friends as 'Cocky' or 'The Doctor') was a remarkable man. There were many strings to his bow: Consultant Physician at The Middlesex Hospital and the Hospital for Sick Children, Great Ormond Street; cipher-breaking expert with the military during the First World War; and one of the first entomologists to study the genetics of aberration in the Lepidoptera. He lived near Baker Street in a top-floor flat, the rooms of which were crammed with breeding cages and other assorted entomological paraphernalia.

Cockayne was also a brilliant diagnostician, but he had a less than perfect bedside manner. Bernard Kettlewell (Revd A. H. Harbottle, pers. comm.) recounted the story of the day that he asked Cockayne to make a domiciliary visit and give a second opinion on a lady with a worrying and possibly serious medical condition. After examining her, Cockayne agreed with the diagnosis and told the patient: 'Dr Kettlewell is correct. You have so-and-so. I would like you to take the following medication and you will be better in three months.' She was. However, as he left the patient's home he turned to the by now greatly relieved husband, eyed him up and down and said: 'Ah, I see that you have such-and-such a condition. You probably know that there is no treatment.' Turning to Kettlewell, he said: 'He could be dead within a year.' The husband was!

The Middlesex Hospital was evacuated during the Second World War to Tindal Hospital, Aylesbury — at that time an infirmary dealing primarily with mental disorders. Because of the large influx of staff and medical students, accommodation was very cramped and Vincent Lloyd-Hart, Consultant Physician at Aylesbury, recalled Cockayne being allocated a padded cell which had been converted into a single bedroom (pers. comm.).

Dr Cockayne published over 200 papers in the entomological journals. His magnificent collection of butterflies and moths, together with that of Bernard Kettlewell (in all, some 50,000 specimens), was left to the Rothschild Museum at Tring. The Rothschild-Cockayne-Kettlewell Collection is now housed in The Natural History Museum in London, where it forms the basis of the National Collection. In his article, Dr Cockayne tells us about one of the hazards of collecting moths at Wicken Fen. We have included five articles under the title 'It happened at . . .' in this chapter, a further two in Chapter Three, and one in Chapter Four.

IT HAPPENED AT . . . (No. 1) — 'FEN FUN'

Dr Edward A. Cockayne, M.A., D.M., F.R.C.P., F.R.E.S., Tring, Hertfordshire. (1950).

On September 27th, 1930, I joined the late H. Worsley Wood in Cambridge and we went to Wicken for a week-end and stayed a couple of nights at Mrs. Marshall's cottage. The first night we sugared without success for *Cirrhia ocellaris* [Pale-lemon Sallow] and on the second night went into the fen for *Rhizedra lutosa* [Large Wainscot]. The whole of the fen was under water, which came about half way up our gum-boots — a new experience for me. Barnes had put the sugar on and got the sheet and acetylene lamp ready, and the weather was favourable. When it was dark *lutosa* began to appear on the sheet and the sugar, and Wood decided that we should stroll down a side drive and look for them at rest before going round the sugar again. Feeling a little nervous I said, "I suppose we shall be all right," and he replied, "Oh! I know every inch of the fen, and you only have to look for the fringe of reeds to see where the deep lode runs." I walked first with my acetylene lamp and he followed with his. Suddenly I heard a loud splash and turned in time to see Wood appearing above the water with his pipe still in his mouth and his lamp in his hand. I grabbed him and helped to pull him out. What a sight! He was streaming with water and his gum-boots were full of mud. Much annoyed, I said, "Well, I suppose that ends the collecting," and he replied, rather sharply, "You don't think I am going on like this do you?" So we set off for home, Wood making strange squelching noises and complaining bitterly of the cold.

We went straight into Mrs. Marshall's scullery and he struggled in vain to get his gum-boots off. Then I tried, but they were so slippery with mud that I had a long struggle before I succeeded. I emptied their contents into the sink, half filled them with water, shook them, and emptied them again, repeating the performance until I had got rid of most of the evil-smelling mud. Then, not noticing that there was no waste pipe and that a empty bucket was standing near, I pulled the plug out, and all the mud and water poured on to the floor. At that moment Mrs. Marshall came in and to judge by her expression she was not amused. However, she said she would do her best to dry Wood's clothes. So he went to get

Fig. 48. Dr Edward Cockayne. 'He was specially interested in disorders of the ductless glands and in all and every bizarre genetic aberration in the young: many of these he delighted to contrast with analogous manifestations in the field of entomology, of which he accumulated such exceptional knowledge.' (*British Medical Journal*, 1956)

undressed and came down in his pyjamas and my rain coat, and then we had a good meal. Luckily I had a spare pair of flannel trousers and handed them over to Wood. He looked at them and to my astonishment instead of thanking me said, "Good Heavens! You buy your flannel trousers ready made!"

[Cockayne, E. A. 1950. It happened at . . . *Entomologist's Gazette* 1: 157–158].

IT HAPPENED AT . . . (No. 2) – 'THE THING'

Arthur Leslie Goodson, Tring, Hertfordshire. (1950)

A hot, sultry night in August, not a leaf stirring, an uncanny stillness which, between the distant rumble of thunder, made one's nerves play queer tricks, and an intense darkness which could almost be felt.

Such a night it was, when I saw and heard 'the thing'.

The scene was the Reservoirs near Tring, the time about 2 a.m. and during the last round of my sugared trees. Before dark I had treacled twenty or thirty trees and one old post which stood well out in the reeds and close to deep water. Again and again I had forgotten this until this last round when, with visions of a host of rarities, I carefully walked the narrow plank which led to it, reminding myself to keep to the left, as on the right the water was deep. I remember thinking how silly it would be to fall in and then wondering why the thought should strike me when I knew the place so well.

I had almost reached the post and switched off my light to avoid scaring the moths, when the "thing" appeared. It started as an indistinct white figure, standing out even in the intense darkness, but in less than one second it had grown out of all proportions, stretching up before me as a grotesque, incredible white shape, six feet across, with long tapering body and making a slow hissing noise which struck terror into the very roots of my body. With a sudden threshing of the water, it seemed to poise in the air before making its attack . . .

Completely unnerved, I turned and ran blindly, treacle tin going one way, I the other, in a panic-stricken dive to escape this awful thing, but . . . the tin had gone to the left of the plank and to safety, whilst I, in my haste, had turned right.

I came to the surface slowly, to hear the beat of large wings on water and finally the whistling sound as the wings took the air. [I] knew that sound so very well . . . .

Alas, why do Swans look so different, so completely different, in the dark?

[Goodson, A. L. 1950. It happened at . . . *Entomologist's Gazette* 1: 162].

Arthur Leslie Goodson (1904–1976) was one of Lord Rothschild's assistants at the Tring Museum. In 1947 he was appointed senior assistant, and, in 1957, experimental officer. During the war years he compiled with Derek Read an annotated, but as yet unpublished, list of all the known named aberrations of the British Lepidoptera. However, some appreciation of this remarkable undertaking is now possible with the recent launch of The Natural History Museum's Cockayne Website (www.nhm.ac.uk/entomology/cockayne/). It contains around 1700 images illustrating the geographic, seasonal, genetic and major individual variation in British and Irish butterflies selected from the National Collection of British Lepidoptera at The Natural History Museum, London. A similar treatment for the moths is anticipated in due course.

Fig. 49. Lord L. Walter Rothschild Ph.D., F.E.S. (1868–1937), who collected, set and arranged over two million Lepidoptera, which he housed in his personal museum at Tring in Hertfordshire. He also kept live zebras which he broke in himself. He first accustomed them singly to a small trap; and, later on, drove them as a four-in-hand — three zebras and a small pony — down Piccadilly to Buckingham Palace.

IT HAPPENED AT . . . (No. 3) – THE MATCH BOX MYSTERY

Bernard Embry, Uckfield, Sussex. (1951)

The cliffs on either side of Dover make happy hunting grounds both by day and night. Here, during the summer months, the sugar patches will attract a galaxy of moths when nothing will come to sugar in the woodlands inland. An added attraction is the peace and solitude of the place. Between the rounds one can sit and watch the lights of shipping passing through the Straits.

One July night a year or two before the war things had been much as usual and not a soul had been seen the whole evening. About midnight it was decided to go home and so steps were taken towards the place where the bicycle had been left. Arriving there the light of a torch revealed a match box on the saddle of the bicycle. The box was not mine so clearly it had been left there by some other human (or superhuman) agency. Feeling very much as Robinson Crusoe must have done when he saw the foot-print in the sand . . . "I stood like one thunder-struck, or as if I had seen an apparition; I listened, I looked round me – I could hear nothing, nor could I see anything". But something could be heard as one approached nearer. Yes, there was definitely a scratching noise coming from that match box. Something was trying to escape or was demanding release. Immediately a host of questions arose. What could it be? Would it bite? Was it venomous? Would it leap out at me or would it just crawl out? Summoning up my remaining courage (and with glances all round) the box was at length carefully opened sufficiently to reveal a huge female specimen of our Garden Tiger Moth, *Arctia caja*, which, after being forced into the box, had become almost embedded in its own eggs.

And this is really the end of the story because the mystery was never solved. One can only surmise that someone had taken an interest in my nocturnal activities and had satisfied his curiosity unbeknown to me. Later on when he found the moth he evidently decided to make an anonymous gift of it the next time I should be going that way.

[Embry, B. 1951. It happened at . . . The match box mystery. *Entomologist's Gazette* **2**: 201].

IT HAPPENED AT . . . (No. 4) –
'THE CASE OF THE CLERICAL COLLAR'

Arthur A. Lisney, Dorchester, Dorset. (1951)

. . . Another entomological story concerns the late Rev. Canon Foster, who, some miles from home, was collecting at night along the sides of a river or canal. He was lying flat on his 'tummy' on the bank examining the vegetation by the water's edge for larvae. Absorbed in his task he was suddenly aroused by the voice of the 'law' who, on hearing the explanation of what was taking place, was not impressed, presumably in the belief that the clerical collar was a neat disguise for one on some nefarious outing. The Canon was unceremoniously marched off to the police station and, as his home was not on the telephone – nor was there anyone in the neighbourhood to corroborate his story – he ignominiously spent the rest of the night in the cell!

[Lisney, A. A. 1951. It happened at . . . *Entomologist's Gazette* **2**: 105–106].

IT HAPPENED AT . . . (No. 5) —
COLLECTING IN THE BURREN DISTRICT

Bryan P. Beirne, Ph.D., F.R.E.S., F.L.S., Ottawa, Ontario. (1952)

Dr Bryan P. Beirne (1918–1998), who showed an interest in entomology from a very early age, was born in Rosslare, Co. Wexford, the son of a policeman. He published his first article in *The Irish Naturalists' Journal* at the age of thirteen years, after capturing a specimen of the Large Thorn (*Ennomos autumnaria*) — a species previously unknown in Ireland. At the remarkably early age of sixteen he entered Trinity College, Dublin and subsequently graduated with a Ph.D. in Entomology; he was then elected to the teaching staff. At the age of twenty-six he was elected a member of the Royal Irish Academy. During this period he published a number of papers and larger works, which included *British Pyralid and Plume Moths* (1952) and *The Origin and History of the British Fauna* (1952). He discovered more than thirty new insect species. In 1948 he emigrated to Canada where he was appointed Senior Entomologist to the Department of Agriculture in Ontario.

Fig. 50. Professor Bryan P. Beirne (*c.* 1985). 'A large man . . . warm-hearted and genial with a great sense of humour . . . he was a marvellous story-teller. He had a deep and lasting interest in Irish Entomology.' (Dr James P. O'Connor, *Irish Naturalists' Journal*, 1998)

The following quotation from a newspaper — the *Galway Observer* of July, 1928 — may serve as a warning to entomologists who hope to visit the Burren District to collect "butterflies of the Malachite species" or other large, green Lepidoptera. I cannot vouch for the accuracy of the report, but, judging from notes in the entomological journals, there were at least three English lepidopterists collecting in Galway or north Clare in the summer of 1928.

"Arrested as Lunatic.
"Englishman's Experience in Galway.
"The Pursuer Pursued.

"An extraordinary story comes from Ardrahan. Recently an Englishman who is visiting Ireland to secure rare species of butterflies, set out, as was his wont, to make some captures. He was in hot pursuit of a butterfly of the Malachite species when a number of men engaged in turf cutting gave chase in the belief that the man was mad. They caught up with him and despite his protestations held him firmly. The man was naturally very excited and the fact that he spoke with a strong Cockney accent almost unintelligible to the captors confirmed the men in the impression that they were dealing with a lunatic. The Civic Guards were sent for and one of these recognised the stranger who had been stopping at Ardrahan. Explanations and apologies were forthcoming. The Englishman rather enjoyed the experience and to show that he bore the men no ill will invited them to Ardrahan where he stood treat."

[Beirne, B. P. 1952. It happened at . . . Collecting in the Burren district. *Entomologist's Gazette* 3: 2].

INTOXICATED INSECTS

H. T. Dobson, jun., New Malden, Surrey. (1878).

During the fine and glorious evenings which we experienced in July, 1876, I was somewhat amused by the nocturnal visits of a certain *Triphæna pronuba* [Large Yellow Underwing]. While collecting at sugar in the early part of the month, a friend called my attention to this peculiar but ragged individual, which was fully enjoying our sweets. In due course he became intoxicated, and had to give way to the obvious result; but naturalists tell us that alcohol acts upon the lower forms of animal life exactly in the same way as it does upon man. Now if we admit this, then we have a right to believe that its excessive use will tend to shorten an insect's life: whether it was so with this *pronuba* is a question that puzzles me, as for more than three weeks this dissipated character took every opportunity of using our sugar, and there we found him five or six times a week as drunk as usual. However, I am inclined to think that the alcoholic mixture nourished him, so much so that he lived to a longer period than the usual term; and probably his career was then cut short simply by the ravages of some insectivorous creature.

(We remember trying sugar every suitable night through a mild winter, and seeing a certain specimen of *Cerastis vaccinii* [The Chestnut], which we had marked, at the sugared tree on upwards of fifty occasions, and only lost sight of it about the middle of April. — Editor).

[Dobson, H. T., jun. 1878. Intoxicated insects. *The Entomologist* 11: 117–118].

A CURIOUS VISITOR AT SUGAR

Edward Hopley, Regent's Park, London. (1867)

I had "sugared" abundantly along the lovely "Water's Meet" valley near Lynmouth, N. Devon, on the evening of the 14th June last, and, on re-visiting, early the ensuing morning, the scene of operations, found at the foot of one of the trees a melancholy object for compassion and warning.

The common bat (*Vespertilio pipistrellus*) lay in prostrate humiliation before me, so far gone as to appear "tight"-ened even to death! On attempting to lift him, however, a rollicking, one-sidy flounder or two, accompanied by a hiccupy squeak, affirmed "all right" so unmistakeably, that, solemnly registering one more vow against the Circean cup, I lifted him carefully by the collar of his coat, and deposited him in the broad space made by the branches of a noble oak-tree, some five feet from the ground, in order that he might recover and regret at leisure and in safety the ignoble example to which he had yielded, and the firmament from whence he had fallen. On my return, some hours later, my jovial brother collector had departed — "nor in the cleft, nor near the rock was he."

[Hopley, E. 1867. A curious visitor at sugar. *Entomologist's Monthly Magazine* 4: 89].

SEARCH THE GAS-LIGHTS

Arthur Naish, Bristol, Gloucestershire. (1856)

I should recommend those collectors who live in the suburbs of towns, where the gas-lamps are alight all night, to be up early in the morning and look on the outside of the glass: they will be amply repaid by the capture of many an insect they little thought frequented their neighbourhood. We have found it so at Bristol. The collector who was first out of bed in the morning had all the sport. This led to a rivalry as to who should be out first. He who was out at five o'clock and found another had been half an hour before him, was sure to be out at four the next morning; and if two collectors happened to be out together there was regular racing for the lamps. At last there was nothing at all to be taken; and then it was found that one of the collectors was *out all night*. Now go what hour of the night you like to Ashley Hill you see one or two nets waving round the lamps; and it is curious and instructive to observe the various hours at which certain insects appear.

> We catch all night
> By the pale gas-light,
> And go home with our sport in the morning.

[Naish, A. 1856. Search the gas-lights. *The Entomologist's Weekly Intelligencer* 1: 163–164].

A CORNISH POSTSCRIPT – 'HE FED A BUCKET OF GREY AND BROWN MOTHS TO THE CHICKENS'

From a letter to the Editor of *The Entomologist's Record*, 31st March 1957:

When Colonel Henry George Theodore Rossel of Lanteglos-by-Fowey, Cornwall, went on holiday, he arranged with a kindly neighbour to run his mercury vapour moth trap each night. He assumed that his instructions to this non-entomological neighbour were adequate until:

[He] rang up yesterday to say (*horresco referens*) that he had "fed a bucket of grey and brown moths to the chickens" . . . Anyway, to-morrow I am sending him the following to pin up in the shed where he opens the trap in the morning:

> Remember not to throw away
> Moths because they're brown or grey;
> Girls come in different tints and sizes –
> The plainer ones may be the prizes!

[Rossel, H. G. 1957. A Cornish postscript. *The Entomologist's Record and Journal of Variation* 69: 119–120].

Colonel H. G. T. ('Chris') Rossel (1894–1971) had a lifelong interest in butterflies and moths. Educated at Felsted and Sandhurst, he then joined the Indian Army. During the First World War he served in Mesopotamia and was mentioned in Despatches. On leaving the army he retired to Fowey in Cornwall. It was said that as a raconteur Chris Rossel was unsurpassed. He used to tell the story of a holidaymaker who, crossing the River Fowey on the ferry, noticed the light of his moth trap up on the hillside. The ferryman's reply to his enquiry about it was, 'Oh, that's the Colonel's moth lamp'. To which the irate reply was: 'My God, you Cornish are all the same – I can never get a word of truth out of any of you!'

A BRUSH WITH THE LAW

It has never been generally accepted that the 'delightful pastime' of butterfly and moth collecting, as our Victorian forbears termed it, was ever likely to lead to criminal activity, or could even result in a civil action. The only exception would appear to be the nefarious activities of certain nineteenth-century dealers who fraudulently duped a naïve butterfly-hunting public with rare specimens said to have been caught in Britain, but which had usually been imported from either France or Belgium (see p. 294). Indeed, some of the more outspoken collectors longed for the day when these 'Kentish Buccaneers' were challenged in a Court of Law. But as far as we can ascertain this never happened. Be that as it may, certain other entomological activities did attract the attention of the police and judiciary as will be seen from the following three articles, although today such 'criminal' activities seem very trivial. With this in mind, we were interested to note that two well-known clerical lepidopterists readily admitted to trespassing onto private property in search of rare specimens (see pp. 126 and 168); while Ernest Neal (1994) wrote that his father, the Revd Frederick Neal (Fig. 79), showed 'little regard' for 'Trespassers will be Prosecuted' notices.

There is no evidence that any of these gentlemen was ever caught and brought before the Bench. This may, of course, be due to luck. But there is little doubt that they were in a markedly better position than most to ask a higher authority to look kindly upon their endeavours. Perhaps a case of 'forgive us our trespasses...'?

ENTOMOLOGY AND CRIME

Col. P. A. Cardew, Wimbledon, London. (1938)

The recent case of a gentleman being hauled off to the police station as a suspect, because he was incautious enough to carry an overcoat whilst wearing another, makes me wonder whether any other entomologists have had experiences similar to that which befel me one windy day last autumn. I was "fence-hunting" – often quite an interesting pastime during, or after, stormy weather even in the suburbs. I had examined and left several moths, including a fine *Catocala nupta* [Red Underwing] which had settled high up on a rather exposed fence. The wind had slightly displaced one fore wing, leaving a vivid patch of crimson and black visible – a bad "give-away" for an insect usually so beautifully camouflaged. A few minutes later I was accosted by a seedy-looking individual on a bicycle, who announced that he was a "police officer", producing, in confirmation thereof, a decidedly grimy small pocket-book. He told me that on several recent occasions he had seen me walking up one side of the road and down the other, stopping and examining fences at intervals, and he wanted to know "what I was up to". I laughed and asked him if he thought

I looked like a prospective cat-burglar. Evidently we were not amused at this, so I led him back to the *nupta*. His face rather fell when he saw it, and I could not resist pulling his leg by pointing out that if Sherlock Holmes had had suspicions of my designs, his first action would have been to imitate exactly what I had done – stopping in the precise

spot and examining the fence, "when", said I pointing to *nupta*, "he could hardly have missed *that* could he?" We parted good friends, and he assured me that he did not propose to waste any more time "a follerin' of gents like you, Sir"! I am sure his private opinion was that I was ripe for Colney Hatch rather than Wormwood Scrubs!

[Cardew, P. A. 1938. Entomology and crime. *The Entomologist* **71**: 67].

MOTH HUNTING IN HUNTINGDONSHIRE, 1905, AND A SEQUEL IN THE HIGH COURT OF CHANCERY

George Lissant Cox, Royal Infirmary, Liverpool, and Justin Brooke,
Emmanuel College, Cambridge. (1906)

During last year's beautiful summer the writers spent an all too short holiday of eighteen days — namely, from June 17th to July 4th — collecting in various parts of Huntingdonshire.

We concentrated our efforts almost entirely on the Noctuæ, and in this brief time either captured or observed no less than seventy-one species. This large number was mainly due to the extraordinary attractions of sugar. Our red-letter day was June 27th, when the average number per tree was one hundred and fifty, and the limits of belief are almost reached when one of us, on a small oak, counted two hundred and eighty insects. Truly an *embarass de richesses!* The entire treacle-patch would be covered, while a jostling crowd carpeted the ground and herbage at the foot of every tree. Still more wonderful, perhaps, was the fact that many moths would fly wildly around and around the sugarer, when, only shortly after sunset, the night's round was being prepared. A few actually committed suicide by flying right into the tin!

This attraction showed an interesting gradual increase from June 17th to the 27th, and then an almost uniform decrease. By July 19th only as many units were seen as thousands a month previously. There were no aphides till July. . . .

The sequel, adverted to above, as reported in the 'Daily Graphic,' March 30th and 31st, 1906: —

Mr. John Ashton Fielden, owner of the Holme Wood Estate, Holme, Huntingdonshire, sued for an injunction in the High Court yesterday to restrain Messrs. George Lissant Cox, Rupert Brooke, Neville Brooke and Justin Brooke from trespassing on his property. Mr. Rawlinson K.C., for the plaintiff, said part of Mr. Fielden's estate consisted of a very valuable game reserve, which was drained land from an old mere. It covered some two hundred or three hundred acres, and was so valuable for sporting purposes that as many as from four hundred to six hundred pheasants had been "bagged" in a day. In the spring of last year the pheasants were sitting in the covers, and on June 19th the defendants came down into the neighbourhood. They erected a sheet on the roadway at night, and displayed lanterns for the purpose of catching moths and other insects. The reclaimed land was famed for its valuable insect specimens. The defendants were warned by the keeper on the first evening that the surrounding covers were preserves, and they were told to be exceedingly careful not to disturb the pheasants. They said they understood, and remained in the roadway, where they had a right to be. They stayed in the neighbourhood for about ten to twelve days, when the keepers warned them that they were doing what they were not entitled to do. Of course they had a right to walk on the high road.

Mr. Buckmaster, K.C. (for the defendants): But must not sit down. (Laughter.)

Mr. Rawlinson: Well, to put it strictly, they must not.

Mr. Buckmaster: What happens if you are tired? — I do not know, but you must not sit down. What would you do?

Mr. Rawlinson: Well, I should go to the nearest licensed house. (Laughter.)

Continuing, counsel said the defendants were told to take their sheets down, and on the

Sunday night the keepers saw two of them go on to the railway embankment, over which the plaintiff had sporting rights. They went wandering about, swinging lanterns in the covers, where also it was found they had placed "sticky stuff" on the barks of trees. It did not, said counsel, seem a great deal to complain of, but such conduct would seriously injure a sporting estate, while there was also the risk of a big fire. Apparently these defendants came down to spend a holiday in the neighbourhood. When spoken to, they said they intended to return in the following year and bring a caravan. (Laughter.)

Mr. Justice Buckley: What are these defendants?

Counsel replied that one was an undergraduate, and one a medical student. Two of them were under age. The plaintiff was claiming an injunction and damages.

Mr. Buckmaster: Are you asking for an inquiry into the number of butterflies which were caught?

Mr. Rawlinson said there was nothing about an inquiry. These young men had tendered a shilling in satisfaction of any damage done, but of course that was not satisfaction. It had been determined long ago that a game-preserver was entitled to substantial damages against persons who, after warning, trespassed on his property. There was one case decided where £500 damages were given, although there was not a single farthingsworth of damage done.

Jackson, one of the plaintiff's keepers, said he ran after the boys (the defendants) with his stick uplifted, but not with the intention of striking them. He always went about carrying his stick up.

Mr. Buckmaster: So that it is handy for striking if you come across a poacher. (Laughter.)

Mr. George Lissant Cox, one of the defendants, denied he had committed any act of trespass on the plaintiff's land, or disturbed the game. In July last year, when he was in Huntingdonshire, he was a medical student.

Cross-examined: They had five lamps between them, and he thought they had a right to do as they had on the roadside. At first it was his intention to write to Mr. Fielden for permission to go on his land, but he did not do so because he thought permission would be refused. (Laughter.)

Mr. Rupert Brooke, another of the defendants, said he and his two brothers (who were also defendants) were the sons of Mr. Arthur Brooke, J.P., of South Kensington and Dorking. Except for going once on to the roadside and once into the plaintiff's covert one night they had never trespassed or committed any damage.

Cross-examined by Mr. Rawlinson: What is the sticky stuff you used? – Treacle. (Laughter.)

Mr. Rawlinson replied that he knew nothing of moths, but confined himself to partridges. Other evidence was called.

Mr. Buckmaster submitted that the action was a frivolous, vexatious, and contemptible one, and asked the judge to dismiss it.

Mr. Rawlinson pointed out for the plaintiff that a landlord was entitled to his rights, and was perfectly entitled to preserve his land from any sort of trespass.

The Judge, having reviewed the evidence of the alleged trespass by the four boys, said he thought it was not a case for an injunction. They had no intention of infringing anybody's rights. There was also a claim for damages. There was no evidence whatever that any damage was done. In the circumstances it seemed to be an oppressive action. He would make an order for the payment of one shilling out of court to the plaintiff, which had been paid in by the defendants, but the plaintiff would have to pay the defendants' costs.

[Lissant Cox, G. & Brooke, J. 1906. *Noctuæ* in Huntingdonshire, 1905, and a sequel in the High Court of Chancery. *The Entomologist* **39**: 127–132].

Although this report in the *Daily Graphic* is probably correct, the *Peterborough Advertiser* (31st March and 7th April, 1906) and *Peterborough Citizen* (4th April 1906) provided further details:

. . . Squire Fielden [apparently] had not only ordered his gamekeepers to take "the necessary steps" to prevent them [the moth catchers] from trespassing again, but had instructed his solicitor to there and then serve a writ on the four young lepidopterists. This was subsequently followed-up by having this 'gang of desperate men' (a description mockingly used by one of the defence counsel) brought before the High Court.

In summing-up the case and giving judgement, Mr Justice Buckley refused to grant the restraining injunction, remarking that it was clear to all that the young men had conducted themselves in a civil and courteous manner at all times, and on being served the writ had given their word of honour not to return. Nor could he find any convincing evidence to warrant the accompanying claim for damages. Mr Justice Buckley then went on to severely criticise Squire Fielden, describing the legal steps he had taken against Cox and his friends as 'oppressive to the last degree' and an abuse of the process of the court.

Winding up the proceedings, Mr Justice Buckley awarded the plaintiff a nominal one shilling damages, but by way of demonstrating his extreme displeasure at Squire Fielden's actions ordered him to pay the four defendants' costs incurred by the case.

[Mitchell, J. 1993. Lepidopterists before the bench. *The Entomologist's Record and Journal of Variation* **105**: 42].

THE PERIL OF PURSUING ENTOMOLOGICAL STUDIES AT NIGHT

CROYDON PETTY SESSIONS, April 20. [1861]

— Present, T. Byron, Esq. (Chairman), J. W. Sutherland, E. R. Adams and W. R. White, Esqrs.

"*Mark Richards* was summoned on the charge of assaulting David Thomas Button, at Addington, on the 14th inst. Mr. Charles Richards appeared for the defence.

"The complainant, who described himself as a decorative painter at Peckham Rye, and also an entomologist, stated that he was passing through Addington Wood, near this town, on the opposite side of the Archbishop of Canterbury's estate, on the evening of the 14th of April. He had a lantern in one hand and a stick in the other, being in search of insects, when the defendant rushed out from behind a bush, seized him by the collar, and told him he had no business there. Complainant did not recognise Mr. Richard's authority, but immediately walked off into the path, when he said to defendant that he thought he had broken his arm. The defendant then seized him by the collar and threw him into the Archbishop's land, calling out "Dick! he is on your side now."

"Cross-examined — He had a white handkerchief on the top of a stick he was carrying that evening, for the purpose of catching insects flying in the air, a very common practice.

"Alfred Harper, an ivory turner, at Mansfield Street, Kingsland Road, stated that he was with the complainant, when he saw Mr. Richards come towards Mr. Button and strike him a heavy blow on arm. The defendant swore at him at the same time.

"Cross-examined — This was about nine o'clock in the evening. Mr. Richards did not speak to Mr. Button before he struck him.

"William Shrosbree, a naturalist, living in Essex Street, Kingsland Road, corroborated.

"Mr. Richards, for the defence, said his client was keeper in the service of Mr. Lewis Lloyd, and seeing these people wandering about that gentleman's wood at night, he first told them they had no business there and ordered them away. Seeing that Mr. Button was holding a stick up, and thinking he was going to strike him, he certainly did make a blow at the man, and he (Mr. Richards) submitted that the defendant's conduct was excusable, seeing that the complainant was trespassing and had no business on Mr. Lloyd's property. He should call a witness to prove that the defendant really had spoken to Mr. Button in the first instance, and if he established that, he hoped the magistrates would say that the defendant had not exceeded his duty on that occasion.

"William Turner, labourer, in the employ of L. Lloyd, Esq., at Addington, who was present on the evening in question, deposed that the defendant had said "What are you doing here?" As no answer was returned the defendant struck at the net which Mr. Button was carrying.

"Mr. Button said it was most important for the successful study of insects that he should watch their habits at night.

"The Chairman remarked that Mr. Lloyd did not want persons to study insects on his ground, and as the complainant had the leave of the Archbishop he had much better have kept on his Grace's ground, and not gone on that belonging to Mr. Lloyd. There appeared to have been an assault committed by the defendant, for which they fined him 7*s.* and 13*s.* costs." — Paid. — *From the 'Sussex Advertiser,' April* 23, 1861.

[Anon. 1861. The peril of pursuing entomological studies at night. *The Entomologist's Weekly Intelligencer* **10**: 38–39].

ENEMIES TO THE ENTOMOLOGIST

Percy Rendall, Ladbroke Square, London. (1886)

Bats, nightjars, and toads have been so long recognised as the sworn enemies of those who go sugaring for moths, that I venture to draw the attention of those who are interested in the above science to a hitherto unrecognised foe, as far as my reading goes. Whilst sugaring last year at Lyndhurst, we were much troubled by the long-tailed field-mice (*Mus sylvaticus*) that frequented our sugared trees, as we thought, at the time, attracted by the luscious liquid we used. Though we noticed that there were never any moths on the same trees, we simply thought that they frightened away the insects, and waged war to the knife against them, finding they only returned when scared away. This year, however, whilst sugaring in Sussex, my greatest fears were confirmed, for one *Mus*, as I was standing quite still with my light thrown full on the sugared bark, came fearlessly into the circle of light, ran round to my side of the tree, sat up, looked at me and then at the tree trunk, up which it ran, and seized a luckless specimen of *Miana strigilis* [Marbled Minor] in its mouth, and ran off with it. After that, I saw at the bottom of more than one of my trees the remains of moths, whose bodies alone had been eaten by the insectivores in question.

[Rendall, P. 1886. Enemies to the entomologist. *The Entomologist* **19**: 234].

'THE HUNT FOR *PALLUSTRIS*' — FENLAND NATURE RESERVES

Towards the end of the nineteenth century, the Hon. Nathaniel Charles Rothschild, alarmed at the destruction of favourite wildlife sites as a consequence of progressive urbanization, came to the conclusion that specific areas — the 'good spots' — should be designated as nature reserves if Britain's biodiversity was to be preserved. In 1899 he purchased 305 hectares of Wicken Fen, Cambridgeshire; and two years later, he donated this to the infant National Trust as Britain's first nature reserve. He purchased Woodwalton Fen in 1910, formed the Society for the Promotion of Nature Reserves (SPNR) in 1912, and then proceeded to draw up a preliminary list of almost 300 specific sites across Britain that were deemed 'worthy of preservation'. Woodwalton Fen is now owned by the Royal Society for Nature Conservation, but managed by the National Trust.

Fig. 51. The Hon. N. Charles Rothschild M.A., F.E.S. (1877–1923). 'The father of conservation'. He bought Woodwalton Fen for the nation in 1910. He was a world authority on fleas; during an expedition to Egypt and the Sudan he discovered the plague-carrying oriental rat flea — 'the vector *par excellence* of the Black Death'. He named it *Xenopsylla cheopis* after the Egyptian pharaoh Cheops.

Fig. 52. The Rothschild bungalow has provided accommodation for innumerable entomologists visiting the Fen. The figure on the verandah is Eric Classey, photographed during a successful trip for *H. pallustris* (Marsh Moth) in June 1937.

When the Hon. N. Charles Rothschild died Woodwalton Fen was then managed by his daughter Miriam Rothschild, ably assisted by James Stuart the estate manager at Ashton — the Rothschild's family home near Peterborough. She remembered Stuart as 'a Scotsman with many gifts, including management, and also an impeccable character with enormous respect and devotion to my father'. Rothschild built a bungalow in the Fen as his headquarters (Fig. 52) and this building was raised on stilts to avoid floodwater. The keeper at that time was called 'Old' George Mason (Fig. 53), an excellent entomologist. And when he retired, his son became the subsequent keeper.

Charles Rothschild was extremely popular with the local inhabitants, some of whom were memorable characters. George Holland, who lived in one of the cottages on the Ashton estate, was a shoemaker 'totally uneducated, but an ardent lepidopterist whose killing bottles were always stuffed with moths'.

A strange, solitary man with a long beard, he was much given to taking long walks in the woods. Although a devout Christian, he went through life thinking that he was pursued by the devil.

Mr Jackson was another Fen inhabitant. Miriam Rothschild (1908–2005) remembered him as a turf cutter and 'total eccentric'. Apparently, he only wore trousers when visiting the King's Lynn market to sell his turves. At other times, practically naked, he used to climb on his roof to shout at intruders. A widow in the village thought that as he was at least seventy and never wore clothes he must be loaded with money. She had reckoned that by marrying him she might outlive the old man and so inherit a fortune. Unfortunately, Jackson lived until ninety and she predeceased him.

Fig. 53. 'Old' Mason, the gamekeeper at Woodwalton Fen (1937). George Mason started working there in the early 1920s and managed the colony of the Dutch race of the Large Copper after its introduction in 1927 by Captain Purefoy. Three generations of Masons have been involved now with the Fen and its conservation.

There is no doubt that Charles Rothschild was the father of nature conservation and his first project, Wicken Fen, was a moth hunter's paradise with its great local prize — *Hydrillula pallustris* (Hübner, 1808)* — the Marsh Moth. Never fully recovering from a breakdown in his health in 1916, in which overwork was a major contributing factor, his unexpected death seven years later would leave a large and unfilled void. In *Nathaniel Charles Rothschild 1877–1923* Miriam (1979) wrote of her father:

> Although he had founded the SPNR in 1912 and promoted its work with great enthusiasm, his death in 1923 from encephalitis lethargica brought the work of the Society virtually to a standstill and, with its loss of momentum, conservation in the modern sense of the word virtually ceased to exist in the United Kingdom. N.C.R. was, in fact, a lonely and isolated figure, and without his foresight, inspiration, knowledge and tremendous drive, nothing happened at all for the next 30 years. Charles Rothschild detested the rigid Victorian formalities which he had experienced in childhood and he not infrequently voiced, even in his own comparatively informal household, a wistful hankering for life in a mud hut. His wife, whose special brand of humour was, to him, a never-ending source of delight, would retort with her incorrigible Hungarian accent: "And where would the secretary live?"

---

* In *The Scientific Names of the British Lepidoptera — their History and Meaning* (Emmet, M. A., 1991. Colchester, Harley Books), Maitland Emmet points out that Hübner's original spelling was an error for *palustris* 'pertaining to a fen: from the habitat'. Until recently, most authors have spelt it with a single 'l'.

ONE OF THE WILL-O'-THE-WISPS OF FENLAND

James W. Tutt. F.E.S., Blackheath, London, S. E. (1894)

J. W. Tutt, a great Victorian, who would have backed the ideals of Charles Rothschild to the hilt, gave a wonderful description of his first visit to Wicken in *Random Recollections of Woodland, Fen and Hill* (1894). After discussing his proposed holiday with a Cambridge friend, Tutt ventured into the fens.

. . . Reaching Fordham I began to feel puzzled. "How far is Wicken?" "Four miles or more," was the answer. "Is there any chance of my getting a trap to take me there?" "Yes, up at the village," and I began to make for that village, which I afterwards discovered was considerably more than a mile from the station; but as I left the station, a happy-looking individual, in a rather dilapidated-looking cart, with a well-fed grey mare between the shafts, sang out — "Are you Mr. So-and-so?" Feeling rather astonished, I remarked that I was Mr. So-and-so, when the man informed me that he had been told by my friend at Cambridge to meet me and take me to Wicken, and thus was explained to my satisfaction why the happy-looking individual in the dilapidated cart, sat comfortably and sleepily outside Fordham station waiting for a train from which the only passenger who alighted was myself. However, I was very thankful for his presence, hoisted myself and baggage into his cart, and was soon on the way to Wicken . . . My driver's name was Bailey — by the by almost half the people in Wicken are named Bailey, and everyone is certainly a relation of everyone else. How these relationships exist according to the strict canon of the Book of Common Prayer, I have never thought it worth while to enquire. This I leave to the parson, who in that out-of-the-

Fig. 54. Dr James S. Sequeira M.R.C.S. (*left*) and Mr (E?) Turner collecting at Wicken Fen, Cambridgeshire (*c.* 1890).
It is Britain's oldest nature reserve — the first plot of land on the Fen was purchased by the National Trust in 1899.

way nook has apparently so little to do that energetic mental exercise of this description, in some shape or other, must be absolutely necessary for existence. . . .

We at last arrived at our destination, and I was located in a cleanly, well-ordered establishment, where I was soon happy in discussing my dinner, plain but well-cooked and with a supply of fresh vegetables and fruit. How quiet it all was after London, hardly a sound until I heard a whistle up the street! Immediately after, the landlady, an old lady of more than seventy summers, knocked and said "Any letters, sir, the postman is going?" to which I gave a most emphatic "No." I afterwards found that there was a Post Office in the street at a little shop, that is, there was a letter box from which the letters were collected every day at 5 p.m., but, as the thirty houses or thereabouts were scattered over a street some half a mile long, the postman after emptying the letter box blew his whistle as he went along to inform those people who had letters to post that he was ready to convey their letters to Soham (from which they would be forwarded) if they were not too lazy to bring them to him. The general postal arrangements, too, were primitive. Besides this free and easy method of collection there were one or two very characteristic points in the business. The postman, who lived at Soham, started from there about seven a.m. and reached Wicken at eight, his Wicken delivery occupying perhaps an hour owing to the scattered position of the houses. Then he went on to Upware, another village still deeper in the Fens, and still more scattered, some three to four miles from Wicken, where the delivery was finished shortly before mid-day. There was no time to go back to Soham then, quite a two hours' walk, and return to collect the letters, so the postman must stay at Upware. Now Upware consists essentially of one important house, styled "Five miles from anywhere," and the name is highly suggestive of its pleasant and entertaining position. As it is a pub, and the postman is a teetotaller, a little diplomacy must have been necessary in the first instance for that postman to spend every afternoon of his life in that pub, but he has managed the business, and there he waits until at four p.m. the whistle sounds, the people stand along the road with their letters, and the journey back to Soham *via* Wicken begins, the day's tedious and monotonous work ending at about seven in the evening. . . .

I went to bed early on the night of my arrival; at half-past nine the place was as quiet as a grave, but I saw some weird-looking lights in the Fen. I thought they were Will-o'-the-wisps, but afraid to expose my ignorance, I would not ask, and thinking of those lights I got into bed; but I meant to have a night to see those Will-o'-the-wisps, and to fathom the mysteries connected with some strange-looking individuals, whom, with big lanterns and great bags, I noticed wending their way to the depths of what as yet was known to me only by the name of "The Fens." Very suspicious-looking characters indeed they were, I hardly knew what to think of them.

It was early next morning when I awoke, and opened the latticed window of my bedroom. The scent of the roses was delicious, so also was that of the lavender with which the path was lined. I noticed "the early bird catching the worm" in the shape of a small boy on his way to work knocking down some plums out of a large tree near the gate. . . .

After a late breakfast I strolled out and made for the Fen. The rank growth, the network of bushes and flowers struggling for the mastery which I had expected to find were not noticeable from a distance, but when I got farther into the Fen, and, attempting to cross a level-looking piece of ground covered with sedge, found myself precipitated at the first step up to my waist in water, and discovered that the smooth-looking ground was a dyke, on which the sedge rested so alluringly, and when directly afterwards I tried to cross a piece of rough overgrown ground to reach a smooth-looking path beyond and found after two or three minutes that I could not see a foot before me, and finally when, after a dreadful struggle between my coat and a buckthorn bush, in which the coat got much the worse of the exchange, I was obliged to emerge at the point I went in, I had a greater respect for that Fen than I started with half an hour before. . . .

But I had a special work before me that night, so I returned to lunch and then to rest until my peregrinations should commence again. Those Will-o'-the-wisps were on my mind, and I wanted to meet them at close quarters. I waited until it was nearly dark, and, saying I should be late, I obtained a latch key and departed for the scene of my morning's explorations.

I looked about, but there was no Will-o'-the-wisp to-night. The night was dark, close, oppressive, and thunder was in the air. As I walked on I saw a small light not larger than that made by the light from a lucifer. Suddenly it blazed forth a great brilliant light, which in the haze had a most weird appearance. I walked into the Fen. The trees on the edge groaned ominously, I felt a little as if cold water was going down my back but I went on. Suddenly I dropped one leg into a water hole and my courage went down to zero, the trees groaned, the reeds rustled, a pony which I ran into almost frightened me to death, but I meant to find out what that remarkable light was, so on I went. When I got near my curiosity was still further whetted, ghostly shadows flitted about the light, and I felt inclined to turn back, but a sudden burst of human voice prevented the attempt. "I've got it! I've got it," said that voice. My spirits rose. Ghosts don't talk like that! I thought to myself, and so I went on. Presently I was aware of a light quite close to me. I started back. I saw someone on his knees; a rustling as of pill boxes, a sudden exclamation, and the light was apparently extinguished. What did that individual want? A moment after, and I was aware that someone had run into me, a sudden flash of light in my face, and my companion could see me but I couldn't see him. "Hullo!" said a boy's voice. "Who are you?" I replied. "Who are *you*?" retorted the boy, whom I couldn't see for he kept the light in my face. "I've come down to see what that light is," I remarked. "Hope you'll be interested," said that youngster. I began to boil. "What are you?" I asked. "An entomologist," said the boy, "will you come round with me?" He turned the light off my face, and I saw an intelligent little fellow about twelve years of age, with a bag slung over his shoulder, another on the button of his coat, a green net in one hand, and a bull's-eye lantern in the other. He knelt close by where we were standing, shook a piece of sedge into the net, put the lantern on the ground, his hand into the bag at his side, and his head into the net which he held between him and the light, and as I stood behind him I saw moth after moth running up the net, and as each one came up the boy remarked, in a tone of disgust, "*Impura – oculea – umbrosa* [Smoky Wainscot, Ear Moth and Six-striped Rustic]," then changing his tone of voice he said, "Fine form of *fibrosa*," and into a box went a remarkable rich purplish moth, the box being dropped into the bag in front of him, and then in delight he called out, "*Hellmanni* [Mere Wainscot], " and I saw him carefully boxing a miserable-looking little whitish moth at the bottom of the net. "This is one of the species my father and I have specially come after," said the boy, and I accompanied him half amused and half astonished as he went his round, stopping short with unerring accuracy at the points where he had "sugared," as he informed me. We approached my Will-o'-the-wisp, and as we got nearer I found it was a large lamp with powerful reflectors shining full on to a white sheet to increase the bright surface. To this, moths were coming in large numbers, sticking on the glass of the lamp or on the sheet, and from these my companion's father was busy selecting, transferring the chosen ones to small pill boxes for removal from the Fen. The bright and gaudy ones were rarely captured, the most dowdy and uninteresting-looking specimens were those that created the greatest enthusiasm among those infatuated collectors, who worked on in the dark hours of the night, and spent a hard-earned holiday thus, in preference to kicking their heels at the sea-side or lounging in laziness at a holiday resort, and they were happier — far happier — undoubtedly in spending their time in their own way. . . .

[Tutt, J. W. 1894. One of the Will-o'-the-Wisps of Fenland. From: *Random Recollections of Woodland, Fen and Hill*. Swan, Sonnenschein & Co., London].

Tutt's description of his visit to Wicken Fen is possibly based on an actual experience. With this in mind it is of interest to read and compare the following account of visiting Wicken Fen by Lt. Col. A. Maitland Emmet, written in 1972. As Emmet was born in 1908 he could not have visited the Fen during its heyday in the latter half of the nineteenth century; his source of material would have been the numerous papers published over the past 150 ycars.

WICKEN FEN

Lt. Col. Arthur Maitland Emmet, M.B.E., T.D., M.A., F.L.S.,
Saffron Walden, Essex. (1972)

Lieutenant Colonel Arthur Maitland Emmet (1908–2001) was one of the country's greatest microlepidopterists of the twentieth century. The youngest child of an Oxfordshire parson, he went on to be Chaplain of University College, Oxford. After graduating in classics he taught Latin, English and Greek at St Edward's School, Oxford for twenty years. He held the Presidency of both the British Entomological and Natural History Society and the Amateur Entomologists' Society and was Vice-President of the Royal Entomological Society of London. In addition to having been a prolific contributor of articles to various entomological journals, his writings included: *A Field Guide to the Smaller British Lepidoptera*; *The Smaller Moths of Essex*; and *The Scientific Names of the British Lepidoptera — their History and Meaning*. In 1978 he became joint editor with John Heath of the series *Moths and Butterflies of Great Britain and Ireland*. Basil Harley remembers him as 'a tall, well-built man with a great sense of humour. He enjoyed life to the full and nothing gave him more pleasure after a day in the field than a pint or two of beer at a nearby pub with his friends.'

Fig. 55. Lieutenant Colonel A. Maitland Emmet (1986). A European authority on microlepidoptera and a prodigious writer, his obituary in the *British Journal of Entomology and Natural History* includes a bibliography of his literary output extending to over eight pages and containing around 245 references.

Let us imagine it is the late nineteenth century and that you and I, the pair of us, are planning an entomological holiday to Wicken around midsummer. First we must decide where to stay. Some of our friends recommend the Lord Nelson at Upware, well known for a landlord, Mr. William Denson, who is friendly to entomologists. The inn has an attractive sign for which it is far-famed; it bears the caption 'No hurry — five miles from anywhere!'. If we stay in Upware, we must approach the fen from a different angle, past the ash trees on whose trunks Mr. Bond used to take *Apatele strigosa* (D. & G.) [Marsh Dagger]. Our guide will be the landlord's son, Gaston, but he, alas, is no entomologist. Though Upware has its points, we decide in favour of Wicken village so as to be close to the local professionals and in a position to reap the benefit of their experience and help. So now we must choose whether to stay at the Red Lion or the Maid's Head, which is reputed to be outrageously expensive, or to take lodgings with the Marshalls at the old post office, Mrs. Phillips at 'The Sycamores', Mrs. Bullman who understands entomological appetites or the Asplands who keep the new post office. We decide in favour of the last of these hosts, because Mr. Isaac Aspland owns a slice of the fen and, if approached in a tactful manner, he makes it available to collectors free of charge; for we have heard a most outrageous rumour that some of the Wicken commoners who own plots in the fen are demanding sixpence a night from entomologists for the privilege of collecting on their ground — a preposterous imposition!

Another advantage of staying in Wicken is that the station at Soham is more handy, and a letter to Mr. John Bailey will ensure that he is there with his cart to meet us. Had we chosen Upware, Waterbeach would have been our railhead and the five-mile drive to our inn would have taken a tedious hour.

We have another letter to write before we travel, and that is to enlist the aid of one of the professional collectors. They have a real love of nature and are excellent entomologists; they are also renowned for their devoted service to visitors which is quite untainted by mercenary considerations. They include the cheery Mr. Solomon Bailey, Mr. Tom Rowlinson, Mr. John Clark of the Black Horse Inn and Mr. Albert Houghton, the local bootmaker, who is credited with the capture of the last specimen of *Laelia coenosa* (Hübn.) [Reed Tussock]. It is a hard decision, for we will be in good hands whichever we select. Our choice falls on Mr. Bailey.

Fig. 56. Solomon Bailey of Chapel Lane, Wicken. Many of the people and places mentioned in this article are featured in Anthony Day's *Wicken: A Fen Village in Old Photographs*.

Now we are all set for our journey. We have to change at Ely, where we pick up a slow train which delivers us at Soham in mid-afternoon. John Bailey and his horse await us, and soon we are jogging at a steady trot along the Wicken road. On our arrival we find our driver's brother Solomon there to greet us and we eagerly ask him for news of the season. It has been a mixture of good and bad, we hear. Cold east winds have prevailed and for this reason light on the fen has yielded disappointing results. However, our mentor shows us a prize, captured only the previous night; it is a fine specimen of *Hydrillula palustris* (Hübn.) [Marsh Moth], the first to be taken on the fen for two years. A coin is passed and the moth is ours. Are we tired after our journey, or would we like to collect on the fen that night? Of course we want to go out collecting and we are told that all we need to do is present ourselves with our nets and pill-boxes at the beginning of the lane leading to the fen at 9 o'clock. Mr. Bailey will do the rest. Oh! there is one more thing: do we smoke? We do, and we are advised to bring our pipes and a plentiful supply of tobacco and matches, for the midges of Wicken are a hungry breed.

Off goes Mr. Bailey to make his preparations and we unpack our gear. The dinner hour arrives and we sample Mrs. Aspland's cooking, finding it much to our liking. We have brought some bottles with us in our luggage, but we resist the temptation to linger long in gossip over our port and hasten down to the fen for our rendezvous with Mr. Bailey. 'I've sugared you a round,' he says, 'and it starts here on these elms; but light is the best thing for catching these beasties on a good night like this.'

As we enter the fen, we pass some thatched cottages close to the brick workings. A figure standing in the doorway of one of these houses greets us as we pass. 'Good hunting!' he calls. 'That is Mr. Farren,' says Solomon; 'he has rented the cottage and he or his son is out collecting every night. "Catch-'em-'all" he calls his house; quite small houses hereabouts are called halls.'

As we advance up the main drove, we see wooden posts with bark attached to them driven into the ground at intervals; they are coated with sugar and some of them are 'ours', we are told. These are an innovation and they are gradually superseding the old-fashioned 'knots' tied in the sedges. But we see some of these too, stickily anointed to add to the evening's sport.

Dusk is now falling and we gaze in wonder, for the fen is lighting up. At intervals along the drove no fewer than five beacons blaze forth, and we look curiously at the one which is to be the centre of our own activity. Driven into the ground is a stout pole and attached to it, about five feet up, is a kind of aquarium. Three sides are of glass and the fourth is of metal, lined with a mirror. Inside the aquarium are four paraffin lamps shining brightly in the gathering darkness. An 'Eddystone Lighthouse', says Solomon Bailey; it was invented by Mr. Abbott.' Two or three yards away upwind is a vertical sheet stretched between two poles, and the mirror of our lighthouse is adjusted to throw its brightest light on to this sheet. Mr. Bailey explains how we operate. Some of the moths come and settle on the sheet or run up and down it, but the main idea is to create a chamber of light in which we can use our nets to catch the moths blundering around in the beams.

It is a warm, moist, windless night with none of those low mists which are so fatal to success, and soon the moths begin to arrive. As their numbers increase, so does our respect for the wisdom of Solomon. For he recognises each species by its flight or the way it runs or sits on the sheet, and he is as ready with their scientific names as any university scholar. But it is not only the moths that come to our light: the mosquitoes are attracted too. So, mindful of the advice we were given, we light our pipes and blow tobacco smoke over each other's faces like friendly horses indulging in mutual tail-whisking.

At first only common moths appear, and leaving the sheet we take up a lantern to make the first round of our sugar, marching to the music of the long-drawn reel of wakeful grasshopper warblers. Not much has yet come, but to our satisfaction we box a few *Apamea unanimis* (Hübn.) [Small Clouded Brindle], *Polia nitens* (Haw.) [Pale Shining Brown], and some nice forms of *Celaena leucostigma* (Hübn.) [The Crescent], all in good condition.

On our return to our 'Eddystone Lighthouse' we find that the pace is quickening and we take some of the typical fenland insects such as *Phragmataecia castaneae* (Hübn.) [Reed Leopard], *Meliana flammea* (Curt.) [Flame Wainscot], *Chilodes maritima* (Tausch.) [Silky

Wainscot], and *Simyra venosa* (Borkh.) [Reed Dagger]. As the night progresses, we find that many of the insects have their exact moment for putting in an appearance, and Mr. Bailey can tell the time to within half an hour by the species of moth coming to the sheet. Still there is no sign of *palustris* but Solomon tells us to be patient, as it is a late flier. His words prove correct, and it is not until three in the morning that a solitary specimen appears. This puts an end to all thoughts of bed, but our optimism is disappointed and no more *palustris* come to our lamp.

By now dawn is beginning to break, heralded by corncrakes in the sedge, and we notice that the other collectors' lights have been dowsed. Knowing that we are interested in microlepidoptera too, Bailey tells us to keep a good look-out, for some of the rarest gelechiids do not fly until daybreak, and suddenly we find the pretty little geometer *Sterrha muricata* (Hufn.) [Purple-bordered Gold] disporting itself in the dew all about our feet as we struggle to keep *Monochroa divisella* (Doug.) [a gelechiid moth] from damage in our sodden nets.

But by now we are wet and cold and sated with our captures and it is indeed time to depart. We offer to help Mr. Bailey carry the collecting gear home, but there is no need; he packs it all up in a tarpaulin and stows it under a convenient bush where it stays handy for a future foray.

And so to bed by daylight, happily exhausted and sleepily wondering how we shall ever find time to do all our setting.

On the next day we make a late start. The fen is reputed to be a poor place for collecting by day except for *machaon* [Swallowtail], which is now past its best. So we turn our eyes elsewhere and as it is a bright afternoon we send a message to John Bailey to ask if his cart is available. It is, and we book for the short excursion to Chippenham Fen, only five miles away, to look for *Eustrotia bankiana* (Fb.) [Silver Barred]. The trip is a success and we net five *E. uncula* (Clerck) [Silver Hook] as well. The good weather looks like holding, and on our return journey we engage our driver for the whole of the next day for an expedition to Tuddenham in the Breck country. Our proposed venture involves a full ten-mile journey each way, so an early start is called for. Accordingly, we decline Solomon's offer of another night on the fen and make up for lost sleep instead.

The morrow brings another red-letter day. We while away the tedious two-hour drive with entomological gossip and alternately gloomy and hopeful prognostications about the day's prospects, while John Bailey regales us with tales of the other entomologists he has transported, such as the great Lord Walsingham himself, or a young undergraduate called Mr. Meyrick who licked all his seniors with his knowledge and skill in discovery: the smaller the moth, the better he liked it.

When we reach the ground, we find that our driver knows all the most favoured spots, and as the day advances our nets in due turn envelop *Lithostege griseata* (D. & S.) [Grey Carpet], *Scopula rubiginata* (Hufn.) [Tawny Wave], *Heliothis dipsacea* (L.) [Marbled Clover], *Acontia luctuosa* (D. & S.) [The Four-spotted] and *Emmelia trabealis* (Scop.) [Spotted Sulphur], which we prefer to call by its more familiar name of *sulphuralis* (L.). A rare little plume is there, too, which we refer to as *laetus*. We search clumps of *Silene otites* L. (Wibel) [Spanish catchfly] for *Anepia irregularis* (Hufn.) [Viper's Bugloss], but we are too early for the larvae and we fail to detect the moths in their daytime hide-outs.

The return journey seems long and tedious, and conversation flags. In contented drowsiness we think the same thoughts over and over again, picturing to ourselves the new look our cabinets will assume and the jealous gasps of admiration from our less fortunate friends. No, we will not collect on the fen that night.

And so our week proceeds, with excursions by day and busy nights around our 'Eddystone Lighthouse' or going the rounds of our sugared posts and knots. On some nights sugar beats light; on others, light beats sugar; on others again, when the wind is chill or low mists blankets the fen, our labours are in vain and almost with relief we return to our lodgings for an early bed.

In spite of warnings that our time will be wasted, we do after all spend one day on the fen, for we are anxious to see the Montagu's harriers and short-eared owls that are nesting there. To save us the tedious walk home at midday, children bring us down a tasty lunch fresh from our hostess's kitchen. On the whole, our advisers were right, and apart from a few larvae and micros swept from the edges of the droves, our daylight visit is a failure. One thing surprises us though and that is to see *machaon* in all its stages — imagines worn and fresh, larvae large and small, and even ova and pupae. Solomon Bailey explains that there seem to be two races, the one single- and the other double-brooded. The double-brooded butterflies emerge early in the year and their offspring follow them later in the same season, whereas the single-brooded race flies while its cousins are larvae.

All too soon our holiday — our what? How can a week like this ever be called a holiday? — our sojourn is over, and with farewells to our village friends and promises to return the next year we embark for the last time in John Bailey's cart for our sad drive to the station.

This picture of a bygone era has been culled from many sources, and I believe it to be authentic in its details. The villagers I have named were real people. You can see a photograph of one of them in a recent number of *The Entomologist's Record*, put there by our newly-elected vice-president. It shows Albert Houghton and an unknown companion

Fig. 57. Albert Houghton (1844–1896), cobbler and self-taught lepidopterist (*right*), with an 'Eddystone Lighthouse' at Wicken Fen (June 1892). 'For the entomologist who is no mere dilettante, The Fens probably afford the richest of all localities for Lepidoptera in this country. Amongst the fen-lands Wicken still retains its virgin soil and flora, unspoilt by drainage or cultivation.' (John T. Carrington, 1880)

WICKEN FEN.

Visitors to this well-known Collecting Ground can be provided with **all** requisites (including Fen attracting lamp) for collecting, and attendance.

LARVÆ, PUPÆ & IMAGINES OF FEN SPECIES FOR SALE.

For Particulars, apply to

S. BAILEY, Wicken, Soham, Cambs.

Fig. 58. Advertisement from *The Entomologist's Record and Journal of Variation* (1893).

standing beside an 'Eddystone Lighthouse'. Houghton is a stout, burly man with a luxuriant beard — whiskers that once caught alight in an affray with his lamp, as Farren tells us with a chuckle. Some of Solomon's specimens, beautifully set, are still to be seen in collections. The use of scientific names is not entirely forgotten by the villagers. Recently, as I was leaving the fen, I was asked by one whose memories may well extend back to the last century whether I had taken *palustris.* I disclaimed that distinction, but sensing that there was a story at the tip of his tongue, I asked the purpose of his question. 'We all know *palustris,*' he told me, 'since that night when we were woken up at three in the morning by Baron de Worms running up from the fen and shouting at the top of his voice "I've got *palustris*! I've got *palustris*!" ' I expect Dr. de Worms will tell us that the tale is apochryphal, and I expect that nevertheless we shall believe it implicitly.

The old-fashioned lights which were used on the fen may seem primitive to inhabitants of the mercury vapour age, but they were remarkably effective. Farren tells that in two nights' work J. W. Tutt collected over 800 specimens. Our society's past president would hardly be popular if he were alive today and were responsible for such a holocaust of entomological slaughter, and the zeal which aroused Farren's admiration would surely provoke obloquy amongst contemporary entomologists. . . .

[Emmet, A. M. 1972. Wicken Fen, with special reference to its Microlepidoptera. *Proceedings and Transactions of the British Entomological and Natural History Society* **5**: 46–74].

Hilary Allison (1987), in a perceptive article on the history of Wicken Fen, informs us that 'Serious moth and butterfly collecting seems to have begun at Wicken in the 1850s.' She went on to list the paraphernalia associated with the lepidopterist's art, which was meticulously described by the magazine *Cambridge Graphic* of 1901:

Towards sunset the mothcatcher will start for the Fen wheeling a barrow heavily laden with such articles as he may require. These include a stout wooden box, a big lamp measuring 18 in. high and 12 in. deep, a killing bottle of cyanide and a number of pill boxes of various sizes, three 8ft poles, a white sheet 10ft long by 5 ft wide, a pot of treacle, a lantern, a moth trap and an indispensable net.

Moths were caught by using a net, or by luring them on to plants with a beguiling solution based on sugar and treacle with a strong-scented additive such as beer, rum or fruit essences. A third way was to hang a large white sheet between poles and set a lamp up in front of it. This latter formed a pool of light

Fig. 59. The Five Miles from Anywhere — No Hurry, Upware, Cambridgeshire (*c.* 1910).
A popular waterside inn frequented by generations of collectors. Built in 1811 and originally named The Lord
Nelson Inn, its more popular name was added to the gable end in the 1860s by a Cambridge graduate who drank
with the bargees and lightermen, styling himself the King of Upware. 'The ferry would carry horse and carts but
too many cattle at a time sometimes sank it, leaving them swimming in all directions!'

to which moths were irresistibly drawn. As many as twenty such illuminated
sheets could sometimes be seen at regular intervals along the central droves of
Wicken. A sense of pique over the superior performance of a rival's apparatus
may be detected in Mr G. L. Porritt, who lamented in 1879 that 'when a
number of lamps are on the Fen at one time the Fen has somewhat the
appearance of street lamps. That used by Mr Wheeler of Norwich is a monster
indeed, and after seeing it we were no longer astonished at his marvellous
success with fen moths'.

**John T. Carrington (Fig. 124), writing in *The Entomologist* (1880), recalled that Frederick
Bond (1811–1889), 'who then lived in Cambridge, was the first entomologist who worked
this fen, with system at any rate'. As to accommodation near the Fen, Carrington, who gave
his own address as The Royal Aquarium, Westminster, thoroughly recommended Mr
William Denson's little inn at Upware — the Five Miles from Anywhere (Fig. 59) — and
suggested early booking as the number of rooms was limited; at the same time he advised
visitors to ask Mr Denson to meet their train with his conveyance. He went on:**

> In about an hour we are at our journey's end, and, after the adventure of all
> being ferried across the river, we find Mrs. Denson[*] awaiting us with a savoury
> and thoroughly country dinner, for which the long journey has prepared us. . .
> During the last few seasons the chief mode of collecting Lepidoptera in the
> fens has been with light. This has been found by far the most successful means

[*] Wrongly called Densome in the original article.

for making large "bags" of rare and local species which could not be allured by the charms of "sugar," or indeed any other bait. The way to proceed is to get a "lighthouse," which may be obtained at one of the shops where we buy our other entomological apparatus. It consists of a glass case some two feet square affixed on a pole about six feet high. In this glass case are placed two or four paraffin lamps, as large as can be conveniently managed. These lamps are lighted when the darkness of night has set in. After we have placed our lighthouse in a conspicuous place which will command a good area of the fen, behind our lighthouse, or more correctly, to windward, we must spread a sheet stretched on two poles. This has a double advantage of sheltering our lamps from the wind, while at the same time it forms to some extent a reflector and convenient background on which to see any specimens which fly past the lantern. Having selected our ground and got all in order we light our lamps. At the same time it will be as well to light our pipes, and, if we can also muster some "yarn" about the great catches of other people, it may encourage us, for we must not expect all the good things in the first hour. Watching a light for Lepidoptera is a fine exercise for our patience. We may have to wait an hour — even two, three, or more hours — before our first insect appears; on some nights indeed our visitors do not come at all. . . .

Before closing this article I should say that another way to go to Wicken Fen is by Wicken village. This is reached from Soham Station on the Newmarket and Ely Railway; but Wicken village is some distance from the station.

Accommodation may sometimes be obtained there, but I prefer the Waterbeach and Upware route, on account of its being the shorter railway journey from London, and, still better, you get a hearty welcome from the host of the "Five Miles from Anywhere," who has for many years been used to the eccentricities of entomologists, and who can tell them where to work for many species. . . .

DOES LIGHT ATTRACT MOTHS?

P. B. M. Allan, writing under the pseudonym 'An Old Moth-Hunter' (1954), once quoted the redoubtable J. W. Tutt: 'It would well repay the entomologist . . . to lay down his net for two or three years and devote his time to hunting the lepidoptera in their early stages; at the end of that time . . . his collection would be enriched with species quite unknown to the mass of collectors without souls . . .' Allan went on to ask whether today, as a result of the widespread use of mercury vapour lamps, there are any species 'quite unknown to the mass of collectors without souls'. He continued:

For aught I know souls may hover above the m.v. lamp as gaily as corposants* above the mast-head of ships sailing uncharted seas — if the relations of mariners be true. At all events I hope they do, for the moths' sake. However, be that as it may there is no doubt that the man who pays no heed to the early stages of his quarry is only half an entomologist, if indeed he be so much . . . Yet there have been ardent collectors who formed rich collections though they

* Corposants: an alternative name for St Elmo's fire.

could hardly tell a caterpillar from a slug. I knew one who used to send his butler out with a net to catch butterflies for him and rewarded his services every time the fellow netted an aberration — until he became old and 'careful.' And I knew another who used to return to his nearby Rolls and drink a toast to each specimen he caught. After his captures exceeded the dozen his disinclination to take the field again became stronger and stronger, until at last he went to sleep in the back of his car, whereupon the long-suffering chauffeur drove him home to bed.

In spite of such diversions, the advent of the mercury vapour lamp revolutionized moth hunting in much the same way as the discovery of sugaring had one hundred years before. It was not long before the unpredictable results of moth-trapping stimulated lepidopterists to debate the knotty problem as to why moths were attracted to light, and why they appeared to find some lights more attractive than others.

NON-ATTRACTIVENESS OF ELECTRIC LIGHT: A QUERY

Rev. James E. Tarbat, M.A., Fareham, Hampshire. (March 1922)

Can anyone offer an explanation of a curious phenomenon which has very much puzzled me? In pre-war days the stout electric lamps here attracted a large number of moths. There was one arc lamp in particular, near by, which shed its light upon a house with a cemented front, which always produced an abundance of visitors. On the house front I would often find as many as a dozen moths late in the evening, including such species as *E. autumnaria* [Large Thorn], *S. fagi* [Lobster Moth], *X. aurago* [Barred Sallow] and *C. xerampelina* [Centre-barred Sallow]. During the war the lighting was reduced to a minimum, in consequence of which no more moths were seen at the lamps. Since the war, however, the old lighting has been restored, though with different lamps. These seem to possess absolutely no power of attraction. Not a single moth is ever found now at any of our lamps. During 1921 I only saw one moth resting on the wall of the house mentioned, and that was a ♂ *H. brumata* [Winter Moth] at the beginning of December. What is the cause of this? I have asked the electrical engineer if he can explain, but he cannot. I find the old lamps were called "Flame Arcs"; the present ones, which give a rather whiter light than the old ones, are known as "gas filled" or "half Watt" lamps. It seems to me that there must be some particular ray which was present in the old lamps that is absent in the light produced by the present ones which was the cause of the attraction, but up till now I had been under the impression that all bright lamps were equally attractive to moths. I shall be glad if anyone can explain. One cannot imagine any change in the sensitiveness of the moths to light.

[Tarbat, J. E. 1922. Non-attractiveness of electric light: a query. *The Entomologist* **55**: 64–65].

The Revd Tarbat's letter started a vigorous correspondence which continued for more than five months. Some correspondents supported the idea that certain lights might not be attractive to moths, while others came down vigorously in favour of the opposite. We have selected just four letters from the many as it soon became quite obvious to us that some lepidopterists, like moths, *are* attracted by light.

REPLIES:

A. THE NON-ATTRACTIVENESS OF ELECTRIC LIGHT

Charles Nicholson, F.E.S., Hale End, London E4. (April 1922)

Is it not more likely that the "gas-filled" lamps give off some rays which are distasteful in some way to moths, than that they lack some attraction present in the "flame arcs." I know nothing of the technicalities of electric lighting, but the fact that the new lights give a somewhat whiter light than the old ones suggests that there may be more ultra-violet rays in the former, and these rays are known to be unacceptable to some insects, *e.g.* ants. . . .

[Nicholson, C. 1922. Non-attractiveness of electric light. *The Entomologist* **55**: 90–91].

B. ATTRACTIVENESS OF ELECTRIC LIGHT

W. Gifford Nash, F.R.E.S., Bedford, Bedfordshire. (April 1922)

In the 'Entomologist' for March, p.64, the Rev. J. E. Tarbat introduces a subject of much interest, and one which for some years I had intended to write about. Up to about ten years ago the electric lights of Bedford were very attractive to moths, and my friend Mr. W. B. Brocklehurst, who worked them very assiduously, captured an immense number of insects, including *Notodonta tritophus* [Three-humped Prominent] and *D. templi* [Brindled Ochre]. The lamps at that time were open-type arc lamps. A change was then made to gas-filled lamps and with their advent the moths disappeared. It is quite a rare event to see a moth on a lamp at the present time. The Borough Electrical Engineer, Mr. R. W. L. Phillips, informs me that these latter consist merely of an incandescent filament in an atmosphere of argon or sometimes nitrogen. The best arc lamp in the town was fixed on the east side of a wall of the light-generating station and its rays would not be visible for more than 200 yards as houses spread around it in every direction for half a mile to a mile. Our experience was that a very large proportion of the moths taken at the lamps were males, and that many of those taken must have travelled one or two miles. A good example was *B. piniaria* [Bordered White], which is not found within two miles. It is evident therefore that the moths were not solely attracted by light rays. It would appear therefore that moths are attracted to electric lamps by some other means than by light waves, and the change of lamps may assist in determining the nature of this attractive force. Some years ago an article appeared in a daily paper by Mr. Hubert Stringer entitled, "Moths and 'Wireless.' Do moths use wireless telegraphy?" He noted that the males of many moths are attracted great distances by females, much further than could be accounted for by scent, and that males will approach females down wind. They therefore have some means of communication unknown to us. He remarked on the highly-developed antennæ of the males, which would serve as receiving aërials, and that these differ from the female antennæ, which would be the transmitting aërials. He suggested that tests could be made by placing the female in a box of metal or wire gauze, which would cut off any wireless waves. If the male did not come to that box it would support the wireless theory. He states that definite proof could be obtained by making the female's signals audible. In what way, then, does the change of lamps affect this theory? My friend the electrical engineer informs me that a modern argon gas-filled lamp does not propogate any ætherial waves other than light or heat. The arc light, however, can be made to set up oscillatory impulses and most of the powerful wireless stations employ "arc transmitters." In a street arc lamp oscillations of moderate rapidity may be constantly emitted due to the continually varying electrical state of the vapour between the carbons. Mr.

Stringer, in the article previously referred to, says "the final coup would be to imitate the female moth's wireless 'cry' with such accuracy, by means of the artificial circuit, that the males would be deceived into approaching the latter in the belief that a hidden female was calling." It appears we have a very near approach to this in the "arc" lamp. I believe the vibrations of the female are caused by rapid movements of their wings and not by their antennæ.

[Nash, W. G. 1922. Attractiveness of electric light for moths. *The Entomologist* **55**: 89–90].

C. ATTRACTIVENESS OF ELECTRIC LIGHT

Frank Littlewood, Kendal, Westmorland. (April 1922)

I think your correspondent, the Rev. J. E. Tarbat, is correct when he opines (p. 64) that only certain of the rays of light are the cause of its attractive power for moths. My own experience has been that *all* artificial lights are not attractive, or, at any rate, equally attractive. In the days of the old "ordinary" burners our street gas-lamps here, especially on the outskirts of the town, well repaid the working; but the substitution of the "incandescent mantle" was, entomologically speaking, a retrograde step. . . . The acetylene gas-flame I used myself to find very attractive, and Dr. Lowther has worked the petrol vapour lamps with great success in the district around Grange . . . Visiting me recently, my friend, the Rev. A. Miles Moss (British Chaplain at Pará, Brazil), told wonderful tales of the attractive power of the city arc-lamps there, and especially of the success of his private arc-light installation right on the border of the virgin forest. His opinion was "the *bluer* the light, the better!" His accounts of the numerous Sphingid, Arctiid, and Notodont visitors on a favourable night made me long for the health and the leisure to join him there — to sample the sport and to share the spoil.

[Littlewood, F. 1922. Attractiveness of electric light for moths. *The Entomologist* **55**: 90].

D. THE RELATIVE ATTRACTIVENESS OF VARIOUS TYPES OF ELECTRIC LIGHT FOR MOTHS

James E. Campbell-Taylor, Lewes, Sussex. (July 1922)

Some interesting letters have recently appeared in this Journal anent [concerning] the attraction and non-attraction of present-day electric street lamps for moths, and there is a suggestion that the attraction is some kind of electric emanation rather than the actual light vibrations themselves. The writers, however, appear to have left out of consideration that other sources of light are equally attractive to moths and certain other insects as is the electric one. Both oil and gas lamps are powerful attractions, as also is the acetylene light; and even a candle will serve to trap many insects; it therefore seems superfluous to invoke any other kind of ray than the light-ray itself, notwithstanding that the present type of electric light (the gas-filled incandescent filament) seems to attract much fewer moths. . . . The suggestion of Mr. Stringer that the antennæ of the females might be "transmitters" and those of the males "receivers" is ingenious and imaginative, but it presupposes the power of setting up an electric current in the body of the female, of which there is not the slightest evidence. I have failed with a delicate electroscope to detect any current emanating from a "calling" female, and with regard to his suggestion of putting the female in a metal box, I have done this with the female of *M. rubi* [Fox Moth] and males have come to it. . . .

[Campbell-Taylor, J. E. 1922. The relative attractiveness of various types of electric light for moths. *The Entomologist* **55**: 165–166].

A RARE VISITOR COMES TO SUGAR –
THE BLUE UNDERWING

Charles N. Hawkins, F.R.E.S., Wimbledon, London, S.W. 19. (1937)

On September 20th, 1935, while staying at the George Hotel, Lydd, Kent, in company with Prof. (now Sir) Beckwith Whitehouse and Mr. Frank H. Lees (the latter of whom had arrived that afternoon), Dr. Cockayne and I had the great pleasure of taking a specimen of this rare and very beautiful insect at sugar under somewhat dramatic circumstances.

On the evening of the previous day, the 19th, Sir Beckwith Whitehouse, as his very kind custom was, had run us down to the sugaring-ground in his car and had then gone off to his chosen area while Dr. Cockayne and I decided to work an adjoining round together. There had been a westerly gale for the last two or three days and although it was moderating, the wind had still been strong and there had been rain also during the earlier part of the day. A certain number of common species visited the sugar, but it was not till quite late that anything exciting appeared. Then, as we were approaching a sugar patch, we suddenly saw a very large moth sitting upon it busily engaged in absorbing our sugar. It sat with wings half opened and quivering, and just at the first glance we thought it was a very large *Catocala nupta* L. [Red Underwing]. As we approached closer, however, we saw, to our amazement, that the hind wings had blue bands and that it was, in fact, nothing less than a fresh-looking and apparently perfect *Catocala fraxini* L. [Blue Underwing]. For a moment or two we gazed at it in speechless admiration, fearing almost to breathe lest it should take fright. Then followed a hasty consultation as to how best to secure it. We had absolutely nothing with us in the shape of a box or killing-bottle at all adequate to cope with an insect of this size. Eventually we decided that the only thing to do was to try to net it and then see if we could rig up some kind of receptacle to hold it. Carefully I placed the edge of my net just behind and beneath it, then gently moved the net upward and touched it. Immediately it took flight and I struck. Sure enough the insect was in the net all right, we both saw it well down in the bottom the net. Unfortunately in my haste, instead of turning the net over first I continued my sweep and brought the net straight down to the ground, or rather I tried to do so. Had I done exactly as I intended all might have been well, but as bad luck would have it, the end of the net caught on some projecting snag of wood and in consequence the net was so stretched that when the mouth of it was on the ground the **V** opening at the **Y** was forced to its widest extent and the moth was able to move freely about. Before I could get my hand over the gap or do anything to save the situation the *fraxini* had dived straight through the opening and was away! So close was my hand to the place that I actually touched the moth as it shot through, but a miss was just as good as a mile. It was gone, there was no getting away from that, and the only satisfaction we had was that we had seen something on sugar which neither of us had ever hoped to see in England. At the moment, however, we could not derive much consolation from that and I'm afraid the things I called myself must have raised the local temperature considerably! I must say that Dr. Cockayne was wonderfully restrained in the circumstances, so much so that I have suspected since that he never really expected me to get the insect into the net at all. When we met Sir Beckwith Whitehouse again and told him what had happened he was frankly incredulous and insisted we had been deceived by the light of our lamps, but I think my dejected appearance convinced even him at last that we really had seen something unusual. The rest of that evening was merely a weary plod from sugar patch to sugar patch hoping against hope that we might get a second chance. But doubtless the insect was far too scared to trust itself near sugar again, on that night at any rate. Eventually we packed up and returned to our hotel richer by an unforgettable experience it is true, but with very little to show for our evening's work.

On the next day, the all-important 20th, it was decided that after we had met Mr. Lees we should have another try at the same place, and although we really had no hopes whatever of seeing anything more of *fraxini*, we thought that if such things were about it would be as well to be rather better prepared. Accordingly, in the afternoon, we sallied forth and purchased some tape, and Dr. Cockayne made a most creditable job of sewing it on to both our nets so that the **V** openings could be laced up tightly. It was very much a case of closing the stable door after the horse had gone, but we were not going to be caught that way again whatever insects might turn up! Also he armed himself with a small bottle of chloroform and a good-sized glass-topped metal box in addition to our ordinary collecting boxes. Once more, Sir Beckwith Whitehouse ran us down to the sugaring-ground and we set to work very much as before. He and Mr. Lees went to adjoining rounds while Dr. Cockayne and I jointly worked ours. As it turned out it was very fortunate that we did so, though I have a sneaking feeling that we did not *quite* deserve our luck.

Again the day had been windy and wet, and although it improved in the evening, nothing of interest turned up at the sugar, and we had almost come to the conclusion that it was a really bad night, when at 9.15 p.m. (B.S.T.) we came upon a sugar patch with a single large moth sitting with half opened and quivering wings, feeding at some of the drops which had run down. As we approached we could see the under side of the right pair of wings which looked very white in the rays of our lamps. We could also see that it had a horrid chip out of the right hind wing! We crept up with extreme caution, not daring to get too near, for as soon as the lights fell fairly upon it we saw that the incredible had really happened and that our second chance at *Catocala fraxini* had actually come. It was one thing, however, to see it on the sugar patch but quite another thing to capture it, as we knew to our cost! Members of the genus *Catocala* are notoriously skittish and easily alarmed; this insect's attitude seemed to indicate extreme readiness to depart, and after our experience of the day before we were almost paralysed at the thought of possibly missing it again. Moreover it was sitting not on the sugar patch but on some drops which had run down into a very awkward, rough place where it was almost impossible to box it with anything like certainty. As on the previous occasion the half-opened and quivering wings warned us it might not be safe to approach very near and also indicated there was not much time to spare. Again we held a hasty consultation and decided the only thing to do was to try to net it first, then to chloroform it, and put it into the glass-topped metal box. Very carefully I placed the edge of my net a little below our prey while Dr. Cockayne stood just on one side, at the ready, hoping to get a shot if I failed. All being ready, as we thought, I struck. So did Dr. Cockayne. We both looked in our nets, then at each other. Neither of us had it! The less said about the next few moments, the better! Then we each said we had not seen it fly away and Dr. Cockayne said that just as I struck it seemed to jump backwards and dive straight down. Promptly we both turned our lights on the ground and there it was, sitting just as it had been on the sugar, wings half open and still quivering! My net was over it in a flash and this time there was no mistake. Even so the excitement was not ended. No sooner was the net over it than the insect became very active, trying hard to slip out beneath the edge of the net, and in spite of the invaluable help

'It sat with wings half opened . . . quivering.'

of the tapes, I had my work cut out to place my lamp on the ground safely and to hold the net down securely all round on the uneven surface while Dr. Cockayne got out his little bottle of chloroform. However, these various feats were duly performed and Dr. Cockayne stooped over to place a few drops of chloroform sufficiently near to stupefy it so we could get it into the box. Unfortunately, just at that moment, he caught his foot on a stone or something, stumbled forward a pace and poured half the bottleful of chloroform right over the *fraxini*! The latter took one violent leap into the air, turned over and landed on its back with legs and wings projecting at all sorts of strange angles, and there it lay perfectly stiff and motionless with the greater part of its body and wings looking black in the lamp-light owing to the amount of spirit that had been poured over them. Naturally we thought this was more than anything would stand, but we could now see that the specimen was a female and, as I said before, badly chipped in the right hind wing, so we set to work to try to revive her. Having put her in the box, and the box on the ground, but leaving the lid off, we knelt round and blew and fanned and fanned and blew till every trace of damp and smell had disappeared, and all apparently to no effect, and we eventually closed the box and set off to meet Sir Beckwith Whitehouse and Mr. Lees. The latter met us at the car and soon we saw Sir Beckwith and gave him a hail, "We've taken a female *fraxini* and fear we've killed her". Of course they were both very interested and sympathetic if a little incredulous and naturally wanted to see the catch. We produced the box and then noticed to our delight, that in spite of all, she had moved. Much of the stiff, strained attitude had gone, she had closed her wings properly and was resting on the bottom of the box in a more natural position. We could see no actual movement while we were looking at her but our hopes revived and we placed her in the car to await in peace our return to the hotel. Nothing much else turned up that night, and what did appear seemed very tame after what had gone before, so we soon made up our minds to pack up. On arrival at the hotel we were all very pleased to find that our catch had apparently quite recovered from her unintentional chloroform bath and was actively fluttering about in the box. Having regard to her condition we had, of course, determined to try and get ova, but the problem now arose of how to so this. Once more, fortune favoured us, for Mr. Lees produced a folding breeding-cage which proved to be ideal for the purpose. This cage consisted of a circular metal base with an upper part formed of Brussels net or some such material, stretched over wires which could be folded down when not required, and with an opening at the top, closed by drawing tight a cord threaded through the edge of the material. . . . By the 26th she had laid about 80 eggs and on the following night she laid some 50 more. In all, before she died on October 1st, she deposited 307 eggs . . . .

[Cockayne, E. A., Hawkins, C. N., Lees, F. H., Whitehouse, Sir Beckwith, & Williams, H. B. 1937. *Catocala fraxini* L.: A new British record of capture and breeding. *The Entomologist* **70**: 240–246].

ELECTRICITY FOR ENTOMOLOGISTS

From the Editor of *The Entomologist*:

As electricity is now coming into such general use, entomologists will be interested to know that they can easily have their moth-traps and lamps converted for the electric light at the Sherborne Electric Installation, under the superintendence of Mr. E. R. Dale, son of the late J. C. Dale, who has done so much to promote the use of electricity in Dorset and Wilts. We may mention that amongst the various collections of portable lamps, exhibited at the Sherborne and South of England Horse and Carriage Show, was one to fit on a strap, labelled "County Police," which would also be useful to the entomologist, as the light can be switched on and off instantly. This appears to be the very thing for a sugaring expedition. – ED.

[Editor, 1892. Electricity for entomologists. *The Entomologist* **25**: 214–215].

DANGERS OF COLLECTING AT NIGHT

Peter J. Edwards, F.R.E.S., Dinton, Buckinghamshire. (1996)

Any General Practitioner who is interested in moths must have stories to tell of late night incidents, if only for no other reason than that we are often out in the dark late at night. I remember as a trainee G. P., being struck speechless while talking to a patient on their front doorstep in the early hours, unable to take my eyes off the Large Thorn [*Ennomos autumnaria*] sitting at the side of the porch light.

One December night I was returning from a late call about midnight when I saw a collection of *brumata* [Winter Moth] males flying around a hawthorn hedge in the depths of the Buckinghamshire countryside. At that time I had not seen the wingless females, so I stopped the car and got out to investigate. Unfortunately I had no torch with me so I used an auriscope [instrument used for examining ears] to search the branches and soon had two females safe inside a spare blood sample tube. Engrossed in what I was doing, suddenly I realised I was not alone. A car had pulled up behind mine and two policemen approached. It is amazing how threatening the phrase "Can I help you, sir?" can be made to sound. So I patiently explained what I was doing and watched disbelief spread over the older man's face. Suddenly the younger copper said "Look! there's one," and sure enough it was. Interest was established and so with the aid of two powerful police torches the hedge was searched with considerable success for twenty minutes or so. I often wonder what they wrote on their night's report as to what they were doing.

Just as they were going, the younger policeman said "What a marvellous arrangement. It's like having a housing estate with all the girls stuck in their houses and all the fellows dashing around in their cars."

[Edwards, P. J. 1996. From an unpublished diary].

CAPTURES AT STREET-LAMPS

Hugh W. Shepheard-Walwyn, Winchester, Hampshire. (1898)

Lepidoptera appear to have been unusually scarce this year in this district, and sugaring more or less of a failure. I made several expeditions to Crabbe Wood, but, with the exception of one night, my efforts met with such very indifferent success that I abandoned it and directed my attention to the street-lamps just outside the town. I practically restricted myself to three lamps, though nine-tenths of my captures were made round one, which was in a most favourable situation; and these lamps I worked every night regularly, with very fair success considering the poorness of the season. Nor was I alone in my nightly rounds. Every night, with the most wonderful regularity, I found waiting for me, outside the gate, a sleek yellow-and-white cat, eagerly expectant, in anticipation of the fat juicy beetles which she knew would fall to her share! And if I failed to keep her supplied, which I sometimes forgot to do in the excitement of a capture, which in my eyes was far more important, she would remind me with a loud mew; neither did she give me any peace until I made amends for my shortcomings by throwing her down one of the cockchafers which were swarming round the lamp. She played with it for a few minutes, and then it disappeared with an ominous crunch, and there was a clamour for more of the dainty morsels. Curiously enough, when I was at Oxford, there was a cat which used to follow me round in the same way; I wonder if any other "lamp-workers" have had a similar experiece. But "revenons à nos moutons." . . .

[Shepheard-Walwyn, H. W. 1898. Captures at street-lamps. *The Entomologist* **31**: 294].

ACCIDENTALS

An Old Moth-Hunter. (1954)

It is human to err. It is also human to have 'accidentals'. We all have them, no matter what our pursuit or pastime may be. I was never a great cricketer – though I am second to none in my love of the game – but my cricketing career (if it deserves such a description) was illumined, every season, by accidentals. The ball which by rights should have knocked my off stump out of the ground hit the edge of my bat and went for four. Two of the fieldsmen who rushed for the ball that I skied collided and sustained concussion of the brain, and I and my partner took three runs before they recovered. And there was that never-to-be-forgotten occasion when, fielding at point – point, mark you, not cover – I threw down the wicket of a Cambridge blue who was playing against my home side and thereby morally won the game. It happened early on and it staggered the enemy to such an extent that they fell easy victims to our bowlers' prowess. And once, when sitting in the cockpit of a small yacht in a choppy sea, I aimed with a ·22 rook rifle and fired at a gannet swirling high overhead and, unhappily, hit the bird plumb in the chest. These are things that happen to all of us now and then; but we can never repeat them. Indeed, it would be improper to do so; besides, a fluke which occurs twice lays its perpetrator open to grave suspicion.

Even the most intelligent of men, to wit lepidopterists, are not immune from accidentals. Perhaps we have been beating sallows in vain for an hour and the very last bush we decide to beat, a tall, a noble bush, has a branch just out of reach. "Oh, well, I may as well have a whack at it", we think; so we leap into the air and just manage to smite the branch with the tip of our stick. Whereupon a full grown larva of the Purple Emperor falls into our tray.

At sugaring of course accidentals are not uncommon. And they happen in cages, too. My friend Mr Castle Russell once collected a small number of *machaon* [Swallowtail] larvae in Norfolk. All the butterflies which eventually emerged from them were quite ordinary *machaon* – except one, one that was as black as a hat, as black as a coal-cellar on a dark night. It was in fact as black as the inside of a black cow. You can think of nothing blacker than that? Good. And of course, being bred, it was, and is, in immaculate condition. Never have I set eyes on such a butterfly. Every day when staying with him I came down to breakfast early, so that I could pull out the drawer and have another look at it. I looked at it several times a day. I looked at it every night before going to bed. It was a super-accidental, an accidental *in excelsis*, such a superlative accidental in fact as is granted only to those for whom the gods have an especial affection.

Accidentals, like poets, are born not made. You cannot compass or contrive them by any means in your power. They just happen. So an important question arises: are we morally entitled to attribute them to our intelligence or prowess, or must we accept them with humility as gifts of the benign gods? I remember very well when the captain of our side, after I had outed the Cambridge blue, came up to me as we were going back to the pavilion for lunch, patted my back and said: "That was a marvellous chuck-in of yours, old chap", I replied nonchalantly: "Oh, its nothing to write home about". But I was very young at the time or I am sure I would never have been guilty of such a flagrant *suggestio falsi*. For by every accepted canon of human behaviour it was a beastly fluke.

But the man who, with no thought of *iris* in his head, beats a Purple Emperor larva out of a sallow bush had best beware lest he falls into this trap; for if he attributes to his intelligence or efficiency what is by all the rules of the game a pure 'accidental' he will be shunned thereafter by his friends. No man can tell whether there is a Purple Emperor larva on any particular bush. We can tell the kind of bush which is likely to harbour a Purple Emperor and the situation of bushes which the female butterfly usually selects. Beyond that we cannot go. We can beat scores of 'likely' bushes without getting more than a second instar *O. stabilis* [Common Quaker] or two. At least that has been my experience.

On the whole, then, it is wiser to accept our accidentals with gratitude and humility. Besides, if we claim any personal wisdom or expertness for them the friends to whom we relate them may look at us queerly and say "Huh".

[An Old Moth-Hunter (P. B. M. Allan). 1954. Accidentals. *The Entomologist's Record and Journal of Variation* **66**: 183-184].

SOMETHING FOR CHRISTMAS

J. Herbert Tutt, Blackheath, London, S. E. (1908)

James Herbert Tutt was the eldest of James W. Tutt's five children. For a few years he assisted his father with the publication of *The Entomologist's Record and Journal of Variation* (see p. 301). This short seasonal offering, however, was his only literary contribution to the magazine.

An elderly entomologist was out collecting one evening, when he saw a smallish boy with a net and boxes, but no other implements, dodging about in the dark. The following dialogue ensued:—

"Well, my boy, and what are you after?"

"Moths sir!"

"Have you caught many yet?"

"No sir!"

"Ah! I see; you are a beginner and don't really know how to set about the work. You must get a book about it, with hints. You'll want a lantern and some treacle, and a few other implements. But the best way is for you to get an elementary book — a very elementary one — read it, and then have another try, and I feel sure you will meet with more success."

After thanking the gentleman the boy went home. A few days afterwards the gentleman again saw the boy acting in precisely the same manner as on the previous occasion. Somewhat surprised, he said —

"Well, didn't you get the book I suggested to you?"

"Yes sir! But I couldn't understand it, and it didn't seem to help a bit."

"Oh! The book you got was, evidently, not elementary enough. I told you to get a very elementary book. By the way, what book did you get?"

"Advice to Young Moth-ers."

J.H.T (overheard).

[Tutt, J. H. 1908. Something for Christmas. *The Entomologist's Record and Journal of Variation* **20**: 310–311].

CHAPTER THREE

'I'LL SEE YOU IN HELL' — AN AFTERNOON NEAR OXFORD

'The canon in residence happened to be the Hon. and Rev. Dr. Vesey Stanhope,
who at this time was very busy on the shores of the Lake of Como adding to that unique
collection of butterflies for which he is so famous. Or rather, he would have been
in residence but for the butterflies and other such summer considerations . . .'

Anthony Trollope, *Barchester Towers* (1857)

WHEN BRIAN BOYD (2000) described Vladimir Nabokov and Samuel Beckett as the foremost writers of the mid-twentieth century he noted that although each wrote with eloquence, intelligence, wit and originality, their visions were polar opposites. Nabokov had made butterflies his lifelong personal mark. His short story, *The Aurelian*, written in 1930, brings before us Mr Pilgram the proprietor of a Russian backstreet butterfly store.**

The street started at the corner of a crowded avenue. For a long time it crept on in obscurity, with no shop-windows or any such joys. Then came a small square (four benches, a bed of pansies) round which the trolley steered with rasping disapproval. Here the street changed its name, and a new life began. Along the right side, shops appeared: a fruiterer's, with vivid pyramids of oranges; a tobacconist's with the picture of a voluptuous Turk; a delicatessen, with fat brown and grey coils of sausages; and then, all of a sudden, a butterfly store. At night, and especially when it was damp, with the asphalt shining like the back of a seal, passers-by would stop for a second before that symbol of fair weather. The insects on exhibit were huge and gorgeous. People would say to themselves, "What colors — amazing!" and plod on through the drizzle. Eyed wings wide-open in wonder, shimmering blue satin, black magic — these lingered for a while floating in one's vision, until one boarded the trolley or bought a newspaper. And, just because they were together with the butterflies, a few other objects would remain in one's memory: a globe, pencils, and a monkey's skull on a pile of copybooks.

Stepping through the half-open door, one was immediately assailed by the smells of entomology — sandalwood and naphthalene, formaldehyde and musk.

The whole place was littered with various cases, cartons, cigar boxes. Tall cabinets contained numerous glass-lidded drawers filled with ordered series of perfect specimens impeccably spread and labelled. A dusty old shield or something (last remnant of the original wares) stood in a corner.

One's earliest memories of butterfly and moth catching remain vaguely elusive. My own memories go back, I think, to 1948 (M. A. S.). I was standing on the boundary during a prep school cricket match. Suddenly from nowhere came Mr Holloway, the Latin master, in plus fours and Norfolk jacket. He was running as if for his life, darting this way and that, and all the while he gripped a large green net with which he was clearly trying to trap something. I was amazed. Later, among friends, I asked about this strange activity. 'Butterflies,' said

one. 'And moths as well,' said another; explanations followed. It was some days later that Mr Holloway showed me his wonderful cabinet of Lepidoptera — and I was hooked! At half-term my parents took me to London where I became the proud owner of my first butterfly net, killing bottle and setting boards. We visited Watkins & Doncaster at 36, The Strand (Fig. 61), the London equivalent of Mr Pilgram's Russian butterfly store. It was here

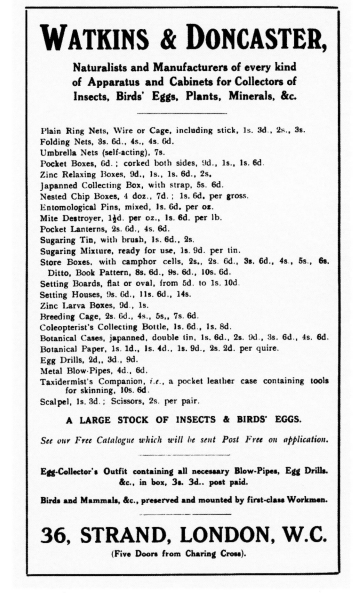

Fig. 60. Advertisement from *Text Book of British Butterflies & Moths*, by L. W. Newman & H. A. Leeds (1913).

amongst the cabinets of specimens, the butterfly nets, mummified Egyptian cats and trays of small instruments that I heard the language of entomology for the first time — a miscellany of strange words. Words such as 'eclosion', 'ecdysis', 'gynandromorph' and 'aberration'. These were to prey on my mind until the arrival some time later of my first butterfly book — a godfatherly birthday present which revealed their true meanings. It was in this famous London butterfly store that I heard one eminent lepidopterist say to another,

Fig. 61. Watkins & Doncaster, 36 The Strand, London (*c.* early 1950s). Richard Ford (foreground) with young customers.

Fig. 62. In 1956 the post-war rebuilding of the Strand led to Watkins & Doncaster moving to 110 Park View Road, Welling, Kent. The business continued there until 1973 before moving once more to larger premises in Four Throws, Hawkhurst, Kent. (*c.* 1970)

'OK then, I'll see you in Hell — Saturday at ten.' I was left wondering what on earth he was referring to. It was not until many years later that I purchased an old butterfly collection and found in it two specimens of the Black Hairstreak labelled 'First specimens known in Oxfordshire, Hell Coppice, 23/6/1918, W. F. Burrows.' Friends then informed me that 'I'll see you in Hell' actually referred to Hell Coppice, a unique locality which I now know to be part of Bernwood Forest, near Oxford. This soubriquet was obviously part of the vocabulary of British entomology — a vocabulary that I was learning fast.

All of us who have collected butterflies and moths have memories, some more distant than others. In this chapter we have collected together a small sample of memorabilia.

THE HAZARDS OF THE CHASE

Revd John N. Marcon, M.A., Pulborough, Sussex. (1976)

Eric Classey (pers. comm.) remembers the Revd John Marcon (1903–1986) as being a 'manic collector'. Apparently, the tall clergyman would drive his motorcycle at great speed on the way to various collecting grounds in the southern counties. The Revd Anthony Harbottle (pers. comm.) recalled that on one of his collecting trips in 1945, Marcon was unfortunately involved in a head-on collision with a Canadian Army jeep and suffered a serious and life-threatening series of injuries. He was apparently certified dead at the scene of the crash by three doctors, one of whom was a Harley Street specialist, but made a miraculous recovery after being many months in a coma. After this he insisted that as he had 'been to the other side and then returned' it might have been 'God's will' that he suffered the crash, and that this was a hint that he should give up collecting. He did precisely this. But in old age, having had second thoughts, he considered that he might by now have been forgiven and took up collecting again.

Bug hunters encounter nerve-racking contingencies as well as adventurous vicissitudes in the pursuit of one of the glories of nature — butterflies. It may be that the hazards of life — at least many of them — contribute to its piquancy!

I expect most collectors have blundered upon keepers, bulls and adders; for all three are part of our English landscape. The writer has been no stranger to these vexations. One Saturday when going through the "stink-works" near Ascot — where the surrounding nettles were a good place for finding *Aglais urticae* [Small Tortoiseshell] larvae — the man told me that Windsor Park Estate were trying to close Swinley Forest. Men on each gate after 1 p.m. and all day Sunday; further, one or two would tour the rides on bicycles to turn people out. If they could do this for a few weeks they could then close the Park as a public amenity.

That acted as no deterrant to an enthusiast. Without more ado, I made over the fence into the "forbidden area". Soon, along the wide passages between the young plantations, there appeared an odd flying insect. Was it a large Grayling flitting by? No. A Fox moth? Perhaps. No, by George, an *Argynnis aglaia* [Dark Green Fritillary] variety; it looked very dark. But settle it would not. Too much bracken made swinging the net hazardous. One must act quickly or it would be seeking new pastures in the plantation. Edging closer it hovered a moment; stretching the net full length a grab was made, hardly daring to breath[e] for excitement. Yes, it was inside, a lovely black male *aglaia* with only two small fulvous spots on the forewings and hindwings smoky, ab. *viridiatra*.

Home for lunch there was no question where to go in the afternoon. Wonder if there is another blackie! Somehow the keepers must be dodged. Later I heard that twelve men were hunting me as I hunted a butterfly! Craft was essential: into the plantation I crept. Some of the young firs kept me well out of sight, but not all. It was 1½ hours before I was spotted, a man on a bicycle 200 yards away on the far side of the plantation. I bobbed down instantly. Had he seen me? A peep through the bushes suggested he had; for he had got off the bike, was looking my way and mounted again pedalling fast. The feeling increased as he turned in my direction. There was nothing for it but to lie flat on the grass and smoke a pipe!

"Hi, there," he shouted in a gruff voice, "no one allowed in here." By dint of "chatting him up" — what the ladies do much better than we mere males — his speech grew less harsh. "I have collected butterflies here since I was a boy: I live nearby: I caught a gorgeous one this morning." Gradually his tone moderated. "Well, I'm afraid you'll have to go," he said finally. A short look round and a great day ended.

A less tense episode was a week after finding an all-black male *Argynnis selene* [Small Pearl-bordered Fritillary] in Abbots Wood in 1955. Hunting the same area I heard voices: gamekeepers I thought, and hid behind a tree. As the sounds subsided I peeped out, and there were two old friends, the Craske brothers.

On another occasion my churchwarden accompanied me on the back of the motorcycle. We headed for the dip behind the Long Man at Wilmington, Sussex — a pocket surrounded by three steep hillsides. Reaching the bottom and preparing to examine such *Polyommatus icarus* [Common Blue] as were resting on the grassheads in the evening, we were aroused by the bellowing of a bull making tracks towards us from the distant flat fourth of the hollow. As it roared ever nearer, foam dripping from its mouth, we could see a single strand of barbed wire as our only protection. Moving away from this was an instinctive reaction. I remember thinking that too much fear was hardly becoming with one of my

Fig. 63. Revd John Marcon. While collecting in Sussex in 1944, the blast from a German V1 exploding nearby lifted him off the ground. It also flushed out the object of 'two and a half days of unremitting search . . . the treasure I had been searching for so long' — a female *adippe* with black forewings. He called it his 'Doodle-bug'. (Marcon, 1975)

Church officers present! Then it struck me that to get close to the barbed wire was the least dangerous place: for if the bull charged through, we could move a few yards along, jump over it while it turned, and make him reverse again and again until he got tired of being torn by the barbs. Ten yards away from the wire we had not seen an electric wire a foot or so above ground. There the beast came to a halt, and we breathed a sigh of relief. Realising the source of our safeguard, yet feeling discretion to be the better part of valour, we dropped all idea of bug-hunting and made a speedy getaway from the scene of imminent disaster, climbing the hill as fast as its steepness would allow: the bull meantime moved parallel with

us, a yard or two away on his side of an electric shock, roaring continuously at his deprivation of victims until we reached the summit.

1945 was a year when *Argynnis selene* were in numbers — and varying — the snakes were too! At an enclosure near Dunsfold I counted over 200, none of which were worth a pill-box. Next day after cycling to a further enclosure fruitlessly, there seemed nothing better than to return to where the numbers were. Walking the path towards it a stray fritillary here and there was to be seen. On the ground ten minutes later, discovering that no boxes had been pocketed, I had to go back for them along the same path. I had moved but twenty yards when a sudden hiss made me jump like a scalded cat, to discover an adder on a warm, sandy patch slithering away. Within twenty minutes four good varieties had fallen to the net from a place I had scoured unsuccessfully the previous day, one a largely black female. The total of adders seen, happily innocuously, was five. (More lethal an incident was twenty years earlier, almost treading on a cobra in India when hunting a butterfly that delights in the sap exuding from the bark of an over-enriched tree.)

What could be called a fortunate hazard occurred in the Vicarage garden, 250 yards from the sea at Eastbourne. Wanting a break at mid-morning, I went out to swat some of the numerous Pierids which had recently immigrated in swarms. Having liquidated a few flying round the beds, I went into the field at the back, part of which was for vegetables. At the far end was a marrow mound; on it was one of the few insects seen perched, its expanded wings showing a well-marked *Pieris rapae* [Small White] ab. *fasciata*. Mr. S. A. Chartres had previously seen a cloud of *Pieris brassicae* [Large White] at Whitbread Hollow (near Beachy Head). "Like a snowstorm," he said, "and one was yellow." But he was less fortunate in capturing it.

Having taken a funeral at the local cemetery one autumn, I asked the Superintendent whether he had any spare wall-flower plants. "Come and have a look," he replied, taking me down to a far corner. There my eye immediately noticed an *Aglais urticae* ab. *nigrocaria* with expanded wings close to the small surrounding box hedge. "Keep your eye on it," I yelled as I dashed back in near desperation to the motorcycle, on which a folding net had been tied for just such an emergency. Putting it somehow together as I hared back, I asked, "Is it still there?" "Yes," said the Superintendent, almost as excited as I was as the net was gently lowered!

In the New Forest at Islands Thorn[s] enclosure in 1940 there was great stimulation among three or four collectors when one of them said he thought he had seen "a black *valesina*" (*A. paphia* ab. *nigrizina*) over in Amberwood enclosure. We all dashed off on the longish walk taking different approaches. Nothing more of it was seen there, but after we had left the Forest several days later S. G. Castle Russell caught this very variety — if the original was not an hallucination, common when collectors are together — at the opposite end of Islands Thorn[s] two miles away, and not in prime condition. The hunt in my case was not without compensation.

THE THIRD PORTION OF THE COLLECTION OF VARIETIES OF BRITISH BUTTERFLIES FORMED BY THE REV. J. N. MARCON

139	Machaon, an unusually pale variety, with the eye-spots on the hind-wings salmon-pink (Norfolk Broads, June, 1931, L. W. Newman)	1
140	P. Brassicae, a perfect male ab. flavescens (Holloway, N. London, bred W. King) and a greyish-tinted male (Somerset, 1896, ex Madison and Sidney Webb colls.)	2
141	Ditto, *an outstanding underside variety, probably unique, pale blue instead of yellow* (*Monk's Wood, Aug.,* 1908, *H. A. Leeds*), FIGURED *Frohawk's Butterflies, Pl.* 3, *Fig.* 20, *and recorded "Text Book of British Butterflies and Moths," Newman and Leeds*	1
142	P. Rapae, a male with smoky grey borders to the fore-wings (Thirsk, April, 1902) and a female extreme ab. Fasciata (Eastbourne, July, 1947, J. N. Marcon)	2
143	Ditto, two females, ab. ochrea, extreme forms with full data	2

Fig. 64. From the catalogue of Debenham, Storr & Sons, Ltd., Covent Garden, London. The auction took place on 21st January, 1948 and involved the third portion of Revd Marcon's magnificent collection of British butterfly aberrations. The Small White mentioned in the article is part of Lot 142.

Having tired of the long trapse up and down the wide gap, full of blackberry blossom, between Amberwood and Sloden enclosure, I thought to try the latter. There on a thistle looked a curious *paphia*: it flipped up, circled and came back. Immediately the net went into play and it proved to be a very nice female *Argynnis adippe* ab. *magnipuncta*.

A less happy experience in the Forest two years later occurred to Col. V. R. Burkhardt. It was at the top end of Oakley enclosure (to which I had introduced him and Russell), where he saw an *Argynnis paphia* extreme ab. *confluens*. Twice he had his net over her and she had eluded him. Two days later I met him. "There it is," he said, as it settled on a favourite bramble. He got his net over it, jerked it down before it was properly inside and away it flew. I left him, expostulating at his crazy idea of capture! At 3 p.m. he had not seen it again. At 4 p.m. he left disconsolate. I went down "his" ride. At last over a stream on an opposite bramble bush there she was. My goodness! But how to reach her? The bracken too thick to skirt around without disturbing her. Plunging into the stream I waded towards the bush. It was an awkward position from which to strike; before I could decide what to do she was away again. Pushing through the bracken I saw her flirting with a male. The moment had come! I struck and missed both — a mad thing to do, nearly as bad as the Colonel's! It seemed to be the last I should see of her. Hastily swallowing a mug of tea I returned to the scene of defeat. After a while, to my surprise and delight, I caught sight of her. She went from flower to flower, from bush to bush without pausing. At last she was on the ride again and settled on a low bush. I held up my hand to Russell approaching and stalked her to within reach, clapped my net right down and thought she had got away. But no, there she was, a beautiful beast! When offered to Burkhardt he would not take it.

It was in the same enclosure, after a tiring morning, I decided to take a break at 3 p.m., and start refreshed at 4 p.m. when *paphia* would come down for a final two hours feed. Arriving at the ride where the motorcycle had been parked against a rut, I was concerned to find it on its side with the petrol leaking out — it was wartime, too! Having righted it I sat down to enjoy the harvest cider I had been given; drank the lot and in due course staggered up the ride singing lustily!

Three anecdotes to conclude this ramble. The late Mr. Jack Craske was at Newlands Corner in 1944, looking at hundreds of *Lycaenopsis argiolus* [Holly Blue] that had emerged. It was a hot day of low, heavy cloud, with most of them resting. Against a dark background he was examining as many as were within reach. Amongst them was one with wings closed

'There on a lone bramble was the blackest male *paphia* he had ever seen.'

130

which he thought was torn. A little later it occurred to him that he ought to have another check. Looking more closely at the "tattered" insect it proved to be magnificently radiated on the underside of all four wings. A short while after he netted a halved gynandromorph. So that was a good day's work!

I had a similar though less dramatic experience. Looking over a fence at a bush on Mount Caburn there was a *Coenonympha pamphilus* [Small Heath] perched. It appeared torn, as part of the upper wing was showing. Rather dispassionately the net was swept over the bush; inside was a homeotic *pamphilus*.

The last yarn concerns the late Castle Russell. Always keen on *Argynnis paphia*, and with splendid captures to his credit (now at the British Museum (Natural History)) he was in his favourite enclosure in the New Forest, Islands Thorn[s]. Walking along the metal road that runs through it, there on a lone bramble was the blackest male *paphia* he had ever seen — more extreme than anything Percy Bright had, he told me. His method of capture with this species was always to lower the net slowly over the insect; when far enough down a slight jerk with the hand holding the bag and "up she rises". This time the extended branch, with no thorns nearby, offered little hazard to capture. Sweeping it off the flower seemed easy; he took careful measurement, aimed the swing with pinpoint precision and struck at the prospective prize. Lo and behold it was not in the net! Where had it gone? Had he missed it? Perhaps he had knocked it down with the frame of the net. For half-an-hour he searched the grass beneath and around meticulously: he never saw it again.

What a hobby we have! The glories of nature, such as sunsets, butterflies, the view from many a height, a full moon shining on a becalmed sea, indeed most of our entomological haunts make us pause and ask: Why? Wherefrom? To what purpose? Happy is the man or woman who can find satisfaction in reflecting on such things, and rejoice in the answer he gives.

[Marcon, J. N. 1976. The hazards of the chase. *The Entomologist's Record and Journal of Variation* **88**: 213–217].

In *Living with Butterflies* (1967), L. Hugh Newman remembered the Revd John Marcon:

> This tall, wiry clergyman, with the booming voice, was one of the best known figures on the collecting grounds of southern England between the two world wars. His parish was at Eastbourne, and in the time which he had at his disposal for collecting butterflies he managed to cover a great deal of country [often on a motorcycle] and was usually to be seen, if only for an hour or two, at most of the well-known localities for Blues and Fritillaries. He had phenomenal luck, too, and had amassed a wonderful collection which was known throughout Britain.

On one occasion, while out collecting at Folkestone, Marcon was accosted by a tramp asking for money:

> Brushing him aside, striding the wall, walking down the slope and netting on the way, took only a minute or two. Five *Lysandra bellargus* [Adonis Blue] were visible inside, one a halved gynandromorph. I shouted to the boy friend accompanying me, who was still conversing with the tramp, "got something good here". The latter, suspecting his fortunes might rise, hurried down with the boy to where the treasure was being safely housed. It seemed a moment of expansiveness, so I took out a shilling and handed it to the vagrant, who departed I hope as delighted as I was.

[Marcon, J. N. 1978. Further memoirs of a butterfly hunter. *The Entomologist's Record and Journal of Variation* **90**: 167–169].

THE INFLUENCE OF CHILDHOOD ON AN ENTOMOLOGIST –
AND A VERY RARE FRITILLARY

Rupert D. G. Barrington, B.Sc., Bristol, Avon. (1999)

Rupert Barrington (b. 1965) is a television producer and writer of wildlife and science documentaries. He worked with the BBC for twelve years and now works for Granada. His programmes have won awards in the United Kingdom, as well as Europe, Japan and the USA. He tells us that he has been fascinated by insects for as long as he can remember, and has focussed his attention especially on variation in British butterflies.

It was suggested by [A. D. A.] Donald Russwurm that I put on record the circumstances surrounding the capture of a very rare and extreme melanic aberration of *Argynnis aglaja* L. [Dark Green Fritillary] in Ireland in July 1998. This seemed an opportunity to pursue, initially, a train of thought that has intrigued me for some time. That is those experiences early in our lives that headed us down a lifelong pathway of entomology as opposed to any of the other avenues of interest that life has to offer. This line of thinking seems to lead naturally to the incident concerning the melanic *A. aglaja*.

Sir David Attenborough was once asked "When did you acquire your interest in nature?" He replied "When did you lose yours?" His point was that most, if not all, children seem to have an innate interest in wildlife. In many it doesn't last or, if not entirely lost, then the desire is lost to experience it in the dirty knees, middle of a nettle patch, hands-on sort of way. Why? Perhaps their human environment discourages it (though that has failed to deter many a naturalist), or perhaps, more crucially, their early experiences of nature just did not fire something deep enough within before some other experience did.

The great American scientist Professor E. O. Wilson, a world authority on ant biology amongst many other things, was a childhood naturalist and a really keen one. That early passion led to his becoming arguably one of the great thinkers of the 20th Century. His autobiography (1994. *Naturalist.* Island Press, Washington DC) closely examines how his childhood experiences shaped the rest of his life. He writes "hands on experience at the critical time, not systematic knowledge, is what counts in the making of a naturalist. Better to be an untutored savage for a while . . . better to spend long stretches of time just searching and dreaming." He did just that as a child, spending much of one summer, for example, just sitting on a jetty at Paradise Beach, Florida, staring into the water below.

One of his most vivid memories from that time was of the moment when the shape of a huge Ray materialised from the dark sea bed and floated beneath his feet. It was far bigger than anything he had ever seen before — it was a monster. But it was not just a monster in the physical sense. One can imagine the child gasping in wonder, because to him it was a

Fig. 65. Rupert Barrington (2003), lepidopterist and producer of award-winning television wildlife films. He has been particularly successful with the breeding of some of the rarer aberrational forms of the Meadow Brown and Marbled White.

"monster" of the mythical kind; something of a type or on a scale that he had not previously realised could exist in his own experience of the world. He tells us this story because he feels that if the child is receptive then such compelling events burn deep in the memory, and compelling events in childhood can set a pattern of behaviour or interest for life.

I wonder if it takes some kind of "monster" experience in childhood to turn many of us into entomologists. If so then the definition of "monster" must be a little broader than just "very large things". It must be applicable to insects. A monster may be simply a new thing or something that has become a personal myth through old book illustrations perhaps, or tales told by adults. Above all it must be something that stimulates the imagination. After all, Wilson says the child naturalist spends time "just searching and dreaming". Dreaming of what if not of finding something new or special round the next bend or under the next stone? I wonder how many grown-up entomologists, however seriously scientific their intent, cannot relate to that?

The Rev. Greene (1870. *The Insect Hunter's Companion.* Van Voorst, London), of pupa-digging fame [Fig. 99], put his finger on something when he wrote of his childhood butterfly-hunting experiences. "Then, everything was rare. I look back with something very like regret to the time when I used to pin . . . a number of *Satyrus janira* [Meadow Brown] into the crown of my hat and think it a good day's work". Regret, because only in those childhood days could he experience so often the excitement of novelty. In some the thrill associated with the discovery of something rare or special is an intoxicating thing and once set within the mind at an early age one wishes to experience it again and again. Why else would P. B. M. Allan write, in his playful "Letter to a young lady contemplating marrying an entomologist" (1948. *Moths and Memories.* Watkins & Doncaster, London) "I gather from your last letter that you contemplate marrying young Mr Hunter-Bugge, and that he is addicted to the collecting of insects". Addicted, in some degree, is the word. As so often, Allan's light touch masks a penetrating observation. The "letter" continued ". . . when once a man, especially a young one, has become afflicted with this mania it is rarely indeed that he can be cured". In this context it is the collecting of the things of one's dreams that gives the thrill but perhaps, ultimately, the thrill really lies in the finding and the seeing.

Writing of the way he has come to view the world (which, in effect, is the sum of his scientific achievements) E. O. Wilson wrote "although the tributary sources extend far back in the memory, they still grip my imagination, as I write, in my sixty-sixth year. I am reluctant to throw away these precious images of my childhood and young manhood. I guard them carefully as the wellsprings of my creative life". If he could live his life again he would "keep alive that little boy of Paradise Beach who found wonder in a scyphozoan jellyfish and a barely glimpsed monster of the deep." Without the experience of that little boy there might have been no adult sense of wonder at the world in which he lives.

Those "tributary sources" are not the province of entomologists alone. Angler Chris Yates writes books on fishing that are both charming and whimsical, yet full of subtle insight. Nowhere is his writing more lyrical than in describing his childhood inspirations. He writes (1986. *Casting at the Sun.* Pelham Books, London) of having been fascinated by old anglers' tales of the great fish said to be lurking in his village pond. They were supposedly things of a size and beauty that the young boy had neither seen nor even imagined could exist in such a mundane place. He dreamed of "fantastic-sounding creatures that lived in the deepest places in the pond". He experienced also "a change in the way I looked at the muddy pool. Especially in the evening . . . I seemed to sense a shadowy transformation. Perhaps it was just my imagination, but then perhaps the pond really did harbour monsters".

Some time later the boy asked what the movement was that he could see in a keep net belonging to one of those old anglers on the pond. It was a fish that Yates describes as "beautiful, almost terrible. The most miraculous thing I'd ever seen." "What is it?", he had asked in a whisper. "Carp" replied the apparently lugubrious angler."

"Was it strange", Yates wonders "that my infant imagination should have been stirred like this? There was no logical reason for it . . . yet those fish affected me like sparks on petrol". They stimulated in him a life long need to keep returning to the childhood dream, to relive that emotion by fishing for carp in mysterious, forgotten lakes. It is a process he calls "earthing the current".

The need to "earth the current", to touch again some childhood experience, is not a predicament (however enjoyable) confined only to those with an interest in the nature. In some way it may be common to everyone. Stories of the same nature are told by people devoted, for example, to football or mountains, sailing or cricket. Probably scrabble and stamp collecting too. Perhaps today's rather maligned accountants were inspired by an early brush with some gigantic prime number. Who knows? It would be nice to think so.

The "monster myths" that stoked my own precocious interest in insects were told by a grandfather and fuelled by his old books filled with dark, dramatic illustrations. They were tales with a touch of romance about them, like the capture of a Peacock Butterfly that turned out, in the net, to be a Camberwell Beauty, or the unexpected discovery of great, rare Hawk-moth caterpillars the size of an outstretched, grandfatherly finger. I dreamed of rare butterflies and moths in remote and lonely places. The actual finding, for the first time, of some of those "mythical" things was a thrill I cannot forget. Today Lepidoptera and "lost places" are becoming ever fewer in England and I have found myself travelling to increasingly distant parts of the British Isles in my attempts to "earth the current". If those places should be sparsely inhabited and have, attached to them, a certain entomological "glamour", a place in our lore, then so much the better. Islands fit the bill very well.

During July 1998, tired from the demands of work, I travelled with a friend to Western Ireland. After so long confined to the city I needed, once again, to experience open, lonely country with precious butterflies.

Parts of the west coast of Ireland are littered with islands and what might be called "spits" which are cut off by the incoming tide. 7 July was a cool, grey and breezy day and showed no promise of an improvement. However, in this part of the world, exposed as it is to the full eccentricities of an Atlantic climate, one must take the weather as it comes. At the morning low tide we walked across the sand and waded through the tidal streams to reach one such spit that did not appear to have been as heavily grazed as much of the local coastline.

Running down the near side was a high dune and once one crossed it the return route over the tidal flat was hidden from view. I calculated that one could have five hours to examine the area before being cut off by the in-coming tide. I had hoped that this place might hold a good colony of the increasingly scarce, and delightfully named, race *mariscolore* Kane of *Polyommatus icarus* Rott. [Irish race of the Common Blue]. However only a few adults could be flushed from the grass while the odd individual even braved the weather to fly about in the most sheltered hollows, along with a handful of *A. aglaja*. In equally small numbers were adults, mostly male, of a large local race of *Maniola jurtina* L. ssp. *iernes* Graves [Meadow Brown]. The only insects in any kind of abundance were the adults of the Burnet moth *Zygaena filipendulae* [Six-spot Burnet] which were crawling over the flowers in their hundreds. Occasionally, unexpectedly, a Mountain Hare of the small Irish form would bolt away from some grassy tussock.

Climbing back over the dune about four hours later we were greeted not by the sight of rippled sand but by a wide expanse of water. Another calculation, rather more accurate as it turned out, suggested the spit would remain an island for about the next nine hours — a duration that was going to seem rather longer for having run out of food and water. Tired and irritated I dumped my net and bag down and tried to sleep under the shelter of a few trees. However it was too cold so eventually I stalked off round the nearest end of the island. It was almost 6 o' clock and I had had enough of looking for butterflies so I left my net and pill boxes where they were.

On the far side I was walking along the top of the high dune which dropped steeply down to the beach when I was surprised to notice a butterfly flying some way below me. With what I suppose has become second nature I looked at it very carefully, not to see what species it was, it was clearly a Dark Green Fritillary, but to check that it was a typical example. It seemed to take a while before I began to ask myself if this was not, surely, a rather curious-looking Fritillary. It gave an impression of a "flatness" in pattern, an absence of detail, which was immediately exciting.

It turned back on itself, flying low over the grass, clearly looking for somewhere to roost. I followed its movements from the top of the dune, running first one way then the other as the butterfly went back and forth. At one point it flew up near me and settled on a grass head that was bobbing in the wind. I recognised the dramatically aberrant underside from the lovely illustration of an ancient specimen in Don Russwurm's book on aberrations (1978. *Aberrations of British Butterflies*. Classey, Oxford). The butterfly now in front of me was a childhood "monster" — something so rare and dramatic that I had never expected to see its like in my own lifetime. I had studied that book, that very plate, since the age of thirteen. I knew the upperside of this butterfly would be almost entirely black.

I contemplated throwing my coat over it, then realised that, as I would have no idea what to do next, some horrible, inept disaster would probably follow. Anyway it was soon off again and resumed its hawking up and down, inspecting one clump of grass after another. Finally it fluttered over a large tussock halfway down the face of the dune and disappeared inside. I slid down after it and discovered the butterfly roosting head-up, out of the wind. There was nothing for it now but to wait until it was properly settled for the night. Half an hour later it had not moved so I judged it safe to make a dash for the net, having first tied my coat firmly to a shrub to mark the spot. The butterfly remained where I had left it and I was able to drop the net gently on top. It was a male ab. *wimani* Holmgren and one of the most extreme melanic fritillaries on record.

Locals told me that they had experienced some very hot days a few weeks before, which would have been around the time the larva of this butterfly was pupating. The adult coloration in this species is not nearly so sensitive to the effect of extreme temperature during the early pupal stage as, say, *Argynnis paphia* L. [Silver-washed Fritillary], in which species hot days at pupation regularly result in melanic adults. However, it seems most likely that this was the reason behind the appearance of my strange butterfly.

Before finally leaving the island at 10 pm I sat and watched the light fade. Though still cloudy the last light had taken on a curious, almost luminous quality. The green grass which covered several small islands in the bay was now of a remarkably intense hue and the sand

'The butterfly in front of me was a childhood "monster" – something so rare and dramatic that I had never expected to see its like in my lifetime.'

dunes stretching away along the coast seemed to give out a pale, ethereal glow. The water that lay in ripples on the sand, or ran across it in small streams reflected, more brightly than seemed possible, the darkening sky. There were Curlews calling and probing the sand alongside small huddles of Oyster Catchers. Not a human sound could be heard. The previous year I had watched a fox walking on the shore just where I was sitting now, quite intent on its business of hunting down crabs under the seaweed. It would prod and nip before grabbing and quickly crushing them. I remembered this and was sorry not to see it again. Sitting there then, Chris Yates' words came to mind. This was "earthing the current".

Finally, at the risk of labouring a point, I might add one further quote on the theme of this piece. It was written by no less a man than the great Charles Darwin who had been a fanatical beetle-hunter in his youth. In old age he reflected on those days that had been filled with the thrilling promise of rare finds and judged them to have been among the best of his life. Despite the great achievements of his later years he never forgot that sense of excitement and once wrote to a friend, "Whenever I hear of the capture of rare beetles, I feel like an old war horse at the sound of a trumpet". In this sentiment, if in nothing else, I feel that Charles Darwin and I might have understood one another. . . .

[Barrington, R. 1999. The influence of childhood on an entomologist — and a very rare fritillary. *The Entomologist's Record and Journal of Variation* **111**: 261–265].

HOW I CAME TO START COLLECTING

Ian R. P. Heslop, Burnham-on-Sea, Somerset. (1967)

My first (and for a long time only) nature book was "The Little Naturalist at the Seaside" presented to me (I have it yet) at Christmas 1909 by a much loved aunt in Wiltshire (she died four years ago at the age of 95), which radically influenced my outlook on the world about me. Also there was a picture inter alia of a moth — without its name — on the inside of the cover which in the following year, even at the age of only just six, I was able to recognise as frequenting the profuse euonymus hedges in the vicinity.

The very earliest recollection I have of any physical connection with the Lepidoptera, however, is when at the age of just seven in the year 1911 I lay, really ill (from mumps), for seven weeks in bed at my home in Bristol. To interest me, someone (it may have been my grandfather) brought me a number of caterpillars of the Small Garden White (as I later knew) feeding on Nasturtium from the garden. I watched them pupate. And later, when they emerged, they flew about the room settling upon the flowers and occasionally pausing at my pillow; until, delighted as I was by their presence, I asked my nanny to let them go out of the window. Somebody else had added to these a butterfly which he had found at rest in the evening beside a path through a clover field at Redland Green. It was quite unharmed, and I have the clearest possible recollection of it: it was undoubtedly a Pale Clouded Yellow.

Later, when I was better, I desired to see this same clover field; and I was duly walked to it, only to find that it had just been cut for a second crop. However, I was allowed to play in the hay while the ladies retired to the trees to shade themselves from the heat of that incredible August. Since no one had thought of equipping me with a hat, I soon found myself back in bed again with a headache the like of which I have never known since.

In the following year, 1912, the family holiday was at Cromer. Here on one rainy day (how I remember the fearful storm and shipwreck that occurred in that holiday), someone in the hotel casually mooted the possibility of an outing to the Norfolk Broads.

Somebody else, I clearly remember, mentioned the Swallowtail butterfly. Probably the whole conversation arose only in relief of boredom, but somehow or other the grown-ups (including my parents) found themselves let in for the project. It was a beautiful day as we set out. But, alas, our horse-brake became jammed with another vehicle in the narrow streets of Cromer (how steadily and patiently those horses, which were uninjured, did stand!); and the whole project was, with unconcealed relief, abandoned and never revived. The grown-ups clearly felt that they had done their part; and that the merciful intervention of fate should be accepted without demur. No one took the slightest notice of the tragic disappointment of a very little boy who had so wanted "to see the Swallowtail butterfly": (as it happens I have still not seen the Norfolk Broads). A day or two later, on a visit to Pretty Corner, I was sufficiently alerted to notice the large grey butterflies (which I later knew to be Grayling) flying briskly about the heath, and to ask whether these were Swallowtails: only to meet with the rebuke that they were "just butterflies".

Well, I could make my own opportunities; and in the following March I set out on the Bristol Downs with my previous summer's shrimping-net and the express determination of finding the very kind of butterfly that had cheered my sick-room nearly two years previously. And so on 20th March 1913 I with the aforesaid implement actually caught a very early specimen of the species: my first butterfly — which I still possess — a Small Garden White. I was not again to see a specimen of this species flying on just such an early date for precisely forty years.

I continued so to use the shrimping-net until the following year, when a neighbour said she would report me to the R.S.P.C.A. if I caught another butterfly; and, to emphasise her remarks, took away my shrimping-net. I can still see the look of gloating exultation on her face as she deprived me of my solitary possession, other than my clothes. For a time I was reduced to trying to knock down specimens with a stick. It is surprising that in one or two so taken, there was but slight damage.

At about this time too I suffered from the intrusions of the hordes of honorary relatives who seemed to infest every household in those days, and who appeared to regard children as existing solely for their entertainment. Many was the specimen I lost through having some vivacious or wanton finger poked right through it as it lay in my collection housed in soap or confectionery boxes with a layer of corrugated cardboard at the bottom of each to receive the common pins. My grief at such an event seemed to occasion the greatest amusement. The contagion of indifference, or worse, spread to the domestic staff: and on one occasion I found a member thereof flicking a duster in my boxes. My livestock (however discreetly or remotely housed) was consistently thrown out in the bushes, or scalded. All in all, it is scarcely to be wondered at that of the total of some 250 specimens of butterflies and moths that I took from 1913 to 1917, inclusive, less than 30 have survived. These survivors do, however, include a specimen of the Scarce Hook-tip.

There was one particular excitement in those early days which perforce has progressively become rarer over the years and which perhaps may not now recur (since I have already taken 67 species of butterflies in Britain), though I am always hoping: and that was the catching of species of butterflies new to me. This was an especially vivid experience in the case of the taking of two new species in one day. And on each of just two occasions (both in

1918) I caught three. With better facilities I could of course have stepped up the rate but as it was I just had to be content with the patch of green (any such far more productive then than now of course) nearest to my home, with rare exceptions, and perhaps I derived the greater satisfaction from the comparative infrequency of the occasion. And also I learned, in the hard way, to make the best possible use of whatever facilities were available to me: hence perhaps now my self-taken 67 species. Looking at my diary I see that in my first collecting season, 1913, I took four different species of butterflies. In 1914 I added four, in 1915 six, in 1916 one; and in 1917 I added four. I had of course some near misses during this time: including in 1917 a Brown Hairstreak in Leigh Woods, a place in which I have never seen or heard of this butterfly since and a species which I was not to take until 1926 in Huntingdonshire (although I did see one specimen in the Forest of Dean in 1924).

At about the time of the start of the Great War the decision was made for me — I was 10 — that my career was to be in the Royal Engineers. And the edict went forth that (apart from stamp-collecting which had always been fostered) my "hobby" was henceforth to be machine-drawing only. This was just a word to me; however, I managed in part to satisfy the requirement by making drawings of steam engines. But butterflying was definitely taboo. I had, however, the support of two school-friends whose parents not only strongly encouraged them in entomological activities but managed to convey a little of their own attitude to my family; with the result that in the following year, 1915, there was some slight relaxation of the ban (though not before a treasured capture — as it then was — a Common Yellow Underwing, was reft from me and released before my face). And these two friends in 1914 also surreptitiously lent me each his own book on British Butterflies (Edward Newman's and A. M. Stewart's), since I had none. I had had a natural affinity for Latin ever since I was introduced to the language at the age of six; and I now learned the Latin names (most of these were genuinely classical) of the butterflies and larger moths in a week or so, incidentally to the marked discomfiture of a genteel loafer of mature years who essayed to patronise me with them.

It is a curious fact, however, that early in 1913 my father had bought copies of *The Entomologist* for me retrospective to the beginning of that year. And, although my sight of this journal ceased very soon, my father must have inadvertently kept the subscription continuing after he returned to India; for, some years later, I found a whole run of the journal, up to about 1921, in an attic.

It is interesting to recall that in those very early days I thought that the Purple Emperor might be a denizen of almost any oak; and I would be continually scanning the tops even in the fields and lanes just by my home, or on car excursions in Gloucestershire with one of my two friends. How narrowly then I missed sight of a specimen, I was not to appreciate until later. However, I did first see the Purple Emperor, in Somerset, in 1918.

In 1914 one of these friends obtained some superb specimens of the Painted Lady on waste ground near our homes. Although I was precluded from availing myself of the information imparted to me, nothing stirred my nascent entomological imagination more than this beautiful short series which was set for my friend by his father.

I have said that restrictions were eased in 1915: I was permitted to make a primitive net for myself (setting was still on cardboard — but it was, and is, my own). Nevertheless I was not allowed to take this net with me when visiting the close relatives in Wiltshire in 1915. However, on our arrival by car, my uncle, surprised at the omission, lent to me from a cupboard in Edington Church of which he was the Vicar, in the hope that I might be able

to make some entomological use of it, a net normally used for catching bats. And I did in fact, to my infinite joy after my frustration of the previous year, catch with it my first Painted Lady (I have it yet) on the hill top on that day trip on 8th June 1915.

When I was mocked for my devotedness, I replied that I thought so much of the occasion that I would on the exact 50th anniversary of the day return to this place and think on these things. I duly kept my vow, not having been to the exact spot in the meantime, with the peals of half a century agone still ringing in my ears.

At Bournemouth in August and September 1915 I caught quite a number of specimens, including my first Graylings: and the family holiday was further marked by an incident wholly fortunate for me. My swimming instructor called out to my parents in the balcony (my father being on short leave from India), "what will you give him if he swims the length of the bath?" The reply came down, "a case of butterflies". Since this was only my third lesson, the promise seemed to carry no danger of fulfilment. However, I swam the 75-foot length of the Bournemouth bath with ease: and the promise was kept — no common outcome in those days when a promise to a child was usually just an expedient. This type collection of British butterflies was to be of the utmost usefulness to me for reference. Furthermore, my father gave me, on 16th September 1915, my first butterfly book — W. S. Coleman's "British Butterflies".

When, however, backed by my father, I enquired for a list of British Lepidoptera, the dealer laughed in my face. There wasn't, wouldn't be, couldn't be such a thing (let alone one with the English names as I had expressed the additional hope). This rebuff left me with a firm resolve, at which (having meanwhile acquired a further book, W. J. Gordon's) I was to make some primitive essays (how then and subsequently I was to value my Latin!) in the following year 1916; and on which I was to embark in earnest in 1917.

In this early period and even up to about 1923 all killing was by means of crushed laurel-leaves: a method having advantages which I still appreciate.

In my first breeding-cage (also given to me in 1915) there emerged in 1916 some Swallowtails from bought chrysalids "from the Norfolk Broads". Although I did not put these in my collection since I had not taken them myself (a principle which I have strictly maintained throughout), I did acquire knowledge thereby; and in this and in my second breeding-cage (purchased from Mountney of Bristol in 1916) I was soon rearing numbers (nearly all subsequently released by myself) of Buff-tips and Common Magpies and the like.

In 1916 also I made the acquaintance of Mr Swaine of Bristol (I was later to overlap by a term the career of his son at Clifton College) who was a friend indeed to me in the pursuit of my hobby. At Clifton, however, where I had been looking forward to enlarging my scope, I soon found that in those days all aspects of Natural History were "nefas". Mr Swaine even lent me a small cabinet. When in 1918 I returned this to him (I take the opportunity of recording that he died in September 1920), having acquired a couple of show cases, I was persuaded by the ladies to scrap a large part of my specimens "to save space": (this was their swan-song, apart from the giving twenty-four years later and while I was abroad of several hundred of my books, including quite a number of entomological ones, to "salvage").

In 1916 also, becoming for the first time the recipient of pocket-money, I saved my shilling a week until I could buy some proper setting-boards (I have kept the saddle kind). My activities in the field were, however, extremely localised until, on 7th June 1917, I became the owner of a bicycle (which, however, I was not to be able to use for two months owing to an initial accident). And, although there was to be no relaxation of the policy that on no account was my career to be of my own choice, after the retirement of my father from India in that year I found in him an ally and companion of ever-increased staunchness in the entomological field. My first packet of entomological pins (white), purchased at this time by my father from Gunn of Bristol, was a boon and a revelation.

I think that in part this change of heart was initiated by natural reaction to a most extraordinary incident. When collecting in the late summer of 1917, I found myself accosted by a horrible old man who asked if he could see my catch. When, out of politeness I handed my collecting box to him, he snatched one specimen from its laurel pad before I could stop him and proceeded to rub all the scales off the wings: expatiating all the while on the pleasurable sensation ("velvet to the touch", etc.) that this process gave him. When I told my father of this incident, he lay in wait on more than one day suitably equipped to confront the character concerned: but we never saw the old reprobate again.

The idea of the Royal Engineers had been dropped – I never discovered why – but deaf ears were turned to my own request to be trained for a zoological degree with a view to proceeding to museum service. Instead it was settled for me that I should go either into the I.C.S. ("plenty of butterflies there") or into the Colonial Administrative Service: and so it remained.

On the 1st of May 1919 I became, with the encouragement of my grandfather and exactly a month before his death, a member of the Bristol Naturalists' Society – a membership I have maintained ever since.

There still remained traces of the old restriction which were manifested from time to time (for example when I alluded to Museums). And it was not until he was dying that my grandfather (also a Robert Dick) told me about his uncle, Robert Dick the great Scottish naturalist and geologist (whose Centenary Exhibition I opened at Thurso last year), a connection which he had actually been asked to keep concealed from me. However, as my grandfather remarked, heredity — without any knowledge of the bearing thereof — had triumphed in the end.

[Heslop, I. R. P. 1967. How I came to start collecting. *The Entomologist's Record and Journal of Variation* **79**: 225–229].

REMINISCENCES OF AN ELDERLY ENTOMOLOGIST

Ronald P. Demuth, Oakridge, Gloucestershire. (1985)

. . . There were no outstanding collecting areas close to Cambridge but further out what other town could better Wicken and Chippenham Fens, the Brecks, Monks Wood, Warboys Wood, Bearshanks Wood and Bedford Purlieus? Needless to say that as soon as the weather got warm we were at them. The travelling was done by bicycle but at some subsequent date Bernard [Kettlewell] got a car, an open Alvis looking like a bath-tub with wheels at each corner and this was a great advantage when I collected with him. This might be the moment to mention Bernard's driving which was fast and when at the same time he was looking for plovers' nests was quite alarming. You might think it was impossible to look for plovers' nests while driving a car however slowly, but this was not so when, as in so much of the country round Cambridge, there were no roadside hedges. Bernard had found that the plover made a discernible special body movement when about to sit on its nest and this is what he spotted, and if the eggs were fresh he (not I) would have plovers' eggs for breakfast. I remember us sweeping round a gentle curve into a long straight road with wide grass verges. Another open car was approaching a long way off. There was plenty of room to pass but the other driver preferred the grass verge criss-crossed with drainage ditches. As we passed, he and his passengers were shooting up and down like jack-in-the-boxes as each ditch was crossed. After a short interval Bernard exchanged his Alvis for an open Lagonda which was able to go faster. . . .

To me the magic of Wicken ended when the bridge was built across the Cam and the long dead end lane from Fordham to Wicken became a signposted holiday route from Birmingham to the East Coast. Up to then, to get from Cambridge to Wicken you bicycled along the muddy path on the flood bank of the Cam as far as Upware where there was an inn on the far bank and you shouted for a ferry and if the wind in the poplars was too strong nobody heard you and that was that. In large letters on the gable of the inn was painted 'Five miles from anywhere. No hurry' but one was in a hurry to catch one's first *palustris* [Marsh Moth]! It was safer to go the long way round through Fordham and double one's mileage. Once at Wicken you turned down the unmarked track to the fen. On the left was Barnes' cottage (the old keeper father of post-war Barnes), and from there to the lode the track was lined by diminutive half-timbered cottages with thatched roofs, each with a pocket-handkerchief sized garden full of flowers. If it was the right season *machaon* [Swallowtail] fluttered from garden to garden. I used to stay at Rose Cottage which lived up to its name. You could just stand upright in its rooms and the staircase was a glorified ladder. The

Fig. 66. The Five Miles from Anywhere — No Hurry (*c.* 1947). 'There was an inn on the far bank and you shouted for a ferry and if the wind in the poplars was too strong nobody heard you and that was that.' It caught fire in 1955 and was demolished a year later. A new inn stands on the site.

building regulations and modern hygiene have rightly seen that all these were destroyed. The gardens are now nettles, good for peacocks but no use for swallowtails which I believe anyhow no longer exist at Wicken.

Wicken was run by a body of well-to-do entomologists for entomologists. I was a subscriber. It was all rather like a Hampshire chalk stream with insects rather than trout as the quarry. I am certain m.v. light traps would have been banned as unsporting. When you arrived you first made your number with Barnes and paid him 10/-. He would allocate you a section of the main drove. At weekends in the *palustris* season the drove was fully booked. If you were Cockayne or Edelsten you got the section you wanted; if an unknown Cambridge undergraduate, a bit of the rest. After a good dinner (I remember a complete roast chicken with bread sauce being put before me) you strolled on to the fen where you would find that Barnes would have sugared your section of cork strips fixed to iron posts, put up a vertical sheet, lit an acetylene burner to illuminate the sheet and provided a table and chair. All you had to do was to catch the moths! Of course this was not all there was to it. There were larvae to search for and bushes and reed beds to explore for the geometridae. Best of all there was tea with Mrs. Barnes. Everyone in the fen made a point of being present and the beginner met the expert. This is where I first met Cockayne who was to become my friend and I his executor. Edelsten was the great wainscot man and was the only collector allowed to enter the reserve, which was the bottom end of the fen cut off from the rest by an unjumpable lode. This caused me great envy and I at once assumed that he was catching species previously unknown in Britain! . . .

On June 22nd (1927) Bernard Kettlewell, his mother and I went to Millook south of Bude in Cornwall for a week's collecting holiday. Millook was the best-known locality for *arion* [Large Blue]. We stayed at a farm known as the Lion's Den with a farmer of the name Burden. Mrs. Kettlewell was a very strong-minded woman. We went by rail to Bude and picnicked in the train. Nothing could be wasted so all the leftovers were collected into little parcels, the window was opened and the parcels thrown at any men seen working on the side of the line, who ducked in terror at this unexpected gift. We took a taxi on to Millook which is approached by a very steep hill down to the sea. As soon as the hill began to steepen the taxi was stopped and we were ordered out to walk to the bottom. Farmer Burden went regularly to Poundstock Market on his pony where he got very drunk and his friends would tie him on his pony for it to find its own way back. Mrs. Burden would untie him on his return. Mrs. Kettlewell witnessed this and was horrified.

Arion occurred on a steep south-eastern facing slope of short grass and thyme and gorse bushes. To make certain no-one missed the spot the owner had put up a notice "Do not catch the flies". It was said by the experts that the time to catch the flies was in the early morning before breakfast but we saw none. The weather was awful and we were probably too early. A Mr. Tongue took the first one of the season on the day we left. *Sinapis* [Wood White] was common but we only saw it on the one fine day. I caught a *repandata* [Mottled Beauty] variety, white with black bands, a beauty. I tossed Bernard for it and tossed the half-crown into a clump of brambles. We casually mentioned this to Burden and next time we passed, the clump had been cut to the ground. Half-a-crown was real money in those days. I got, and still have, the *repandata*. . . .

July 9 (1931). I left Aberdeen for Lerwick this morning accompanied by Pennington and Poore, both keen collectors but probably not as keen as I was. Pennington was a complete Edwardian and a long since extinct species. I suppose he was in his late fifties and was getting bald and with a big black spade beard. In fact he looked very much like Edward VII. His father had been Liberal M.P. for Guildford and Pennington, a bachelor, though he slept near Lancaster Gate, spent all day at the Reform Club where he was very difficult to dislodge. (I remember telephoning some exciting entomological news one evening. After a long wait a club servant replied "Mr Pennington does not speak on the telephone during the dinner hour." So he never got the news!). When he collected he carried a large silver hip flask which contained a mixture of marsala and soda-water and the trouble was that Unst was dry. Unst had until recently been the centre of the herring fishery where herring were cleaned, salted and barrelled for the Polish trade. The fishing crews got so horribly drunk that it was decided to make the whole island dry. In 1931 all the crews had gone but the dryness remained and consequently a large case of mixed drinks had preceded Pennington to the Nord Hotel at Baltasound, the island capital. This was permitted for visitors but the locals were not so lucky. The steamer 'The Earl of Zetland', the 'Old Earl' to avoid confusion with the modern boat, called twice at Unst and real drinking enthusiasts would bicycle down to the first port of call and as soon as the boat cast off the ship's bar would be open and they would drink steadily for half an hour until Baltasound was reached when they would push their bicycles unsteadily ashore. Luckily the Earl did not run daily! . . .

On this Unst expedition I had hired a car and the island was suffering an exceptional drought so that the peat hag was as hard as brick and I could drive the car to places which in a wet year it would have been impossible to reach. I drove the car well off the road one night and parked it so that the headlights shone down on the ground to see what would be attracted. Someone passing saw it and reported to the Island policeman "a car right off the road with its nose in a ditch. The driver must be dead or badly injured as he hasn't switched off his headlights." Out bicycled the policeman to find a busy lepidopterist at work and we both laughed at the report. Next night I was at Burra Firth . . . and I was seen from the lighthouse shore station slowly walking back and forth with my bright light. "Someone with a bright light poaching salmon" and out came the policeman on his bicycle and after a seven mile ride not so pleased to see me. "Please sir, tell me where you are going each night." I followed this good advice as next night I was on the cliffs of the west coast and my light was seen from the neighbouring island of Yell where no light had ever been seen before. Our policeman was again alerted: "Bright light half-way down the cliff near Petaster. Think there must be a wreck. Shall we call out the life-boat?" Our policeman did not tell me his reply. For the life-boat to have appeared below me crewed by eight lusty men of Shetland could have been an encounter I would have preferred to avoid. I might mention that on August 16th I collected under the aurora borealis which dimmed the value of my light. It was uncanny and impressive. Great beams of light like searchlights appearing over the northern horizon, getting brighter, flickering, fading, getting brighter again. I had no idea the aurora showed itself so early in the autumn. . . .

1949 was Annus Mirabilis! In early March I married Veronica Drake. In the summer the Robinson brothers ran the first m.v. light and it was the year of *lunaris* [Lunar Double-stripe], *compta* [Varied Coronet] and *büttneri* [Blair's Wainscot], though all three had been first found several years earlier.

Veronica was an ideal entomologist's wife. She quickly picked up the technical jargon and learnt her species and was just as keen as I was. When the rain was pouring down and I would say "Come on let's pack it up," she would say "Let's give it another half hour," and we were often rewarded. She was also a professional and highly-skilled electrical engineer so when m.v. lights came along and something went wrong, all I needed was to wait until light was restored. . . . We were again at Ham Street with our m.v. light on July 29, 30 and 31 and again between Sept. 8 and 13 and on this occasion there was a blue light deep in the woods and there were the Robinson brothers and I think Robin Mere, running their light off a petrol engine and generator. We could not let this go unchallenged so as soon as we were back in London we set about getting something similar. There were no neat little Japanese generators on the market then, but we found a firm in Acton who could marry a Villiers engine to a generator and fix them in a frame suitable for handling. The trouble was that it was far too heavy to move singlehanded and although I could lift it out of the back of the car I could not lift it back in again and Veronica's presence was always required. While it was being prepared, and this took a long time, we had to continue to plug into friendly houses. And how friendly the owners were! What we wanted to do often took some explaining but the answer was invariably "yes", and a great deal of trouble was taken in opening up outhouses or windows to give access to our cables and to other acts from rich or poor. I remember the steaming plates of sausage and bacon which came from a sergeant's wife when we plugged in to some barracks in Ash Vale near Aldershot, or "I've cooked you a little fish" from a lady in West Wales, well after midnight; or when we were connected to an expensive house on the edge of Sandwich golf course and a dinner party was taking place and the men came out in their dinner jackets (with drinks) after the ladies had retired to the drawing room; or the stately home in Hampshire where Ffennel[l] and I had our light on the lawn and the owner came out to say good night "I'm going to bed now. You will find whisky in the Library when you need it." Of course there were disasters too. We were staying near Nairn at a farm guest house and plugged our light into a disused turkey hut, and on testing there was a tremendous bang and a blue flash and a lot of smoke. The evening meal was nearly cooked. The proprietor explained to the guests that a cold meal would be substituted. A guest said she didn't mind provided she could have a nice cup of tea. No tea either! The farmer husband had not yet begun milking. No milking either. We had blown the main fuse and only the Electricity Board could replace it and with considerable charge, waived by them when I explained the circumstances, but no tea, no milking, no collecting that night. On another occasion, much later as we then had a Robinson trap, we plugged into an Irish farmhouse. What we didn't notice was a tethered goat and that we were within the limits of its chain. The goat exploring its territory dragged the chain across and completely decapitated the trap. . . .

[Demuth, R. P. 1984–1985. Reminiscences of an elderly entomologist. *The Entomologist's Record and Journal of Variation* **96**: 189–195; 264–272; **97**: 13–19; 46–50; 97–105].

> There was a young fellow named Harris,
> Who was honeymoon-making in Paris,
> But he rushed home to Kent
> With but half of it spent,
> When he heard that they'd taken *lunaris*.
>
> R.S.

[R. S. (Air Marshal Sir Robert Saundby) 1951. *Entomologist's Gazette* **2**: 108].

REMINISCENCES OF ANOTHER ELDERLY ENTOMOLOGIST

Brian O. C. Gardiner, Cambridge, Cambridgeshire. (2003)

Brian Gardiner (b. 1923) is well known for his studies of the Large White (*Pieris brassicae*) and, in particular its pale blue ab. *coerulea* Gardiner. He was educated at Uppingham and St Bartholomew's Hospital Medical School, where he studied anatomy and physiology, before deciding that a medical career was not for him. At this time he was offered a temporary post under Norman Riley in the Department of Entomology at the Natural History Museum, London — an offer that was readily accepted. Following this, he joined the Unit of Insect Physiology under Sir Vincent Wigglesworth at Cambridge.

He has written some 250 papers on various aspects of entomology and once bred 34,000 caterpillars of the Large White in three weeks.

Fig. 67. Brian Gardiner. He released 3000 butterflies at The Rolling Stones Hyde Park concert in 1969.

Although I do not remember it, my life as an entomologist started when I was about six or seven according to my mother, who repeated the tale on a number of occasions. During one of her tea parties little Brian took a dislike to a certain Mrs Blackie, wife of the local bank manager, so he went off into the cabbage patch, collected some caterpillars (*Pieris brassicae?*) and proceeded to put them onto the back of the good lady, much to mother's horror. No doubt I was suitably chastised, but if so it did not put me off collecting caterpillars.

My next lesson on entomology was that cricket takes precedence over collecting. At school in Sandgate (about 1936) I spotted on the sports pavilion a very large moth which was not unlike the Red Underwings I was already acquainted with. I was almost certain then, and still am with the benefit of hindsight, that it was a Clifden Nonpareil (*Catocala fraxini*). Before I could take action, it was my turn to bat and of course the moth had gone by the time I was bowled out for a respectable thirty-three runs — my only consolation. Sandgate, of course, is within moth-flying range of Lydd where Dr E. A. Cockayne and others had first taken it in 1935, and it continued to be found in this area of Kent into the 1950s.

My next memory of note is catching my first gynandromorph, a Holly Blue (*Celastrina argiolus*), at Dover while under 'light, desultory artillery fire' as my father called it. Although I have since bred a few gynandromorphs, this is the only one I have ever caught in the wild.

Looking back over the years it is the good things that spring to mind rather than the unpleasant. Although I have heard of vandalism and disapproval being directed at moth-hunters from certain members of the public, on the whole I have often found the latter both interested and, on a number of occasions, helpful — such as the local farmer at Chippenham Fen who, after a cold and unproductive night, offered us breakfast; eggs (then rationed) straight from the hen. On another occasion, when John Renouf and I went light-trapping to the controversial White Wood, Gamlingay, lugging our 2 cwt generator, we were spotted by a local landowner who promptly offered us several hundred yards of extension cable and the use of his mains supply. This was the night when we took the Heart Moth (*Dicycla oo*), the only recent record for Bedfordshire. So why is White Wood controversial? Because older records for some species, such as the Bath White, are recorded there for Cambridgeshire, when the wood is actually across the road in Bedfordshire. For many years too, Messrs Pye of Cambridge gave us the use of a generator whenever we wanted it. Weighing in at around 2 cwt it was not to be taken far from the car, but it did have the ability to support my 400 watt m.v. bulb.

Over the years, the majority of the hundreds of hours spent collecting have been humdrum and routine, although a few, for one reason or another, stand out and remain with happy thoughts in one's memory. I still remember the thrill of seeing and catching my first Swallowtail (*Papilio machaon*) on Wicken Fen. I never even thought then that less than 20 years later, using Norfolk stock, I would be breeding them by the hundred and taking them out to the fen in an attempt to re-establish them there after they had become extinct. In those days, having first obtained a permit from Dr Thorpe at the Department of Zoology, one cycled along the towpath of the river Cam until reaching the bank opposite the 'No Hurry, 5 Miles from Anywhere' Inn, rang the bell and took the sixpenny ferry over the river and hence on to Wicken. Swallowtails were first reported from the fen in 1851 by R. Julian (*Naturalist*, **1**: 170-171), who, with a party of undergraduates, had rowed up the river Cam and even carried their boat for half a mile overland, shooting birds and collecting eggs on the way.

Another early memory is the great migration year of 1947, spent chasing Clouded Yellows in the broiling heat in the neighbourhood of Hatfield Forest, accompanied by a charming young lady, also of an entomological turn of mind. Is that why I remember it rather than for my first ab. *helice*? Quy Fen, Cambridge, also has happy memories as it used to swarm with insects, including several species of the blues and skippers, as well as Mother Shiptons, Burnet Companions, Netted Heaths; but above all for the many dragonflies that inhabited the old coprolite pits, then large ponds and not at that time overgrown, and ideal for cooling off in the heat of the day or skinny dipping on a warm evening at midnight while living in the hope that the Marsh Moth (*Hydrillula palustris*) might turn up at the light. This moth had been first confirmed as British when recorded from there in the nineteenth century.

There was the occasion when Claude Rivers and I met up with Eric Classey and Robin Mere, but decided to go our separate ways: they to Woodwalton Fen as they were also after *palustris*, and us to Holme Fen, which was a more un-explored area. We found *palustris* and on going to Woodwalton just after dawn to announce our success what did we find? Why, just an abandoned car which had broken down in the middle of the fen and no *palustris* to match ours!

There is no telling what some people's reaction to insects may be. Together with some friends collecting at Hampstead Heath, we came across a hornet's nest in a hollow tree and proceeded to catch a few as they flew in and out. Soon a small crowd had collected, wondering what these mad people with nets were doing. Finally, showing them a hornet in a pill box and saying 'Hornets' their exodus was rapid. The highlight of the day, however, was John Riley's capture of *Volucella zonaria* (*Entomologist*, **79**: 247), the nest parasite of the hornet.

I was once showing an eminent doctor around an insectary where there was a large colony of nearly full-grown Garden Tiger (*Arctia caja*) caterpillars. Picking up a handful to show him he fled the building at a rate that would have made Sebastian Coe an 'also ran'. It turned out that he had an absolute conviction that hairy caterpillars were deadly poisonous and I do not think that my insouciance in handling them actually convinced him that some at least were not. Conversely, when showing insects to 7–11 year old children, those they liked to handle most were bird-eating spiders and the handsome *Dipetelogaster maxima*, the world's largest blood-sucking bug (4ml capacity).

Having handled millions of insects over the years I have been fortunate in never having had any allergic reactions to them. I was informed, however, some years after being stung by the larvae of the Venezuelan *Lonomia cynira* that most people were dead within hours. Fortunately for me they were harmless when fed on English beech and only deadly when they sequester the poison from the leaves of their normal South American foodplant.

[B. O. C. Gardiner, 2003. Reminiscences of an elderly entomologist. Unpublished].

AN ENTOMOLOGIST'S WIFE

Mrs Elizabeth E. Harper, Newtonmore, Inverness-shire. (1960)

Commander Geoffrey Withington Harper R.N. (1902–1973) lived in the Cairngorms, Inverness-shire, for twenty-one years and built up a large collection of Scottish butterflies and moths — said to be the most comprehensive collection ever made of the Scottish Macrolepidoptera. After training at the naval colleges of Osborne and Dartmouth the Commander served on a number of famous ships including *HMS Furious* and the ill-fated *HMS Hood*. In this article Mrs Betty Harper warns prospective entomological wives of the dangers that lie ahead.

This summer, my husband broadcast a short talk about his hobby of collecting moths, on "Woman's Hour". I wonder if I could give you the woman's point of view on this interesting activity?

I am the wife of a retired Commander, R.N., and the mother of a medical student son; both are rabid entomologists, and I don't know which is the worse.

My life has fascination, many complications, and not a few snags. To dewy-eyed young women about to marry, or toying with the idea of marrying an entomologist, I would not exactly give the advice "not at any price", but I do urge a little caution.

Entomology is a hobby which is all-absorbing. In some men I have seen it assume proportions almost amounting to mania as the men grow older and become more and more interested and involved.

The men with this hobby, or sometimes profession, represent a cross-section of society. Few women take it up on their own, perhaps because as a sex we intuitively foresee the snags involved. As for the men, I have known all the well-known professions involved. Admirals and Air Marshals, Parsons and Politicians, even an occasional Prime Minister, Doctors, Publicans and, paradoxically, Policemen too. Perhaps entomological Policemen are a little less tempted to break the law than the others. Men in settled jobs bordering on boredom are also intrigued. The Civil Service, Bankers, and those men known vaguely as "Something in the city", men drawn from all walks of life, some with titles and all kinds of decorations, all may be bitten by the bug of "bug-hunting" and join a closely-knit fraternity.

I think their wives fall into three categories. First, the very disapproving. These wives are mainly elderly; they have tried, but have had too much of it. Secondly, the very young women. These start married life in a flush of enthusiasm for their husband's hobby, and soon they find themselves involved in a morass of entomological apparatus, feeding larvae, hatching ova, breeding cages, tins and all the associated activities. Thirdly, the nit-wits. I myself fall into this category with the women who try to keep domestic order, their men-folk fed, and who know the commoner kinds of moth but are not expert in any way at all. We can, if the know-how is carefully explained to us, sometimes find pro-cryptic moths on tree trunks, caterpillars and chrysalids here and there; often indeed we spend our outings in this way. I think my category dislike the more austere forms and manifestations of the fever, such as collecting in the pouring rain, in a marsh, or hanging by one's eyebrows over the top of a high cliff at night in a howling gale. I have known entomological wives do all this and more without a qualm, and never lose their glamour or their hairset. To these women I pay due homage; they should have some kind of memorial.

If you do become an entomologist's wife, gone are your hopes of married and domestic security. Rather like a doctor's wife, you will be on call at all hours by your man and his entomological friends. In the spring and the autumn, as well as the summer, there is dusking and sugaring. For the benefit of the uninitiated, this means painting a patch on fence posts, tree trunks, or foliage with a sticky mixture of black treacle, beer and assorted flavourings such as rum or amylacetate. This is varied by your husband returning to see if the moths like the mixture at all hours of the night.

It may also mean complaints from the neighbours, and dealing with these, too, is also strictly an entomologist's wife's province, privilege, or however you view the matter!

Now, the question of cooking for a husband who is an entomologist. If you are a 'Cordon bleu' expert, or even just a very good cook, say good-bye for ever to such dishes as omelettes, hot soufflées, and the like. When your omelette or soufflée is looking mouth-watering and lovely, and should be eaten instantly, your husband will only say with maddening calm that he can't possibly eat it yet! He has fifty young caterpillars to feed, and that will take another 20 minutes at least. "Run away and don't bother me, there's a good girl", he will say cheerfully and thereafter (temporarily) forget your existence. So confine your cooking to meals that will not spoil if kept hot for an indefinite period.

Gone, too, are your hopes of a settled annual holiday. You will mention timidly to your husband how much you would like a fortnight of shopping, or even shop-gazing, a few new clothes and gaiety in some fashionable sea-side resort. If you have married an entomologist, he will say: "Nonsense! my dear girl, such and such a moth emerges in the wilds of Norfolk . . . Scotland . . . or Ireland, and I particularly want you to come with me and hold the lamp, or feed the caterpillars, or some other strictly entomological job". He will add, absently, "Don't bring too many clothes, will you? because I shall have to bring so much gear myself!" This latter statement is only too true, and eventually we set off with an unlimited number of tins, jars, nests of glass-topped boxes, paraffin lamps, methylated spirits, treacle. Caterpillars which have to be fed must of course come too, and add to these the eggs about to emerge into tiny caterpillars, chrysalids about to emerge into moths, and maybe a temperamental female moth which your husband wishes to lay eggs for him, and which must be coaxed into ovipositing with a mixture of sherry and treacle! All this is no exaggeration and strictly truthful. Nowadays the inevitable mercury vapour outfit comes too. This last item is a decided snag to an entomologist's wife. Mercury vapour lamps give forth a rather ghastly blue light, and are a great attraction for moths. Clever entomologists have adapted these electrically so that they can run them off car batteries, from the household supply, from fearsome (so called) portable engines which can be carried up mountains, on to bogs, the cliffs, the sea-shore, or wherever the moths occur. The entomologists themselves are so used to the mercury vapour outfit by now that they take it for granted as an absolute necessity.

BUT. The neighbours, the Police, the Customs, the Coastguards and the gamekeepers are not always so well informed. They see a strange and rather horrible bright blue light at night and immediately assume that anyone out at that hour must be poaching, smuggling, burgling, or engaging in some other nefarious activity.

Many times, as an entomologist's wife, I have soothed down officialdom, alarmed householders, and the like. One and all, they find it difficult to believe that anyone out late at night can be up to any good. They are also difficult to persuade that anyone who is engaged in really criminal activities would never advertise their presence with a noisy engine and a bright blue light.

Still, all this is just part of an entomologist's wife's duty, and with me now, it is all routine. Many famous stories have been told of well-known entomologists, in the two world wars, being arrested as beautiful blonde spies. This I can understand perfectly. To entomologists, war is an incident, a nuisance, but not to be taken seriously at any cost. They are quite unaware of anything except the moth, the caterpillar, which they must obtain in some particular place, at the precise time of the year when it occurs. They are oblivious of wars, and similar complications. My husband, in the last war, often spent his spare moments ashore at his favourite hobby. In uniform or in plain clothes he was often suspected, and sometimes this could be alarming, or annoying.

To go from the wartime experiences to peacetime. One of the best-known entomologists of my acquaintance was once a policeman. On his beat one night he saw the extraordinary phenomenon of a parson who had climbed up a lamp-post. To his query "what's going on here?", the parson, being an entomologist, was not one whit abashed. He simply slid down the lamp-post and explained to the policeman how moths are attracted to light, so that in the end the policeman became so intrigued that he became a famous collector.

I hope that I have made you see, as future entomologists' wives something of the fascination as well as the complications of this way of life. For myself, undoubtedly, I get irritated to the point of exasperation, but not for anything would I miss meeting these famous and learned men, and their usually stoical and sometimes learned wives. I too am always learning and, speaking purely in the third category of the nit-wit, I might someday do or learn something useful. Who knows? At least one never leads a dull life.

[Harper, E. E. 1960. An entomologist's wife. *The Entomologist's Record and Journal of Variation* **72**: 169–171].

THE WEST COUNTRY REVISITED

Walter Dannatt, F.Z.S., Blackheath, London, S. E. (1909)

Contrary to my usual custom of spending my holiday on the Continent, I last season decided to give old England another trial. Having re-read a very interesting article by Mr. A. E. Gibbs in the 'Entomologist' (vol. 39) on a holiday he spent at Polzeath, and what specimens he collected there, I decided to follow out Mr. Gibbs's directions, and accordingly caught the 6.20 a.m. train from Waterloo (a comfortable corridor), which did not stop between London and Salisbury. At Okehampton we had to change into a slower train, but the scenery being so beautiful one did not regret the slower progress. I reached Wadebridge at one o'clock; it had been raining, and I at once inquired at the station about a conveyance for getting my stock of treacle, carbide, "setting house," and other heavy luggage taken the seven miles. As luck would have it there was a carrier going that way there and then. I next asked about accommodation; one man informed me he knew of no place where one could stay, but the carrier's boy, who now came upon the scene, informed me that there was a lady who "took people in," and I felt greatly relieved until the boy added he did not know if the lady in question was "full up" or not. However, I decided to risk it, and immediately made for the Station Hotel, and, having lunched, the rain seeming over, I mounted my bike and made a start. After a mile or so the rain came on again so much so that I took shelter under some trees; after some time I donned my waterproof suit and decided to ride through it, the clouds cleared, and it was then pleasant travelling, and at length I reached Polzeath. I was told the name was originally Hayle, and it was altered because the people would insist on pronouncing it as if it was the infernal regions.

I found the lady was "full up," and I had to search elsewhere. The next Cove, Trebetherick, contained a boarding-house, principally used by golfers, but was then almost empty, and Mr. Buse, the landlord, made me very comfortable, the *ménage* was excellent, and the charges were very moderate. There are only two or three more houses in the place, and these are farms. The spot is really just at the mouth of the river Camel (from which Camelford takes its name). A few minutes' walk brought me down to the sea (or river, whichever one likes to call it). It seemed an ideal spot for "sugaring" — there was a row of posts, also sand-hills, and a field of thistles and ragwort — and I decided to give it a trial the same evening; but, alas, the only thing I took out of the common was *Agrotis valligera* [Archer's Dart], one specimen; *Leucania conigera* [Brown-line Bright-eye], *L. lithargyria* [The Clay], and, of course, the ubiquitous *Xylophasia polyodon* [Dark Arches] were plentiful.

The next day I decided to search for Mr. Gibbs' spot, so fully described, as before stated; having discovered it, I decided to work it the same evening. I may say along the road during the afternoon I discovered a wing of *Agrotis lunigera* [Crescent Dart] in a spider's web, so I knew one of the moths which I had hoped to get was about. I had never taken this species,

although I had tried Freshwater for it, but Mr. A. J. Hodges told me the time of appearance given by Newman is incorrect, and that is probably the reason why I had never captured the insect. I took but one specimen of *lunigera* that night. I think the place must have altered considerably since Mr. Gibbs was there; there are very few posts, and they are across a ditch and much overgrown with foliage. The other Leucanias I have mentioned appeared again. The next night I was more successful, and secured three *lunigera*; altogether I captured seven during my stay. I saw nothing of *Neuria saponariæ* [Bordered Gothic], *Hadena adusta* [Dark Brocade], and *Triphæna interjecta* [Least Yellow Underwing]; never having previously taken these species, I was naturally disappointed. Mr. Gibbs thinks a house is now built on the spot where he used to get them. *M. rivata* [Wood Carpet] and *E. mensuraria* [Shaded Broad-bar] were netted. I was detained a whole week by the English weather (I won't say climate). An American, on being asked what he thought of our English climate, replied, "I guess you ain't got no climate, it's all weather," and this is generally true so far as my experience goes.

The first fine sunny day I rose at seven, and cycled to St. Ives. As this article is for a scientific journal, I must not give too much of what, for want of a better appellation, I may call "domestic" news. I will then not give details of the very pleasant spin over the moors, up hill and down dale, in the fifty-five miles' spin to St. Ives. At Hayle Bay the sand-hills are enormous, reminding one of the Boulogne–Abbeville route. Large quantities of red valerian and wild flowers are found along the cliffs at St. Ives, but I netted nothing of importance. Delayed a few hours next day by the weather again, I was late in leaving for Land's End; I found a comfortable hotel there, and a landlord that Charles Dickens might have made use of. He told me that if I purchased curiosities and other things he had for sale and sent them to my friends, they would exclaim, "How kind it is of my friend to send me these pretty things." Well, to return to the Lepidoptera. I treacled rocks and flowers suitable to hold that substance, and the result was the common species before mentioned. It was very lovely at Land's End, the sun was shining brightly when I left, and I had an enjoyable spin to Penzance, went over St. Michael's Mount; but if one has visited Mont St. Michel in Normandy, it is only a waste of time to visit the English mount. I, however, discovered some *Silene maritima* [sea campion] in the castle grounds. I had been searching in vain for this plant in Polzeath in hopes of getting *Dianthœcia barrettii* [Barrett's Marbled Coronet]; although I found some plants on my return, and visited them by night, I saw nothing of the moth. Having trained to Truro, I rode the rest of the way *viâ* Padstow Ferry to Rock (but I don't advise anyone to go this way, at least, not with a bicycle), and reached Polzeath in time to treacle the same night.

Having sent home some of my luggage, I left for Tintagel and Boscastle, sugared along the cliffs of the latter place, but had no luck. At Bude I found a few sand-hills, and had the same bad luck with regard to captures. The most charming spot I think I have ever seen (Clovelly) was reached the next day, and thence, *viâ* Bideford and Barnstaple, to the famous Braunton Burrows. I stayed at a very comfortable golf house at Saunton, above the Burrows; the latter comprise three miles of sand-hills. Finding no posts I sugared flowers, but nothing other than common species were taken. I cycled the three miles on the sands to the lighthouse, and then found I was opposite Instow, from which place I once, years ago, joined some entomological friends and went for a picnic to the lighthouse; I had no idea it was Braunton Burrows at that time. I collected a quantity of sticks, stuck them in the sand-hills, and sugared them the same evening, but the same bad luck attended me.

I may mention I was trying a new experiment on this tour; instead of "papering" my captures (readers may ask what captures? and with reason, for as yet I had very few), I was setting everything I took while fresh, and for this purpose was carrying a "drying-house" with me on the front "luggage-carrier" of my bicycle; this mode of setting things when fresh is much preferable to relaxing and setting specimens after one's return home. I always experience a difficulty in relaxing and setting British moths when once they have become dry, the antennæ are almost always stiff and refuse to go in the desired position. Mr. Newman's new relaxing-tin may overcome this trouble; so far I have found it very useful, I have left an insect in for over a month without any appearance of mould. After leaving Braunton I made for Barnstaple, and soon got on the Lynton Road, which, winding as it does in and out along the valleys over moors in places and through woods occasionally, makes cycling very enjoyable. A sharp descent brings one into the picturesque village of Paracombe.

At length one arrives at the model town of Lynton, which owes its popularity largely to Sir George Newnes, M.P. A long and steep descent, rather too rough to ride down with any pleasure, and one is in the bright little village of Lynmouth. After having selected an hotel, I made my way along the Lynn in search of the hemp-agrimony, and noting two or three likely looking places, visited these later in the evening and was rewarded by a specimen of *Toxocampa craccæ* [Scarce Blackneck]. This moth does not settle like a butterfly, with closed upright wings as I expected, but like a *Triphæna*. I stayed three days longer in hopes of taking additional specimens, but saw no more. Along the Lynn immense quantities of valerian are found, and the cottage-gardens are full of it. It grows along the cliffs in profusion, and this is its natural habitat I conclude. In the daytime the agrimony is a tremendous attraction for all kinds of insects. *Macroglossa stellatarum* [Humming-bird Hawk-moth], the Vanessidæ, Theclas [Hairstreaks], and many other lepidopterous insects I saw, as well as Hymenoptera, etc., in quantities.

On leaving Lynmouth I was told I should have a three-mile walk up Countessbury Hill before I could mount my cycle, but by the aid of my 50-inch Pedersen gear I only had to push my machine for about one mile. The road continues undulating for some distance just skirting Exmoor until one reaches Minehead, where the coast is very flat. The Exeter route was now followed, passing the quaint little town of Dunster. The road winds along the valleys, and is practically downhill to Exeter. I stopped a night at Star Cross, but Dawlish Warren, like Deal and so many of our collecting-grounds, is being ruined by golfers; besides this, a railway-station has been built there, and numerous bungalows, so that there is not much ground left from an entomological point of view.

I did some hedge-beating one afternoon in hopes of disturbing *Callimorpha hera* [Jersey Tiger], when I heard a voice say, "You won't get *hera* there, it is too dusty." I turned round and saw a clergyman in a trap with a harmonium; he informed me that he it was who first discovered the species there, but, he said, "*hera* is not a coast insect, it is a garden insect," and added, "you would be more likely to find it in the lanes at the back, away from the main road." This I tried, but was not fortunate enough to get a specimen; the only thing I netted was a dwarf *Pieris rapæ* [Small White] exactly one inch across the wings. Feeling a bit sick of seeing my setting-boards so empty I decided to look up my friend Mr. Walker, of Torquay; this I did, and he took me to his spot for *Leucania putrescens* [Devonshire Wainscot]; we got a dozen each the same night.

I was informed that it was no use trying to catch this insect before 10 p.m.; if netted they are so wild that they soon become useless as specimens. Mr. Walker put me up to a dodge that was entirely new to me. When there are no posts or suitable places to treacle, cut a number of flower-heads of the wild carrot, treacle these and place them about in hedges and other convenient places.

We went to a fen out Newton Abbot way one night, but owing to a puncture I was not able to be there in time to sugar. *T. pastinum* [Blackneck] is found there; the only thing at all out of the common which I got was *Noctua umbrosa* [Six-striped Rustic]. Leaving Torquay, the next day I cycled to Exeter and trained home, after a very enjoyable twenty-three days, having seen perhaps the best of Cornwall and Devon.

I may say my "drying-house" travelled over the two hundred and sixty odd miles, much of which was literally, "up hill and down dale," admirably; hardly a pin or brace was loose. Of course I had some "packing," consisting of some of my clothes outside the "drying-house" to lessen the jolting. I should like to add that I am desiring a companion for a three-months' collecting trip to the West Indies, starting in May.

[Dannatt, W. 1909. Entomology in Cornwall and Devon in July, 1908. *The Entomologist* **42**: 67–71].

FURTHER REMINISCENCES OF A BUTTERFLY HUNTER

Revd John N. Marcon, M.A., Pulborough, Sussex. (1980)

At an early age most boys collect something, whether it is stamps, birds' eggs, cigarette cards, coins or even match-boxes. At nine or ten the craze overtook me: stamps and cards were the first enthusiasm. A cousin gave me an 8 in. storebox with a set *Arctia caja* [Garden Tiger] in it. How proud I was of the bright colours of this moth; it was frequently fished out of the playbox to show other boys at school.

Not much was added for a couple of years, but on a holiday at South Brent in Devonshire, walking up a lane several butterflies were spotted, including a Silver-washed Fritillary. The excitement was renewed; my father hastily made me a sort of frame from strong wire, whilst my mother sewed me up a homely net; and I sallied forth up the same lane with delight and expectation.

Moths and butterflies were alike in their attraction in those days and any unoffending specimen imprisoned by the windowpane was added to the collection. I even put a moth into my spectacle case when out on a training day in the O.T.C. at Puttenham, discovered among the heather whilst preparing to charge! Light and sugar were activities after a first visit to the New Forest in 1922. I can still remember the thrill of catching the first *valesina* [bronze-coloured female variety of the Silver-washed Fritillary]. But time for day and night pursuit of the hobby became inevitably restricted by the need for studying for a degree: so the craze had to be limited; butterflies were chosen, and it was not long 'ere an aberration became a very special acquisition.

What an excitement it is for an entomologist to see a variety! They are always rare and requiring numbers of insects, much persistence and good fortune. It is a thrill which exceeds almost everything in life. It may be only a good minor, but the heart beats faster; and if a major it arouses the blood pressure to fever pitch! It may be minutes or hours or even days before the prize is safely in the pill-box, but what a sensation it is!

In days gone by one used to reckon on the capture of one good variety each year and be satisfied with that: often fortune favoured an expansion of this, and some years quite a considerable enlargement. It was rare for all species to be scanty — as is our misfortune today; there were almost always one or two that were prolific, if one could discover which

they were in time and have the leisure for a massive assault on their habitat; and then the fun and the dogged pursuit began!

1933 was an exceptionally early spring and very warm — almost June weather for three weeks. A visit to Pamber Forest on May 22nd proved this; *Argynnis euphrosyne* [Pearl-bordered Fritillary] males were worn and over, though a few females were about in reasonable condition. It was a week later, my car having a punctured radiator, that a friend took me from Chingford to Fisherlane, Dunsfold. Three or four other collectors had already arrived. *Argynnis selene* [Small Pearl-bordered Fritillary] being the main quarry as it was well out. I was fortunate in seeing my first var. *confluens* the other side of a ditch; the sight made me so nervous it seemed many minutes before I could catch it. Walking a few yards further a female *euphrosyne* was fluttering along, divided between nectar from a late flowering Bugle and finding a suitable violet on which to lay an egg. Better have a look at it came the thought and the net was brought into play. It looked normal on the upperside, but in captivity the underside quickly showed the pearly spots on the hindwings to be black. F. W. Frohawk figures it in his *Varieties of British Butterflies*, plate 13 — ab. *ater-marginalis*. The only regret was it should have been caught a week earlier.

Next year, living at Worthing, a young Balliol man came and asked to borrow some setting boards. At the inevitable discussion amongst collectors he said he had been up Salvington Hill to a wood at the top of the Downs where he'd seen four or five *Polygonia c-album* [Comma]; and one was a 'black devil' similar to var. *suffusa* by F. W. Frohawk. Needless to say we set off at once to the wood through which a track ran. Hunting for one and a half hours produced no result save the sight of one hen *c-album*, quite typical. We gave up the search disconsolate — and for my part incredulous. In the afternoon my wife suggested a picnic somewhere with the children. The locality for a bughunter provided no difficulty — the wood on top of Salvington Hill! Back and forth I traipsed, in and out of glades but no sign of the 'black devil'. At last returning to the car a *c-album* was spotted sunning himself high up on a hazel leaf. With a jump the net was in reach — quite normal. Sighting two others higher up, a long pole from the car had to be fetched. Alas, these were types too! At the end of the track where the car was parked, there low down on a bush was the coveted trophy. It has not fallen to my lot to capture as many of this form as Major-General Lipscomb has of a similar form of *Aglais urticae* [Small Tortoiseshell] — his must be a record with the net — but the luck of the game has provided opportunity of securing three *c-album* v. *suffusa* (or, no-doubt wrong-headedly, as I should prefer to call them v. *nigrocaria*!).

Next day the New Forest was visited and a stay with Mr and Mrs Clarke. They were always most hospitable: a note says she always gave us two eggs and four rashers for breakfast 'to stimulate the hunt' — what price that nowadays? And one slept in a feather bed: once down one slept in the billows around and could hardly move — not that one wanted to after 6-8 hours on the slog! Clarke said he had missed a good *Argynnis cydippe* [High Brown Fritillary] in Roe Wood and a black *Limenitis camilla* [White Admiral] in Frame Wood. We decided to start with Roe, indeed stayed all day as *cydippe* were fairly numerous. Mr Bright and his chauffeur had been there the day previously. Clarke stayed in one corner of a clearing with bushes and brambles, I in another. He was determined to catch what he called the 'Covered Wagon' — I think that was the name of a song. Whenever we met he started to sing the 'Covered Wagon', have you seen it yet? No. After half an hour an odd beast was spotted: could it be the black hindwing one? It settled in an awkward place which took ten minutes to approach circumspectly, and then only from underneath with three others on some thistles. All four were swept into the net and one was a slightly suffused hindwing female *cydippe*. The ticker added a few beats, but this was not IT. Five minutes later there was a shout from Clarke; he'd just missed the 'Covered Wagon'. We chased madly round and eventually he to his corner. Presently there was a wild yell: he had boxed the 'Covered Wagon'. It was the finest *cydippe* variety I had as yet seen — black hindwings with marginal fulvous spots and the forewings heavily fasciated. Needless to say we arrived home exhausted but exuberant: and did we down some cider?

Later that year a picnic with the family was the cause of another delight. We had gone to the top of Chantry Hill, Storrington. The advantage of taking the car to the top, as one can still do today was a desideratum; the view on both sides is magnificent. Within a few moments I was on the North face of the Down, and a second or two later amongst the dozen or so *Polyommatus icarus* [Common Blue] flying was a pink one. 'There's a variety here', I stupidly shouted to the others, engaged in removing the tea basket from the boot. 'Stupid' because one should never speak when something good is sighted: it may fly away or, more likely, one would miss the prize. However it kindly obliged in flying around and was plainly visible amongst the others — presumably a kind of albino. F. W. Frohawk figures it in his *Varieties of British Butterflies, var. opalizans*, plate 28 (though it is more striking than in the copy I have).

It is never the expected that happens. In mid-July 1939 I went to the Chiddingfold Woods, with the intention of working what fritillaries were available, starting in the Hambledon area Vann Copse, where the Craske brothers had collected with success: then moving to High Street Green, where a meadow by a stream invited inspection. Somewhat surprisingly *Aphantopus hyperanthus* [Ringlet] were abundant and a certain number netted in the hopes of a var. *lanceolata*. Working leisurely before long an odd one was seen; the rings round the underside spots were smoky yellow, not clean yellow. This induced a more exacting search. Before long an even odder one was in the net, an underside with a large

deep black patch on one hindwing and the yellow veins showing through distinctly. It was figured in the *South London Entomological Society Proceedings* 1939/40. Melanic? Yes. Homeotic? No-one seems to know as yet. The day ended with another smoky one rather better than the first. It looks as if all three are linked together with the same gene. It then rained in torrents, the car was bogged and only when three men came along were we able, with the aid of sacks, to get it on the highway again!

Beeding proved prolific that same year for *Lysandra coridon* [Chalk Hill Blue]. Several collectors were at work there and at Erringham Down. One used to start at the latter in the morning, the former in the evening. The tally included some not met with before, a bluey-black one v[ar]. *plumbescens*, three *pulla*, four *viridescens* and a well-marked gynandromorph: but the best of the bunch came from Beeding, when the sun was so warm that the blues were flipping off their perch at 6 p.m. Waiting until a cloud obscured it one hastened to the chalk pit, examining the undersides up the path; and there in the pit itself, visible several yards away was a heavily marked male *ultra-radiata*. Two days later working along the Down from the pit a curious male was flying, which seemed in the sunshine to have only two wings. It

Fig. 68. J. C. B. 'Jack' Craske, who captured a female *ultra radiata* Holly Blue and a halved gynandromorph within the space of twenty minutes one hot summer's day on the North Downs in 1944.

Fig. 69. R. M. 'Bob' Craske was 'the most famous and successful variety hunter to ever live in Sussex. He was the last of the line of a family of collectors, which commenced with his great grandfather during the 1840s'. (Colin Pratt, *British Journal of Entomology and Natural History*, 2001). See Plate 3.

proved to be a fresh halved gynandromorph. One couldn't believe it!

Mr Castle Russell tells of how he and his wife were examining *coridon* at Danbury, one of his favourite collecting grounds. As they sat down to lunch his wife asked, 'What luck?' 'Nothing as usual', he replied. 'Then why didn't you catch that *semi-syngrapha* close by?' The question was repeated. 'All right then', and he got up to catch it — it was a halved gynandromorph! On another occasion he was alone, away for a week. Having hunted fruitlessly for three days he was about to abandon it and go home. On the point of entering the car he noticed alongside it one of the best *ultra-radiata* females ever taken. He decided to stay the week as planned!

[Marcon, J. N. 1980. Further reminiscences of a butterfly hunter. *The Entomologist's Record and Journal of Variation* **92**: 34–37].

The two Craske brothers were amongst the most successful of all aberration collectors. But they were private and independent, which may explain why both their names and collections are rather less familiar than those of people such as John Marcon and Sidney Castle Russell.

John Christopher Beadnell Craske (1902–1958) started to collect butterflies seriously after returning to Sussex from a seven years' spell tea planting in southern India. In 1932 he formed a collecting partnership with his brother Robert which lasted until his death. John's obituarist, Alan Collier (1959), suggested that:

Immense enthusiasm, inexhaustible patience, and extremely hard work contributed to his success in the field, where it was always a delight to meet him. One of his most enduring qualities was his genuine and generous appreciation of another collector's modest captures. Many of us must have felt that perhaps, after all, some of our geese were really swans!

Robert 'Bob' Mervyn Craske (1909–2001) was described in his obituary (Pratt, 2001) as:

A brave and modest winner of the Military Cross, successful Empire Games long-distance runner, and a practical joker, Craske was a remarkable, utterly charming, and quirky man of military bearing who positively loved butterflies; he was also the most famous and successful variety hunter to ever live in Sussex. . . . A great but quiet philanthropist, and utterly addicted to collecting . . .

Fig. 70. Two remarkable underside aberrations of the Chalk Hill Blue taken by Bob Craske (x 1¼). *Top*: male ab. *extrema* Bright & Leeds. Pitstone Hill, Tring, Hertfordshire. 1952. *Bottom*: female ab. *extrema* Bright & Leeds. Beachy Head, Sussex. 1947.

One discovery he made, and which brought him particular pleasure, was that of a previously overlooked aberration of the Marbled White (*Melanargia galathea*), a species in which major variation is but rarely encountered. Ralph Tubbs (1978) later named it after him: ab. *craskei* Tubbs.

Rupert Barrington (pers. comm.) considered that although the Craske brothers were perhaps less well known than some other collectors:

For sheer concentrated thoroughness they stood alone. Jack even spent one night sleeping, or trying to, at the base of Shoreham Down one particularly good year so that he could get first crack at it in the morning. But he got nothing. Bob (who came down by train) met him looking tired and dishevelled as he was walking into town for breakfast.

Bob's son Peter remembers his father 'insisting that we hide our nets and, on occasion, lie full length on the down whenever a Lewes–Eastbourne train went by one locality', in case they were spotted by a rival collector. '[A]nd it was always a point of honour for him to be very reticent about his success if he should meet another collector on the down. "No, very little here. Peter and I were just thinking about going!"' Another occasion he recalled was Bob and Jack returning from a collecting trip and discussing their catches — much to the alarm of women riding in the same train compartment:

On overhearing Jack inform Bob that he'd 'got an absolutely marvellous female. Black as night!', and that he was taking home in the hope of persuading her to breed, I remembered a woman getting out at the very next station and secreting herself in the "Ladies Only" compartment immediately behind the driver.

WEST COUNTRY TOUR

An Old Moth-Hunter. (1953)

In this article Phillip B. M. Allan (1884–1973), the doyen of entomological story-tellers, recounts memories of a collecting trip to the West Country in 1900. Although he was only sixteen at the time, the memory of this trip was such that he was able to recall it in detail no less than fifty-three years later.

When I was sixteen I made an entomological expedition by bicycle into the West Country; for in those days I collected and I wanted to add several species to the cabinet which an indulgent parent had given me. The maker of the bicycle called it a "road racer"; but before the coming of the motor-car there were precious few country roads on which one could 'race'. In dry weather most of them were blanketed with dust two to four inches thick and in wet weather the potholes were miniature ponds of similar depth.

I wandered through Dorset, stopping wherever the mood took me — which was quite often, for the bicycle and I did not agree on the subject of road racing — and I remember making a sketch of stocks on a village green — I think it was one of the several villages called Gussage which were dedicated to various saints. Doubtless the stocks have long since been used for firewood. On heaths I found *Plebeius argus* [Silver-studded Blue] and, here and there in chalky spots, *Cupido minimus* [Small Blue]. This little butterfly always seems — in my experience — to have rather restricted habitats. One never finds it in profusion over a hundred and more acres as one does *Lysandra coridon* [Chalk Hill Blue] and other Blues, at least I never have. Even on such a wide expanse as Newmarket Heath it is confined to a few acres. *Leucophasia sinapis* [Wood White] was common, on 26th July, in Burlescombe Wood, Somerset, and perhaps it is common there still, if the wood has not been felled.

On the 27th of July it rained. Not just summer showers but a dour, soulless, downpour which soon had me wet to the skin. Strapped inside the frame of my bicycle was a more or less triangular case — (Good God! says the purist; how on earth can a triangle be "more or less"? — Pay no attention, reader — the bottom angle was square) — which fitted the frame of the bicycle nicely and was about four or five inches thick. In

Fig. 71. 'Far from the Madding Crowd'. Entomological illustrator, enthusiastic lepidopterist and a president of the British Butterfly Conservation Society, Gordon Beningfield (1936–1998) in Hardy country, near Powerstock, Dorset (*c.* 1980). See Plate 4. This idyllic photo is evocative of P. B. M. Allan's youthful excursion.

this were stored my spare shirt, vest and socks, sleeping suit, shaving tackle (perhaps 'down-remover' would be more accurate considering my age), bath-sponge, soap, towel, hair-brushes, and entomological impedimenta. All these things, especially the sponge, had a great attraction for the rain. When I reached Moreton Hampstead I was in much the same condition as a Persian cat which has been floating about off the port of Basra for a week or two.

The White Hart inn looked inviting, so I dismounted, discarded the bicycle, and asked if I could have a meal and my clothes dried. The landlady, who was a fat motherly woman, took me to a bedroom, told me to strip and put my clothes outside the door, and in an hour they would be returned to me dried and a hot meal ready. Till then I was to lie in bed. So I lay naked in bed until a pretty young maid came in with my clothes and told me that dinner would be ready in five minutes. I told her not to be in a hurry to go, so she sat down beside the bed and put her arms around my neck and kissed me. . . . She really was very pretty, and I was very young. . . . I thought this was an excellent introduction to Devonshire. However, she was afraid that mistress would come up after her if she didn't hurry, so off she went, and I got into my warm dry clothes.

When I came downstairs I was shown into a parlour with a cheerful fire, and presently the little maid brought in a large roast fowl, a steaming hot boiled gammon, and a truly royal dish piled high with potatoes and French beans. The accoutrements were a quartern loaf (home baked), half a pound of butter, and a large round cheese. If I had been hungry when I arrived I was ravenous by now, and I consumed the whole of the fowl except bones and chitin and most of the gammon. I also ate the best part of the loaf and nearly — but not quite — all the vegetables, at least half the butter, and a considerable lump of cheese. These were washed down with a pint of good ale — very different from the stuff one is served with today. When I had finished my meal the landlady brought me half a pint of "sherry wine" to "keep off the chill". I was only sixteen, but I manfully deposited this also in the correct receptacle. I then pulled up an armchair before the fire and felt that I should not require anything further to eat for several days.

When I awoke the rain had stopped, so I paid the reckoning (which probably did not exceed two shillings), kissed the pretty little maid, mounted my road racer, and departed. But I don't think I rode very fast after that meal and I expect the bicycle wobbled a bit. Later in the day I arrived at a little beerhouse in a desolate spot which seemed to be plumb in the middle of Dartmoor. It was called Warren House and a more uninviting place I had never stayed at before, having previously led a somewhat sheltered life. I could not foresee that there would be many days, and nights, in years to come when such a house, with walls and roof intact, would seem to me the height of luxury! The landlord, having looked me up and down, scrutinised my throat, apparently so that he would know exactly where to cut, and the landlady seemed to be wondering how much money I had on me and what my clothes and shoes would be worth. I felt very lonely and far from aid. . . . Actually, they were excellent folk, and they fed me well. I stayed the night, a daughter giving up her room to me, and in the morning my throat was intact and the money in my trouser pocket ditto. Next day the sun shone and I netted *Argynnis aglaia* [Dark Green Fritillary], fresh and frisky, as they flew about the old workings of the long-abandoned Vitifer tin mines. Again I doubt if my reckoning, which included a vast breakfast, amounted to more than a shilling or two.

Fifty-one years later I came to the Warren House once more and found that except for an outhouse or two it looked very much as it did at the time of my first visit. But the road was now a motor road, and the little beerhouse probably sold more liquor in a week than it formerly did in a month, at least in summertime. While I was renewing acquaintance with it my wife found four full-grown larvae of *Anarta myrtilli* [Beautiful Yellow Underwing] on the ling overhanging a bank at the side of the road. I should never have found them in a month of Sundays, so perfect was their procrypsis.

Next day I bicycled to Dartmouth and found *Melanargia galathea* [Marbled White] flying everywhere. I had never caught this butterfly before, so I made hay while the sun shone. Then I turned back coastwise and was beset by *galathea* all the way to Bridport. In a narrow hillside lane above Dawlish a brilliant tigermoth was cavorting in the hot sunshine. I recognised "hera" as we then called it; for in the early 'nineties the magazines had had a good deal to say about *Euplagia quadripunctaria* [Jersey Tiger]. But by the time my net was ready the insect had disappeared in a cottage garden and although I lent over the hedge and watched for some time it did not reappear. Shortly afterwards another, with yellow wings, flew across the lane. I pottered about all afternoon but did not see any more.

At the top of the hill into Charmouth a man asked me if I had seen a lion, as one had escaped from a travelling circus the previous night. As I was armed only with a butterfly-net I took the hill in top gear and let the road racer race. The initial note of a donkey braying on the other side of the hedge caused my legs to revolve almost as fast as the spokes of the bicycle. At Lulworth Cove I lay face downwards on the grass near the top of the cliff while little brown butterflies flew about me in plenty. But I was chary about harming the colony, so took only six and felt guilty at that.

Thence I made my way to Salisbury, and on the hills named Dean, Pepper-box, and Whiteparish *L. coridon* [Chalk Hill Blue] and *Hesperia comma* [Silver-spotted Skipper] were abundant and in perfect condition. I knew nothing about aberrations in those days so took about half a dozen of both sexes of each species, all of them as normal as could be. Indeed I think I should probably have discarded an aberration as being an imperfect specimen. At Streatley-on-Thames I found that the colony of *Lysandra bellargus* [Adonis Blue] which I had discovered there a few years previously was still flourishing, with *H. comma* and *L. coridon* all about the chalk hills on both sides of the river. So far as I remember it did not rain again after I left Moreton Hampstead.

Those were happy days and perhaps even happier in retrospect. *O mihi praeteritos referat si Jupiter annos!*

[An Old Moth-Hunter (P. B. M. Allan). 1953. West Country tour. *The Entomologist's Record and Journal of Variation* **65**: 355–357].

P. B. M. Allan, the 'Old Moth-Hunter', wrote his own obituary notice and this was published in *The Entomologist's Record* the year following his death in 1973.

O. M. H.

The auto-obituary of the late P. B. M. Allan appears here-under having just come to light from beneath a collection of dry *leaves* eminently suitable for pupation.

BENEATH THIS TREE LIE
THE EXUVIAE
OF
AN OLD MOTH-HUNTER
WHO WENT TO EARTH
The 31st Day of December 1973.

From earthly *cage* by *Atropos* set free
His hope is *pinned* to Immortality;
Mors pallida Hor. caught him in her *net*:
The *bush* no more he'll *beat*; for here he's *set*.
His nights with *sugar*, *lamp*, and *sheet* all past,
Now, *box'd securely*, lies *relaxed* at last.

READER!
DIG NOT HERE
BUT PONDER ON THE
METAMORPHOSIS
THAT AWAITS YOU

[Allan, P. B. M. 1974. O. M. H. *The Entomologist's Record and Journal of Variation* **86**: 171].

WHAT HAS BECOME OF THE BRITISH SATYRIDAE?

Professor Raphael Meldola, D.Sc., L.L.D., F.R.S., F.E.S., F.C.S.,
Brunswick Square, London, W.C. (1911)

Professor Raphael Meldola (1850–1916) was one of the leading chemists of his day and an authority on aniline dye-stuffs derived from coal-tar. His work in this field was considered so important that he was awarded the Davy Medal of the Royal Society in 1913. Meldola also published important studies on insect mimicry and in this work was associated with Darwin, Wallace and Bates. When the Epping Forest and County of Essex Naturalists' Field Club (later renamed the Essex Field Club) was founded in 1880, Meldola was elected its first President. He was President of the Entomological Society of London 1896-97. In his

Fig. 72. Raphael Meldola, whose work was 'associated with that of Darwin, Wallace and Bates'.

obituary in *The Entomologist* (1916) he was described as 'a small, trim, wiry figure of somewhat severe appearance, but with a whimsical sense of humour and ready wit'. His collection of Lepidoptera was bequeathed to the Oxford University Museum.

Among the reminiscences of my early collecting days some forty odd years ago is the abundance of certain species of Satyrid butterflies in the London district in localities from which they have now disappeared altogether, or have become so scarce as to appear notable when observed. It is not altogether a case of "urbanization," because many of the districts frequented by me in my youth, such as Epping Forest, the chalk downs south of Croydon, &c., are still open spaces and more or less rural. Moreover, the species which I have in mind are generally less abundant all over the country than they used to be, so that some wider cause than the spread of cities must be sought for. It is noteworthy that the Satyridæ should apparently be so especially affected by adverse conditions. Let me, in the first place, state the facts from my own memory. In the late sixties and early seventies *E. ianira* [Meadow Brown] was abundant round and about Leyton, in Essex, and in the Epping Forest district generally. It swarmed among the long grass of the Hackney Marshes and all along the Lea valley. It is now a comparative rarity in this district; two years ago a few specimens were noted, as a kind of curiosity, in the marshes between Ponders End and Chingford, but the predominance of this species is evidently a thing of the past. During the same period *P. egeria* [Speckled Wood] used to sun itself on the southern wall regularly every summer in our garden at Leyton, and was fairly common in the Forest. I have not seen it in the latter district for more than twenty years. So also *P. megæra* [Wall], which could always be seen in the Forest glades, has practically disappeared from this locality. The same remark applies to *E. hyperanthes* [Ringlet], which used to flutter in swarms over the bushes in the Forest, and which is now quite extinct in the district, according to my experience. *E. tithonus* [Gatekeeper] was never common in the Forest or its environment, but could always be seen at the right season. In the country round Twickenham and Anerley, which I also used to frequent at that time, this butterfly was quite a conspicuous feature of hedgerow insect life. I have seen the bramble-flowers crowded with this butterfly season after season, and, paraphrasing Hans Breitmann, I ask, "Where is that species now?" At the time referred to, the chalk downs along the Caterham Valley (Riddlesdown, &c.) used to be favourite localities with collectors. The commonest Satyrid then was *S. semele* [Grayling], which was out with *L. corydon* [Chalk Hill Blue] (common), *L. minima* [Small Blue] (rare), and *Z. filipendulae* [Six-spot Burnet] (abundant). One morning's visit to Riddlesdown at that period sufficed to fill up one's "series" of all these species. *Semele* has disappeared from the locality, so also, according to my experience, has *L. minima*. *L. corydon* and *Z. filipendulae* still linger on in the more remote and less frequented coombs of the chalk downs, but they have disappeared from their former habitats, and are getting scarcer in their present localities.

The question raised in this note is, of course, only part of the general question of the causes of the fluctuation in numbers of British species. The answer cannot be given in terms of one factor: it is not always a simple case of the over-running of localities by "humanity," because I have found, and my experience is confirmed by others, that the decline of the Satyridae is pretty general. The causes which in districts undergoing "urbanization" are operative to the extent of producing local extinction appear to be also operative, although in a lesser degree, in the rural habitats of those species which used formerly to be abundant. What these causes are I am not prepared to state dogmatically, but it seems to me worth while putting my recollections upon record before they fade, for there must be many of my contemporaries whose experience of former times will coincide with mine. Other species and the representatives of other families have, as we all know, been observed to decline locally, but in no other case within my knowledge has such a general family decline been noticed as that which is made manifest in the Satyridæ by a comparison of the present state of affairs with that which existed forty years ago. It has been suggested, and with some reason, that the protection in modern times of small birds by Act of Parliament has some connection with the decline of certain British species of Lepidoptera. This may be the case, and, if so, the enemies of the Satyridæ must be sought for among those insectivorous birds which hunt among grasses for food, for the larvæ of this family are all grass feeders. To this suggested cause may be added the fact that the Satyridæ are not migratory, and that losses by increased persecution are not made good by occasional immigration from the Continent, as in the case of the Vanessidæ. It is also possible that improvements in agricultural practice

have had something to do with the decline of some of the grass-feeding species, but this cause can hardly be assigned in the case of species which frequent woodlands and heaths. I may add, with reference to the latter, that even the commonest of the heath-frequenting species, *C. pamphilus* [Small Heath], is a rarity now in the districts referred to as compared with its abundance in former times.

[Meldola, R. 1911. What has become of the British Satyridae? *The Entomologist* **44**: 146–148].

THE NAME AND IDENTIFICATION OF THE NEW CLOUDED YELLOW

Revd Anthony H. Harbottle, Bude, N. Cornwall (1950)

Previous to 1945, lepidopterists recognized only two British species of Clouded Yellow butterflies: *Colias croceus* (Clouded Yellow) and *C. hyale* (Pale Clouded Yellow). However, in that year, the Belgian lepidopterists Lucien Berger and Maurice Fontaine described a third species, although they did not at that time give it a specific name. Berger then published a further description, together with the name *Colias alfacariensis*, in *The Entomologist* (1948), its publication antedating the second part of Berger and Fontaine's paper in the Belgian journal *Lambillionea*. According to Jacques Hecq, the editor of *Lambillionea* (pers. comm.), Berger, in doing this, established priority for his authorship of the name, thus depriving Maurice Fontaine, '*le veritable découvreur*' of this species, of the credit that was his due. Because of this the 'New Clouded Yellow' continues to be known as Berger's Clouded Yellow rather than 'Fontaine's Clouded Yellow'. It is very similar in appearance to *C. hyale*, and subsequent examination of presumed *C. hyale* specimens in British collections revealed that *C. alfacariensis* had, in fact, previously occurred in this country for many years, albeit unrecognized as such.

In this article the Revd Harbottle describes his first encounter with this new species.

A sweltering sun in a cloudless sky was intensified by the reflected brilliance of the cliffs that it bathed. Such were the conditions under which, on Tuesday, 26th July last, whilst on a very brief visit to the Dover–Folkestone area of Kent, I fortuitously came across a small colony of the new British species of butterfly, *Colias australis*, Verity [Berger's Clouded Yellow].

At 11.30 a.m. (B.S.T.) my attention was suddenly drawn to two pale butterflies frisking a few feet to my left. By their flight, which was now swift and reckless, together with the depth of their colour, I suspected their true identity from the first. I made a hasty and ill-judged swipe with the net, missed both, and gave chase to one, cursing my lack of skill. Several times every ounce of energy was exerted to gain on the insect, which eluded every stroke of the net. Eventually, having tired of the sport, it careered from my ken altogether.

Periodically this process was repeated, and the steep slopes helped the butterflies to win every time.

Later, however, at about 1.0 p.m. I caught a male, which promptly flew out of the only hole in the net! Stung into alacrity I had it replaced by another within a few minutes. This insect was less fortunate and, upon examination, proved itself to be a male *C. australis* in immaculate condition.

At this juncture my luck seemed to turn, and within the next three hours I had secured four males, making a total of five in all. Their condition varied from good to perfect.

I saw only one female, which was very fresh and of the white form. It came with great speed and directness at me, and, before I could regain my balance after the first and only lurch, it had vanished. I was bitterly disappointed, for I had determined from the outset to try and breed the species.

During this first visit all the *C. australis* were remarkably restless, incessantly quartering the ground, which was carpeted with *Hippocrepis comosa* [horse-shoe vetch], and they scarcely, if ever, settled.

On the morning of Friday, 12th August, I paid my second visit to the same site. Conditions, although

Fig. 73. Revd Anthony Harbottle (1996). The Queen's Chaplain at Windsor and the first person in this country to have bred Berger's Clouded Yellow.

not so ideal as before, were otherwise more pleasant with a slight breeze and considerable cloud.

At first, to my dismay, it appeared that all the *C. australis* had either died or migrated elsewhere as not one was to be seen. After strolling about for an hour, however, I saw what I thought was a female *C. australis* flitting lazily along the bank and frequently settling on the purple thyme heads. Having caught it, I boxed it, and thought: "pity, *helice*" [white or cream coloured female form of *C. croceus*]. Not unnaturally I kept pulling the box out and looking

167

at the creature, and, as it was yellow and heavily bordered, I eventually reached the quite erroneous conclusion that it must be a male *Colias hyale*. However, I refrained from killing it.

A little later I netted a male *C. australis*, and, in so doing, smashed the ferrule of my umbrella, which I was using as a stick and which I eventually left in the compartment of a railway carriage. This male, which was slightly worn, I boxed.

Things were going very well and I was very happy until, in about an hour's time, I was informed in no uncertain manner by a railway official that I was trespassing, and I was told to clear off. This I readily and apologetically consented to do, and perched myself just the other side of the railway's property but within full view of the beloved hunting-ground. This forthright devotion to duty on the official's part proved to be a blessing in disguise. Almost immediately I observed a female *C. australis* of the white form. A brief moment passed before it settled, I saw the massive forewing discoidal spot, and I at once knew it for what it was. I slammed the net over it and boxed it. It was in perfect condition. A few minutes later I caught a second male, although I think I had to trespass to do so. I eventually made my way into Folkestone, taking two *C. croceus* ab. *helice* en route.

On the following day I secured two more *C. australis* males, one in the usual spot and the other, curiously enough, on a southerly bank the Dover side of Folkestone.

I dedicated what was left of the day to the gathering of a dozen plants of *Hippocrepis comosa*, which, having packaged into a large tin, I posted to Bude with full instructions to my painstaking and long-suffering aunts, so that the foodplant would be ready and available on my return.

I paid a final and futile visit to the spot on the Sunday morning and at lunchtime scraped some chalk from the White Cliffs into an empty flour bag, which was destined to belch chalk to the dismay of porters until I arrived home. These elaborate plans were necessary as *Hippocrepis comosa* is not indigenous to the neighbourhood of Bude.

Having completed several journeys of a more mundane nature, I eventually reached Bude early on the morning of Wednesday the 17th. The three live imagines had been fed periodically on water, but the white female unhappily died just before I reached home. The male was obviously on its "last legs", but the other yellow and heavily marked insect was still somewhat vigorous. My belief was that it was not *C. australis* had been strengthened by the fact that, when at rest, its body was raised high on its legs from the ground, whereas, in the case of the other two butterflies, the legs were splayed outwards causing the head and thorax to touch the ground. By way of contrast the two *C. croceus* ab. *helice* which I was keeping for ova were even more robust, although they had not enjoyed such assiduous attention.

After a hasty breakfast I proceeded to pot up in the chalk a few of the better plants, and by 9.45 a.m. I had enclosed by muslin in a large pot of *Hippocrepis* the male together with the yellow insect, which, by now, I had begun to suspect was neither ab. *helice* nor *C. hyale*, and if any doubt remained then wishful thinking dispelled it.

The day was fortunately hot and sunny, and I kept a constant vigil beside the insects. The male was torpid, but not so the other insect, which, having arched the abdomen several times, eventually deposited an orange ovum on a terminal shoot of the *Hippocrepis* just after 10.30 a.m. Thus not only was this a female *C. australis*, but a fertile female too. In a frenzy of excitement I grabbed the male and killed it, setting it half an hour later together with the already dead white female which had the enormous discoidal spots. During the remainder of the day seven more ova were laid. On the 18th there were two more ova, twelve on the

19th, and on the 20th six. Thereafter the female ceased ovipositing and no amount of coaxing would persuade her to resume. On the 28th, now sadly worn and frayed, she died.

On 23rd August the first ovum hatched, followed during the next four days by all the others except one, which proved to be infertile. Three of the young larvae were unaccountably lost, and, of the remaining twenty-four, five died in their first instar.

All but three of the nineteen larvae ceased feeding and entered into hibernation at the beginning of September. Twelve of these sixteen larvae hibernated in the second instar, three in the third instar, and the remaining one in the fourth instar.

Two of the other three larvae, which did not hibernate, fed up rapidly in the sunshine, and, having spun up thirty-six hours previously, they both pupated practically simultaneously on 18th September.

One pupa was malformed and turned black within three or four days: the other, however, throve and at length coloured up on the 28th September, but the imago — a yellow female as I later discovered — failed to emerge.

The remaining larva spun up on the 22nd and pupated on the 24th Sept. At midday on the 6th October there emerged from this pupa a perfect third brood male *C. australis*, which I believe constitutes the first British specimen to have been bred in captivity. . . .

[Vallins, F. T., Dewick, A. J. & Harbottle, A. H. 1950. The name and identification of the New Clouded Yellow butterfly. *Entomologist's Gazette* **1**: (part 3), 120–125].

ENTOMOLOGICAL REMINISCENCES

By an Octogenarian, Deal, Kent. (1883)

My first introduction to Entomology took place when I was about fifteen years old. I was taken to see a collection, and was quite pleased with what I saw. An entomologist of the name of Sluse, who was clever at drawing and painting, induced my father to cultivate a taste for collecting, but he confined his efforts to the garden, consequently his knowledge never extended much further than "tortoiseshells," "peacocks," and "aldermen," [Red Admiral], as he called them. I often assisted him in taking those species common in cottage gardens. Soon after I became acquainted with a man of the name of Weatherhead, from whom I learned my first lesson, and with him I went to Colney Hatch Wood, where we frequently collected. I also about the same time became acquainted with Daniel Bidder, a coleopterist, who introduced me to the forest in the neighbourhood of Wanstead. I frequently made excursions to that place with other boys, having for our primary object the collection of blackberries, but I always had an eye to such insects as were flying at the time.

Charlton Pits was then a fine place for *Sesia ichneumoniformis* [Six-belted Clearwing], I took two dozen one afternoon; they feed on the black knapweed (*Centaurea nigra*). I also went to Birch Wood with young Bidder, and we worked with the net, sugar not then being known. We found a moth very plentiful on the wing, and as we did not know it we only took half a dozen each. We showed old Bidder our captures, and he said, "Why did you not take more, — in fact all you could?" He also said, "You will never get such a chance again." In this he was right, for I did not take *Toxocampa pastinum* [Blackneck] again for many years. During these early days I was shown *Papilio machaon* [Swallowtail], and all my thoughts were to get some. I was told that the nearest place at which they were procurable was Whittlesea Mere, and I started one Saturday afternoon with a great box. When I got about ten miles from

home in the East of London, I began to enquire if I was right for Whittlesea Mere, and was surprised to find that no one could tell me; and it was not until I overtook a waggoner that I learned that it was somewhere in the Isle of Ely. I rode in his waggon all night, and in the morning he called me and said that he must turn off to Cambridge, and that I must keep straight on; and it was afternoon when I reached Whittlesea. Great was my surprise to find it a village; and as I could find no "swallow-tails" there, I began to enquire if any butterfly-catchers ever visited there. They said that there was one some time ago, but could not inform me where he lodged, and, what was still more discomforting, they could not tell me where I could find a bed. However, I was fortunate enough to find one at the Ferry House, about two miles over the marshes, and felt very thankful after my long journey. The next morning I enquired of the children if they knew what a swallow-tail butterfly was, and I heard with joy that they not only knew it, but that there were lots about there. "All right," I thought, "this is the place for me." "There goes one on the other side of the river," cried one, and I was soon across the river. "Where is it?" I cried. "There," said they, and it was with feelings of great disappointment that I beheld only a "tortoiseshell." No *P. machaon* did I see that day, but at dusk I took several things, among which were two Nonagrias [Bulrush Wainscot]. Not bad things, and if I had known what they were I should have taken more. When the man of the house came home he told me that he could tell me where the butterfly men stopped, and he would direct me in the morning. After breakfast he told me that I was to go to a place called Ho[l]me, then across the seven fields to Yexley [*sic*]. Off I went in good spirits, and got there by noon, and found the house, and enquired if any fly-catchers stopped there. Oh yes! Mr. Chant and Mr. Bentley had stayed there! "All right," thinks I to myself, and after dinner I went out and was overjoyed to see *P. machaon* flying gaily over the reeds, but I could not catch them, as they were out of my reach. However, the next day I had them in a turnip-field, and it was a splendid sight to see them flitting over the turnip-blossom. I stayed there a fortnight, and then walked home, nearly eighty miles, well content with my captures.

Perhaps it may interest some to know how the locality for *Polyommatus hippothoe* [see p.37] was discovered, and how that butterfly came to be exterminated. About forty years ago Mr. Benjamin Standish (the grandfather) heard that *dispar*, as then called, had been seen in the Fens. *Dispar* was known and figured in 1792 and 1795. He got a painting of the butterfly, coloured by his father, and went down to the Fens and showed it to people there, but no one knew anything about it. Mr. Drake, at the 'Checkers,' told him that a man lodged there who worked in the Fens, cutting reeds, who was a most likely person to know. When the man returned from work Standish showed him the drawing, and said, "Do you know anything about a butterfly like this?" "Yes," said the man; "I saw some to-day." "Well," said Standish, "what shall I give you to take me to the spot?" "No!" said the man, "I intend to take a lot up to London." Standish then offered him five shillings to take him to the place, but the man would not divulge the locality, even for a promise of two shillings for each insect captured. The landlord, however, told Standish where the man worked, and he was successful in finding the place, and took a fine lot of *P. hippothoe*. It soon got wind among the folks at the Fen that they were worth two shillings each in London, and two men came from Cambridge and secured a large quantity, which they took to London in boxes full, and sold them at sixpence each. I went down about three years after, and got some of the larvæ. They appeared to be very local, and most numerous where their food-plant – *viz.* the water-dock – was most abundant. The larva was collected by all persons, young and old. I bought two dozen larvæ of an old woman for ninepence, from which I bred some fine specimens, and sold them at one shilling each. I wish I had them now. Mr. Cole, at Holme Fen, took a large quantity of them. His back-yard was close to their locality. The last time I was there Mr. Cole said he had not seen one for some years. There was the food-plant in plenty on the same spot, but no larvæ. They had been too closely hunted for. However, I solaced myself by taking *Nonagria ulvæ* [Silky Wainscot] in Cole's stack-yard. As soon as it got dark they came out of the cut reeds and had a fly. They ran up the inside of the reeds like mice, but how they turned round to get back I cannot make out. I took some nice varieties. In 1847–8 Mr. Doubleday was down in the Fens, and found *Zeuzera arundinis* [Reed Leopard] in the dykes. He told a man he employed, who lived there, to look after them. He did so, and found the pupæ. I went down the next year, and found the imago. An account of them I published in the 'Zoologist' for 1850, as stated in the first volume of the 'Entomologist's Annual,' and that is the only account I have seen. About this time sugaring was discovered by Mr. Doubleday, who, in his vocation as a grocer, noticed that the moths swarmed round his sugar hogsheads in the back yard. There was a great desire among working entomologists to know how it was made, but the secret was retained by a few. All kinds of scents were tried, but were not found of much use. A man of the name of Courtney made some up, and sold it at one shilling and sixpence per pint. This discovery caused many rare things to become common. *Acronycta ligustri* [The Coronet] was a rare moth, and I have seen fourteen shillings refused for it, and that was even a wasted one. But sugar found them in plenty, and I am of opinion that there are few things really rare. You have only to find out their habits and food-plant. Look at *Aleucis pictaria* [Sloe Carpet], only one taken in fourteen years, yet they existed in plenty on the bloom of blackthorn. Although a man searched Dartford Heath fence a fortnight without success, a few yards from him they swarmed at blackthorn. Since then they have been found in many places.

In the year 1847 Mr. Hindley and myself made up our minds to go to Dover and collect. We started in the steamboat to Margate, and walked to Deal. The wind was blowing very hard, and we had a difficulty in landing. But we arrived at Deal safely. The next morning it poured with rain, but we walked to Dover through it. When it cleared somewhat, we made up our minds to return, thinking that little could be done if we continued our proposed expedition. In walking across the sandhills, making for Sandwich, we took from the stems of grass two specimens of a *Lithosia*. This was in broad daylight. These I showed to Mr. Doubleday some days after, and he pronounced it to be a variety of the common one, but to make sure he sent it to his friend Herrich-Schäffer, who averred that it was *Lithosia pygmæola* [Pigmy Footman]. One of these specimens Mr. Robinson, of Limehouse, had, and one I retained for my own collection.

Some twelve years after I thought I would go to Deal and try to find them again, and I was rewarded by finding them in plenty. I appear to have been the only person who collected on the south coast of Kent for some years. There was a man from Dover, who visited St. Margaret's Bay some years ago, of the name of Leplastre, who was a watch-maker. He seems to have taken *Stigmonota leplastriana*, which was named after him. In one of my rambles I went to St. Margaret's Bay; the weather was hot and thundery, at which time insects leave their retreats and fly. I captured during that evening a Noctua which I did not know, as it was much wasted. When Mr. Doubleday saw it he said that it was much wanted, and I promised to go again for it next season. I did so, and took seven the first night on the blossom of the bugloss, and several of *Plusia orichalcea* [Slender Burnished Brass]. The place is now destroyed by the inroads of the sea. In Mr. Stevens' sale a short time ago it was stated in the catalogue, — "*P. orichalcea*, five taken by Mr. Harding at Deal," and "another lot taken and bred by Mr. Harding at Deal." The truth is that I never bred one; I took one just out of pupa, which is of a yellow colour. An entomologist at Canterbury has sent out some specimens, which he has stated were taken by me. I have seen them, and they were never taken by me. There appears to be a manufactory at Canterbury for the produce of rare things. I may have taken in all some eighteen or twenty of *P. orichalcea,* seven of which were taken in one night.

During another of my rambles to Deal I procured *galii* [Bedstraw Hawk-moth] larvæ, and I also fell in with a small brown moth in large numbers; that was *Acidalia ochrata* [Bright Wave].

One stormy Saturday I was at Darenth Wood. At dusk I took seven *Xylomiges conspicillaris* [Silver Cloud], one of which laid several eggs; but what to feed the young larvae on I did not know. In a book it said "feed on vetch," but I could not get them to feed on anything else but blackthorn, which they took readily to; and I succeeded in breeding fifteen fine ones. A strange habit I noticed in the larvæ was this, that if I opened a door in the room where they were they would all fall down and lay among the dead leaves for an hour before they would take to their food again.

[An Octogenarian (H. J. Harding). 1883. Entomological reminiscences. *The Entomologist* **16**: 127–132].

ONE SUMMER HOUR

Robert Adkin, F.E.S., Eastbourne, Sussex. (1932)

Robert Adkin (1849–1935) was one of the last members of that great group of late nineteenth-century lepidopterists that included Henry Stainton and J. W. Tutt. He built up a famous collection of some 47,500 specimens which he left to the Natural History Museum, London. A modest man, who refused the Presidency of the Royal Entomological Society, he was described in his obituary by W. G. Sheldon (1935) as 'one of the simplest and most unassuming of personalities . . . always keenly on the look-out for something that was wanted, and when that something was found his usual remark was, "I'll see to that", and see to it, he invariably did'. In the following note, written less than three years before his death, Adkin remembers a quiet moment in his home town of Eastbourne.

In the past inclement season, when one heard little but complaints of the abnormal scarcity of butterflies, it is pleasant to be able to record an abundance, even though local. At the western end of the Parade here is an almost precipitous bank; it is not primeval, but it is very old — evidently the side of an old chalk-pit. When I first knew it, some seventy years ago, the foundations of the old lime-kilns were still standing, the floor of the pit was grass grown and two or three trees of some age grew at its upper end; it must have been out of use for many years even then. Although the pit has been transformed into a recreation ground and a tea châlet built at its lower extremity, the bank still maintains its natural wild flora, in addition to which a few plants of red valerian and garden scabious have established themselves. At about noon on August 9th I visited this bank; it faces due south. The sun was shining brightly and a light northerly breeze was blowing. On my way there along the Parade I noticed a few odd specimens of *Pieris brassicae, P. rapae* [Large and Small Whites] and *Colias croceus* [Clouded Yellow] flying wildly, but on the bank they were in dozens, feeding at the flowers or flitting gently between them; *Pyrameis cardui* [Painted Lady] and *Aglais urticae* [Small Tortoiseshell] were equally common. The bank has been a haunt of *Polyommatus thetis (bellargus)* [Adonis Blue] so long as I have known it, and it is gratifying to know that it still lingers there; I saw several specimens, as well as a few *P. icarus* [Common Blue]. The flowers and the butterflies made the whole bank a mass of scintillating colour, as pretty a sight as I have seen for many a long day. On a subsequent visit a few days later the butterflies were somewhat less numerous, but the places of the absentees were more than taken by hosts of *Plusia gamma* [Silver-Y]. *Pyrameis atalanta* [Red Admiral] and *Vanessa io* [Peacock] were not represented, but a few specimens were noted in my garden; neither species was, however, particularly common last autumn.

[Adkin, R. 1932. One summer hour. *The Entomologist* **65**: 52].

LUCK AND COINCIDENCE

Col. Sidney H. Kershaw, D.S.O., Aspley Heath, Buckinghamshire. (1956)

Colonel Sidney Hardinge Kershaw (1881–1964) was born at the Rectory, Fledborough, near Nottingham. Educated at Repton and Sandhurst, he became commanding officer of his army regiment the Fifth Fusiliers, and in 1917 served on the staff of General Lord Allenby. On retirement from the army he settled at Aspley Heath, near Bletchley, where he was able to pursue his interest, first developed as a schoolboy, in the Lepidoptera. His collection of foreign butterflies was bequeathed to the Nottingham Museum.

For some years I have been helping with a survey, under Nature Conservancy, of some woods on the Buckinghamshire border which might prove suitable as nature reserves. On a routine visit to one of these, not far from Bletchley, I started out on 21st July. It was a wood in which a few years ago one might hope to see *euphrosyne, selene* [Pearl-bordered and Small Pearl-bordered Fritillaries], a score of *camilla* [White Admiral], fives times that number of *paphia* [Silver-washed Fritillary], plenty of *aglaia* [Dark Green Fritillary], a few *cydippe* [High Brown Fritillary], and, if you were lucky, some *M. aurinia* [Marsh Fritillary]. Now alas! *selene, aurinia* and *aglaia* have disappeared, at least for the time being, *cydippe* is very scarce, while *camilla* and *paphia* have about held their own.

I spent from 10.30 a.m. until 3.30 p.m. in the wood; it was a dull, warm day until 1.30 p.m. when the sun came out, but about half past eleven I saw a grand *camilla* ab. *nigrina* close to me. Handicapped by having a *paphia* in my net I was clumsy and missed it; it retired to a tree-top to think things over. It was pure black with a few tiny white spots.

At 1 p.m. I saw a *semi-nigrina*, with a continuous but very narrow white line, but it did not come near enough for a stroke.

I began to notice a marked difference in flight and general colour between *camilla* normal form and ab. *nigrina*; the former floated and soared and looked orange and black on the wing; the latter fluttered and dipped and looked slaty blue.

Naturally I stayed in the spot and had my sandwiches; the sun came out but nothing

happened until 2.10 p.m., when my first *nigrina* drifted down and pottered about over bramble blossom. This time I made no mistake; it was a grand specimen with a lovely deep underside. I saw at least two other *nigrina* flying around a maytree, but they would not come down, and the sun went for keeps. I packed up and caught the bus home.

What was the reason for this concentration of *nigrina* in such a small area? Was it the lively warm weather from 3rd July onwards which enabled the (to my mind) more delicate pupae of this variety to emerge successfully? The late Mr. Castle Russell once told me that he had seen some of his *camilla* pupae showing distinct signs of emerging as *nigrina* through the pupa-case, but all failed to emerge.

Next day I went to the wood again and met my first *cydippe* of the season, a male, and a female *tithonus* with extra spots on the forewings; I netted the latter and went on to look for more *nigrina*! Nothing was moving in the *camilla* line and the sun disappeared, but as I was moving bus-wards I saw a pair of *paphia in cop.*; the male was normal but the female had a quarter inch band of silver round the outer margin of each hindwing. I netted them and they separated, when I was able to release the male and examine the female's top-side. Very dark, with the spots inside the margins much elongated and broadened at the external end into the shape of harpoon blades. Apart from her silver bands her underside was plain and drab, but she was in excellent condition. I set her for top-side. At the time I did not know how she had spent the previous evening; please remember also that she was *in cop.* when netted.

A very busy week followed and I could not visit the wood until the afternoon of 27th July. This time I was accompanied by J.B., a young but experienced entomologist. I soon saw a *nigrina*, flying high over the oaks, but it never came within reach, and I was just thinking of leaving to catch my bus when I saw my *semi-nigrina* again near the top of a tall maytree. Minutes ticked away and it *would* not come down . . . Finally I handed over to J.B. and sprinted for the bus, as I was being met by a taxi at my home stop. . . .

Now to return to the *paphia* var. Last week I was showing my season's catch to another friend (S.H.) and he at once recognised the insect, after asking whether it had a quarter-inch band of silver round the hindwings on the underside. That clinched its identity. Then he told me *his* story of the 21st July. Arriving just after I had left he had spotted a pair of *paphia in cop.* high in a tree; the male opened and closed its wings from time to time, but the female remained closed and S.H. could see a broad band of silver round her hindwings. He watched them for some time, but the pair did not move.

Now S.H. is a very active, determined and patient man, but this pair of *paphia* eventually got to the end of his patience: he shinned up the tree, got into position for a sweep, and carefully freed his hand and net. At this moment either his foot slipped or a small branch gave way; at any rate the branch shook, and the *paphia* sailed off to a safer tree.

The pair were now on an outer branch of an unclimbable oak; but S.H. was far from beaten yet; he searched around and at last found a long enough stick, heavy and sufficiently rotten at the thin end for him to force the brass Y of his net into it. Once more he was in position for a sweep . . . but just then the male *paphia* decided that it was time to make a move and he carried his lady-love up to the safety of a tall and even more unclimbable oak.

Apart from throwing a stick up on the chance of disturbing them there was nothing else to do, and he could not come next day. However, I am glad to say that on his way out of the wood (it was on 30th July), he took a grand ab. *nigrina* with a very fine underside. He had surely earned it and had not had my wonderful luck in being given two second chances.

[Kershaw, S. H. 1956. Luck and coincidence. *The Entomologist's Record and Journal of Variation* **68**: 21–23].

THE BATH WHITE

Revd William H. Hawker B.A., M.A., Horndean, Hampshire. (1859)

The Reverend William Henry Hawker (1828–1874) was educated at Rugby School, and later graduated from Trinity College, Cambridge. In addition to being a botanist and zoologist (elected a Fellow of the Zoological Society in 1860), he was also a member of the Alpine Club and spent several winters at Menton in France making many excursions in the then almost unexplored Maritime Alps. For the last seven years of his relatively short life he was Vicar of Steep, near Petersfield in Hampshire.

There is something almost irritating in the tremendous luck that seems so often to reward a beginner's first labours in the field of Entomology, and it is not to be wondered at that the older collectors, whose lucky day has long gone by and whose rare captures now are the result of downright hard work, should be a little jealous. I was a very young hand when I took my six Lathonias [Queen of Spain Fritillary], and, not knowing what they were, gave one of them to the friend who named them for me. I was but a neophyte when I found *Cloantha Perspicillaris* [*Actinotia polyodon* — Purple Cloud] in a spider's web, and for ever so long thought myself supremely fortunate in having captured an "antler moth." Now the above insects were all got without the least Science, trouble or merit on my part, and yet, I suppose, they would be considered as almost equal to the whole of my subsequent captures. And I believe that the experience of many an entomologist would show the same thing. Here is a case in point. A few Sundays ago I had the great pleasure of seeing, on my way to church, a female *Pieris Daplidice* [Bath White], the first I have ever seen alive in England. Whatever my impulse may have been, I could hardly, in the face of several of my congregation, cry "hats off in chase;" the chance was missed and I never saw the fair one again. However, the next morning I wrote to some of my neighbours to put them on the look-out, and a few days after one of them called and said that he was going back to school the next day and wished before starting to show me a few of his last captures. I opened the box and beheld three *Daplidices*, one male and two females, all in good order, especially the male, which appeared not long out of the chrysalis. He took the first specimen before he received my note, the others after. His elder brother, who also collects, was with him, but did not get a single one, and so had to console himself with the reflection "Won't I hunt for the larvæ, old boy, while you are grinding away at Virgil." The two females had evidently laid all their eggs.

[Hawker, W. H. 1859. *Pieris daplidice. The Entomologist's Weekly Intelligencer* **6**: 186].

IT HAPPENED AT . . . (No. 6) – 'BOATING AT KENMARE'

Bryan P. Beirne, Ph.D., F.R.E.S., F.L.S., Ottawa, Ontario. (1953)

Late in July, 1947, I stayed for a time with Mr. P. P. Graves at Glengarrif, to collect in Kerry and west Cork . . . Dr. and Mrs. H. B. D. Kettlewell arrived at Kenmare, and we all arranged to spend a day investigating Uragh Wood, at Lough Inchiquin on the Kenmare Peninsula. The late A. C. Forbes, former Director of Forestry in Ireland, had told me that this was one of the very few woods in Ireland that apparently was untouched by man. It was to be expected from this that rarities, such as *Leucodonta bicoloria* Schiff. [White Prominent], might occur there. . . .

Graves and I drove over to Kenmare and set out for Lough Inchiquin, following the Kettlewells. They flashed off at excessive speed and, though I was accustomed to the narrow, winding, country roads and was driving a fast German sports car with front-wheel drive, I was unable to keep up with them. Eventually we found them waiting for us at the entrance to a mountain track up which we had to travel for several miles to reach the lake. This trip was accompanied by only minor incidents: a hub-cap of the Kettlewell hired car was somewhat dented by contact with a projecting boulder; and at one point Kettlewell stopped and emerged from his car carrying his haversack of glass-bottomed pill-boxes which he placed on the road, got into the car, drove over it, and got out and picked up the remains without comment or explanation. Graves and I watched these proceedings from the car behind with some amazement.

When we arrived at Lough Inchiquin we found that the only practicable way of reaching Uragh Wood, on the steep opposite slopes, was by boat. There was only one boat on the lake, privately owned and in a locked boathouse. Its custodian, a certain one-eyed Maguire who lived nearby, had departed for the day. However, the Kettlewell charm and blarney and a package of cigarettes persuaded Mrs. Maguire to hand over the key.

We got out the boat and proceeded across the lake, somewhat erratically. At the opposite side I jumped out, into apparently bottomless mud. After several similar attempts a suitable landing-place was found. We spent a pleasant day collecting in the woods which, though very wet, looked as if they had strong potentialities for Lepidoptera. We found no special rarities, however. At one stage, hearing loud shouts from the Kettlewells, Graves and I thought

Fig. 74. Dr Bernard Kettlewell is known to thousands of entomologists throughout the world for his research into industrial melanism.

they had found at least *bicoloria,* but on making our way toward them, with great difficulty through swamps and tangled vegetation up the hillside, we found that they were merely calling their dogs.

At the end of the day we rowed back across the lake to the boathouse. The problem now was to get the boat up the ramp into the house. The Kettlewells and I pulled on the sides, which broke away in our hands. Dry rot. We then noticed a block and tackle affixed to the end wall of the boathouse. We attached the rope to the boat, and pulled. Nothing happened, and we pulled harder. A section of the end wall of the boathouse fell down. At this, Graves, who was gazing through the aperture in mild surprise, pointed out that we would be late for dinner and we made a rapid departure for Glengarrif, cravenly leaving Kettlewell to explain to and placate One-eyed Maguire. I never heard how he did this.

[Beirne, B. P. 1953. It happened at . . . *Entomologist's Gazette* 4: 34–35].

Bryan P. Beirne seemed remarkably accident prone. Clearly 1947 was not one of his best summers, and after the adventure at Kenmare he suffered further mishaps on the Burren of Clare.

IT HAPPENED AT . . . (No. 7) —
'THE STRONGEST MAN IN COUNTY CLARE'

Bryan P. Beirne, Ph.D., F.R.E.S., F.L.S., Ottawa, Ontario. (1953)

Accidents are said to happen in threes, an adage which I can confirm from personal experience. In the summer of 1947, Dr. Fergus O'Rourke and I went on a collecting trip to the Burren district of Co. Clare. We stayed at a hotel near Corofin for eight days, during seven of which there were almost continuous high winds, heavy rains, and low temperatures.

One morning we drove down to the village and on our way back passed the only other car that had been seen at the hotel during our stay there. Concluding from this that there would be no other car coming from the hotel we proceeded up the winding driveway at a more rapid speed than usual. Rounding a blind corner we met an unexpected arrival and had a head-on collision with his car. The other car and its occupants were undamaged but the front of my car was smashed in rather badly. However, a hotel employee, who claimed to be the strongest man in County Clare, fixed it up with a sledge-hammer.

As collecting Lepidoptera was out of the question because of the weather, we decided to go out on the lake in a boat that afternoon to see if we could pick up some aquatic insects. We got into the boat at the back of the hotel and pulled on an oar. The oar broke in the middle, and we were swept into the nearby mill-race. We had to jump into the water to above our waists to get ourselves and the boat ashore.

After a change of clothing we agreed that we would play it safe and do nothing more that day but sit in the hotel and read books. While we were thus quietly engaged, the strongest man in County Clare appeared at the door: "You left your car under the tree outside." "Yes." "Well, the tree has fallen on it." It was an evergreen oak and the weight of the water on its leaves had been too much for it. Nevertheless, it was not an occurrence that one might reasonably expect in early July. The sledge-hammer had to be brought into operation again to straighten out the V-shaped bonnet of the car.

The net results of the day's activities were a considerable reduction in the resale value of the car, and no Lepidoptera.

[Beirne, B. P. 1953. It happened at . . . *Entomologist's Gazette* 4: 35–36].

THE BOG AT THE BACK OF BEYOND

An Old Moth-Hunter. (1965)

We had a good lunch at the Forsyth Arms, so good in fact that as I sprawled in an easy chair after coffee I was glad that a younger man was to be at the wheel that afternoon. My companion had been content with a mere half-pint of lager beer; for it is his rule (and should be everybody else's) to be abstemious to the verge of teetotalism when in charge of a car, especially if the car be a high-powered one and the distance not inconsiderable.

"Have you got that map?" said he, anxious to be back on the road.

I pulled out the map and, unfolding it, spread it across my knees. "The best thing we can do", said I, "is to make due north for the coast, then 'run our easting down' as the sailors say, along the coast road. About sixty miles I make it".

He took the map from me and scrutinised it. "But why go all that way round?" he asked. "There's a road here right across the hills, going almost straight in our direction — if a mountain road can ever go straight for more than fifty yards. It won't be more than forty-five this way".

"It's not motorable", said I. "Most of it is marked by a dotted line. I expect it's been washed away in several places, near the tops of the hills. And just look at it" — I leant across him — "It goes miles and miles from anywhere. Right over the back of beyond. If anything happened to the car when we got well up into these hills we'd have to walk miles and miles before we came to even a village. I know these tracks across the hills. Most of them ought not to be marked on the map at all. You might do it in a jeep, but not in a car sixteen feet long".

Fig. 75. Dr Philip Allan (1884–1973). He was 'an ardent moth-hunter at the age of eight', and as 'An Old Moth-Hunter' he was widely regarded as 'the doyen of entomological raconteurs'.

"Let's ask somebody. The landlord ought to know what state it's in". He got up and went in search of the landlord. Presently he came back and reported that the road over the hills was doubtful though the first six miles of it were all right, being used almost daily by the inhabitants of outlying farms.

"And after the first six miles?" I asked.

"He's never been more than six miles along it, so he doesn't know. I vote we try it. We can always turn back".

I thought of a recent incident when he had been obliged to drive the car backwards for nearly a mile until a farm gate made it possible to turn. However, there are always farm gates . . . . "Very well", said I. "Let's have a go".

We climbed out of the village by a road which only an optimist would have called 'serpentine'; for it consisted chiefly of hairpin bends. These happened whenever the road narrowed to about nine feet, and there was invariably a minor precipice at the most acute part of the bend.

When we came out on to a plateau which extended for a couple of miles my companion stopped the car and we just sat and stared. I am sure we could see for thirty miles in every direction. Doubtless there were farms tucked away in valleys over which we gazed; but of these we saw nothing — nothing but ridge after ridge of russet-purple hills and peaks which met the clouds at every horizon. The cool air was as exhilarating as vintage champagne: one could not drink enough of it. "I must look at that Lychnis", said I, indicating a wide pink patch of ragged robin a few paces from the car. "Might find eggs of *conspersa* [Marbled Coronet]." But it wasn't the Lychnis nor the chance of *conspersa* that impelled me to get out of the car: I just wanted to walk about in that marvellous air at the wonderful spot.

We found no *conspersa*; so presently, glutted with mountain air and scenery, we got back into the car and drove on, now along the top of a ridge and across gently undulating plateaux, now up a hill, now down one, but climbing all the time and every few miles stopping to look down upon little farmhouses and green meadows and coloured specks that were cattle, all nestling in the valleys far below the road along which we drove.

After we had been going for about three-quarters of an hour, while scrutinising the map I noticed something thereon that caught my attention. "Pull up for a moment", said I to the driver. The map showed, ahead of us and a mile to the right of our road, a pale-coloured patch about an inch long and nearly an inch wide, such a patch as is used on ordnance survey maps to denote low-lying ground — swamps and fens. No track, not even a dotted line indicating a footpath, crossed this patch anywhere, and it was contained by 2,500 feet hills on all sides except at one end, where it was bounded by a ridge that came down nearly to the 2,000 feet contour.

"A bog of sorts", said my companion. "Looks rather an interesting place. Must be about a mile long and nearly a mile wide. Shall we go and have a look at it? There's a track of some sort going off the road we are on: we might pull in there and walk down and inspect".

I agreed and when presently I estimated that we were near the spot where the track branched off we slowed down to walking pace.

Even so we had passed the track before we saw it. "That must be it", said I, pointing backwards to a narrow cleft in the ridge that bounded our road. We backed, then drove the car on to the grass in the cleft, and walked through the rift to prospect.

In a few minutes we were on the other side of the ridge and stopping simultaneously had our second thrill that day. We found ourselves looking down into a great oval punchbowl, the floor of which was a patchwork of greens and browns. Neither of us spoke; for the silence was unbroken even by the hum of an insect and the scene we gazed upon was truly impressive. At last "Gosh!" said my companion, and we started to clamber down among the bracken and bilberry and boulders till at length we came to the edge of the 'floor'.

It was more of a fen than a bog, for it was a watery place; no wonder there was neither track nor footpath across it. The brown patches were reeds and the green was a lush growth of marsh and fen flora. There were one or two shallow pools at the edge we had now reached, and I noticed *Alisma*, figwort, silverweed, a patch of water-mint, the amphibious persicary, and many other common marsh plants. I wondered what moths would come to light and sugar in such a spot. . . .

My companion explored botanically while I wandered on, gazing over this strange place we had come to all unexpectedly and noting reed birds — buntings with black heads, a snipe, and once a *Larus ridibundus* [black-headed gull] whose mocking laugh echoed eerily from the sides of the great bowl. It was indeed a desolate spot, the kind of place where any rare plant or insect or bird might occur. My eyes lighted upon a tall dock plant with huge leaves — *hydrolapathum* [water dock] without a doubt . . . .

I stopped suddenly in my walk. It was Thomas Edwards, an accomplished zoologist, curator of a museum and Associate of the Linnean Society, who told Edward Newman that he had seen, and chased, a large copper butterfly in this part of the country and had come close enough to see that it was a male. "It settled several times in full view", he wrote, "I repeatedly fell in pools concealed by the tall reeds and grasses, and at last was so completely tired that I gave up the chase". . . . And *hydrolapathum*, the foodplant of the coppers, here! . . . . I sat down on a boulder and gazed across the bog. Could Edwards have come to this lonely place, and could it have been here that he saw and chased — ?

At that moment my companion came up. "I've just seen a fritillary", said he. "Oh! Was it *aurinia* [Marsh Fritillary]?" (Although he is a botanist he knows most of the butterflies).

"May have been; it flew rather like *aurinia*. But it seemed to be a brighter colour; quite a brilliant beast. It was going fast, over there", he extended an arm, "and when the sun caught its wings it looked quite red. Expect it was a new var", he laughed.

I said nothing at all, because all of a sudden I felt — rather as I should have done had my companion remarked "there's a plesiosaurus wallowing about over there". Also I had remembered that *aurinia* is not on the wing in July.

"Anyhow you won't catch it", he went on. "You couldn't even force a canoe through this, and if you jumped overboard from one you'd probably go in up to your neck. Quite a sanctuary for birds and insects isn't it. Rather a discovery. I wonder if anybody's ever explored it".

I got off the boulder. "Show me just where you saw this fritillary", I said. "Then I'll sit and smoke and perhaps I'll catch sight of it too while you're exploring along this side. Don't go too far".

We walked back to where he had seen the butterfly, and I sat and stared over the bog, glancing every now and then at my companion as he jumped across hummocks and stooped over pools; for it was a dangerous place and a false step might have landed him in difficulties.

But the butterfly did not appear again, and after an hour we toiled up the ridge and so back to the car and resumed our journey.

When we had gone a mile or two we came to a cross-roads and there we saw a shepherd lighting a stump of pipe. We stopped and I got out of the car, ostensibly to ask him the way but really to make enquiry about the bog. Being a shepherd he was a contemplative man, therefore polite. He had English, and he spoke it slowly and correctly.

"We call it 'Bhuig na Bhodaich' ", he said in answer to my enquiry.

I racked memory and translated "the bog of the bogle".

He thanked me with his eyes and nodded.

"It's a strange place", said I. "Who is, or was, the Bhodaich?"

"I do not know", he said. "It was called that very long ago".

"Before you were born?"

He nodded gravely; then: "They say it was there before the hills".

I thanked him and got back into the car. "It was there before the hills", I repeated as we drove off. Then all at once I turned to my companion. "Do you know", said I, "I believe he was right. It was there before the hills were thrust up from the earth's crust. It's been there for millions of years".

And now, sometimes, when I lie in bed waiting for sleep to come, I see with my mind's eye that strange silent bog hidden far away in the hills at the back of beyond, the bog that cannot be glimpsed from any road, the bog that was there before the hills; and I hear the murmuring conversation of the reeds as they discuss the two strangers, and the taunting laugh of the pretty little gull, and the *'scape, 'scape* of the snipe, which is bird-language for "Catch me if you can!"

But most of all I think of a butterfly that was "going fast over there, and when the sun caught its wings it looked quite red . . . ."

[An Old Moth-Hunter (P. B. M. Allan). 1965. The bog at the back of beyond. *The Entomologist's Record and Journal of Variation* **77**: 33–36].

IRISH LEPIDOPTERA — THE BURREN OF CLARE, 1950

On the discovery of *Calamia tridens occidentalis* Cockayne (syn. *Luceria virens* Linn.) —
The Burren Green — in Ireland.

Lisney, Arthur A., Classey, Eric W., & Robinson, Hugh S. (1950)

General Introduction [E. W. Classey]: . . . In August, 1949, my good friend Captain W. S. Wright, of Co. Antrim, wrote to me to say that, whilst botanizing on the Burren during the early part of the month, he had found a green moth which was strange to him. The insect was found, during the hours of daylight, sitting on a bracken frond. Captain Wright had no entomological gear with him at the time and he had to empty a match box to accommodate the moth, a female.

I was puzzled at the time as to what the moth could be but when, later in the month, I received another letter to say that Seitz' "Macrolepidoptera of the World — Palearctic Fauna — Noctuae" had been combed and that the only thing the moth looked like was *Luceria virens* L. [at that time without an English name], my casual interest became an insatiable desire to see the insect and check the identification.

My desire was sated when the moth arrived in England (together with Captain Wright), for a short visit, in September 1949.

It was certainly *L. virens* and the question of its status then posed itself. For my own part I was incredulous at any theory about it being a casual or vagrant specimen, for one thing the West of Ireland was just about the most unlikely place in Great Britain (this, of course, in the Geographical sense — as should be understood throughout the whole account) for a migrant or stray insect — and, for another, the unique character of the Burren and its almost unworked state, from the entomological viewpoint, immediately sprang to mind.

Fig. 76. Hugh Robinson's Bentley (HAA 16) on the Burren, Co. Clare, Ireland (1950).

The question was thoroughly discussed between Captain Wright (W), Dr. A. A. Lisney, Messrs. H. S. and P. J. M. Robinson (P), Mr. Barry Goater (G) and myself (C) when we met at Freshwater in early October 1949 and, at a later date, by Dr. E. A. Cockayne and me, and it was decided to mount a full scale entomological expedition to the Burren the following August (1950). . . .

The Robinsons were the designers of the apparatus used on the trip and this apparatus was one of the primary requisites of success. Hugh Robinson's car, a specially converted Bentley, was used to transport the heavy gear and all the personnel, with the exception of Captain Wright, from Rosslare to the Burren and back. Captain Wright brought his van, equipped with further apparatus, from Antrim, to meet us at Cashel, Co. Tipperary, and we redistributed ourselves, for comfort's sake, in the two vehicles before commencing the last half of our journey. . . .

Narrative [H. S. Robinson]: We arrived at Fishguard at 5 p.m. on Friday, 4th August, and after the usual formalities presented a schedule of the contents of the Bentley to the Customs Officer. After the first shock his behaviour was admirably controlled. . . . Last on at Fishguard first off at Rosslare, and we were cunning enough to arrange this. The car came under the crane, but there were some anxious consultations. "Two-and-a-half-ton" shouts the foreman, and the craneman, a little shocked, starts to lift. The front wheels came off alright but the rear end stayed obstinately down and the dusty old van began to look like a forlorn spaniel begging for a bone. In the end they took her up aslant and dumped her on the deck. Was it our imagination, or did the ship really have a permanent list all the way to Rosslare? Cold meat, salad, hyoscine hydrobromide, bacon and egg (I suppose someone got some sleep) and last on was, as we had designed, first off.

The Customs again and our now notorious schedule, our first experience of hearing *lepidoptera* described as "the flois" — and RAIN. We were to meet W at Cashel and we were very depressed. We stopped at Waterford for a real breakfast and felt much better, but it still rained. As we arrived at Cashel the sun came out and W's cheerful voice came rolling down the rock. Our cramped passengers transferred gratefully to the second car and we spent the afternoon catching butterflies at Greenfields. We considered doing a night there, but we were all exhausted so we made an uneventful journey to Gort and our beds. My diary says "a magnificent high tea and Guinness at 10d. a pint", but all I remember is blissful sleep.

Sunday, 6th August, a windy day but fine and warm. We ate an Irish breakfast and took sandwiches — at least that is what they called them. What we found was a whole chicken, a whole ham and a couple of loaves of buttered bread. W took us to X [the site where his specimen was taken in 1949] by a "short cut". Never have I seen or experienced such roads. The new springs stood up manfully but the Bentley rattled and banged until we feared a complete disintegration of car and equipment. The grey-white dust of the Burren limestone covered everything and we looked like grey ghosts when we arrived; but the sun shone, we brewed tea, ate our lunch, rested and considered our comfortable stomachs. We gaped reverently at the spot where W had found *virens* the year before, but we shot appalled glances at each other. Could anything fly on this barren, exposed slope? Well, it wasn't my job; I was only the driver. Finally, P settled on a line of traps as well out of the wind as we could manage and took G and I as assistants. W and C decided that sandhills would be more likely and W's pilot set should go there.

We worked like blacks among the rocks, and ran a continuity trial on a thousand yards of cable, returning exhausted to Gort for tea. More Guinness ("every pint you drink saves you 10d., so we must keep at it"), and back to the gear. Goodbye and good luck to the sandhill party, the generator coughs politely, clatters through her warming up and settles down to a steady roar. I am no longer only the driver and the electrical controls leave no time for thinking for the first twenty minutes. The meter hands gradually cease their tremors and the cold light from the great lamps shows up the rocks in sharp silhouette. The wind begins to drop and our hopes to rise. In the gathering dusk a few insects start to fly and we watch eagerly for our quarry. Soon there is a black ring of night round the lamp we are watching and the cones of light from the further traps show faintly in the damp air. There are plenty of insects, many very different in form from our own and we are busy with net and pillbox, but there is no sign of *virens*. Did W's come off a ship sailing into Galway Bay? Is it a sandhill insect? At 10.45 I go down to the sandhills to see C and W, they are cold and have two *tritici* [White-line Dart]. *Virens?* Never heard of it. At 11.10 I am back at the lamp. Nothing. A cloud of despondency descends on us all and we contemplate the baleful lamp miserably. At 11.15 *pallens* [Common Wainscot] flutters in the grass on the far side of the sheet. It looks bigger than the English one and we may as well have it. I net it desultorily and peer through the net. It appears to have a greenish tint and I search frantically for a box. After a panic-stricken struggle I look at it in the light of the lamp and announce with what I hope is reasonable calmness that I think I have *virens*. This produces a weary and cynical laugh — probably P — I force the box into his hands, he and G bend doubtfully over it. I draw a veil over the ensuing scene. The cloud of despondency vanished, the night was calm and we, who had been cold were warm. I sat proudly on my rock. Even if I *was* only the driver . . . I

'The wind begins to drop and our hopes to rise . . . Soon there is a black ring of night round the lamp . . .
and the cones of light from the further traps show faintly in the damp air.'

looked about alertly and carefully — was that a feather on the grass at the edge of the field of light? I took an unostentatious saunter round the circle. This time I had a box. It was certainly a moth and appeared to be drying its wings, white and silvery, over its back. I boxed it carefully and remembered to put a twig in the ground at the spot. Close to the light it was possible to see, between the parallel wings, the beautiful malachite-green surface. A freshly emerged female *virens*.

C and W came in at midnight with the score of *tritici* raised to five, but nothing else. We assumed a proper air of cynical misery and denied any catch of interest. P wondered innocently whether C could identify the insect in the upturned box — yes *that* one. We were not disappointed! We took eight that night, including one female, there was a shower at midnight and by 1 a.m. they had stopped coming in. We went back to Gort and dreamed of endless broods.

My diary tells the hopeless tale of the following days better than any narrative: —

Monday, 7th August. P ill and stayed in bed all day. We decided that P and I with C and G alternately each night should man the big set at X, while W should take the other man and set up his pilot set in as many places as possible. This would give us a good guide to distribution and leave the big set fixed till a better locality turned up. Very cold and windy. We took one male *virens* on switchboard, and a mouse and a bird came to our sheet. W took *bractea* [Gold Spangle]. We returned at midnight and saw a badger on the way home. P had crawled out of bed to get the radio working. I dropped a rock on my foot and was very uncomfortable.

Tuesday, 8th August. A dreadful day. Rain and gales. We took a few *anomala* [The Anomalous] and a rubbed *bractea*. W took nothing.

Wednesday, 9th August. I was ill and stayed in bed all day. Weather foul. The others went out and returned empty handed. P broke one of W's bulbs.

Thursday, 10th August. W was ill. The rest of us found new accommodation nearer to X. Weather still bad so we gave up and went to bed early. P broke W's bed.

Friday, 11th August. All well and much refreshed. Gort Fair — a pandemonium of cattle, and Irishmen with sticks looking exactly like Irishmen with sticks. Went to new digs and to X. W found a plant of white heather and we all wore a piece. P found *virens* pupa. Weather a little better. A beautiful fresh *virens* came at 10.15 and by 3 a.m. we had ten. C and W came back having done three localities and taken eight *virens* in the last (Y) [a new locality]. All the catch were male. We arrived back soaked but happy.

"P found *virens* pupa" — but not quite as simply as that. You will remember that I had marked with a twig the place where the female was found drying her wings. The following day we marked out with a tape a square yard round this twig and G made a list (an astoundingly long list it was) of the plants within it. We then took the whole area to pieces leaf by leaf and root by root to a depth of an inch — and found nothing. P, ever persistent, decided to go on after we had retired in despair and at about 1½ inches found the empty pupa case and extracted it without damage.

Saturday, 12th August. Moved big set to Y, this took us most of the day. Turned out very cold (46°F) and we took nothing of interest. Good audience!

I must break off here to explain about audiences. By our third day at X we had usually assembled, by dusk, up to twenty people, some of whom had walked as much as ten miles from surrounding villages to see "the great lights and the gentlemen catching flois". They were enthusiastic, polite and kind, and brought us water for our tea and cheered us on. Our

185

equipment was never touched and we found the crowd, though occasionally embarrassing in their enthusiasm, a pleasant lot. By the end of our stay we had begun to look forward nightly to a good "house" and we were quite upset when on our last night most of them deserted us for the circus!

Sunday, 13th August. We had a day of indulgence and went over in our best clothes to Gort where we had LUNCH. We were just about capable of standing in the afternoon. In the evening we patronised O'L's bar till dusk and then, distended and sleepy, we watched our traps till midnight. Seven male *virens*.

Monday, 14th August. Everyone slept in the afternoon except C who nobly set all the *virens* and a dozen or two of the best of the other things. Wet and windy. Mrs. O'L gave us a sprig of white heather. Five Guinness and five male *virens* and we packed up at midnight.

Tuesday, 15th August. A sunny morning and afternoon, we hopefully re-sited the big set but rain started in at 6 p.m. and by 9 p.m. was torrential. Wind high and temperature down to 45°. We spent the evening in O'L's with the Garda. Twelve Guinness and no *virens*.

Wednesday, 16th August. Barometer down to 999 millibars, promises badly for to-night. An appalling night. Barometer down to 990 with torrential rain and gales. We abandoned the lamps (after replacing a defective lead in the torrent) and retired to bed. We could see the lamps blazing on the hill from our bedroom, but it was little comfort.

Thursday, 17th August. A dismal day. We found this morning that the two high pressure lamps had been fractured by the rain. Two battered male *virens* were in the traps. W left for home — a depressing end to his part of the expedition — and we had little enough time ourselves. In the evening G took one male *virens* sitting on the grass and P took one female. Cold and windy night.

Friday, 18th August. Packed all equipment to go tomorrow.

*   *   *

There is little more to relate — a weary, dishevelled and dirty party arrived at their several homes on the Sunday night. The wives were probably pacified with nylons — but we still miss the Guinness. . . .

[Lisney, A. A., Classey, E. W., Robinson, H. S. 1951. Irish Lepidoptera — A brief introduction. *Entomologist's Gazette* **2**: 85–99].

Accompanying this article was a plate depicting the new discovery. It bore a caption: 'The Claddagh'. However, this suggested name obviously did not meet with universal approval, judging by the following letter to the editor of the *Entomologist's Gazette*.

'THE CLADDAGH'

Philip P. Graves, Bantry, Co. Cork. (1952)

Dear Sir,

"Claddagh" means a sea beach in Gaelic. The Claddagh is the fishermens' quarter in the city of Galway. "Claddagh rings" are imitations of old fashioned amulets once made by the Claddagh people in Galway. I cannot for the life of me see why this name has been applied to *Luceria virens*. The moth is not found in Galway city, nor, as far as I can make out, on the beach, nor has it anything to do with "Claddagh rings". As it stands, the name has a decidedly stage Irish air, suggesting obsolete or obsolescent words or phrases such as "spalpeen", "shillelagh" and "top of the morning". Would not "The Burren Green" be a much better name? The term "Burren" is used for the limestone "crags" or pavements of North Clare and the neighbouring parts of Co. Galway where the moth is very likely to turn up. Such a name would therefore be applicable and explicable.'

I remain, dear sir,

Faithfully yours,

Phillip P. Graves

[Graves, P. P. 1952. "The Claddagh". *Entomologist's Gazette* 3: 74].

Logic won the day.

LEPIDOPTEROLOGICAL REMINISCENCES

Alexander H. Clarke, F.E.S., Earls Court, London, W. (1906)

Alexander Henry Clarke (1839–1911) was elected a Fellow of the Entomological Society of London in 1867. In this short communication to *The Entomologist's Record* he recalls seeing butterflies in parts of London which today would seem remarkable.

As a matter of ancient history I may mention that in 1855 and 1857, *Augiades sylvanus* [Large Skipper] was abundant, and *Polyommatus astrarche* [Brown Argus] and *Hesperia malvae* (*alveolus*) [Grizzled Skipper] by no means scarce, on the West London Railway embankment at Wormwood Scrubbs, and especially on that portion of it which runs alongside Latimer Road. I also took a *Polyommatus coridon* [Chalk Hill Blue] ♀, and saw another in Ladbroke Square, Notting Hill, on August 14th, 1864.

[Clarke, A. H. 1906. Lepidopterological reminiscences. *The Entomologist's Record and Journal of Variation* **18**: 24].

THE PAINTED LADY IN GREAT NUMBERS
NEAR HUNSTANTON

James M. Barrett, King's Lynn, Norfolk. (1904)

It was on a Thursday in October last that we were driving to Hunstanton. After passing Heacham there is a rise by Heacham Hall and then a short piece of level road till you come to the bottom of that steepest hill in this part of the country – Redgate Hill. Just after climbing this hill, and in Hunstanton parish, I first noticed a butterfly dash past, and during the next quarter of a mile of road, more particularly on the right hand side, the Painted Ladies kept rising from the roadside in scores, flying round us, or settling on the road or on flowers growing in the hedge side. I drove slowly to have a good look at them; there were rather pale ones (not worn) and lovely rich coloured ones. They were in splendid condition, and were very alert and shy, not a bit as though they had come off a long journey. It was a lovely bright day, and they appeared to be enjoying the sunshine and the flowers, and they sailed about as these butterflies *can* sail. I think this, the first company we saw, covered three or four hundred yards of the road side, and were particularly attracted by the flowers of knapweed. This was a little after 12 o'clock noon. About ten minutes later we passed Chilvers' Gardens. These are about half an acre in extent, partly upon the same road and about half a mile from the sea, and were laid out in flower beds. There were a good many beautiful asters, but bordering all the beds and paths were masses of lavender in full bloom. This lavender was perfectly alive with Painted Ladies; I could not possibly estimate the numbers, but there must have been thousands. I did not think of migration, as the butterflies were in such splendid condition! It looked as though the warm sunshine had hatched off a big brood. It is rather difficult to decide whether they were moving in any given direction, for they kept rising as we passed, flying on ahead, and around us; but the flight was certainly very local, since from the place where I saw the first to Chilvers', which seemed to be the attractive spot, could not be more than half a mile. Roughly, the road is a mile from the sea.

[Barrett, J. M. 1904. *Vanessa cardui* in great numbers near Hunstanton. *Entomologist's Monthly Magazine* **40**: 61–62].

Although James Barrett suggested that migration was not the reason for this multitude, we disagree. These butterflies were all in pristine condition, the locality was just one mile from the sea and the weather was perfect. The wings of newly hatched butterflies soon become damaged by contact with grasses and other plants, whereas newly arrived migrants tend to be in good condition as their wing-scales are not damaged by flight across the English Channel or North Sea.

Plate 1. Scarcer than Gold-dust. (Unless stated otherwise, specimens from M. A. Salmon collection.)

(a) Dark Green Fritillary (*Argynnis aglaja*): male ab. *wimani* Holmgren. Co. Mayo, Ireland, July 1998. R. D. G. Barrington (page 132). (R. D. G. Barrington coll.)

(b) Hybrid between Adonis Blue (*Polyommatus bellargus*) and Chalk Hill Blue (*Polyommatus coridon*): ab. *polonus* Zeller (page 300). North Downs, June 2004. A. M. Jones. (A. M. Jones coll.)

(c) Swallowtail (*Papilio machaon*): male ab. *discoflava* Salmon. Wicken Fen, August 1911. G. Brooks.

(d) Almost ab. *duplex*! Clouded Yellow (*Colias croceus*): typical female with left forewing of the form *helice* Hübner. Hove, Sussex, October 1947. J. B. Purefoy (page 292).

(e) Silver-washed Fritillary (*Argynnis paphia*): bilateral gynandromorph (*left*: male; *right*: female ab. *valesina* Esper). Burley, New Forest, Hampshire, July 1961. J. B. Purefoy.

(f) Another South Downs 'special' (pages 158–159). Chalk Hill Blue (*Polyommatus coridon*): female ab. *antiextrema* Bright & Leeds + *postalba* B. & L. + *limbojuncta* Courvoisier. Shoreham, Sussex, August 1955. R. E. Stockley. (R. W. Watson coll.)

(g) and (h) Orange-tip (*Anthocaris cardamines*). *Above*: gynandromorph. South Devon, 1947. G. R. S. Willson. *Below*: male ab. *salmonea* Oberthür. Sowdens Bridge, Pelynt, Cornwall, May 1972. A. P. Gainsford.

(i) Small Tortoiseshell (*Aglais urticae*): female ab. *maculomissa* Goodson. Amberley, Sussex, August 1907. W. G. Pether.

Plate 2. Extract from the diary kept by T. G. Howarth whilst a Japanese prisoner of war (page 262). Complete with the red censorship stamps, the inter-leaved drawings depict the early life stages of the butterfly *Euploea phaenareta castelnaui*, a 'crow' member of the family Danaidae.

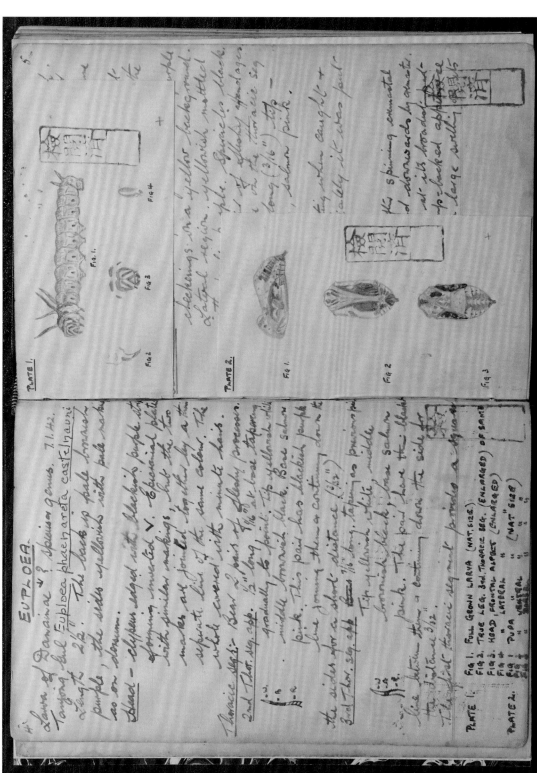

Plate 3. Aberrations of the Small Pearl-bordered Fritillary (*Boloria selene*) from the Craske collection (Natural History Museum, London). Bob Craske (page 159) was proud that his captures should have become part of the National Collection. 'It will let people see what used to be possible.'

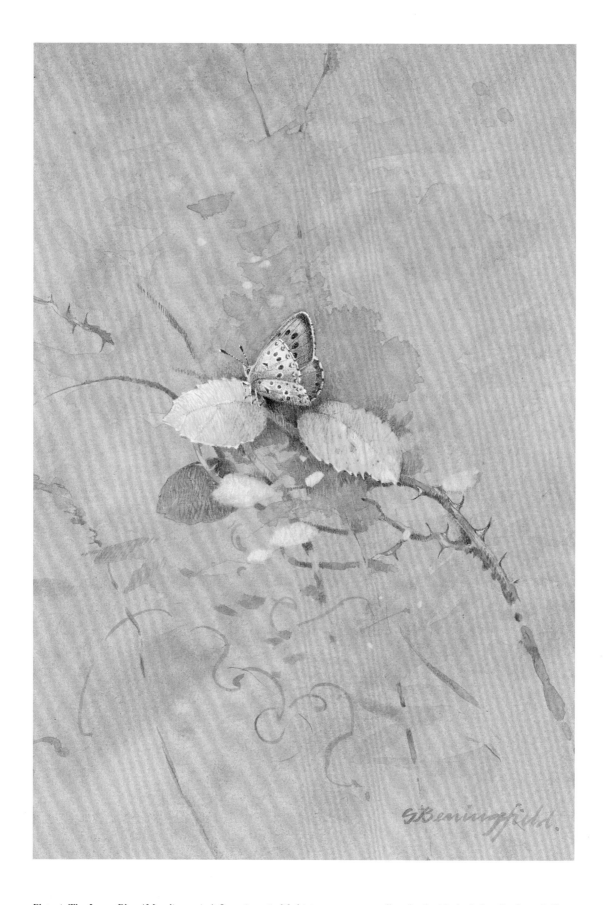

Plate 4. The Large Blue (*Maculinea arion*). Its enigmatic life history was eventually solved with the help of walnut shells (page 48). Detail from an original painting by Gordon Beningfield (Fig. 71). He began his career with a company that specialized in ecclesiastical art and furnishings. Later on, the English countryside and its natural history were to be his source of inspiration. His first book (*Beningfield's Butterflies*) was published in 1978.

Aglais urticae
Caught by Capt. E.B.Purefoy
East Farleigh 28·7·1942

Plate 5. (above) Spring Butterflies (*c.*1924). Original watercolour by Frederick W. Frohawk (Figs 22 & 27).

(below) Small Tortoiseshell (*Aglais urticae*) ab. *leodiensis* Cabeau. Original watercolour by F. W. Frohawk,
painted at the age of eighty-one. His work was all the more remarkable for the fact that he was almost
completely blind in one eye — a legacy of contracting typhoid in his teens.

Plate 6. 'A really good insect cabinet is something like a safe investment of money, the interest being paid in the pleasure and profit the owner receives from studying the contents' (Edward Newman, 1871). A Thomas Gurney twenty-drawer butterfly cabinet c.1880 (see page 65). A thirty-drawer mahogany cabinet made by him cost £18 in 1890.

This particular cabinet was once owned by Captain Edward Bagwell Purefoy (page 47), whose detective work did much to unravel the mystery surrounding the life cycle of the Large Blue. It is now in the possession of one of the authors of this book.

Plate 7. (a) 'Mahogany Entomological Cabinets On A New Principle. Ten Shillings per Drawer.' So began Charles Brady's advertisement in *The Entomologist* for April 1878. It continued: 'This New and Improved Cabinet, as exhibited at the Great Entomological Exhibition, Royal Aquarium, Westminster, gained universal admiration for the light effect of the drawers and other improvements, combined with acknowledged superior workmanship, and extremely moderate price. Reference can be made to several Gentlemen who have purchased these Cabinets.'

The drawers with their solid mahogany bases, extremely narrow frames, intricate double seals, hidden bearer runners and camphor cells, and fine dove-tailing are typical Brady trademarks (page 63). In 1890 his thirty-drawer mahogany cabinet 'with cornice' was priced at £16 5s 0d; a forty-drawer cabinet could be purchased for £20. (A. S. Harmer coll.)

(b) Rare glazed display box made by Brady & Son for Leonard T. Ford (page 68). The 1901 Census records Charles Brady's occupation as a show case maker and his sons James and Edward as apprentices.

(c) Cabinet made for George Nobbs (page 67). The base of each drawer is solid mahogany three-eighths inch thick.

Some idea of the relative cost of a quality cabinet at the time may be gauged by the fact that when Mr Nobbs entered Royal Service as Head Gardener at Osborne House, Isle of Wight in 1894, his starting salary was £80 per annum, rising by £5 a year until his salary reached £100. He was entitled to a cottage and garden. (A. S. Harmer coll.)

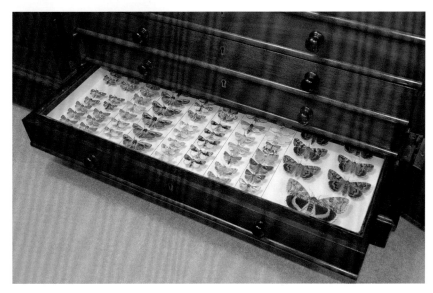

(a)

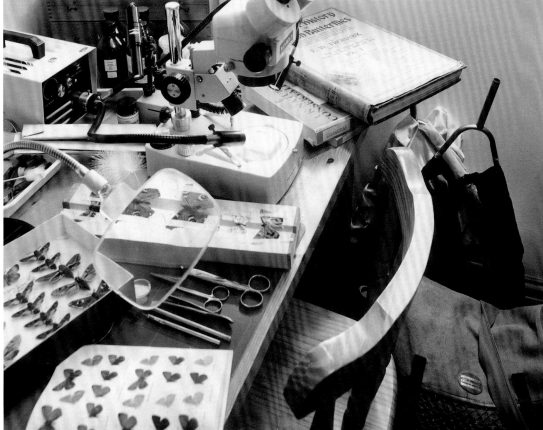

(b)

Plate 8. Tools of the Trade: the lepidopterist's equipment. (a) 1900. (b) 2000.

CHAPTER FOUR

'FIVE MILES FROM ANYWHERE' —
BUTTERFLY HUNTING IN THE BRITISH ISLES

'Sebastian Knight's college years were not particularly happy. To be sure he enjoyed many of the things he found at Cambridge — he was in fact quite overcome at first to see and smell and feel the country for which he had always longed. A real hansom-cab took him from the station to Trinity College: the vehicle, it seemed, had been waiting there especially for him, desperately holding out against extinction till that moment, and then gladly dying out to join side whiskers and the Large Copper.'

Vladimir Nabokov, The Real Life of Sebastian Knight (1941)

I went out into the village at about half-past nine in the dark quiet evening. A few stars penetrated the soft sky; a few lights shone on earth, from a distant farm seen through a gap in the cottages. Single and in groups, separated by gardens or bits of orchard, the cottages were vaguely discernible: here and there a yellow window square gave out a feeling of home, tranquillity, security. Nearly all were silent. Ordinary speech was not to be heard, but from one house came the sounds of an harmonium and a voice singing a hymn, both faintly. A dog barked far off. After an interval a gate fell-to lightly. Nobody was on the road.

IT WAS WITH THESE LINES from *In Pursuit of Spring* (1914) that Edward Thomas (1878–1917) remembered a personal and quiet moment during his long journey from London to the West Country. The year was 1913 and at that time the English countryside seemed to stretch onwards for ever — at least from Dover to Land's End. His journey was made only just in time, for within two decades the green fields were in full retreat. Long gone were the days when butterfly hunters like James Francis Stephens (1792–1852) could stand transfixed by the incredible sight of 'myriads [of White-letter Hairstreaks] that hovered over every flower and bramble blossom'*. That was in the long summer of 1820, but who today can remember even seeing five White-letter Hairstreaks at the same time? Today there are few who can recall distant scenes such as those described by Stephens or Thomas.

Most of the articles selected for this chapter were written during the nineteenth century, with just a handful since the Second World War. In a search for our lost countryside we found that earlier writers, albeit without Edward Thomas's gift of poetical prose, gave tantalizing glimpses of the England that existed in the long ago. One of these was Roland Trimen (1840–1916). Fresh from South Africa in 1858, he gave a memorable account of his day out in the lanes and woods around Dorking. 'The whole stretch of country from Betchworth, and far away to the South, where the distant wooded hills melted into the sky, lay like a map before me, — everything bright and glowing under the glorious June sun.' Surely it is the memory of experiences such as this that leads the earnest butterfly hunter to pick up his net and venture into green and distant places.

* Stephens, J. F. 1828. *Illustrations of British Entomology* — (Haustellata). London, Baldwin and Cradock.

APPEARANCE OF THE BATH WHITE IN LARGE NUMBERS

Although the Bath White (*Pontia daplidice*) is common in the Mediterranean region of Europe and freely migrates, it has always been considered a rarity in this country. C. B. Williams (1958) calculated that perhaps only 400 specimens had been recorded during the period 1826 and 1944 (including about 200 reported to have been seen on the coast of Dorset in 1906). Both 1906 and 1945 (when a total of 650 was recorded) were years in which unprecedented numbers appeared in the English southern counties.

Fig. 77. Carrington Bonsor Williams F.R.S. (1889–1981). The great authority on insect migration.

a) 1906: 'A COUPLE OF HUNDRED OR MORE AT LULWORTH COVE'

I think it of sufficient interest to record what must be a unique occurrence of a swarm of *P. daplidice* [Bath White] in this country. My attention was recently called to this remarkable incident by the Rev. F. L. Blathwayte, after having seen the specimens captured by Mr. W. W. Collins, who has kindly given me the following particulars of his observation: "I captured the Bath Whites in 1906 at the latter end of July, or early in August, on the Dorset cliffs, west of Durdle Door, which is west of Lulworth Cove. I cannot tell the exact day, but I was in camp west of Lulworth, not far from the edge of the cliffs. I went off with my net one morning and saw what I took to be a large hatch out of *P. daplidice*; it is not possible to say how many — the best of my recollection a couple of hundred or probably more, as they were hovering about on the upper part of the cliff. I easily captured the four (2 ♂♂, 2 ♀♀) Mr. Blathwayte has seen." The occurrence suggests that an immigrant female in the spring laid its eggs in this particular spot and the resultant butterflies all emerged about the same time, and kept to the same part of the cliffs where the food-plant flourishes.

[Frohawk, F. W. 1938. Unrecorded occurrence of *Pontia daplidice* in numbers. *The Entomologist* **71**: 66].

It appears that Mr Collins failed to place data labels under his specimens or he would have been able to check the precise date of his captures. In 1945 Dr Henry Bernard Davis Kettlewell (1907–1979) returned from a truly remarkable four days' collecting in South Cornwall and was quick to publish extracts from his diary:

b) 1945: THE BATH WHITE, SHORT-TAILED BLUE AND PALE CLOUDED YELLOW IN SOUTH CORNWALL

July 14: Fine and sunny. At 9 a.m. (G.M.T.) I went round the hotel gardens to look for larvae of *H. peltigera* [Bordered Straw] on the banks of marigold, as I had found it the previous day commonly on *Ononis*. I noticed an insect fly out of a herb bed which I at first thought was *Abraxas grossulariata* [The Magpie]. It came to rest in some parsnips, where I procured it by picking it up between my finger and thumb. To my amazement it was a newly hatched female *P. daplidice* [Bath White]. I hastily returned to the hotel to get my net, and whilst running through the garden I saw first a *hyale* [Pale Clouded Yellow] and then

another *daplidice*. On returning with my net I caught the *hyale*, which was a fine male. A quarter of an hour later I caught my second *daplidice*. It was somewhat worn, but the normal green pattern of the underside was entirely replaced with grey-black. It was a female. I found no more in the next half hour, so I crossed the road into a small valley which was entirely taken up with allotments. *Pontia daplidice* was flying freely here, and I rapidly had two in the net together. Altogether I took 37 during the course of the day, and could have taken several more but for the fact that I spent a great deal of time following the females, endeavouring to find on what they were ovipositing. . . .

July 15. The weather broke entirely. Northerly gale and about an inch of rain fell in a few hours. . . .

July 16: Fine intervals after 11 a.m. Strong S.W. wind. It was apparent that the storm had killed many *daplidice*. *Pieris rapae* [Small White] was also much scarcer. At about 2 p.m. (G.M.T.) I noticed a Blue moving about on a patch of hop-trefoil. I turned back to look at it, as I suddenly realized that it had had an

underside like *Celastrina argiolus* [Holly Blue] and it would be an unlikely place to see this species. To my amazement I found it was a fine male *E. argiades* [Short-tailed Blue] in good condition, its two tails being obvious on close examination. At this stage an awful feeling of unreality came over me, which was not altogether helped by seeing another *daplidice* flying towards me. This was secured, and with four others, made a total of five for to-day. The ground was systematically worked for further Blues, but no further specimens were encountered.

July 17: Strong east wind with hot periods. . . . Later in the day I tried a fresh spot about a quarter of a mile from the allotments. *Daplidice* was flying commonly here in the few brief moments of sun which were given me. Altogether 12 were taken during the course of the day . . . Between July 14 and 17 a total of 54 *daplidice* were captured and others seen . . .

[Kettlewell, H. B. D. 1945. *Pontia daplidice*, *Everes argiades* and *Colias hyale* in South Cornwall. *The Entomologist* **78**: 123–124].

Kettlewell discovered that *P. daplidice* were ovipositing on hedge mustard (*Sisymbrium officinale*). He subsequently obtained ova from collected *Sisymbrium* and from the eight females he set up to lay on his return; a female *C. hyale* taken on the first day also obliged him with eggs. Both species were bred through successfully.

Dr Bernard Kettlewell was one of the great characters of British entomology. Educated at Charterhouse, Caius College, Cambridge and St Bartholomew's Hospital Medical

School, he settled into general practice at Cranleigh in Surrey. Unhappy with the newly formed National Health Service, Kettlewell emigrated to South Africa before returning to work with Professor Edmund Brisco Ford at Oxford.

Sir Cyril Clarke described him as 'a household name to everyone interested in natural history, and known to thousands of entomologists throughout the world for his research into industrial melanism'. Ronald P. Demuth remembered him for quite different reasons: 'Bernard never did things by half. Fast sports cars were driven at excessive speed. When looking for larvae with me, he would consider it a failure if he did not find twice the number that I did.' A characteristic picture was painted by L. Hugh Newman: 'I've so often been collecting with him – drenched to the skin, the wind blowing his dark hair into his eyes, without thought of food or mealtimes, but determined not to give up the search, whatever the weather and discomfort of it all.' When Kettlewell died he left instructions that when his beloved dog passed on, its ashes were to be sprinkled over his grave.

One week after Bernard Kettlewell had caught fifty-four Bath Whites in South Cornwall, the Revd Anthony H. Harbottle was out and about at Bude, North Cornwall. He also found the Bath White in considerable numbers and kindly sent us the following personal account of his meeting with it:

c) 1945: 'I TRIED, WITHOUT SUCCESS, TO THROW MY COAT OVER IT.' THE BATH WHITE IN NORTH CORNWALL

I saw my first Bath White on 22nd July. It was a female, very worn and it settled on the road as I wheeled my bicycle up a hill on the outskirts of Bude. I tried without success to throw my coat over it. A short while later, armed with a net, I caught my first specimen nearby. It was a male in good condition and I saw another male shortly afterwards. During the remainder of July a further thirty specimens were recorded and two more in August, the last of the immigrants on the 12th of that month, bringing the total to forty-two butterflies. On 28th July I secured between my finger and thumb, two females ovipositing on *Sisymbrium* [hedge mustard], growing on the Bude Golf Course. I was able to breed a number of these, the first emerging on the 24th September and the last the following year on 6th May. A third brood occurred, but it was partial, there being just two males and three females. These were uniformly larger and of a slightly more intense coloration. On 23rd July I caught a suffused female, which is now in the National Collection. The last specimen recorded from the area was a very large male taken on the golf course on 2nd October 1945. The total number of Bath Whites recorded from Bude in 1945 was forty-seven.

[Harbottle, A. H. H. 2003. Personal communication].

See also: Harbottle, A. H. H. 1950. The occurrence of *Pontia daplidice* Linn. in North Cornwall in 1945. *Entomologist's Gazette* 1: 49–50.

Not everyone, however, was to be so fortunate that year . . .

IT HAPPENED AT . . . (No. 8) – 'THE LUCK OF THE IRISH'

Bryan P. Beirne, Ph.D., F.R.E.S., F.L.S., Ottawa, Ontario. (1952)

Some years ago I spent a few days in the middle of July collecting at Killarney. The weather was bad most of the time, with strong winds and frequent heavy rainstorms. One afternoon, however, there was bright sunshine, and I collected in a sheltered glade by the lake shore in the woods of Ross Island. There I saw the largest number of species of butterflies that I had ever seen at the one time in Ireland. Fourteen of the 38 species reliably recorded from Ireland were present . . .

I was busy collecting Microlepidoptera, but noticed casually that the specimens of *napi* seemed to be rather large and well marked. They flew rapidly with the wind through the glade, without pausing at the scabious and other wild flowers that were abundant there. They appeared to be in rather good condition for remnants of the first brood and were perhaps rather early for the second brood. This puzzled me vaguely for some months, until reports in the entomological periodicals provided a possible explanation. It was in 1945, the year of the great *Pontia daplidice* invasion. What I had seen were almost certainly that species. And I had not troubled to capture even a single specimen, although I must have seen at least a dozen.

[Beirne, B. P. 1952. It happened at . . . *Entomologist's Gazette* **3**: 42].

AWKWARD INCIDENTS IN AN ENTOMOLOGICAL CAREER

Claude Morley, F.E.S., F.Z.S., Monk Soham, Suffolk. (1918)

Claude Morley (1874–1951) was one of the most colourful entomologists. From Epsom College he proceeded to the Ipswich Museum, where he studied under the Curator, Dr John E. Taylor, and afterwards, the British Museum, where the fruit of his labours — *The Ichneumons of Great Britain* (1903–1914) — was published in five volumes.

It was due to his hard work that the Suffolk Naturalists' Society came into being in 1929. His obituarist commented that 'in the quietude of his "moated grange" in Monk's Soham, Morley worked with the zest of the born scientist. . . . Not only was his knowledge encyclopaedic, but he brought to his studies that gift for tabulation, classification and arrangement which [Henry] Havelock Ellis held to be a characteristic of East Anglians.' He was described by Dr Kenneth Blair as being a 'delightful personality, with a strong sense of humour, he was highly individualistic, even eccentric, with a hatred of modern "progress", and would have no wireless, telephone, electricity or summer-time — "lying-in time" he always called it'.

A number of Claude Morley's more whimsical writings such as *The Beatific Babblings of Bugland's Bard* were published under the authorship of 'Maud Clorley'.

Fig. 78. Claude Morley. His more whimsical writings were published under the authorship of 'Maud Clorley'.

Insect-hunting leads one, by its very fascination, into strange places and predicaments; and our experience on April 26th, 1904, was most diverting, though it might have ended — as it would often do, if mantraps and spring-guns were not abolished — in serious consequences. Presence of mind is a useful possession upon such occasions, as old John Scott found when, ordered by the owner off his grounds, he sturdily commented that (when there is but one man's word against your own) might is right . . . From Brandon, Elliot and I had ridden our bicycles from the Lakenheath road, opposite Northcourt Lodge, to a cottage in Elms Covert, where an aged keeper directed us down a road known as "Shakers," when our compass showed a southerly direction and we sought east. So we branched off across a heath which was half gorse and wholly heather (any botanist understands this kind of proportion) of about a foot's growth, and rode as straightly as may be along rabbits' tracks of six inches or less in breadth to Elveden Warren; thence, avoiding Warren Lodge, we emerged upon the Bury road at the classical "Diastictus Place" [*] as designed. No lonelier spot exists in Suffolk. There we stacked our machines and fell to investigating the rabbit holes beneath the turf wall bounding the high road, whence *Onthophilus sulcatus* [a local beetle] and other rarities may be retrieved with sufficient persuasion and labour. Presently I saw, on rising to stretch, a man stalking something unknown in a crouching position from the warren, and I drew Elliot's attention to so novel and interesting a spectacle, continuing myself half buried in the bunny-hole at which I was at work. Ere long the man approached and asked somewhat brusquely the object of our subterranean investigations. At the same moment I became aware of a county policeman alighting from his bicycle in my rear. Here, then, was our quartette — an unfair one surely, for who does not know that a bobby's word is more than that of a mere private individual! Fortunately Bluebeard was no less than the Brandon constable, who knew we were staying at the "White Hart" there; and a further reference to a local cousin (Arthur Elliot, Esq., J.P., of Elveden) straightened matters entirely, though the keeper, after his kind, still rejected the evidence of our collecting-tubes, and considered, in a retrogressive undertone, leptophilous coleoptera to be pernicious examples for the local yokel.

When all the world and love is young your best collection is made. I had a delightful landlady at Lowestoft, and on August 3rd, 1904, this good dame (her heart, if not her head, merits the title) cooked three "hard-boiled" eggs. With these upon my person by way of lunch, I sallied forth to the Kessingland sandhills on the Suffolk coast. Upon arrival at these dunes I became utterly absorbed upon the capture of the Culicoid bug, *Metacanthus puncticeps*, which was quite new to me, and abundant on *Ononis spinosa* [rest-harrow]. So obsessed therewith was I that I rolled from patch to patch of food-plant in the most abandoned manner — till I heard something *give*: thought I, "The eggs, by George." Most gingerly my fingers sought them in their snug retreat — and found them. Found, too, they had NOT been hard-boiled; sincerely I wished they had. How Newbery and his niece did laugh!

[Morley, C. 1918. Awkward incidents in an entomological career. *The Entomologist* **51**: 163–164].

[*] *Diasticticus* — a very rare ground beetle known only from Suffolk.

THE CLOUDED YELLOW

The Clouded Yellow butterfly (*Colias croceus* or *C. edusa* as the early lepidopterists knew it) is a frequent visitor to our shores. Once in a decade or so, vast numbers wing their way across the English Channel, and clover fields, especially across the southern half of England, appear to come alive with these very attractive yellow butterflies. The late Lt. Col. A. Maitland Emmet (1989) tells us that the 'great *edusa* years' were 1877, 1892, 1900, 1913, 1928, 1937, in six of the years 1941 to 1950, and 1983.

Fig. 79. Revd Frederick Neal collecting Clouded Yellows at Broadstairs, Kent (1928).

The following brief notes confirm our impression that the Clouded Yellow and its two cousins, the Pale Clouded Yellow (*C. hyale*) and Berger's Clouded Yellow (*C. alfacariensis*), retain a special affection in the hearts and minds of butterfly hunters. The Pale Clouded Yellow is a rare migrant to Britain and although small numbers are seen most years, it has never been as frequent as the Clouded Yellow. In the first letter, an enthusiastic tyro has the afternoon of his life; while in the second, an old hand attempts to show that some rarities are not always as rare as we think.

ALMOST TOO GOOD TO BE TRUE!

William C. Chaney, New Brompton, Kent. (1857)

Yesterday I had the pleasure of making acquaintance with my first specimen of *C. Hyale* [Pale Clouded Yellow]; it was flying over a saintfoin field in Wigmore Wood: after a smart up-hill chase I succeeded in capturing it, and found it to be a male, rather wasted, but nevertheless a glorious prize. Returning home over Darland Hill, thinking of my *Hyale*, and wondering whether I was too early for *Edusa* [Clouded Yellow], great was my surprise and astonishment when there arose, almost from under my feet, an apparition (for I could hardly believe in the reality): there, floating before me was what appeared to be *Machaon* [Swallowtail]; but no, it could not be! What! *Machaon* on the top of a Kentish chalk hill, high and dry, scarcely out of the smoke of Chatham! The idea was preposterous. I stood motionless; but there was no disputing the fact, — it was indeed *Machaon*. I therefore bestirred myself, and, after a little dodging to and fro (I had but a small pocket-net, and the wind was very high), I succeeded in capturing it, when it proved to be a fine female, in splendid condition, but minus one tail, which I strongly suspect became detached in the scuffle. I had just boxed my second prize, and was continuing my journey homeward, when another stranger attracted my attention, — a white butterfly, but the under wings too yellow for *Rapæ* or *Napi* [Small and Green-veined Whites]. What could it be? I soon captured it, and found, to my great joy, it was a splendid female *Colias Hyale*. Thus, in less than one hour, I became possessed of a pair of *C. Hyale* and a Kentish *P. Machaon*.

[Chaney, W. C. 1857. *Colias hyale. The Entomologist's Weekly Intelligencer* **2**: 171–172].

NOT SO RARE AFTER ALL!

Roland Trimen, Brighton, Sussex. (1857)

I find this species [Pale Clouded Yellow] unusually common near here this season. On Monday last, on approaching a lucerne field, I beheld a green net waving about, and having introduced myself to the individual who bore it, he kindly led the way to some lucerne field in the vicinity, where he informed me he had captured seven *Hyale* [Pale Clouded Yellow]. The day, though windy, was fine and bright, and eventually I succeeded in taking eight specimens of this insect, and my companion took four more. Three others were captured in the same field by a small boy. Of *C. Edusa* [Clouded Yellow] very few are out yet. *Eremobia ochroleuca* [Dusky Sallow] is not uncommon on the flowers of knapweed.

[Trimen, R. 1857. *Colias Hyale. The Entomologist's Weekly Intelligencer* 2: 172].

THE CLOUDED YELLOW AT ANDOVER

Henry T. Stainton, Lewisham, London, S. E. (16th August 1856)

A specimen was seen at Andover the other day by an entomological friend, whose ardour has nearly evaporated.

[Stainton, H. T. 1856. *Colias Edusa. The Entomologist's Weekly Intelligencer* 1: 165].

THE CLOUDED YELLOW AT FOREST HILL

Charles G. Barrett, Mile End, London. (18th August 1856)

While riding in the train last Wednesday on the Brighton line I saw two specimens of *Colias Edusa* flying on the bank: I therefore got out at the next station, Forest Hill, returned to the place and caught them both, but could not find any more: they were in excellent condition, and could not have long emerged from the pupa.

[Barrett, C. G. 1856. *Edusa* at Forest Hill. *The Entomologist's Weekly Intelligencer* 1: 165].

INSECT HUNTING IN ABBOT'S WOOD

W. C. Dale, London, E. C. (1879)

The very interesting account of the New Forest that has lately appeared in the 'Entomologist' (*Entomologist*, **12**: 75, 96, 120), under the title of "A Lepidopterist's Guide to Lyndhurst," cannot fail to have excited in the breasts of many youthful entomologists a longing to visit the beautiful spots so faithfully described by Mr. Bernard Lockyer. Two difficulties, however, generally stand in the way — time and expense. Many a young clerk, tied to his desk in the bank or the merchant's office, can only get a day's holiday at the most; and the question with him is where to go in the shortest time, at the smallest possible expense, with the greatest certainty of taking a large number of species. My object in writing these few lines is to answer this question. A journey to Brockenhurst or Lyndhurst averages three hours, at an expense of twenty-two shillings. The wood that I shall name can be reached in one hour and forty minutes at an expense of nine shillings and eightpence. This wood, almost equal in beauty to the New Forest, is known as Abbot's Wood, and is within twenty-five minutes' walk of Polegate, a station on the London, Brighton, and South Coast

Railway. One of the company's fastest trains (the "paper train") leaves London Bridge at 6.40 a.m., and slips carriages at Polegate at 8.20. A train returns from Polegate at 9.42 p.m., arriving at London at 12.5. My imaginary clerk may, therefore, spend the entire day at the scene of action, with time also for some sugaring. To find the best road to the wood, ask any of the officials at Polegate to point out two red-brick villas known as "Sunnyside;" follow the road in front of these, and you will come into the Hailsham Road (the privet-hedge on your right hand and the old blackthorn on the left will repay attention). In front of you, on the left, stands a pinky-white cottage with a black slate roof; go on past this cottage down the road, and take the first turning on your left — a beautiful and productive lane, leading by a stile at the top on the right hand into a field. This is the "White Field," one of the finest sugaring-grounds in the county. *Ophiodes lunaris* [Lunar Double-stripe] has been taken here, and *Catephia alchymista* [The Alchymist] hard by. *Melitaea athalia* [Heath Fritillary], *Arge galathea* [Marbled White], and the three large Fritillaries swarm in good seasons. *Apatura iris* [Purple Emperor] may be seen with certainty every year (about 18th July), in the left-hand corner nearest to the wood. I know one particular branch of a certain oak which, year after year, is a favourite throne of the "purple monarch." At the top of the white field (whence you get a lovely view of the sea) is one of the numerous woods that go to make up Abbot's Wood — these are Gnat Wood, Folkington Wood, and Cophall Wood. Folkington Wood has lately changed hands, and it is just possible that some difficulty may be experienced about going over certain portions of it. The owner of the "pinky-white cottage" will, I am sure, give all necessary information on this head; and his son (a remarkably intelligent youth) knows the best spot where to look for *Apatura iris*. The following is a list of the butterflies I have myself taken in the locality [A long list of previous captures and their dates follows] . . . I think I have said enough to prove that Abbot's Wood will furnish a mine of entomological wealth to a diligent and systematic collector.

[Dale, W. C. 1879. Insect hunting in Abbot's Wood. *The Entomologist* **12**: 155–157].

THE PURPLE EMPEROR

Revd G. M. A. Hewett, M. A., Winchester, Hampshire. (1895)

I am one of the fortunate men to whom the heading, which I have just written, not merely suggests entrancing visions of what might be, but calls up actual memories. Fortunate, surely I may say, for though the splendid insect, which takes its fair name from the goddess of the rainbow, is no great prize, compared with many a meaner and less showy specimen, yet I am inclined to fancy that most of us are boys enough to look with more complacency on its purple splendour than on one of those dull little *Caradrinidae* [noctuid moths], which is really so much greater a prize. I know one gentleman, at any rate, who, at a very early date in our entomological acquaintance, wrote to me 'I do like pretty insects.' I wonder if his tastes have since been corrupted and made severer by his own successes with regard to those same dull little *Caradrinidae*. But though I have the luck to live within reach of *Iris* [Purple Emperor], yet I must at once make the somewhat humiliating confession that I have never taken his Majesty or her Majesty in a net. I hope that this confession will lessen the jealousy of less happily situated mortals. I will go even farther, and say that I have never even seen him near enough to swear to his identity. I have seen large butterflies round the oak-tops at Lyndhurst, but what of that? We have all seen large butterflies round the tops of trees, and murmured quietly 'Look at those Fritillaries.' However, the confession pains me. I hope no one will quote my own words against me in parallel columns. I am not a great statesman, but I do like insects which I have caught on the wing, and had some difficulty, too, in catching. I would go a long way to make sure of netting *Iris*. But, though I would go a long way, yet I cannot screw up my courage to carry about high meat or a 30-foot net. The former makes one so very unpopular in a railway carriage, and the latter so very ridiculous. An ordinary net is bad enough. I shrink from unpopularity and ridicule.

But though I have to confess with sorrow that I have never taken on the wing the King of British butterflies, I can at any rate boast of having a fair series of my own getting, gotten, too, with quite as much pains and trouble (though with less unpopularity I hope) as if I had sallied forth with a dead cat in my pocket and a net on the top of a large pole, to be the terror of my neighbours and the delight of small boys.

Let no one think it a light matter to breed *Iris*. First and foremost, in my case at any rate, there is the anxiety. I have bred what I suppose are rarer insects, but never have I felt care for my precious larvæ sitting so near my heart, as when I have had two or three of these splendid larvæ feeding up. Three, four, or even five times have I changed their food during the day, and in the night my sleep has been broken by visions of monstrous earwigs scaling the walls of the pot, patiently gnawing their way through the covering, and finally chewing with huge relentless jaws and fiendish appetite, one after another, my precious infants. I have writhed in agony at the vision, and cried aloud to the monsters to spare my treasures.

But beyond these troubles of the imagination, which are really very imaginary as the larvæ are very healthy and hardy, there is the much more serious difficulty of getting the beasts. Even in an *Iris* country, they are not to be found on every sallow bush, and much patient work has to be done with the beating tray. One every two hours is a fair allowance. Of course, if one comes in the first half-hour or so, the heart is emboldened to go on; but after an hour and fifty minutes it is rather difficult to toil through those remaining ten. Nor is there very much else to pick up meanwhile — a few *Poecilocampa populi* [December Moth], possibly half-a-dozen *Trichiura crataegi* [Pale Eggar], though this is rather a large allowance. No great bag at the best. But when at last the little green slug is seen on the tray, feeling about with its horns to discover what strange place it has landed in after its unexpected fall, then one remembers no more the hours of hard work, but sits down contemplatively, lights another pipe, possibly even sips a wee drap to the health of the treasure, and seeks out the best and cleanest pill-box, which is carefully perforated and filled with the best of sallow leaves. Who would care to pick up the infant in his fingers, at the risk of squeezing him unduly? Nay, choose with care a clean sallow leaf and let him crawl on to it ever so slowly; then lay him with trembling fingers in the box, to be anxiously looked at at intervals during the rest of the day. Often have I felt inclined to rush for the nearest train and take him home at once, knowing full well that if any box is to be lost or crushed, this is the one which an unkind fate has her evil eye upon.

Although never having taken the Purple Emperor on the wing, the Revd Hewett obtained his series by beating for the larvae, 'gotten . . . with quite as much pains and trouble . . . as if I had sallied forth with a dead cat in my pocket and a net on the top of a large pole, to be the terror of my neighbours and the delight of small boys'.

I once took five in a day — others have done better. I can tell you now where each one was. I began my day about eleven in the morning by a little sulky pond, with a water-hen's nest on a branch which touched the water. I can see the nest and eggs now. After beating round the pond on the outside without result, I determined to reach to the inside branches. My foot slipped as I tried the first, and I was wet to the knee, with a bootful of mud. Being so situated, I utilised the position and beat lustily, with the reward of number one. Of course I at once peopled every branch in imagination with dozens. But though I wet both legs and spoiled my boots, and nearly spoiled my temper, I got no more. It was lucky that I got one, or I might have given up. Number two came in about an hour, out of a little, stunted, shabby-looking sallow in a pine ride, which I was tempted to pass by, as unworthy of the effort of beating. So far I was doing well. Then came a terrible blank of over two hours. So I sat down and rested and refreshed my interior machinery. I had finished the best of my country, full of splendid sallows, so there was nothing to do but beat gradually homewards. After an hour of fruitless labour I came across the ideal sallow, standing alone in an opening among a grand group of oaks. How many someone else had got out of it, I shall never know. It had been well beaten. I tried it over again with no result, until I spied a little branch in the middle, apparently untouched. I got a corner of the tray under it, shortened my stick, and with some difficulty gave it a vigorous tap. The tray would not come out, and I could hardly see into it. At last I worked it carefully out, and oh joy! there were two little pairs of horns anxiously working from side to side. I will draw a veil over my unseemly joy. Only let me point the moral, 'Always beat little inside branches.' I did not care much what happened now, and beat carelessly homewards; but my luck held, and I got one more out of a small sallow right in among some pines.

So much for what was to me an eventful day: and why should I relate the duller days when I have only one or none. Let ill memories rest. Only let me exhort any who have the chance, to take their trays in May and work the sallows, whether they be standing high and dry, or in the middle of a marsh. *Iris* wanders very far from its unapproachable haunts among the oaks in search of sallows, and you never know on what stunted little bush may be feeding the horned head, which is so dear a prize, if not to all, yet at any rate to G. M. A. Hewett.

[Hewett, G. M. A. 1895. *Iris. The Entomologist's Record and Journal of Variation* 6: 145–147].

REPORTED OCCURRENCE OF THE SCARCE SWALLOWTAIL IN SUSSEX

Herbert Goss, Surbiton Hill, Surrey. (1892)

The following is an extract from a letter received from Mr. Charles E. Morris, of 4, Oriental Place, Brighton: — "I am sure you will be interested when I tell you that whilst working Robin's Post Lane, Polegate, yesterday (June 13th), upon some cowdung in the road I came across a very fine female *P. Podalirius* [Scarce Swallowtail]. I instantly identified it, being most familiar with the insect, having caught many three years ago in Switzerland and Northern Italy. I had at least five or six strikes at this one, but somehow, through excitement or surprise, failed to obtain it. The tails were intact, the ground colour much whiter than usual (possibly bleached), but otherwise in good condition. It was a very large one, undoubtedly a female. I noticed quantities of the foodplant in the locality. How it came there I cannot tell. I need hardly tell you I followed it as far as I could, trespassing through more than one hop field; for several moments it rather toyed with my net, and then went over a hedge."

(The fact that large numbers of the pupae of *P. Podalirius* are imported into this country, and that some of the resultant butterflies may accidentally escape, or be intentionally set free, should not be lost sight of. The pale colour seems to indicate the var. *Feisthamelii*, which is the more southern form. — Eds)

[Goss, H. 1892. Reported occurrence of *Papilio podalirius* in Sussex. *Entomologist's Monthly Magazine* **28**: 190].

Entomological history is full of reports of rare and wonderful captures. As we have already seen (see p. 31), some of these reports are quite fanciful. The Scarce Swallowtail is not uncommon in continental Europe (with a range that extends northwards across France to southern Belgium), so it is quite likely that occasional specimens migrate to Britain. Early writers such as Thomas Mouffet (*c*.1553–1604), John Ray (1627–1705) and John Berkenhout (*c*.1730–1791) all mentioned the Scarce Swallowtail, but there is no evidence that they regarded it as British. That had to wait until 1803 when Adrian Haworth reported that the Revd Dr Abbot of Bedford took a specimen in Clapham Park Wood. Some twenty years later the Revd F. W. Hope took a second specimen, this time near Netley in Shropshire, and a few days later observed, but failed to catch, a third specimen. P. B. M. Allan (1980), who investigated these Shropshire records, believed that there may have been a small breeding colony in that locality. However, that is still open to question and since those early days less than ten other reports have been published.

THE CAMBERWELL BEAUTY AND A VESTRY MINUTE

Henry Rowland-Brown, M.A., F.E.S., Harrow Weald, Middlesex. (1911)

Describing the village of Camberwell, where Robert Browning's grandparents settled, and in 1782 their eldest child was born, the late Professor Hall Griffin writes: "The square embattled church-tower . . . stood at the base of the pretty tree-clad slopes of Denmark Hill, Herne Hill, and Champions Hill, amid hedgerows and oak-trees, surrounded by well-stocked pastures and their overshadowing willows and flowers and fruit-trees, which were the haunt of the butterfly. Was not the Camberwell Beauty famous? Indeed, when the Browning household moved to Camberwell, the parish authorities had just been busy 'apprehending' the too numerous caterpillars, and in a single season had secured some four hundred bushels. A generation later, in 1810, Dame Priscilla Wakefield, in her 'Perambulations,' described Camberwell as a pleasant retreat," &c.*

In the hope of discovering the authority for this entomologically

* 'The Life of Robert Browning' . . . By Professor Hall Griffin. Completed and edited by Harry Christopher Minchin. Methuen & Co., Ltd., 1910.

amazing statement, I wrote to Mr. Minchin to ask if Professor Hall Griffin had left any note to indicate the sources thereof. Mr. Minchin, however, could throw no additional light on the problem, so at his suggestion I turned to Mrs. Wakefield's 'Perambulations in London,' published in 1814, on the off chance of finding an allusion to this plague of *Antiopa* larvæ! But Dame Priscilla is silent on the subject. "Camberwell is a pleasant retreat for the citizens who have a taste for the country, whilst their avocations call them daily to London" — that is all the information vouchsafed by "Yours affectionately, EDWIN," the imaginary writer of her Letter xxix.

But the mystery is explained to some extent in 'Old and New London; the Southern Suburbs,' vol. 6, p.279, by Edwin Walford, where, after expatiating on the rural charm of Camberwell, the author transcribes a Vestry Minute, to the effect that in 1782 caterpillars so abounded in the parish that the overseers spent £10 in "apprehending" them, at the rate of sixpence a bushel; the caterpillars being cited as "dangerous to the public in general"; and immediately afterwards Walford mentions that the Camberwell Beauty, "the delight of entomologists, is still one of the finest butterflies of the season . . . It was abundant when Camberwell was a straggling parish." Thus, setting aside the question of the normal abundance of *Antiopa* in Camberwell, or anywhere else in Britain at this time, it is clear that Browning's latest biographer read the same paragraph, and jumped to the conclusion that the caterpillars "at sixpence a bushel" were those of the insect he introduces to emphasize the rusticity of the then suburban London.

Meanwhile, one would like to know to what pest the entry in the Vestry Minute really refers. But unfortunately the record is no longer available on the spot, for, as the present Vicar, the Rev. F. F. Kelly, kindly informs me, St. Giles' Church was entirely destroyed by fire in 1841, and only the register-books of births, deaths and marriages were saved. Was it *Stilpnotia salicis* [White Satin Moth]? Perhaps some reader of the 'Entomologist' can supply the missing data?

[Rowland-Brown, H. 1911. Unrecorded occurrences of *Euvanessa antiopa. The Entomologist* **44**: 68–69].

This extraordinary note by Henry Rowland-Brown provoked the following reply from the distinguished lepidopterist Robert Adkin:

Possibly some light is thrown upon the question of the identity of the larvæ referred to as those of the Camberwell Beauty, in the quotation under the above heading, given by Mr. Rowland-Brown (*antea*, p. 68), by the following note which occurs in Humphreys and Westwood's 'British Moths,' vol.1, p. 91, where it is stated of the larva of *Porthesia chrysorrhoea*, L. [Brown-tail]: — "It feeds on various plants, especially whitethorn, in June, and has at times become so remarkably abundant as to cause a serious panic to Londoners, especially in 1782, when prayers were offered up in the churches against the enemy; and the churchwardens and overseers of the neighbouring villages, after offering rewards for collecting these caterpillars, attended to see them burnt by bushels." It will be noted that both the date and the measure by which the quantity of the caterpillars was estimated are the same in the two accounts, and I think we should not be far wrong in assuming that Professor Hall Griffin's Camberwell Beauty caterpillars were none other than those of *Porthesia chrysorrhoea*.

[Adkin, R. 1911. Unrecorded occurrences of *Euvanessa antiopa. The Entomologist* **44**: 112].

A SECOND LOOK AT THE CAMBERWELL BEAUTY

A. Russell, Ashford, Kent. (1857)

I send you the particulars of the capture of *Vanessa antiopa* by me in the month of August last, should the same be worthy of notice for 'The Substitute.' I was strolling out on a fine Sunday morning, in the beginning of August, when my attention was directed to a most beautiful insect. Not having a net with me I cautiously advanced, hoping to secure it with my cap as it rested on a spray in a dry ditch by a hedge road, but before I could manage that away it went over the hedge, and after it I went, falling down on the other side; but again on my legs, not much the worse for my fall, and keeping my eye on the object of my pursuit, in a short time I came up to it. Another attempt, but no such luck, having missed it in striking. It again started with increased swiftness, and I after it at the top of my speed, blowing fearfully and almost done, considering I had run a good quarter of a mile. I soon lost sight of it; but after an hour's search I again started my game, which again led me such a dance I shall never forget, but after three misses I made a hit, and you may judge my pleasure when I was informed it was a most perfect specimen of a British Camberwell Beauty.

[Russell, A. 1857. *Vanessa Antiopa. The Substitute* No. 17: 196–197].

ANOTHER LOOK AT THE CAMBERWELL BEAUTY

C. Nelson, Pitcox by Dunbar, Lothian. (1858)

On Thursday last, when out with my gun, I had the pleasure of seeing, but not capturing, a fine specimen of this insect: I watched it for a time sailing on the outskirts of a wood, sheltered from a stiffish breeze blowing at the time. Now and then it would mount nearly to the tops of the trees, its flight resembling that of *Io* [Peacock] more than any other butterflies I have seen on wing. At last it settled on a bit of rail: I had no net, so tried my hat, and missed it: a few strokes of the wing brought it within the influence of the wind, and in an instance it was lost to view, — "Sic transit," &c. I looked again for it on Friday and Saturday, but "Never, never back again did that beauty come."

[Nelson, C. 1858. *Vanessa antiopa. The Entomologist's Weekly Intelligencer* 4: 187].

YET ANOTHER LOOK AT THE CAMBERWELL BEAUTY

Charles Roberts, Wakefield, Yorkshire. (1858)

On Thursday last I had the pleasure of seeing this insect in a perfect state in King Street. I gave chase, and it alighted on a mill window-frame: not having a net there at the time I struck at the insect with my hat, but missed it; then it flew to the top of an elm tree close by. I left some parties to watch the insect till I went for my net, but on my return the insect had taken its flight without their seeing it: I have not since heard of any one capturing it.

August 30th.

Since my note of the 30th ult. this insect has been captured by a schoolboy, not more than one hundred yards from the place where it was first seen, and is now in my possession.

September 2nd.

[Roberts, C. 1858. *Vanessa antiopa. The Entomologist's Weekly Intelligencer* 4: 186–187].

THE MONARCH AT EXMOUTH

Revd John Hellins, Exeter, Devon. (1886)

A few days ago I was passing a cab-stand, when one of the men whom I have long known as a steady fellow, and the biggest "cabby" in Exeter, but certainly never imagined to be a brother entomologist, asked me to give him my opinion about something he had to show; and taking a box from under his driving seat, he opened it, and, to my surprise, displayed a specimen of *Danais Archippus* [The Monarch or Milkweed] unset, but in very good condition.

He told me it had been captured at an open window in Exmouth by some friends of his whilst lodging there during last August, and had been brought to him by them on their return, just in the state in which I saw it. He had not the slightest notion of the real character of his specimen, thinking it must be one of our British species not common in this neighbourhood; in fact, I have no reason whatever to doubt that he gave a true account of its capture.

[Hellins, J. 1886. *Danais Archippus* at Exmouth. *Entomologist's Monthly Magazine* **22**: 211].

THE MONARCH BUTTERFLY IN DORSET AND DEVON

Frederick W. Frohawk, F.R.E.S, M.B.O.U., Sutton, Surrey. (1933)

I recently received a letter from Mrs. M. Wood, dated September 13th, stating: "Col. Wood and I went to Exmouth last week, and on the cliffs between there and Budleigh Salterton I caught a female [*Danaus*] *plexippus* [The Monarch or Milkweed] on September 5th, about midday on a bright sunny morning, with a strong gale blowing from the east. The butterfly was trying to fly out to sea against the wind, but was blown back when I caught it. It is in quite good condition except a chip out of one lower wing."

The most remarkable observations made on the appearance of *plexippus* I know of are six specimens seen off the Dorset coast by Mr. Bower. Towards the end of July last, while 3 miles out at sea, no less than five of these great butterflies passed by his boat, flapping slowly along just above the surface of the sea, making for land. He tells me that they were all together, but what struck him most was their leisurely flapping flight, and their great size. Again, remarkable as it is, on the morning of August 16th he was also out at sea, almost in the same place, but about 3½ miles out when to his surprise, another single specimen passed by, heading for the coast; it was flying exactly like the others, and quite differently from any other British butterfly he knows. I happened to be on the Dorset coast that day, which was fine and very warm, with a rather strong easterly breeze. The six specimens alluded to bring the number of *plexippus* seen and captured this year up to twelve, which is the largest number yet recorded in one year. The previous largest number occurred in 1885, when nine were recorded.

[Frohawk, F. W. 1933. *Danaus plexippus* in Dorset and Devon. *The Entomologist* **66**: 250].

TWO DAYS HUNTING OF BUTTERFLIES AND MOTHS IN SUFFOLK

D. T. B. (1856)

I left London July 21, and when riding from the station to the "Old House at Home" I noticed a good number of the *Thecla W-Album* [White-letter Hairstreak] on some thistles by the road side. There I had found them for several years previously: three years ago I took thirty specimens in a few minutes. This time, however, my nets were as yet all packed up, so I did not disturb them. After spending a pleasant evening with old friends I arranged my nets and boxes ready for the morrow. Morning arrived, and I started at 5 o'clock for a wood where I expected good sport. On my way there I beat three splendid specimens of *Halias Quercana* [*Bena prasinana* L. — Scarce Silver-lines], and a number of other things from some young oaks. On I walked, net in hand, ready for *W-Album*; but alas! the destroyer was before me: a labourer was that moment engaged in trimming the hedge-row, and my hopes were like the blooming thistles — prostrated: not a *Thecla* to be seen. After pelting the neighbouring elms till my arms ached, I succeeded in dislodging a few, and at last captured half a dozen with great difficulty with my Emperor net, for they would not come down, but flew hurriedly round the tops of the trees when disturbed and soon alighted again. I was sadly disappointed, as I had promised to supply a number of friends with this species. *W-Album* is very uncertain in its flight: I have sometimes seen the hedges swarming with them; the next day they would be on the tops of the elms and not come down for several days. Some years ago I suddenly lost a whole colony of them: I had daily seen them round the elms, but one morning I missed them. Two days after I found them swarming on a field of mustard in full bloom a short distance off: they did not then attempt to ascend to the trees, but kept flitting about like the

Small Copper and Blue Butterflies. Arrived at the wood I chose a small open space to commence operations in, where the honeysuckles and brambles bloomed prettily round the low bushes. In a few minutes a fine female *Argynnis Paphia* [Silver-washed Fritillary] was in my net: I pinned her to a bramble, and in a very short time captured fifteen beautiful males. Now and then *Sibylla* [White Admiral] swept over the bushes out of reach, and though they once or twice deigned to wheel round my head not one would alight. This was very trying, as I knew that had been a favourite place with them in former seasons, but it was plain they had chosen a fresh spot for their "Metropolis." However, I patiently waited; and so quiet did I stand for an hour that a fox trotted past within forty yards of me, and a jay repeatedly fed her young in a tree over my head. At last I shifted my quarters and forced my way through the wood, — no easy matter, as there are no glades or paths of any description, but only a small open space here and there: I reached the edge of the wood, and found the extreme border had been cleared of timber: this space was about half a dozen yards wide and the entire length of the wood, without trees, but overgrown with bramble, honeysuckle, and wild flowers of every description. What a scene was there for a naturalist! I gazed in wonder and delight. The noon-day sun was shining in all his glory: not a sound was to be heard but the hum of insects that were there in hundreds! — in thousands! One long bright belt of insects and flowers lay before me: the beautiful *Sibylla* floated gracefully past, and fearlessly alighted on the bramble at my feet. *Paphia*, "Silver Queen," was on every knot of bloom; *Adippe* [High Brown Fritillary], too, sported merrily round, chased from flower to flower by *P. Sylvanus* and *Linea* [Large and Small Skippers], that were there in swarms; there flitted the quiet-looking *Athalia* [Heath Fritillary]. Contemptuously snapping his wings at intruders sat the bright-winged *Rhamni* [Brimstone], *Urticae* [Small Tortoiseshell] and *Hyperanthus* [Ringlet] too were present in hundreds, while myriads of gaily-coloured flies and bees, and a strange ichneumon-looking thing as big as a hornet darted rapidly past me every moment. Driving furiously along was that Jehu of moths *L. Quercus* [Oak Eggar]. There, too, on a sandy hillock lay another old acquaintance, a fine adder, neatly diamonded with umber and black, and coiled round like a watch-spring. In the dry ditch at my feet lay several large snakes, already disturbed by my presence, and slowly gliding away over the dry leaves; one, in particular, was bright with yellow and green. A pretty lizard lay gasping in the sun on an old gate in front of me, the pathway to which was overgrown with pretty yellow flowers gaily studded with numbers of *C. Phlaeas* [Small Copper]. After watching the various things round me for some time, I went to work with my net, and succeeded in taking thirty fine specimens of *Limenitis Sibylla*, fifteen of *Adippe*, thirty-five of *Paphia*, five *Athalia*, and numbers of all the others I mentioned, filling every box and using every pin I had with me. Next morning at six o'clock I was on the road to another wood, about eight miles distant, in search of *Apatura Iris* [Purple Emperor]. I arrived there about half-past eight o'clock, but the old keeper was dead, and I tried in vain to get leave from his successor to enter the wood. "There was nothing there," he said, "and it was no use trying; besides he expected some gentlemen there to look at the timber, and he would have no fly-catchers about." I was sadly vexed, as I had set my heart on capturing *Iris* that day, but 'twas no use pleading. However, at last he said I was welcome to hunt in the "Little Thicks." This was a small wood half a mile further on. Thither I proceeded, and in the course of the morning I captured about thirty *Adippe*, forty *Paphia*, thirty *T. Quercus* [Purple Hairstreak], four *T. W-Album*, three *polychloros* [Large Tortoiseshell] . . . Just as I was thinking of leaving the keeper's son came up: luckily we had met before in some woods in another locality where he had been keeper some years back: he recollected me, and we seated ourselves on the grass in the shady glade and discussed the merits of a large stone bottle of excellent home-brewed he fortunately had brought with him: from that we got to a trial of shooting on a small heath close by, and at last I was allowed to visit my favourite wood, that had been forbidden ground in the morning. The keeper's clock struck five as I entered: I began to feel plain symptoms of weariness, but I walked down the glade. "What gleams through the wood in the bright sunshine?" 'Tis *Iris* by Jove? I was in an instant as strong and fresh as when I started in the morning. My twelve-yard bamboo went together in a twinkling, and I was ready. He comes again! He is on the oak; one sweep — he is safely pinned in the hat of the keeper, who runs to the house to find me another box (all mine being full). A few minutes after I saw another *Iris* seated with closed wings on the outside bough of a magnificent oak. It is mine — a fine female! Soon after I thought I saw another hanging from the underside of a bough of an immensely tall oak. I could but just reach it, and was delighted to find a splendid pair (*in coitu*) safe in my net. I caught another beautiful male soon after, and I then left off, as it was half-past six and I had a long walk before me. As I was walking back

'One long bright belt of insects and flowers lay before me . . . There, too, on a sandy hillock . . . a fine adder . . . coiled like a watch-spring . . . A pretty lizard lay gasping in the sun.'

through the glade the large Fritillaries were retiring for the night. I several times stopped to notice them: they chose generally a spreading oak; they alighted on the outside boughs and proudly marched up and down the leaves, apparently fanning gently with their wings, and turning round in a most amusing manner. In a few minutes they would then quietly creep under between the leaves, and I saw no more of them. One incident I had almost forgotten to mention. In the morning I found a fine female Oak Eggar (*L. Quercus*) in the hedge: I enclosed her in a piece of net and pinned it to my arm. I was soon surrounded by males that crawled and fluttered all over me: I might have taken scores if I had wished. I was pleased to find that all the specimens I had taken in these two days were beautifully perfect and fresh, with few exceptions. Among the specimens of *Paphia* was one spotted with white on the upper side of the front wings [possibly ab. *caroffana* Cabeau].

[D. T. B. 1856. Two days hunting of butterflies and moths in Suffolk. *The Substitute* No. 13: 151–154].

PHENOMENAL NUMBERS OF RHOPALOCERA LARVAE AND IMAGINES

Sidney G. Castle Russell, M.I.E.E., Cranleigh, Surrey. (1955)

Many years ago, when butterflies of various species were generally abundant throughout the country, larvae and imagines of certain species occasionally appeared in phenomenal numbers. Frohawk in his *Natural History of British Butterflies* [1924] records authenticated instances of abnormally large numbers of *Euphydryas aurinia* [Marsh Fritillary], one at Church Stretton, where they swarmed to such an extent that roads and fields covering a large area were blackened by countless thousands, and a similar swarm was observed at Ennis, Co. Clare, Ireland.

Sometime in the early 1930's Sir Charles Langham, a well-known entomologist in Ireland who used to visit this country in order to collect with me, wrote and told me of an instance of phenomenal abundance of *E. aurinia* in a village close to his own demesne of Tempo Manor, Co. Fermanagh, Ireland. The villagers were alarmed at the immense numbers of caterpillars in the village and sent to Sir Charles to advise them what to do in the matter as they feared the destruction of their crops. Accordingly he visited the place and found the village and a large area of adjacent ground, on which was an abundance of devil's bit scabious, and various crops covered with immense numbers of *E. aurinia* in various sizes, the majority being full grown. Each of the cottages was surrounded by banks of peat which had been erected in a futile effort to keep the caterpillars out of the rooms. Sir Charles told the villagers that nothing of any effect could now be done but that within a week or so all the caterpillars would have changed into chrysalids and butterflies. He added that no harm would happen to the crops, etc., as the caterpillars would only eat the common weed known as the devil's bit scabious or honeysuckle.

The episode of this swarm of caterpillars got about, and at last it reached the ears of a Member of Parliament who mentioned the matter in the House of Commons and another member undertook to make inquiries. He got in touch with Sir Charles Langham and asked him to investigate the matter. In due course Sir Charles sent him a reassuring report on the incident, which was communicated to the House and reported in the daily newspapers. Although I remember reading about the matter in the *Morning Post* I have quite forgotten the date.

More than fifty years ago I was fortunate enough to witness a similar instance of phenomenal numbers of *E. aurinia*. Wishing to acquire a series of this species to add to my collection, I was informed that I could find the larvae on a certain hill on the Wiltshire Downs in early May. The locality was some six miles from the nearest station and to get to the spot I had to hire a pony trap (no motor-cars were then available). On arrival we found a wide road at the foot of the hill black with live and dead full-fed larvae through which horse traffic, chiefly farm carts, occasionally passed. The whole of the hillside from top to bottom was black with the larvae as were also all the surrounding scabious fields. It was impossible to walk anywhere without treading on numbers of larvae. It was a most imposing sight and one I have never forgotten.

I also witnessed a vast swarm of the Large White, *Pieris brassicae*, when, one spring, I was staying at the Royal Sandrock Hotel at Niton, I. of Wight. One evening a lady called at the hotel and said that she had been told there was an entomologist staying there and that she would like to see him. I was accordingly notified and accompanied her to her house. The garden and some three acres of cabbage crops had been devastated by an immense swarm of the larvae which had stripped the whole area bare and were walking about full-fed searching for places to pupate. All the rooms in the house were full of the caterpillars which had even penetrated the beds and inside them. It was really an unpleasant sight and to the inmates a disgusting one. There was nothing I could do to assist in the matter except point out that within a few days all the caterpillars would have turned into pupae, the great majority of which would be killed by ichneumons. Of course very large numbers of *P. brassicae* occasionally occur in all districts as is well known, but the one I have mentioned was exceptional.

As regards phenomenal numbers of butterflies I have seen three such. At Aldershot in 1887 in a wood nearby there was a large open copse which was full of small birch trees on each of which there was such a swarm of *Thecla quercus* [Purple Hairstreak] that with two

209

sweeps of the net on one particular tree I could catch fully a hundred of the butterflies. Although this species can often be seen, especially in the New Forest, in large numbers sitting on the bracken, etc., the area in which they occur is usually very limited in extent.

The other species concerned was *Celastrina argiolus* [Holly Blue]. On one occasion in the spring during the 1890's the holly trees on the borders of Holmsley Enclosure, New Forest, were each surrounded by hundreds of the butterflies of which there were vast numbers. On the second occasion in early August in an enclosure near Brook in the Forest there were phenomenal numbers of the same species. This was very unusual as many of the old time collectors used to assert that the Forest never produced a second brood. This, however, was not true and I invariably met with examples every autumn.

In the last instance I met with a well-known member of the South London Entomological Society who was working for aberrations, and judging from those he showed me he had been very successful. He remarked that never in his long experience had he met with such large numbers. At the time I was more interested in looking over the large fritillaries, which were in very great abundance also. Since then I have met with *C. argiolus* in large numbers in Kent, especially in the Rochester district in the spring and autumn.

Castle Russell, S. G. 1955. Phenomenal numbers of Rhopalocera larvae and imagines. *The Entomologist's Record and Journal of Variation* **67**: 111–113].

TWO OR THREE DAYS IN THE ISLE OF THANET

H. C. & Co., Brockley Lane, London, S. E. (1858)

The day after our rattle down by train last week we sallied forth on a capturing expedition, — two sportsmen and one to attend to the *impedamentæ*. We had the good luck to meet with, among other specimens, one *C. Cardui* [Painted Lady], which, after a most provoking and zigzag chase, was fairly under our net; an hour after we we fell in with others of the same species, and captured four of them: these chose for their resting-place the flat-tiled roof of a house, and many a tuft of grass and bit of old wood did we lodge there in trying to drive them to a lower spot, so much do their wings, when folded, resemble the general colour of such a roof that they can scarcely be detected, though known to be there: we unfortunately had to leave four behind, which no doubt claimed the victory as theirs, but resolved in our own mind to return the following day and take them. Jogging along the road for that purpose, our attention was suddenly arrested by a *Colias Edusa*, then a *C. Hyale* [Clouded Yellow and Pale Clouded Yellow], then another of the latter; these, after a most earnest up-hill and down dale chase at the very height of our speed, we made our own, but had the mortification to miss two other *C. Edusa*. The day after we visited the *A. crataegi* [Black-veined White] districts, and succeeded in taking thirty-two: running, in our zeal, into a hay meadow, we were at once summoned to heave-to by a farmer's man, who, instead of prosecuting us "according to the utmost rigour of the law," did what was much better, — kindly told us where we "might catch lots of them things:" no sooner said than done; plunging at once into the wood pointed out, we soon took many *M. Athalia* [Heath Fritillary]; further on we took one or two *A. crataegi* just from the chrysalis, and scarcely developed. Having outrun our time we were unable to return to head-quarters, so sought a lodging in a neighbouring watering-place. While one of our number was negociating the terms, and the affair proceeding well, the other two made their appearance with nets and collecting-boxes under their arms, at the door: suddenly there was a pause, and the matter seemed falling through, but was finally concluded, our worthy landlady apologizing for her hesitation by saying she feared we "were some of them wandering music people," and should not like a noise in her apartments. After a refreshing tea and a night's rest we departed, leaving behind us, by our becoming deportment, the firm conviction that we were not of the "banjonian" species, but merely a knot of quiet, sober butterfly catchers. On revisiting our farmer friend's wood we struck into a partially cleared portion of it, and sighted two paler yellow Lepidoptera. "*Colias Hyale!*" was shouted out, and after a rapid hunt over that most dangerous of all hunting-grounds, at the risk of broken shins and sprained ankles, one was captured, which turned out to be a poor old *G. Rhamni* [Brimstone], with wing like a piece of seaweed! Do not, dear sir, suppose that the list below were killed for the mere pleasure of the sport; no, our cabinet being quite in its infancy, we secured them in hope of being able, by exchange, to fill up some of its wide gaps. The following is the total of our week's captures:- [A short list of butterflies and moths follows.]

[H. C. & Co. 1858. Two or three days in the Isle of Thanet. *The Entomologist's Weekly Intelligencer* 4: 116–117].

A DAY'S COLLECTING NEAR DORKING

Roland Trimen, Russell Square, London. (1858)

On an intensely hot morning, towards the end of June, I equipped myself, according to my almost invariable custom during my stay at the bright and cheerful little town of Dorking, for the capture of my beloved order of insects, Lepidoptera. I also provided myself with some lunch and a flask of water, — for entomologists are not above such things, my experience, indeed, going to show that they as a body yield the palm of an excellent appetite to no other class of individuals, — and last, not least, with a huge pocketful of gooseberries, which I can confidently recommend on an excursion as a most successful allayer of thirst.

Fig. 80. Roland Trimen
F.R.S. (1840–1916).
'I equipped myself . . .
for the capture of my
beloved order of
insects, Lepidoptera.'

Thus, armed at all points, I passed quickly through the town, and soon emerged upon the open road to Betchworth. Having reached Betchworth Park, I left the road, and proceeded to take a foot-path which led directly to Box Hill, across the river Mole and some fields of grass and beans: thus I soon entered the steep, chalky lane that runs between tall hedge-banks, and, passing under the railway, brings one to the foot of the south-west corner of the Hill. In the lane sundry *Zerene procellaria* [Pretty Chalk Carpet] and *Bapta temeraria* [Clouded Silver] issued from the hedge, at the gentle hint of the beating-stick, and were in consequence captured. Just as I emerged upon the little open space at the end of the lane, I perceived a slight motion among the tall heads of grass by the shady hedge; on approaching I could at first see nothing, though the outline of a moth had plainly represented itself to my eye at a distance; after a little search, however, I discovered a most lovely specimen of *Chlorochroma vernaria* [Small Grass Emerald]: as the delicately beautiful insect hung on the slender grass stem, motionless, save for a slight quivering of its spotless wings in the cool breath of air never absent from a shady hedgerow, and looking like an exquisite leaf just animated with the breath of life, it seemed to be so perfectly in its place, and so in harmony with all around it, that the idea of capturing it at first seemed to me like a sacrilege. Need I say that in a minute or two this feeling was conquered by the *amor habendi*, so inherent, alas! in all, and more especially in entomologists? Yes! I drew a large chip-box from my pocket, and enclosed the lovely creature and the pendulous head of grass at "one fell swoop," and then, without staying to view the ruin I had made, — the temple without its goddess, — I put the box in my pocket, and, turning through the hedge to the left, emerged on the foot of Box Hill.

The shady seat under the yew tree looked so tempting that I resolved to rest before commencing the ascent. Lying at full length on the broad seat, and quietly making my first assault on the store of gooseberries, I began to think what tree it was whose dark branches nearly hid the sky from my view. "Ah, a yew!" — one can't find much on yew. What does Mr. Shield say about yew in June?" Out came Mr. Shield's 'Practical Hints:' under "June" an excursion to the Hilly Field is given: "Let us beat the yew trees on the slope. What is this plain-looking, yellowish insect I have beaten out? A good beginning — *Lithosia helvola* [Buff Footman]!" I thought to myself, "Why shouldn't *Helvola* be in this yew tree as well as those in Headley Lane?" I accordingly arose and smote the yew: down came spiders and earwigs in abundance, but no moths. I went round to the other side: surely that was a moth that flew out over the field! Whack! whack! A narrow-looking moth falls on the ground, — a *Lithosia* certainly. It was one I had never captured before, and decidedly "yellowish," and though I did not know it then, I afterwards found it to be *Helvola*. I felt very thankful to Mr. Shield, and whacked away for some time without further results in the way of Lepidoptera, though three or four other orders were numerously represented. By the way, I always thought it very strange how "few and far between" are the moths one gets by beating: earwigs, beetles, Diptera [flies] and Cimicidae [parasitic bugs] are very abundant, and many queer-looking things one doesn't know what to make of are to be found in the net. I don't know whether the Lepidoptera allow themselves to be beaten in like manner and abundance into the nets of collectors of *other* orders; if they do it would be very convenient for the Lepidopterist to make exchanges of his "rubbish" for the "rubbish" of other 'Pterists.

After the capture of *helvola* I proceeded to ascend the Hill. The handsome *A. Filipendulæ* [Six-spot Burnet] whirred lazily about on the slope, and the beautiful bee orchis attracted attention by its profusion. On the chalky foot-path the brilliant and active *Cicindelæ* [tiger beetles] were gleaming in the hot sunshine, ever and anon taking short flights as I approached. On the summit I rested for awhile to look back upon the beautiful and wide-extended view beneath. The road from Dorking, the railway with its impatient train panting to be off at the little Box Hill Station, the whole stretch of country from Betchworth, and far away to the South, where the distant wooded hills melted into the sky, lay like a map before me, — everything bright and glowing under the glorious June sun.

I then struck into the wood . . . Just as I was near the end of the wood on the Mickleham side, an old man in a smock-frock rose from a stump, where he had been sitting, and informed that it was "a fine mornin'." In this I agreed with him, and was passing on, when he said, "Would ye like me to show ye where Major Labberleer (Labelliere) was buried, sir?" I had read the story in the guide-book, and was therefore not desirous of seeing where this immortal personage was buried: I therefore said that I didn't mind about it, and wouldn't trouble him, &c. However, he wouldn't leave me, and dinned into my ear the following, as I walked on: — "He was berried sum years ago, bein' a officer o' mareens, with his 'ead downwards, for he said that, as the world was turn'd topsy-turvy, 'e couldn't only come right at last — by bein' — so deppozerted — " (I walked rather too fast for him). "Lor' bless ye, sir, — I've showed that 'ere grave o' his'n — undreds o' times, — man and boy, on this hill — for fifty year!" I observed that I thought it a great waste of time, when he became quite savage, and swearing as hard as his short breath allowed him to, he retired in a state of discomfiture. . . . Feeling by this time somewhat weary I drew forth my lunch, and reclining under a friendly yew and oak that mingled their branches overhead, resolved to make myself comfortable. This, however, the Diptera would by no means permit, and, observing how they assaulted my sandwiches, I wounded a corpulent gooseberry, and placed it in front of me on the grass, at the same time making the sandwich-suckers retreat. A large bluebottle settled about eight inches from the gooseberry, and, after rubbing his hands, made a leap forwards of about three inches; other blue and green bottles now advanced from various quarters and gathered around the prey: the first bluebottle darted upon the gooseberry and buried his tongue in the pulp: two green-bottles followed his example, and were quickly succeeded by others of different sorts and sizes, till at length the whole gooseberry was completely hidden by struggling flies. Now was the time to improve upon the proverb of "killing two birds with one stone," — with one stone I resolved to immolate thirty at the least. I picked up a large flint, and let it drop exactly on the gooseberry; but on lifting it, one bluebottle and two small flies were all the slain! The agility of these creatures is truly wonderful, and their courage is scarcely less so, for a few seconds only had elapsed and the crushed fruit was covered completely as before. But soon other devourers showed themselves; a number of ants came to share the booty, and it was amusing to see how frightened the bulky flies were at the approach of one of these energetic little creatures.

After a short rest I proceeded to return through the Hilly Field into the lane. The sun was very powerful, and both water and gooseberries were exhausted; I accordingly asked at the farmhouse in the lane for some water, and having drunk it, astonished the girl who brought it by suddenly going close up to the wall and pinning a moth sitting thereon: it was *Hadena dentina* [The Shears] that I thus appropriated, and I answered the damsel's look of wonder by displaying the contents of my collecting-box. What she thought of me I know not, but her "Lor' now! what'll ye ever do with 'em all?" was amusing to hear. On reaching Burford Bridge I was much interested in observing the evolutions and manoeuvres of a number of the brilliant *Calopteryx Virgo* and *C. splendens* [damselflies], which were sailing and darting about among the luxuriant bed of reeds and aquatic plants by the side of the stream. Another *H. dentina* and some magnificent male stag-beetles completed my captures before reaching home, where I found the first specimen of *Vanessa Polychloros* [Large Tortoiseshell] just emerged from the chrysalis, and, what was quite as acceptable, a good dinner awaiting me. . . .

[Trimen, R. 1858. A day's collecting near Dorking. *The Entomologist's Weekly Intelligencer* 3: 174–175; 181–184].

Most articles written about collecting trips or entomological holidays appear to describe heroic adventures where rarities and exciting specimens were readily discovered and captured in large numbers. With this in mind, it was refreshing to read the next article which describes a visit to the Norfolk Broads; a visit that was to prove memorable for the poor quality of the entomology encountered.

A WEEK ON THE NORFOLK BROADS

George Lissant Cox, Birkenhead, Lancashire. (1904)

On the evening of July 30th we arrived at Wroxham and boarded our wherry, 'The Caistor Maid.' A small rowing-boat carried the entomological apparatus — a sheet with the necessary poles, and twelve five-foot posts, on which were nailed pieces of cork, in imitation of Bailey's well-known row in Wicken Fen. The day had been fine and sunny, but in the evening it clouded over, and we had heavy rain from the south-west. The journey and the rain prevented an energetic evening, and we contented ourselves with putting up a few posts close to our anchorage, some few hundred yards below Wroxham and at the edge of the fens. To our dismay we found that sugar was as unattractive here as in other places this year. Not a single insect came on this favourable night. My friend Mr. J. H. Wybrants, however, netted two *Toxocampa pastinum* [Blackneck], and a few common wainscots, *Epione apiciaria* [Bordered Beauty] and *Cidaria testata* [The Chevron], were captured flying round the boat.

Next day we sailed to Irestead Staithe, close by the entrance to Barton Broad. The day was fine and sunny, and the wind south-east, a combination which favoured us for the rest of the week. We noted a very large number of *Pieris brassicae* and *P. rapæ* [Large and Small Whites], flying over the fens on either side of the river, and at Irestead Staithe were greeted with the first *Vanessa io* [Peacock] of the season.

Near the Staithe, and overlooking the large fens bordering Barton Broad, we put up the sheet, a motor-bicycle lamp doing duty for the more classical paraffin lighthouse. The night was warm, clear, and with little dew. At dusk we both netted one *Nonagria brevilinea* [Fenn's Wainscot]. But, alas, even an imposing row of posts, and the best of treacle and rum would not tempt our usual friends. . . . Light was just as bad, for only one *Odonestis potatoria* [The Drinker], one *N. brevilinea*, and a few common wainscots, came to the sheet. Next night we were in a poor locality and did not go out. On Aug. 2nd, however, we reached Potter-Heigham, and in the evening erected the sheet and posts overlooking the south edge of Whitesea Broad. After a fine hot day we had a clear cool night and a fair dew. The first insect boxed off the posts was *Nonagria neurica* [White-mantled Wainscot], but this proved to be the only gem of the evening. . . . On Aug. 3rd we had two expeditions to the Norfolk coast. The first was *via* Summerton, including a sail in the dinghy for about four miles, and a two and a half mile walk to Winterton-on-Sea. On the coast we saw the lyme-grass, and resolved to return in the evening, for was it not time for *Tapinostola elymi* [Lyme Grass]?

So, after an "all-night tea," my friend and I cast off in our rowing-boat. This time we went by Whitesea Broad and Horsey Mere, for the staithe at the latter is only about a mile and a half from the coast. We started off with the sheet, five poles, innumerable boxes, and a bag full of impedimenta. The sun had nearly set as we reached the marshy land behind the sandhills, when, to our horror, we found them securely barricaded with a barbed-wire fence, our path blocked by a locked gate, and two keepers waiting our approach. Eventually we were allowed to go on, but only on the condition that we walked straight to the sandhills, and thence northwards out of this preserved property. So we had two more miles against time, and in loose sand. No time now to look for the precious lyme-grass, and we were content to erect the sheet at the edge of the forbidden land. Luckily there were a few plants of ragwort, and these, together with some twisted marram grass, were duly sugared. The night was very warm, with a stiff south breeze, and quite clear. Insects were, however, scarce. Nothing came to light except one *Odonestis potatoria*. On the sugared ragwort the only insects of any note were four *Leucania littoralis* [Shore Wainscot] and an immense female *Cossus ligniperda* [Goat Moth]. After the first two rounds we could find nothing fresh, and as the unsugared ragworts were absolutely unproductive, we made off for home, this time along a road to the staithe. The five-mile row by moonlight across the meres was splendid, and enlivened by the furious approach of two gamekeepers, who took us for poachers.

Thursday, Aug. 4th, was the record hot day of the year. In the evening we anchored at the edge of Ranworth Fen. Here, indeed, we were on famous ground. Sugar was, however, an absolute failure, no doubt on account of the aphide-laden sallow and alder bushes. No insects were seen at honey-dew. At dusk we netted some *Cænobia rufa* [Small Rufous], one *Tapinostola fulva* [Small Wainscot], and, also three *N. brevilinea*. Light was better. Five *N. brevilinea* settled on the sheet, but had to be carefully netted, as they would fly off at the least alarm. . . . After eleven, however, it turned cold, and with a heavy dew falling no more insects appeared, and so our last night on the Broads came to an end.

[Cox, G. Lissant. 1904. A week on the Norfolk Broads. *The Entomologist* **37**: 325–327].

WITHERSLACK AND AMBLESIDE A CENTURY AGO

Russell E. James, Highgate, London, N. (1904)

Looking through the magazines one finds many notes from Wicken, the Broads, and the New Forest, and, although kept rather quiet, one knows of many a trip to north Cornwall. Even Forres and Rannoch get their full share of attention, but a careful search reveals scarcely a note on the "mosses" from the pen of a south countryman. Moreover, I have only met one London man who knows anything about them. Mr. C. F. Johnson [Fig. 10], of Stockport, whose acquaintance I had the pleasure of making last year, on the Deal sandhills (which, by-the-by, still retain much of their past richness), spoke so highly of Witherslack that I resolved to try it. The result was that July 6th found me settled at the Derby Arms, for six days' work. From the expense point of view one could scarcely have a cheaper holiday. The London and North-Western Railway runs a fast train to Grange-over-Sands every Wednesday, at cheap fares (22s.), returning Monday, Wednesday, Monday week or Wednesday week. Thence four-and-a-half miles of good road brings one to the Derby Arms, where the accommodation and catering are such as are rarely found in a country inn, albeit the tariff is the very moderate one of 5s. per day, inclusive of everything. The Lancashire collectors know a good thing when they get it, and have hitherto kept it pretty much to themselves. The lake district can easily be got at from here, as 3s. day excursions are run from Grange to Ambleside, the steam yacht trip down Windermere *en route* being delightful. Favoured with perfect weather, I was kept hard at it, in spite of treacle failing utterly. The moss commences some quarter of a mile back from the inn, and other fine collecting ground

Fig. 81. An entomological gathering outside the Derby Arms, Witherslack, Westmorland. (*c.* 1904).

is situated immediately at the front door. The first morning on the moss was very windy, but, in the sheltered parts, I found *Coenonympha typhon* [Large Heath] in great abundance and lovely condition. Great care is necessary in moving about, as one's leg frequently disappears well up above the knee, either into a large hidden crack or into a bog-hole, in either case a highly dangerous occurrence if on the run. A week could be devoted to *C. typhon* alone, as the variation shown is most interesting. With so many things to do, however, I could not give up too much time to the one species, but the 150 odd specimens I brought home with me are an extremely variable lot, several inclining strongly in the same direction as *Epinephele janira* [Meadow Brown, but presumably the Ringlet] ab. *lanceolata*. . . .

Immediately opposite the inn is a high grassy bank, with patches of undergrowth. Here and in the meadow above many interesting species occur. *Polyommatus astrarche* ab. *salmacis* [Castle Eden Argus] was in plenty, with a fair proportion of the type and all grades in between. These were in fair condition, but *Cupido minima* [Small Blue], although common, was very worn. I heard that this latter species had been almost exterminated here by some Lancaster dealers, but it is evidently now holding its own well. A fine race of *Polyommatus icarus* [Common Blue] also occurs, one male being quite as brilliant as that of *P. bellargus* [Adonis Blue], and all large, with strongly marked females. An equally brilliant race of *Rusticus aegon* [Silver-studded Blue ssp. *masseyi*] is said to occur about a mile away, but I failed to find the spot. This bank and meadow are also home the home of *Phothedes captiuncula* [Least Minor]. After four nights' vain search at dusk I found this little Noctuid flying in the sun in plenty one afternoon, about 4.30 p.m. to 5.30p.m. They occasionally rested on the ox-eye daisies, and, although many were worn, I got a very decent series by careful selection. . . . Although the time was all too short, and much ground left untouched, I could not resist trying for *Erebia epiphron* [Small Mountain Ringlet]. Two day trips were made to Ambleside, the first to Kirkstone Pass and over the eastern and souther sides of Red Skrees, being a total failure. *Melanthia albicillata* [Beautiful Carpet], *Nudaria mundana* [Muslin Footman], and *Melanippe tristata* [Small Argent and Sable] were taken off walls on the way up to the pass, and some strongly marked *Pieris napi* [Green-veined White] netted on higher levels; *Erebia*

epiphron, however, failed to put in an appearance. On the second trip (July 11th) I determined to go farther afield. Again ascending the Kirkstone Pass, I, this time, climbed right over Red Skrees, from opposite the Kirkstone Inn. For some three hours I wandered on the high fells towards Grasmere and Helvellyn, without seeing a sign of my quarry, only getting some nice *Crambus furcatellus* [a crambid moth] and a single *Nemeophila plantaginis* [Wood Tiger]. Late in the afternoon I found the species, its unmistakeable sooty appearance being very conspicuous at quite a distance. It was exceedingly local, and confined to a few acres of rather marshy ground, to all appearance exactly like that over which I had been working all the afternoon. Probably early in the day it would have been abundant. As it was I got 24 very fair specimens, and a little later on three more, some 500 feet lower down. As nearly as I can ascertain the elevation of the first locality was 2300ft.–2400ft. An attempt to obtain ova proved successful, and with a view to the best chance of bringing the larvæ through hybernation I distributed them between Messrs. E. Joy and L. W. Newman. I do not know whether the full-grown larva has yet been described, but do not recollect seeing a description. Given good weather, this trip to Ambleside makes as fine a day as one could wish for. . . .

James, Russell E. 1904. Lepidoptera at Witherslack and Ambleside. *The Entomologist's Record and Journal of Variation* 16: 297–300].

AN ENTOMOLOGICAL TRIP TO SHETLAND, JULY 1938

Charles G. M. de Worms, M.A., PhD., A.I.C., F.R.E.S., Egham, Surrey. (1939)

Another colourful character was Baron Charles de Worms (1904–1980). Educated at Eton and Cambridge University, his career in chemistry included work at the military defence laboratory at Porton Down and the Royal Cancer Hospital, London. Among the numerous articles he contributed to entomological journals was one in which he described his 'main summer holiday' in 1937. It was, he wrote, 'on the whole, a successful tour of the British Isles'. Russell Bretherton, who knew him well, remembered that he was 'a kindly man, good with cats, dogs and small children'.

. . . Mr. A. [Archibald] G. B. Russell and I had heard such thrilling accounts of the amazing "bags" and variety of insects in these northerly regions that we thought we would try to see for ourselves what this remarkable country could produce. Having gleaned a good deal of useful information from previous visitors, we decided to set out in early July. As it is only possible to reach Shetland by boat twice a week from Aberdeen, on Mondays and Thursdays, we considered we might put in a profitable week-end by making the Lake District a stepping-stone to the North.

We accordingly started from London by train on the evening of July 8th, reaching Witherslack towards midnight, somewhat late to do any serious collecting. However, our appetites were well whetted when another entomologist returned with a very fresh series of *Perizoma taeniata* [Barred Carpet] he had secured in the local woods at dusk. But at the same time we heard ominous news of the weather during the previous week. On the following day we thought we would see whether *Erebia epiphron* [Small Mountain Ringlet] was still on the wing, and made a very long and tedious journey by 'bus to Langdale. We reached the top plateau of the Pikes in the early afternoon, but not a glimmer of sun or sign of an insect. After a wait of two hours we made the descent empty-handed and reached Witherslack in the early evening, where Mr. N. G. Wykes, who had joined us, had had better luck, obtaining

Coenonympha tullia philoxenus [Large Heath] and the usual day-flying moths. At dusk we visited the locality for *P. taeniata* and in spite of a deluge we managed to secure two good specimens by agile strokes of the net among the yews. We were able to confirm Mr. Smith's interesting observation about the time and duration of flight of this elusive and obscure insect.

We had high hopes that the next day, Sunday the 10th, the weather would relent, but a continuous downpour made collecting impossible. We joined the train at Oxenholme that evening and after a three-hour wait about midnight at Carlisle we boarded the night express, reaching Aberdeen in time for breakfast on the 11th. As our boat did not leave until 9 p.m. we had the whole day to spend in or near the Granite City, which was new to both of us. After a brief tour we took a bus to Muchalls, ten miles to the south. We arrived soon after 11 and at last found the sun shining. A short walk southwards along the cliffs brought us to some grassy slopes. It was not long before we came across *Aricia agestis artaxerxes* [Northern Brown Argus], flitting about in the vicinity of of the large patches of rockrose chiefly growing in the most precipitous places. The insects were only just out and not in very great numbers. However, we secured quite a fresh short series. Among the butterflies also on the wing were plenty of *Argynnis aglaia* [Dark Green Fritillary], including some very dark forms of the female. There were still a few *Polyommatus icarus* [Common Blue] and *Cupido minimus* [Small Blue], together with numbers of the very bright northern *Maniola jurtina* [Meadow Brown]. Day-flying moths were equally numerous, chiefly *Malenydris didymata* [Twin-spot Carpet] and *Odezia atrata* [Chimney Sweeper]. On our way back to Aberdeen we called on Mr. G. Hartley, who very kindly showed us his wonderful series of Scotch butterflies. After a quick dinner we boarded the boat for the North, the "St. Sunniva", a very well-appointed and extremely comfortable vessel, not much larger than a big sea-going yacht, upon which lines it was apparently constructed. In spite of the large crowd on board we had very good quarters and, what was more, an almost record calm sea journey. It is about 180 miles from Aberdeen to the south point of Shetland and 215 miles to Lerwick. The passage, which normally takes 16 hours, we covered in just over 14. We sighted Shetland about 10 a.m. on the 12th and gradually skirted along the coast, which was in some ways a remarkable contrast to that of north-east Scotland. The high cliffs and undulating hills completely devoid of trees and high vegetation were very imposing. Not less interesting was the amazing variety of bird-life, much of which was new to us, especially the fulmar petrels.

We ran into Lerwick just before midday in very sunny weather and decided to complete the journey overland to our destination, the most northerly island, Unst. After lunch we set out by car along a very good road and through some fine rugged scenery. We were surprised at the length of the group of islands, between 80 and 90 miles from the southernmost point to furthest north. But we found our cross-country route not so easy and none too cheap. After 25 miles across the mainland we had to transfer to the first ferry-boat all our luggage, some dozen pieces; then came a somewhat perilous crossing of the channel to the island of Yell. We next had a further 18 mile journey along a very winding road to Uyea sound, which divides this island from Unst. Here we embarked on an even smaller craft in which we did the 3-mile crossing which was made the more interesting owing to the amazing number of birds, especially eider duck, guillemots and kittiwake. It was here that we had our first view of the bonxie or great skua, for which this part of Shetland is famous. Another 7 miles by car across Unst brought us about 4 p.m. to our destination at Baltasound, where we were greeted at the Hotel Nord by Mr. E. J. Hare and Dr. Smart, who had already been there four days. But they had a sorry tale to tell, atrocious weather all the time and very poor collecting. The hotel, where we were made very comfortable for the subsequent week, is situated about half a mile from the head of the sound. In the adjoining grass fields we made our first captures of Shetland lepidoptera. At every step rose numbers of *Perizoma albulata* [Grass Rivulet], ranging from almost white to the completely leaden form *thules*. As conditions looked more promising we decided to set out after dinner for the sugaring ground. All four of us managed to squeeze into Mr. Hunter's very excellent car and were conveyed by a circuitous 6-mile route round the north of the island, halting at the head of Burra Firth, a former whaling station. At 10.30 p.m. we began the ascent of the north-west shoulder of Unst, known as Hermaness, but we did not find the climb nearly so arduous as Mr. Hughes led us to believe. On the way we took a few *Hepialus fusconebulosa (velleda)* [Map-winged Swift], of which there is a very characteristic form. As soon as we approached the top of the heather-covered ridge we came on numbers of the Arctic or Richardson's skua, a much smaller and more slender bird than the bonxie. These kept on swooping at us with a shrill plaintive note. It only took us some twenty minutes to reach the sugaring fence, which runs north and south along the summit of the moor which is capped with peat, and divided by deep gullies, which make convenient beats for sugaring. On this occasion Mr. Russell and I took the more northerly stretch, about a mile in length, while our colleagues covered about two-thirds that distance to the south between the first and second ravines. When we had finished putting on the sugar at 11.30 p.m. the light was just starting to go. But the weather began to fail us, with thick mist and intermittent rain. The first round at midnight only yielded a few *Triphaena pronuba* [Large Yellow Underwing], the large form of *Agrotis strigula* [True Lover's Knot] and two *Hama adusta* [Dark Brocade], which is very brightly marked. However, on a further scrutiny of the posts just before 1 a.m. we saw our first *Crymodes exulis* [The Exile] of the season, a most handsome insect, on the sugar patch. This gave us more heart, but with further adverse conditions another round provided no more insects and we made the descent towards 2 a.m. to rejoin Mr. Hunter, who had had more success than us, landing several sea trout.

The next day, July 13th, we set out exploring the island and were astonished by the luxuriant growth of grass and particularly at the flowers, among which the fine red campion was especially noticeable. In the few sunny intervals we saw several *Pyrameis atalanta* [Red Admiral], quite an event for Shetland, where there are no indigenous butterflies. That night we all four paid a further visit to Hermaness, but a continuous drizzle made collecting very unpleasant and unprofitable. We saw no *C. exulis*, the only new species from the previous night being *Apamea gemina* [Dusky Brocade] and the first *Noctua primulae* f. *thulei* [Ingrailed Clay], the very remarkable dark form of this insect for which Unst is so well-known. We returned somewhat despondent and distinctly empty-handed, but the 14th saw hardly any improvement in the unsettled conditions. The quick change in the weather was extraordinary. One moment brilliant sunshine and in a few minutes heavy clouds would roll up over the hills, bringing a drenching downpour. However, we explored some of the more easterly regions of the island where quite different geological strata prevail, providing barren and rocky hillsides. In the meadows we took some more *P. albulata*. That night a further joint effort on the sugaring ground in bright moonlight yielded another meagre "bag", no sign of *exulis*. On the return journey about 2.30 a.m., near the head of Burra Firth, we stopped by a high bank, where we found the fine dark form of *Xanthorhoë munitata* [Red

Carpet] flying freely, but many were already worn. On the following day, the 15th, there were indications of a distinct improvement in the weather. After spending most of the time setting and going through the first mail we had since our arrival, we once more set out about 10 p.m. with higher hopes. Again the night was clear and the drier conditions attracted a fair sprinkling of insects, mainly *A. strigula* with a few more *conflua*. On the final round at 2 a.m. there were two *C. exulis* in very fresh condition, while Mr. Hare and Dr. Smart took three more on their stretch. This was encouraging, but unfortunately for our friends it was their last night. On the way back the variegated form of *Xanthorhoë montanata* [Silver-ground Carpet] was much in evidence, a very different insect from the Scotch race. The 16th, Saturday, was a very warm day. We made the most of it by a delightful walk over the moors to the west coast of the island, during the course of which we

Fig. 82. Baron Charles de Worms (1960). 'My main summer holiday consisted of a successful tour of the British Isles.'

saw one of the few British nesting sites of the whimbrel. As it began raining towards evening Mr. Russell and I considered it would be well spent by devoting our attention to *Hepialus humuli* f. *hethlandica* [Ghost Moth], of which we had only to date taken a few examples. Just after 11 o'clock all the grass fields round the hotel were a dancing mass of these swifts. It was possible to take half-a-dozen males at a time in the net, each one different from the other, ranging from mottled white to orange and deep brown.

The females, which flew slightly later were no less remarkable, some being almost chocolate in colour. It did not take us long to get all we wanted, and the flight was over in twenty minutes. *X. munitata* was even more numerous in this locality and, if anything, in better condition. After a further fine day on the 17th another wet spell set in towards dark and we confined our activities to the vicinity of Haroldswick, with very little result. Monday, the 18th, however, saw another change for the better. In the afternoon I called on Mr. Mowatt, the local postman, who has had very great experience of Shetland insects. In his company I visited a garden near his house, where there was a large patch of cow parsley. By parting the stems he was quickly able to see any exudation of white frass, which denoted the presence of the larvae of *Dasypolia templi* [Brindled Ochre]. On digging up the roots we soon came across the white maggot-like larvae, sometimes 2 or 3 in a plant and all sizes. It was not long before we unearthed 15. By keeping the roots in a ventilated tin I subsequently bred, in early September, 10 examples, 5 of each sex, the females being appreciably darker than the southern race. With a mild south-westerly wind prevailing Mr. Mowatt prophesied a much better collecting night. With these prospects we reached the sugaring ground well on the early side and worked the whole length of posts, covering about 1½ miles. As soon as we had put on the sugar insects began to flock to it, a marked contrast to our previous efforts. By midnight on every post were several *N. conflua*, *A. strigula* and *T. pronuba*. Half an hour later *exulis* began to arrive, half-a-dozen by 1.30 a.m., but it was not till dawn was breaking that this species made its main appearance. On a double round before 2.30 a.m. I secured a further 13 examples, all very variable and mostly in excellent condition, but not a single female. When we joined forces about 3 o'clock, we found we had 29 *exulis* between us, a very gratifying catch when we had almost given up hope of seeing this fine insect in any numbers. We had also obtained all we could wish for of *N. primulae* (*festiva*) ff. *conflua* and *thulei*, hardly two of which were alike. On the 19th, our last day in Unst, the weather once more deteriorated. However, we were not deterred from making a final attempt. On the way to Hermaness that evening we stopped at Haroldswick and gathered a large bunch of the seed heads of the sea campion (*Silene maritima*), which subsequently was found to be well patronized by larvae of *Dianthoecia conspersa* [Marbled Coronet]. Soon after reaching the sugaring fence a thick mist descended which made it unwise to go far from the line of posts, which were almost devoid of moths. However, just before we were going to return at 2 a.m. we each took a single *exulis*. Mr. Hunter conveyed us back to the hotel in daylight and then, after picking up our luggage, took us on to Uyea Sound, where this time we boarded the "Earl of Zetland", a very ancient vessel of some 60 years' service, which plies between Lerwick and the northern islands. We left Unst at 5 a.m. and, after a very smooth voyage, during which we took an opportunity of getting some sleep, we reached Lerwick at 10 o'clock, and went straight on board the "St. Sunniva". We set sail at midday with many regrets at leaving this delightful country with its glorious scenery and charming inhabitants, nearly all of pure Scandinavian stock. The sea was once more very kindly on the journey south. On board we met Mr. T. Kay, the well-known naturalist, who gave us some most interesting information about the birds of the Shetlands. We berthed once more at Aberdeen in the small hours of the 21st, but did not disembark till after breakfast. Soon after 10 we took the train south in very warm weather. Travelling via the Tay and Forth bridges to Edinburgh, we broke our journey at York about 6 p.m. After dinner we took a car out to Strensall Common, where we spent quite a profitable few hours, but I only managed to find one male example of *Epione parallellaria* (*vespertaria*) [Dark Bordered Beauty] at rest on some rushes. Other insects seen at light included *Geometra papilionaria* [Large Emerald] and many *Acidalia emarginata* [Small Scallop]. Very little came to sugar. Rejoining the car soon after midnight on July 22nd we caught the express at 1.30 a.m., reaching King's Cross four hours later.

So ended a most enjoyable and successful holiday. We felt as if we were almost cut off from civilization in these remote regions, where we could hardly realize we were as far from the Metropolis as is the South of France. But in spite of the 850 miles, the trip by sea or air is well worth while and a sojourn in these wild surroundings of the north cannot be too highly recommended for anyone interested in any branch of Natural History.

[Worms, C. G. M. de, 1939. An entomological trip to Shetland, July, 1938. *The Entomologist* **72**: 60–65].

Dr Leonard McLeod (pers. comm.) is one of the many lepidopterists who fondly recall Charles de Worms' eccentricities:

> He was certainly an unforgettable character. His visits to our home in Provence will undoubtedly be remembered with pleasure by my own family, particularly by my two eldest daughters who used to sit at the dining table open-mouthed at his eccentric style of eating. Without wishing to be critical of a friend, one

can say that he contravened all the table manners which we had tried to instil in our children. Before his arrival, my wife and I had to prepare our daughters for the unknown; one never knew what unusual event would be precipitated by Charles' presence. I recall that on one occasion he even had a car accident between the airport and our house. Fortunately he had hired a car and the damaged vehicle could be replaced with ease; on this occasion the extraordinary events had begun even before his arrival.

Charles always changed for dinner, but his suit and tie were both highly disfigured by food stains. Bowls of cherries and strawberries, perhaps containing 2kg of each, were rapidly consumed; and on other occasions, large quantities of apricots, peaches and nectarines disappeared in the same fashion. The fruit juices which dribbled profusely onto his shirt and tie would certainly have filled a pint glass. At breakfast, entire pots of jam were emptied onto his plate and consumed with a spoon. Once, a large kilogram jar of homemade Seville orange marmalade was emptied onto his plate and eaten in this fashion.

One particular evening, Charles decided to take a bath. The bathroom was on the first floor of our Provençal farmhouse and we heard the hot water running for quite a long time. The taps were eventually turned off and this was followed by an enormous splash. To the great delight of my children and the consternation of my wife, water cascaded down the staircase. On enquiring if everything was all right, Charles explained that he had filled the bath to the brim before getting in it.

In an article in the South African journal *Metamorphosis*, Bernard D'Abrera (1997), author of the monumental '*Butterflies of the World*' series, remembered other occasions:

Some of my funnier experiences have involved such luminaries as the famous Baron Charles de Worms, whose culinary appetite was legendary if not notorious. The great Wicky Fleming [W. A. Fleming, author of *Butterflies of West Malaysia and Singapore* (1975)] once swore that when Charles de Worms visited him in Malaya, he observed the good Baron devour at one sitting an entrée, two roast chickens with sundry vegetables and garnishing, 5 pints of beer, 3 servings of dessert (in addition to the servings of some of the other guests, who had sacrificed theirs in amazement), a whole pineapple followed by several cups of coffee, an entire bottle of brandy, and

Fig. 83. Baron Charles de Worms (*c.* 1975). 'An unforgettable character . . . one never knew what unusual event would be precipitated by Charles' presence.'

then another two rounds of coffee, followed by Schnapps, at which point he let out a very loud burp and said in that growling laconic voice "What ho! And what do you have in mind for breakfast tomorrow?" At one B. M. (N. H.) [*] Christmas party, the good Baron arrived first among the guests, and proceeded like a vacuum cleaner down the assembled trestle tables groaning with goodies, where at the end of the semi-circle Kathy Smiles had placed a plate of coloured polystyrene foam extrusions of different shapes – which were devoured nonchalantly by the good Baron, who then proceeded to let out his customary burp, and begin all over again. . . . Bob Smiles once opined that if you could boil down Baron de Worm's tie, you could make enough soup to keep all the Oxfam shops happy for years.

Because he was short-sighted, Charles de Worms was quite prone to making mistakes, particularly when it came to him boxing specimens. In '*The Aurelian Legacy*' (2000) the expression 'charlesing a moth' is mentioned — a term coined by the Baron's friends to describe the unfortunate effect that sometimes followed his attempts at boxing moths. Often some hapless creature would end up trapped between box and lid, irretrievably damaged. The Rev A. Harbottle (pers. comm.) recalled what must have been the ultimate 'charlesing' incident when the Baron, busily engaged in sugaring tree trunks and without realizing his error, painted over a Blue Underwing (*Catocala fraxini*) that unfortunately happened to be at rest.

THE CHEQUERED SKIPPER IN WESTERN INVERNESS-SHIRE

Fig. 84. Lieutenant Colonel Cyril Mackworth-Praed. 'He was quite indefatigable, even pursuing butterflies in Kenya when he was nearly eighty.' (de Worms, 1975)

Lt. Col. Cyril W. Mackworth-Praed, O.B.E., F.R.E.S., Fort William, Inverness-shire. (1942)

Lieutenant Colonel Cyril Wynthrop Mackworth-Praed (1891–1974) lived at Burley in the New Forest, where he ran a moth trap nightly for over thirty years. 'He could virtually identify at sight every species that came to it down to the smallest of the micros,' recalled Baron Charles de Worms (1975). It was while he was stationed at Inverlochy Castle, Inverness-shire, during the Second World War, that he found the Chequered Skipper. Years later, he collaborated with Capt. C. H. B. Grant to write the definitive six-volume *African Handbook of Birds* series. 'His prowess with rifle, rod, and gun was equally renowned and many stories are told of his remarkable feats with these weapons . . .' (de Worms, 1975). He captained the Great Britain rifle shooting team at the Olympic Games in 1924, where he won a gold medal.

It may be a surprise to British entomologists to know that *Carterocephalus palaemon* [Chequered Skipper] occurs in Western Inverness-shire. It certainly was a surprise to

Fig. 85. The Chequered Skipper, Ashton, Northamptonshire (2003). Owned by the Rothschild family, it was a favourite haunt of butterfly collectors. It is also the birthplace of The World Conker Championships.

Fig. 86. First taken in May 1798 by Revd Dr Charles Abbot in Bedfordshire, the Chequered Skipper eventually became extinct in England around 1976. Fortunately it continues to thrive in Scotland where it was discovered in 1939.

me, and I could not believe my eyes when the first one settled in front of me. Since then however I have seen a considerable number and have taken a small series. I rather hope it may be fairly widely distributed, as the situations it affects are rides in birch woodland and thinly wooded banks, which are extensive in this part of the country. The specimens I have appear to be pale and sharply marked as compared with a series from eastern England. I saw the first one on May 10. There is neither *Brachypodium* nor *Bromus* [False Brome and Brome grasses] in the places it frequents, and in spite of careful watching I failed to spot its food-plant.

[Mackworth-Praed, C. W. 1942. *Carterocephalus palaemon* in Western Inverness-shire. *The Entomologist* **75**: 216].

His announcement would not have been a surprise to Miss C. Ethel Evans — it transpired that she had taken *palaemon* three years earlier, near Loch Lochy in Western Inverness-shire, although she did not publish this fact until 1949. A male caught by her at Bunarkaig on the 18th June 1939 is figured in George Thomson's *The Butterflies of Scotland* and the specimen itself is in the Royal Scottish Museum, Edinburgh.

Even her discovery may very well not have been the first. In 1907 James J. Joicey and A. Noakes intriguingly reported seeing a 'Skipper' during a collecting holiday in Glenshian, Inverness-shire, in early July. Did, in fact, the distinction of being the first entomologists to glimpse Scottish *palaemon* rightfully belong to them? It is certainly found around that area and can still be on the wing in that month — and no other skippers have been recorded from that locality . . .

Mackworth-Praed's discovery of the Chequered Skipper in Scotland came at a time when this butterfly was slowly disappearing from its known haunts in a number of English midland counties. By 1976 it had gone — the last English specimen being recorded from Rutland. Today it can be found in many parts of Argyll and Inverness-shire where at least ninety colonies have been identified, and there is compelling evidence that it is spreading. Thankfully this butterfly has now been removed from the endangered species list.

CHAPTER FIVE

'TRAVELLERS' TALES' — BUTTERFLY HUNTING OVERSEAS

'One step. Steady. Another step. Flop! I got him! When I got up I shook like a leaf with excitement, and when I opened those beautiful wings and made sure what a rare and so extraordinary perfect specimen I had, my head went round and my legs became so weak with emotion that I had to sit on the ground. I had greatly desired to possess myself of a specimen of that species when collecting for the professor. I took long journeys and underwent great privations; I had dreamed of him in my sleep, and here suddenly I had him in my fingers — for myself!'

Joseph Conrad, *Lord Jim* (1900)

GEORGE BLUNDELL LONGSTAFF, M.D. (1849–1921) was almost the last of a long line of Victorian butterfly collectors and travellers. A painting hangs in the hallway of the Royal Entomological Society in London which shows him in a quiet moment, sharing thoughts about butterflies with another great collector of the time — Professor Selwyn Image (1849–1930).* The two men are examining specimens from a large cabinet. Longstaff, beard thrust forward like Sir Arthur Conan Doyle's Professor Challenger, sits gazing into space, perhaps recalling the exact day, the exact moment, when his specimen was taken. As an undergraduate at Oxford an accident deprived him of the sight of one eye. But this handicap did not prevent him from becoming a determined traveller who chronicled in great detail the pleasures and difficulties that confronted him in a host of foreign places. As he travelled, Baedeker's guide in hand, he would eagerly record details of the scenery, the people and the architecture of the places visited, while at the same time hunting butterflies and amassing notes for his lengthy volume — *Butterfly-hunting in Many Lands: Notes of a Field Naturalist* (1912). In later years, he acquired a beautiful estate in North Devon. It was said in his obituary that 'he was an admirable field naturalist — patient, active, and enterprising'.

The more widely did these Victorian collectors travel, the more enthusiastic they seemed to become. Some positively glowed with the aura of conquest. Difficulties over travel arrangements, language, unwholesome food, tropical diseases, or unhelpful natives, were often brushed aside. Some — like Margaret E. Fountaine — 'just ploughed on, telling [ourselves] that there must be something rewarding round the next bend. If only?' Longstaff, like Fountaine, usually listed the difficulties that he encountered. But once these had been surmounted there were always tantalizing descriptions of rare or beautiful butterflies. At times, however, Longstaff was strangely apologetic:

> That I was able to give so much time to collecting was due to the fact that, whereas my daughter and her companion felt the heat so much that they usually kept within doors from about 10 a.m. to 3 p.m., I, for my part, protected by a "solar tope" [*sic*] of the "pigsticker" type, and a spinal pad to my coat, suffered no serious inconvenience from the sun's rays *so long as I took active exercise.*

Once, on a trip to India, Longstaff forgot to pack his butterfly net. On arrival, however, he made it a priority to put matters right. 'The resources of the bazár at Simla only produced a child's butterfly-net, a mere toy, scarce twelve inches in diameter and of a pale yellow colour!

* See Frontispiece in *The Aurelian Legacy: British Butterflies and their Collectors* (Salmon, M. A., 2000. Colchester, Harley Books).

227

Armed with this and a tin cigarette-box filled with triangular envelopes I took the field.'

The wealth of articles on hunting butterflies in foreign lands made it difficult to choose a representative sample. However, after some initial hesitation we followed the example of George Longstaff and 'took the field'.

AN ENTOMOLOGIST'S VISIT TO DALMATIA IN 1873

Anon. (1874)

In Chapter 3 (p. 126) the Revd John Marcon talks of various 'hazards of the chase'. These included bulls, adders and gamekeepers — but he does not mention dogs. In an anonymous article entitled 'An Entomologist's visit to Dalmatia in 1873', the author tells us how he coped with the unwelcome attention of various dogs.

. . . To the traveller Dalmatia will never be attractive; in its physical aspects in many respects like Greece, and, although some of its towns played no unimportant part in history, it lacks the "scenes our earliest dreams have dwelt upon," that will long continue to make us "hail the bright clime of battle and of song" with interest and delight. At present there is not an hotel in the whole country; the two or three, if so many, little restaurants, which are called albergos, at Zara, Spalatro, and Ragusa, may or may not be able to furnish the traveller with a bedroom, but generally the owners know where to find one in their neighbourhood. This is not pleasant; we got, however, clean and tolerably comfortable accommodation, all things considered, and have nothing but praise to accord to what they gave us to eat and drink. It is possible that other travellers may be more fastidious. The men are a fine race, still dressed in eastern style — the belt full of yatagans [*] and pistols, the countryman generally carrying a long gun in addition. If the women are not very pretty, they at least seem a kindly set. Once at Cattaro we were surrounded by a bevy of them, who discussed our appearance and possible nationality, without rudeness indeed, though not without causing us some embarrassment; but, on discovering that we were English, it was gratifying to see from the altered manner that our countrymen were not unpopular. . . .

In all our excursions we were never annoyed by dogs. Knowing their character in Albania and Greece, they had been my dread on entering the country. Near Marathon, I, with two companions, all on horseback, were once pursued by two ferocious brutes, which we had disturbed while glutting themselves on a dead horse; and a few times, when on foot, I have had to sit down and face the enemy till its owner arrived. Once I was a prisoner in this way nearly two hours. The dog is quiet as long as you are seated, eyeing you at a distance that you would gladly increase. I believe the plan of sitting down is alluded to by Homer, and was not quite understood until it was explained by a traveller some years ago. I never cared to try throwing a stone at them, which is so efficacious with dogs in general. I noticed that the owners struck them over the fore-legs when refractory. In one of my walks I recollect having to pass one not far from the road, and it struck me I would try another plan. Before the dog noticed me I began talking to it in English, and in the most soothing tones I could command. At first it looked puzzled, then, lifting up its head and dropping its tail, it poured out a long howl, during which I passed quickly on. English must have been a novelty that astonished it. I had no opportunity of trying this plan a second time.

[Anon. 1874. An entomologist's visit to Dalmatia in 1873. *Entomologist's Annual,* pp.164–170].

[*] Yatagan: a Turkish sword with a single-edged blade.

A CLOUD OF BUTTERFLIES

J. W. Slater, Tollington Park, London, N. (1879)

A strange occurrence is reported from Wetzikon, Canton Zurich. On June 14th the commune was invaded by an immense swarm of butterflies, a kilometre wide, and so long that the procession took two hours to pass. They were principally of the kind known in Switzerland as *Distelfalter*, which feed on nettles and thistles. They flew from two to ten metres above the ground, and went off in a north-westerly direction. *Distelfalter* is the common German name for *Cynthia cardui* [Painted Lady].

[Slater, J. W. 1879. A cloud of butterflies. *The Entomologist* **12**: 180].

CANNIBALISM IN THE BLACK-VEINED WHITE

James Cosmo Melvill, Prestwich, Lancashire. (1883)

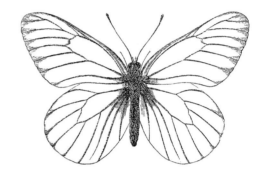

On June 26th last, whilst walking with my brother from Visp to Zermatt, we came, soon after passing Stalden, upon a sudden turn in the road where it crossed a small mountain stream. Here disported a perfect flock of *P. crataegi* [Black-veined White]; so plentiful were they that by one sweep of the net it was possible to capture eight or ten at once. A step or two further we saw what at first sight seemed to be a living and moving white flower in the road, but it dispersed and flew off in various directions at our approach, with the exception of some three or four individuals, which we carefully watched upon perceiving that they were feasting, with extended proboscides, on the juices of a fallen comrade of their own species that had evidently been trodden under foot that morning. These three or four it was impossible to drive away from the spot; they seemed half-stupefied with their repast, and only flew away a yard or so when disturbed, to return again at the first opportunity to their cannibalistic employment, and, as it appeared to be, enjoyment. Upon repassing the same spot a few days afterwards we again noticed a large flock of the same species by the stream. Though abundant throughout Switzerland, I never saw them in such countless swarms as here. . . .

[Melvill, J. C. 1883. Cannibalism in *Pieris crataegi*. *The Entomologist* **16**: 15–16].

BUTTERFLY-CATCHING IN THE NEIGHBOURHOOD OF MONT BLANC

James W. Tutt, F.E.S., Blackheath, London, S. E. (1894)

Overhead the sky is of a lovely blue. The sun's rays pass through the larches and fall upon a sloping hollow that is filled knee-deep with scabious and thyme, marjoram and gentians, umbellifers and trefoils, barberry and juniper. Two lazy fellows are lounging idly in the shade at a little distance from each other, each trusting that the other believes him to be working as hard as possible while he is really glorying in his own laziness as he feasts his eyes on the snowy dome of Mont Blanc, or on the necklet of cloud from out of which stands up, black and grim, the sharp point of the Aiguille Noire de Peteret. Yonder the Glacier de Brenva shows its white névé, glistening in the brilliant sunlight; whilst The Grammont and Chétif smile grimly across the Dora Valley at the two make-believes on the opposite side. Lovely is the Dora Valley, with its turbid glacial streams, its emerald green, its snow-capped mountains, and its beautiful flowers. Round this delightful spot, in favourable localities, butterflies and moths don't simply exist — they swarm.

Let us glance at some of the butterflies that may be captured round about Courmayeur on a morning in early August.

In the valley below there *Papilio podalirius* [Scarce Swallowtail] flies lazily but gracefully, sipping from every muddy spot. The few *P. machaon* [Swallowtail] we see are worn and broken, and a half-fed larva, picked up on the bank, tells us that we have hit on a time between the two broods or else that the summer brood is past. But *the* butterfly of these slopes is *Parnassius apollo* [Apollo]. A lazy, high-living chap is he, sucking away greedily at the nectar of knapweed or scabious, too intent to mind the fingers that pick him tenderly from his food, simply throwing out his forelegs in a wondering sort of way as much as to say, Where am I now? As we put him back he goes on sucking again, flaps his wings once or twice to satisfy himself that he has discovered where he is and then, after a time, spreads his wings and launches himself in the air so lightly and easily that you fail to see his wings vibrate to keep him in motion. A really fine fellow it is, with its crimson spots varying in size and number, dependent, my companion says, on sex; but this flight makes one think that, in spite of the neuration being so different, the osmaterium of the larva is a better guide, and shows that it has closer affinities to the Swallow-tails than one would otherwise be inclined to suppose. *Leucophasia sinapis* [Wood White] threads its way slowly through bush and grass and occasionally settles as lazily as it flies, in spite of the fact that some of our English collectors think that this species has solved the problem of perpetual motion. In yonder

Fig. 87. James W. Tutt on one of his last collecting trips (1910). He was only in his fifty-third year when he died. His obituarist Dr Thomas Chapman attributed the cause to a combination of over-work, an East End atmosphere and a congenital heart weakness.

fields *Aporia crataegi* [Black-veined White] disports itself, the most diaphanous females reminding one of *P. apollo* and giving one the notion that the most perfect specimens are but in poor condition. With it are *Pieris brassicae* and *P. rapae* [Large and Small Whites], but *P. napi* [Green-veined White] does not put in an appearance, although we met with it later on at Aix-les-Bains. *Pieris daplidice* [Bath White] flits easily along, but a regular "artful dodger" it is. It flies slowly, and you cannot help distinguishing it at once on the wing, notwithstanding all that has been said to the contrary. But for all its slow flight you often miss it; it dodges just as you strike, changes its mind perhaps when the shadow of the net falls on it; at any rate you miss about as many as you catch. *Gonepteryx rhamni* [Brimstone] is just coming out, but no *G. cleopatra* [Cleopatra] are seen. The "Yellows" are in fine condition and in the humour to hunt a fellow on the hillside. You may talk about hunting butterflies but I have quite made up my mind that these Clouded Yellows hunt me. One took me a pretty dance, I nearly broke my neck – and got a peep at him; had after him again – and got a telescopic view at about six yards; then he beamed on me as he turned suddenly and passed within an inch of my nose, just as I was calculating whether I was to sink gracefully on my back on the bank or roll with the loose stones I had incautiously stepped on and thus end my existence; then, when I recovered, I saw him hovering over a flower at the very spot whence I had started; but when I got there he was just sailing away over the larch trees. I didn't give them much chance of hunting me though, for we soon arranged matters satisfactorily, and whilst *C. edusa* [Clouded Yellow], *C. hyale* [Pale Clouded Yellow] and *C. phicomone* [Mountain Clouded Yellow] flew peacefully about the bank I lay in the shade and watched them. Argynnids were in thousands, *A. aglaia* [Dark Green Fritillary] and *A. niobe* [Niobe Fritillary] in dozens; and what grand fellows some of the latter are! what marvellous variations they show in their silvery undersides – and in their uppersides, too, for the matter of that. *A. adippe* [High Brown Fritillary] and an occasional *A. paphia* [Silver-washed Fritillary], together with a much larger but closely-allied species, with a really grand underside of green and red, were mingled with such lovely *A. latona* [*sic* – Queen of Spain Fritillary]. Just out of pupa, they waved their wings airily, now on a flower, then on the rock at one's feet. *A. selene* [Small Pearl-bordered Fritillary] I saw once, I believe, but *A. euphrosyne* [Pearl-bordered Fritillary] was not. A half-dozen other species besides perhaps fell in our way here, but their names are not on British lists, except perhaps *A. dia* [Weaver's Fritillary], which sometimes is and ought not to be. All our British Melitæas occurred and many others besides – *M. cinxia* [Glanville Fritillary] on the hill-side, *M. aurinia* [Marsh Fritillary] high on the mountains, probably long over in the lower regions, and *M. athalia* [Heath Fritillary] here and there, with *M. parthenie* [Meadow Fritillary], *M. aurelia* [Nickerl's Fritillary] and many other species. The larvæ of *Vanessa urticae* [Small Tortoiseshell] occurred high on the mountains, where nine-tenths must starve before they come to maturity, and plenty of imagos as well. *V. antiopa* [Camberwell Beauty], fine strong-winged fellow, was only once seen here, but others appeared in the Cogne Valley, where a pupa and evidences of some hundreds of larvæ in the shape of their cast skins were found upon the willows. *Vanessa io* [Peacock] and *Pyrameis atalanta* [Red Admiral] were in no great abundance, but *P. cardui* [Painted Lady] and its larvæ were everywhere. This species was found up to the highest points we reached, sailing over the top of Mont de la Saxe and the Glacier du Miage, free and unrestrained. *Limenitis camilla* [White Admiral] occasionally haunted a shrubby honeysuckle, and *Melanargia galatea* [Marbled White] kept company with *P. apollo* almost everywhere on suitable slopes. We made a special hunt for *Erebias*, and got some, although *Erebia aethiops* [Scotch Argus] occurred but twice and both times at low levels (at Bourg St. Maurice and Grésy near Aix les Bains), but some allied species swarmed. *Erebia epiphron* [Small Mountain Ringlet] in varied conditions of dotting and spotting was sometimes not uncommon. *Pararge megaera* [Wall] and some allied non-British species occurred, but rarely in the higher levels, although the species was abundant in the Val d'Aosta, whilst *H. semele* [Grayling], fine grand fellows some of them, were met with in many places. *Epinephele ianira* [Meadow Brown], with a double-spotted relation, and *Coenonympha pamphilus* [Small Heath] were not uncommon. Of the Hair-streaks only one, and that a non-British species, occurred, but the lovely Coppers made up for them. Brilliant little gems are the males of *Chrysophanus virgaureæ* [Scarce Copper], and abundantly they skipped from flower to flower, whilst *C. phloeas* [*sic*] [Small Copper] gave us here a bright form, lower down the dark form which Mr. Merrifield has proved to accompany a high temperature and which has helped to prove that melanism is often the result of a physical (pathological) process which may be engendered in a variety of ways. But *Lycaenas* are the insects *par excellence* of the banks here. *L. corydon* [Chalk Hill Blue] and *L. bellargus* [Adonis Blue], *L. aegon* and *L. argus* [Silver-studded Blue], *L. astrarche* [Brown Argus] and *L. icarus* [Common Blue], *L. acis* [Mazarine Blue] and *L. minima* [Small Blue], *L. argiolus* [Holly Blue] and *L. argiades* [Short-tailed Blue], with fine dark *L. arion* [Large Blue] sport here, and quite a dozen non-British species besides: the thyme and marjoram teem with these strange little creatures, which make their wings appear to rotate by a process of moving those on opposite sides in different directions. No *Nemeobius lucina* [Duke of Burgundy Fritillary] were observed here, although a second brood turned up at Aix, but *malvae*-like Skippers were in dozens. How many species there were I dare not say; whether *Pyrgus malvae* [Grizzled Skipper] was in fact one of them it is equally unsafe to assert. *Nisoniades tages* [Dingy Skipper] and some butterflies which resembled but were not it occurred, not here but at Aosta; but here, with the Yellows and Fritillaries, thousands of *Pamphila comma* [Silver-spotted Skipper] dart about diving their probosces deep into thistle and scabious, hustling the Burnet moths, the *apollos*, and even the bees. *P. linea* and *P. lineola* [Small and Essex Skippers], *P. sylvanus* [Large Skipper] and *P. actaeon* [Lulworth Skipper] all occur here, *P. lineola* much the most frequently.

Thus much for some of the butterflies around Courmayeur. Those species which are not found in England find so little favour in the eyes of British collectors that this must be my excuse for not naming them; but when three-fourths of our British species and as many other non-British species besides, can be seen in one or two morning walks among some of the most beautiful scenery in the Alps, with the Sovran Dome of Mont Blanc keeping silent and watchful guard, where, when butterflies and Burnet moths pall, one can turn to lovely flowers, glacial torrents, glistening snow, sparkling cascades, silent and majestic mountains or deep deep blue sky, can watch the filmy haze weave itself into fanciful shapes around the aiguilles yonder and float off a wraith so fairy-like and light that the blue of the sky appears

to pierce it, whilst the sound of the cow-bells comes peacefully from the pastures above and woos the sleepy dream-god, then I feel it safe to assert that there are many worse occupations than catching "Hampstead Heath" *antiopas*, "Dover" *latonas* [*sic*], "Folkestone" *daplidices* and Midland *dias*, on the breezy slopes of the mountains around Courmayeur.

[Tutt, J. W. 1894. Butterfly-catching in the neighbourhood of Mont Blanc. *The Entomologist's Record and Journal of Variation* **5**: 233–235].

BUTTERFLY HUNTING IN GREECE IN THE YEAR 1900

Margaret E. Fountaine, F.E.S. (1902)

Margaret Elizabeth Fountaine (1862–1940) was born at South Acre, Norwich, the daughter of a clergyman. After an early and unhappy love affair she spent much of her life travelling the world — for twenty-eight years in the company of Khalil Neimy, a dragoman, her 'dear companion, the constant and untiring friend'. In 1940 she was found dying by a roadside in Trinidad having had a severe heart attack. Her butterfly net was nearby. Her many adventures were recorded in a diary twelve volumes of which were left, together with ten mahogany cabinets of butterflies, to the Norwich Castle Museum. Later, W. F. Cater condensed Miss Fountaine's life into two volumes — *Love among the Butterflies* (1980) and *Butterflies and Late Loves* (1986) — his text being essentially an annotated and shortened version of the diary.

Fig. 88. Margaret Fountaine, who left to the Norwich Museum 'ten handsome mahogany cases containing in all 22,000 butterflies: rank after rank, drawer after drawer'.

. . . The Greek roads bore in many places a striking resemblance to the partially hardened surface of a ploughed field, and frequently there were no roads at all, but only bridle-paths, for the principal mode of locomotion in Greece is on horseback. This threw my bicycle completely "out of work;" but horses were to be hired everywhere, at from five to seven drachmas for the whole day; though of course such a thing as a side-saddle, was an absolutely unknown item of civilisation. The inns in the country towns and villages are rough to a degree, and hemiptera, other than those to be sought for outside by the entomologist engaged in the study of that class of insects, were in some of these inns extremely plentiful. In fact though the food was bad the accommodation was worse. The Greek innkeeper often seemed to think that to have two sheets on a bed was an unnecessary luxury; and sometimes they provided none at all. Luckily, owing to the kindness of a friend, I was prepared to meet this contingency. Towels also were not visible unless specially ordered. But they managed to provide their guests with a greasy hair-brush and comb, and also with an old clothes brush; to say nothing of a piece of untempting looking scrubbing soap; all of which articles of luxury(?) I used to collect in a heap, telling Marcus (my Greek courier) to cause them immediately to be removed from my presence and never to let them appear again. Nor were these all the contingencies to be provided for in choosing a room in a Greek Hotel, as I would perhaps be told that the charge was one drachma (6d) a night, and then, while I was inwardly congratulating myself that travelling in the "Interior" was at all events not ruinous, I would be shown into a good-sized room, barely furnished, but with perhaps two or three beds in it. I remember at Tripolitza, deciding upon an apartment of this description, when I happened to remark (of course through the medium of Marcus), that those other two beds might just as well be removed as it would give me more space, to which the prompt reply was: — "Oh! but you see someone else may arrive!" — and then I grasped the full horror of the situation; the one drachma a night was for the *bed* and not exclusively for the room. As matters stood I should be liable to return from one of our long butterfly-hunting expeditions into the mountains to find some objectionable Greek female established in another corner of *my* room. The idea was intolerable, but the way out of the difficulty was obvious; I must hire all the three beds in order to prevent anyone else from doing so. But all this and more must be endured by the butterfly collector in Greece, with just as much patience and resignation as he may happen to have at his command. Yet there was a pleasing variety in the quality of these discomforts, and at Delphi, though the so-called hotel was only a little bungalow-dwelling in the main street, with not so many as half-a-dozen rooms in it all told, the landlord of this unpretentious little habitation who was, I had heard, celebrated as the ugliest and most honest man in Greece, proved himself to be quite worthy of both epithets, and also was so far comparatively accustomed to provide for the English tourist, as to be aware that one of our indispensable little weaknesses is the demand for cleanliness in all things. For Delphi being a place of great archaeological interest is on this account occasionally visited by travellers.

There are not very many railways in Greece, and the trains are extremely slow and leisurely in their movements, so much so that there is no sort or kind of objection raised when the passengers walk along the footboards outside the carriages while the train is at full speed, should they be disposed to do so. I did this once myself on the little branch railway from Dhiakopto up to Kalávryta, when I found my quarters in the small first-class compartment next the engine, a trifle too warm in consequence of the hot smoke which was constantly pouring into it. As I knew there was no stop till Zachloróu, and that there were several long tunnels, I considered it just as well not to run the risk of being suffocated in one of them. With Marcus it was a common practice also to get in after the train had well started. The first time I saw him standing coolly on the platform, as we were slowly steaming out of the station, I naturally thought to myself "Why, that fool Marcus has been left behind." But he soon set my mind at ease on this point, by shortly afterwards appearing at the window of my carriage, to have a few minutes' friendly conversation during the journey, a little habit of his to which I soon became quite accustomed. I once asked him if he had carried on these practices during his trip to England, to which he replied "Only once, and then I was told if I ever did so again I should be fined."

Having found the country round Tripolitza so dry and barren as to be apparently utterly unproductive from an entomological point of view, we were returning on the line of railway between that place and Corinth, when the train suddenly stopped in the midst of the mountains, nowhere near any evidences of what could possibly be mistaken for a station, and Marcus appeared to inform me that the cause for this was "the grasshoppers." So many of them were there that to proceed would be impossible, without running the risk of the engine slipping off the rails. I looked out and saw that the ground was covered with one moving mass of orthoptera. There was not a square inch of earth or visible blade of grass that was not densely populated with these creatures, but as I am a lepidopterist and not an orthopterist, I am unable to say to what species they belonged. Impromptu brushes had to be made of the scrub and brush-wood, and these were placed in front of the engine, and by this means the line was swept clear enough for the train to proceed in safety.

The Greek butterflies that I was most anxious to obtain were *Pieris krüperi* [Krueper's Small White], *P. ergane* [Mountain Small White], *Euchloë gruneri* [Gruner's Orange Tip], (*E. damone* [Eastern Orange Tip] I knew must be over long ago, as it only flies in the early spring), *Colias heldreichi* [now *C. aurorina* – Greek Clouded Yellow] (most especially), *Melanargia larissa* [Balkan Marbled White], *Chrysophanus ottomanus* [Grecian Copper], *C. thetis* [Fiery Copper], and *Satyrus graeca* [Grecian Grayling]. All of these I succeeded in taking with the exception of the two last-named species, both of which I should imagine to be July insects, as I left Greece at the end of June without seeing any specimen of them. . . .

In order to secure *Chrysophanus ottomanus* I had been told that I must visit Mesolonghi, another place on the sea-level, but very different from Loutraki. Instead of the dry, arid shores of the Gulf of Corinth, Mesolonghi lay surrounded by low, damp meadows, and unhealthy marshes – a perfect fever-bed of snakes and mosquitoes. Marcus did not appreciate the snakes at all, though he was never so vehement in his protestations that he was "not afraid" of them, as when he had just jumped half a foot off the ground at the sight of one; or possibly on no greater provocation than the rustle of a lizard in the grass! But *C. ottomanus* had to be captured, so snakes and mosquitoes alike must for the time being be put up with. And this was the chosen haunt of this brilliant little butterfly, flashing like a spark of fire amongst the tall green reeds and luxuriant flower-mingled grasses, but it was not so easy to find, and some days elapsed before we came across it all. But at last Marcus, to his great joy, secured a magnificent female. Still we had not really discovered, so to speak, its headquarters, till one day, when Marcus had gone off for a holiday to Patras, and I was out alone, I encountered what appeared to be a rather evil-disposed person, and in order to disembarrass myself of this individual I gave him the slip by pretending to go in hot pursuit after some imaginary butterfly-rarity. Once out of sight I lost no time in taking refuge in flight, by making off in an opposite direction; and by this means I came upon a spot near a little chapel, which we had not previously visited, where *C. ottomanus* (at least the males) flew in some abundance. So the evil-disposed person did me a good turn after all. . . .

To the butterfly collector in Greece *Colias heldreichi* is the one prize before all others, to be sought after and looked out for. And this butterfly I had been given to understand only occurred on the high and lofty mountains – such as the Parnassos – always above the tree-line, at an elevation never lower than 7000ft. Judge, therefore, of my surprise and delight, when one day about the middle of June, not more than a few hundred feet above the village of Soudena, on the lower slopes of Mount Chelmos, as we were riding steadily on, intending to reach the summit, I saw a large dark *Colias*, hovering rapidly over the scrub and brushwood, but, as I found, on consulting my aneroid, that it was only an elevation of 4000ft., I was not sufficiently sceptical of the information I had received, even then, to dismount and catch one, till one of the men who had come with the horses, and was amusing himself by brandishing about my net, suddenly brought for my inspection what I saw at a glance was unmistakably a magnificent female of *Colias heldreichi*. I was soon on my feet and in hot pursuit of every one I saw, which was no easy task over this rock-strewn mountain-side, but the males of this lovely butterfly were flying in every direction, so that I had soon secured several, not to mention another fine female. A day like this is a day to be remembered in the life of an entomologist. It is one which stands out quite distinct, leaving an impression never to be forgotten. The long, toilsome climbs of other and less successful days beneath a blazing sun, the long hours of thirst and fatigue, which have so often brought in the end little or no results, are all compensated for in the joys of the one day, when the enthusiastic butterfly-hunter meets for the first time a treasure such as this, flying everywhere in wild reckless profusion, alluring the excited biped to run heedlessly over ground of the roughest description, now jumping, now slipping, maybe even sometimes falling, but never pausing in the hot pursuit of the fascinating little insect, that will make such a grand acquisition to the collection at home. . . .

[Fountaine, M. E. 1902. Butterfly hunting in Greece, in the year 1900. *The Entomologist's Record and Journal of Variation* **14**: 29-35; 64–67].

This magnificent butterfly, which made such a vivid impression on Miss Fountaine, has a form of the female in which the usual orange ground colour is replaced by white. Abafi-Aigner named it for her in 1901 – f. *fountainei*.

Although many of the tours undertaken by these intrepid entomologists were extremely successful, those of some other collectors were much less so. In 1899 the redoubtable J. W. Tutt set out to investigate the Lepidoptera of the Val d'Herens in Switzerland. While, in 1902, the Reverend Frank Lowe travelled for several weeks through Germany and Italy. The accounts of these two expeditions, both of which were published in *The Entomologist's Record*, suggest that for various reasons they turned out to be anything but rewarding adventures.

COLLECTING LEPIDOPTERA IN 1902

Revd Frank E. Lowe, M.A., F.E.S., Guernsey. (1902)

The Revd Frank E. Lowe (1853–1918) was Rector of St Stephen's, Guernsey (Fig. 20). He was educated at Durham School and Durham Theological College. In his early years he distinguished himself as an oarsman. After an early interest in butterflies and moths he let it wane until: 'One day,' wrote Mrs Lowe, 'I returned from walking on the cliffs. I described to him a brown butterfly I had noticed different from anything I had seen before. The next day we went to identify it, and it was *cinxia* [Glanville Fritillary].' This little discovery re-fired his enthusiasm, and from that time he became an ardent collector and a close observer.

Those who ought to know tell me that negative evidence is nearly as much wanted as positive. This is my sole excuse for recounting my disheartening experiences in June and July of this year. The wish had been — starting at a much earlier date than Mr. Tutt's visits — to add something to his valuable "Contributions to the Fauna of Piedmont." Thanks to his kindness I was provided with all the back numbers of the *Ent. Record* bearing on the localities to be visited. Also, at some little trouble and expense, I had little booklets printed, with lists of all possible butterflies, and the page opposite ruled in columns like a school register, that I might have no need to trust to memory, but simply "mark the attendance" of each species in every locality, with a series of signs to denote "fresh," "worn," etc. London was left on June 4th, and reached again on August 1st. Our trip was to Freiburg in Baden, Turin, Susa, Valle di Pesio, Aosta, Courmayeur, back to Turin, Verona, Bozen, Brenner, and home. Well, we did all this and more, but the whole tour has not given me a single new species for the cabinet, and very few which may serve to renew or extend existing series. Everywhere but at Bozen, where we were too late, insects were so abnormally backward that there was nothing to be done. The weather was generally wet, and always cold for the time of year, but, though the summer species were retarded, there was no consolation of belated spring broods. At Freiburg, June 6th was a dull day, thunder threatening, and nothing stirring in the woods behind the "exercising ground" but a few *Abraxas sylvata* [Clouded Magpie]. The next was a pouring wet day, and I was laid up with neuralgia. Sunday, entomologically a dies non. On Monday, the 9th, as it looked more promising, I was up and caught the 6.0 a.m. train to Neu-Breisach. It began to rain before I reached my destination, and never ceased for more than a few minutes at a time. The motive of the *détour* to Freiburg and Breisach, was the desire of a good series of *Chrysophanus dispar* var. *rutilus* [Large Copper]. Last summer I had taken four in passable condition on June 14th, *viz.*, one male and three females. Two of the latter were boxed for eggs, and ruined as specimens without obtaining ova. This year I hunted up and down the sides of the moat which surrounds the fortifications, in the same spot as last year, but took not a thing, not even *Agrophila trabealis* [Spotted Sulphur], or *Bankia argentula* [Silver Barred], which abounded in 1901. Turning to go back to the station I was "halted" by a sentinel of the 142nd Regiment of the Line, who calmly, but very decisively, barred the way. From his remarks I gathered only one word, "verboten," at which I offered my apologies in English, and again attempted to proceed to the station. At that he manifested more excitement, and signalled to other soldiers who appeared ready to hand. These made me understand that I must follow them. So we marched back with arms at the slope to the guard-room. Here a sergeant, pen and note book in hand, endeavoured to question me, but as he only spoke his own language, and I did not, we got no "forrader." After much delay, I was sent under guard to the citadel, and was again equally hopelessly interrogated by higher officials, who spoke neither French nor English. They evidently suspected me, most unjustly, of knowing German, for — by the way they insisted upon seeing the contents of all my pockets — when I showed a "pocket pistol" of whisky and water, saying "flask," as I had named every other article in turn, one very typical German, in a green uniform, sprang forward, seized the lapel of my coat, and bringing his face down to mine, snarled, "Hein! You no hab Deutsch? 'Flasche' ist Deutsch. A-rrh! vat you said." I gently suggested that the name of the vessel was practically the same to both of us, but that the spirit was good Dewar, and like myself a British subject. Not to prolong an amusing scene which, however, is not entomology, they found at last a private who had been in England, and could speak the language of civilisation. He came, and in a few moments I was discharged, "without a stain on my character." It caused some amusement when I ventured through the interpreter to express regret for the trouble I had inadvertently given, but official dignity was greatly ruffled when, through the same mouthpiece, I asked if I might come again tomorrow. Next day I tried Gottenheim, another haunt of *C.* var. *rutilus*, but with no better luck. The 11th was dull with slight showers. I took, however, two *Aporia crataegi* [Black-veined White] at rest on flowers of scabious. One of these, a female, is of remarkable beauty, apparently just emerged, the underside of the secondaries being of a strong maize colour. The coloration is visible on the upperside, but it is on the underside that the full effect of this unusual tint is seen. . . . Out of conceit with Freiburg we left for Susa, at which little town of classic fame we arrived on the evening of the 16th. Here we had three fine hot days during our stay, which extended to midday of the 21st. Though so much further south, Nature seemed to be little more forward here than at Freiburg. On the 18th, about 500 ft. above Sta. Maria della Luso, I found the meadows filled with the pheasant-eyed narcissus, in its first glory, with *Ornithogalum nutans* [star-of-Bethlehem] and others which formed quite an early spring show. While we were at Susa the only common butterflies were *Aporia crataegi, L. sinapis* [Wood White] and *Pararge maera* [Large Wall Brown], with some remarkable fine *Pararge megaera* [Wall]. One of the latter, a female, measures just under 2½ in., and is as large as a good *P. maera* female. . . . Without doubt there would have been good sport at Susa later, but the hotel was not run on sound principles of sanitary science, to put it mildly, and uninviting, therefore, for a protracted stay. The absentee chiefly deplored was *Polygonia egea,* [Southern Comma] which Mr. Rowland-Brown found so abundant about a week later last year. With empty store boxes we took train to Turin, and on the next day train again to Beinette, from whence, after some difficulties with our driver, we reached Certosa di Pesio at 4.30 p.m. on the 22nd. The old Certosa, or monastery, suppressed by Napoleon, has been converted into a most comfortable hotel and bathing establishment. We were the first visitors of the season, and never more happy in country quarters, but the valley is close and relaxing. Even here we were too early for the summer of 1902. . . .

[Lowe, F. 1902. Collecting Lepidoptera in 1902. *The Entomologist's Record and Journal of Variation* **14**: 330–334].

LEPIDOPTERA OF THE VAL D'HERENS — AROLLA

James W. Tutt, F.E.S., Blackheath, London, S. E. (1905)

Arolla! To how many readers of this magazine does not the name conjure up one of the loveliest vignettes to be found throughout the length and breadth of the Alps? The long vista up the Arolla glacier, closed by the delightful snow-clad Mont Collon, the glorious snow-peak, the Pigno d'Arolla, and then the unpronounceable Zigiorenove glacier, with its huge moraine sweeping away from the foot of the Pas de Chèvres. To the left (looking towards the snow-peaks) the sharp Aiguille de la Za, a long and difficult ascent, and to the right again La Rousette and the Aiguilles Rouges, the slopes from the foot of which to the hotel make a marvellous collecting-ground, whilst now, right behind, at the foot of the Combe d'Arolla are the Dents de Veisivi, on the slopes of which, Mr. Lloyd informs me, *Œneis aëllo* [*O. glacialis* Moll — Alpine Grayling] flies in the greatest abundance. The knoll itself, on which the Kurhaus Hotel is situated, is a delightful flower-garden in the midst of the last and highest big remnant of the forest of Arolla pines, whose delicate fragrance adds such a charm to this delightful valley. And who can describe the flowers? Acres upon acres of yellow and orange hieracii [alpine daisies], and billowy waves of the pale blue alpine forget-me-nots, with occasional masses of white and yellow alone breaking the continuous sheets of beauty they spread everywhere. A few hundred feet above the hotel, edelweiss is in the greatest abundance, and the comfort of the hotel itself marks Arolla, when reached, an ideal resting-place. I say, when reached, advisedly, for the journey to Arolla is not to be undertaken by cripples without considerable forethought, for the Kurhaus Hôtel is situated as nearly as possible at 7000 feet elevation, and there is no means of reaching it except by walking, or on mule-back. Arolla is exposed from early morning till late evening to the sun, a fact that, no doubt, goes far towards producing its wealth of vegetation and its abundant insect life. It is indeed, a place of beauty, an ideal spot for a nature-lover, be he botanist or zoologist.

I have paid two visits to Arolla, the first consisted of four or five splendid days in the third week of August, 1899, whilst the second was a longer stay, from July 29th to August 11th, 1903. The first ended in a perfect holocaust. Following on four or five hard days' work, in which Dr. [T. A.] Chapman and I had amassed a splendid lot of specimens by day, and in setting which every spare moment had been utilised in the early morning and late afternoon, an intelligent mule-driver, in spite of repeated warnings that my large collecting-box and setting-case were insecurely packed, managed to let the setting-case fall down a steep and rocky mule-path, smashing it entirely, and then, to mend matters, carefully put the

Fig. 89. An awkward moment while out collecting. From 'Mountaineering' by C. E. Dent. Badminton Library, 1892.

boards loosely into the box with the set insects. Practically every specimen taken at Arolla was mangled into dust, and not until the man had disappeared, and we were anxious, at Evolène, to know how the specimens had travelled, did we learn the hopeless ruin that had befallen our labour. To attempt to describe the condition of my mind on that never-to-be-forgotten midnight ride down to Sion (for a hurried and peremptory return was necessary so far as the doctor was concerned) were [sic] futile. Thoughts of scraps of the wings of burnets, blues, whites, Erebias, Setinas, fritillaries, broken and bent pins, in huddled confusion under the heel of loose setting-boards, created such demoniacal desires in my heart as I have rarely been possessed of, and till this present day the mere mention of that night has been taboo with everyone cognisant of it; some 1200 perfect alpine lepidoptera, besides several long series of bred and captured insects that were on the boards when we journeyed up, these went down in one fell moment to endless ruin and perdition. That our other box, containing our captures of the preceding fortnight at Evolène and on the Simplon Pass, was left behind at Evolène, and that its contents had not shared in the general ruin was the only redeeming feature of that in some way unsatisfactory summer holiday of 1899. . . .

[Tutt, J. W. 1905. Lepidoptera of the Val d'Herens – Arolla. *The Entomologist's Record and Journal of Variation* 17: 1–6].

Tutt's temper was legendary! Some of his contemporaries admitted quite openly that he terrified them. In time, both F. W. Frohawk and Richard South became victims of Tutt's hectoring criticism and it was after a series of unfortunate and hostile confrontations at the Entomological Society of London that Frohawk, a very mild-mannered man, resigned his Fellowship. However, within months of Tutt's death in 1911 he sought re-election. His daughter Valezina, Viscountess Bolingbroke, remembered her father describing Tutt as 'that windbag!' (pers. comm.).

On another occasion, Tutt took a swipe at one of his most distinguished contemporaries

— the Revd F. O. Morris. The vehicle for this attack was Tutt's *British Butterflies* (1896). When discussing the habitat and distribution of the Glanville Fritillary in Britain, he castigated Morris, 'who seems never to have had the slightest practical acquaintance with the insects of which he wrote . . .', before going further and mildly rebuking his forbears with the comment 'we doubt very much the occurrence of this species in "hay-fields", "woods" and "marshes" as stated by our entomological ancestors'.

James Tutt was also highly critical of Henry Doubleday, one of the most distinguished Victorian lepidopterists. Doubleday possessed a huge collection which Tutt found sadly wanting:

> We suppose no one knows more about his own collection than did the late Henry Doubleday about his; yet, what is there to be learned from that collection (now at the Bethnal Green Museum) after a certain elementary point has been reached? It is useful for reference in order to name species, to see the range of variation in certain species, but there is nothing to tell us whether any particular insect came from the North Pole or the Sahara; nothing to help us to draw any conclusions from one of the greatest masses of Lepidoptera ever collected together. What a different value the collection would have if some system of labelling had been adopted.

In 1892 Tutt turned his attention to the scientific naming of moths. In writing *The British Noctuæ and their Varieties* (1891–92) he commented that 'many individual points have forced themselves upon my notice'. He visited the British Museum to examine type specimens in the National Collection, but found them poorly organized and often wrongly named. In *Stray Notes on the Noctuæ* (1892) he blamed A. G. Butler, who had arranged the collection, for this confusion. 'With regard to hap-hazard criticism, the following is an example from the pen of Mr. Butler, who appears from his writings, to be somewhat if not entirely responsible for the present condition — both in naming and in arrangement — of the national collection of NOCTUÆ.' He went further: 'Mr. Butler excuses his want of knowledge of a species fairly common just outside the London suburbs, because there was no "European representative in the general collection."' And 'One of the most remarkable instances of Mr. Butler's inability to see specific characters, or perhaps, I ought rather to say to distinguish allied species . . .' With this attack on one of the experts at the British Museum he found himself alienated from a good many colleagues.

Tutt did not restrict his criticisms to British lepidopterists alone. On one occasion he openly attacked Herr Otto Staudinger (1830–1900), the greatest German authority on the Palaearctic Lepidoptera. Obviously upset by what he saw as confusion in Staudinger's work he wrote: 'We have not time to work out the point . . . except to say that the chances are always great against Staudinger being right in any of the genera that he has not copied direct from some authority . . .' Dr T. A. Chapman, a friend of many years and Tutt's companion on that disastrous expedition to Arolla, penned in his obituary (1911) that Tutt 'had very little patience for opinions which he saw to be erroneous, no matter in what way; and in his earlier days his contemptuous onslaughts at times gave offence to persons who thought he was attacking not their errors but themselves.' On another occasion Robert Adkin recalled Tutt saying: 'Yes, I know I am often brutal in the way I put things, but I can't help it, and you know I am right.'

THE LARGE 'COPPER', ITS HABITS, AND ONE OF ITS PRESENT HAUNTS

William G. Sheldon, F.E.S., South Croydon, Surrey. (1909)

William George Sheldon (1859–1943) was born at Duffield, near Derby, and educated privately. Elected a Fellow of the Entomological Society in 1905, he was Treasurer from 1918 to 1928 and Vice-President in 1920. As a result of his financial acumen he was largely instrumental in acquiring the premises at 41, Queen's Gate, South Kensington, for the Royal Entomological Society. He was remembered as 'a tall, quiet man, who did not suffer fools gladly'. In the following short article he describes a visit to the Hungarian marshes in search of the Large Copper.

I suppose there is no butterfly that has a greater attraction for the average British lepidopterist than our long lost glory, *Chrysophanus dispar* [Large Copper], and this species was one of the reasons that turned my steps towards the Danube this summer.

On the morning of June 1st last, at the early hour of eight o' clock, I walked out of the little wayside station of Kamaraerdo, some few miles south-west of Budapest, where I had been most kindly conducted by Professor Schmidt to see *C. dispar* alive. The country was very different in character to that frequented by it in Britain, years ago, probably largely in consequence of the partial cultivation of its haunts. A valley some half-mile in width, the sides gently undulating up one or two hundred feet to its vine-clad crest on one side, and to the locally famous Budapest national playground, the Kammerwald, on the other. Except for a narrow strip at the bottom of varying width, the slopes were taken up by cultivation, and produced, in addition to grapes, luxuriant crops of wheat, barley, rye, sainfoin, potatoes and maize; the remaining uncultivated portion being the present stronghold of *C. dispar*. Centuries ago this had been no doubt a quaking, undrained, reedy bog, where the food-plant flourished luxuriantly and the outflow from which found its way to the mighty Danube close by. Modern improvements had changed all this; down the centre ran a ditch, willow-planted, which had drained the water off, and into this ditch emptied at intervals smaller

Fig. 90. William George Sheldon. Like J. W. Tutt and Dr T. A. Chapman, he enjoyed collecting abroad, even travelling as far afield as South America. 'But Sheldon still loved the British Lepidoptera and spent much time on the smaller species, in particular the Tortrices . . . His love for the Wicken Fen area led him to the National Trust, of which he became a member of its Council.' (Henry J. Turner, *The Entomolgist's Record and Journal of Variation*, 1944)

channels, each one of which played its part in the general scheme. This drainage system had converted the surface, leaving it moist indeed, but firm and covered with a thick crop of coarse grass, intermixed with flowering plants, amidst which the great waterdock grew abundantly in places.

The sun shone brightly that June morning, and we had not got ten yards from the railway station, when slowly flying along the grassy side of a ditch I saw my first large "copper" in the flesh, var. *rutilus* [German subspecies of the Large Copper] of course, but a very different object to the rather puny butterfly one usually gets from a dealer if a specimen is purchased;

for, next to our own peerless type, the Budapest is certainly one of the finest, if not the very finest, form to be found anywhere. My largest male and female expand respectively 44 mm. and 45 mm., as against the 46 mm. and 49 mm. expanse of my largest British specimens.

There is no mistaking *C.* var. *rutilus* on the wing for any other European butterfly; the unique coloration identifies it at once. It has very similar habits of flight to the other European species of the genus, the males usually flying briskly but not fast over the long grass, with a jerky movement common to most of the Lycaenidæ, searching for the females; if another male is approached, either flying or settled on the grass, the two will rise in the air and fight together for a few moments, then separate and each pursue its way. It does not seem to be partial to resting on, or sucking at, the numerous flowers that grow in its haunts. I saw two or three specimens at rest on one flower or other, but these were quite the exception; it is very fond of, especially during the afternoon, settling on a grass stem, and opening its wings to their full extent to enjoy the gratifying warmth of the sun's rays. It is then a magnificent object, brilliant beyond one's power of imagination, a patch of living, sparkling, ruddy gold; but even a study of the brilliant upper side does not reveal all the glory of *C. dispar*. If you see a male approaching, flying slowly towards you over the long grass, do not be in a hurry to effect a capture, but watch, and as it passes you will see the sparkling gem-like, red gold, upper side, mingle with the delicate blue-grey under side, and form a natural kaleidoscope, a dream of colour well-nigh incomparable. Certain other species of European "coppers" are brilliant and most beautiful, but there is something indescribable about *C. dispar* that, to my mind, places it in a class by itself for beauty.

The female is, of course, not so brilliant an object. She is generally to be found in some corner away from the usual haunts of the male, presumably after impregnation: one frequently observes her at rest in the morning, or she may be disturbed out of the herbage. During the afternoon she is usually seen flying slowly and steadily over the grass in search of the food-plant.

One gets the impression that *C.* var. *rutilus* is only here for a time, for the whole of the herbage is cut for forage every season when the young larvæ of the first brood are feeding, and it is difficult to understand how any large proportion can reach maturity. Some of the examples I captured were very small, one expanding only 28 mm., evidently the result of insufficient nutrition.

The melodious fluting of the golden oriole, and the unmistakeable "Hoo, hoo, hoo," of the hoopoe, two of our rarest and most beautiful birds, now alas, like the large "copper," extinct with us, or visiting us only casually, added greatly to the interest and charm of a red-letter day in one's entomological life.

[Sheldon, W. G. 1909. The Large "Copper," its habits, and one of its haunts. *The Entomologist* **42**: 219–221].

A STREET BLOCKED BY A MOTH

Capt. J. J. Jacobs, Gibraltar. (1910)

The following rather amusing incident is extracted from the "Gibraltar Chronicle and Official Gazette," dated May 4th, 1910:— "A very large moth was the means of drawing quite a large crowd, and causing some commotion in the Main Street, just outside the 'Welcome,' about 9 o'clock last evening. It was a remarkably large and rare-looking specimen, and somewhat resembled one of the larger sized bats, which most of the spectators took it to be. Attracted by the glare of the electric street lamp, it fluttered about before it was detected by some boys, who were hastily on its track. After a few minutes' diversion on the wing, it settled on the wall of the Spanish Pavilion, about twenty feet from the ground, where it became an interesting target, and had to stand the bombardment of hundreds of caps, hats, and such other missiles from the crowd in the street, which had by this time considerably increased, and blocked the traffic. After some time it was dislodged by a well-directed shot and fell into the street, where a general *melée* took place, each and every one being over anxious to secure the rare and interesting visitor, which eventually got crushed in the scuffle. By this time traffic was at a standstill, but the appearance of a sturdy policeman soon dispersed the crowd."

I believe the insect in question was a large specimen of *Saturnia pyri* [Great Peacock Moth], which occurs commonly in this district. A freshly emerged specimen, rather the worse for wear, was brought to me a few days later.

[Jacobs, J. J. 1910. A street blocked by a moth. *Entomologist's Monthly Magazine* **21**: 162–163].

A FORTNIGHT AT GAVARNIE. HAUTES-PYRÉNÉES

George T. Bethune-Baker, F.L.S., F.Z.S., F.E.S., Edgbaston, Birmingham. (1911)

A twelve hours' journey brought us from Mende to Toulouse, where we arrived at about 8 o'clock in the evening, and as we had to be up betimes in the morning we were glad to go straight to bed after dinner. No doubt it was a very bad thing to do, but it did not seem to have any ill effects in our case. We were down at 5.30 for our *petit déjeûner*, which was enjoyed greatly in the street before people generally were astir, and whilst the air was delightfully fresh. Our first change was at Lourdes, where we had two and a half hours to wait. Half an hour of this sufficed for a good meal, after which I left my friend (Mr. A. H. Jones) to have a needed siesta, whilst I went through the small town to see the far famed grotto with its church above it. It happened to be a quiet day with but few pilgrims, and of this I was glad, as I made my way through the winding street, the Boulevard de la Grotte. On the one side the Boulevard was lined with shops of all descriptions, for the great part, however, with but one object in view, *viz.*, the sale of mementoes of "my Lady of Lourdes" and of all the cures wrought by her marvellous efficacy. The shops end at a small bridge beneath which flows the river, the Gave du Pau, beyond which the ground is all beautifully laid out as a spacious garden, mostly consisting of lawns very carefully kept, up to the ascent to the church, beneath which is the grotto. It was with mingled feelings and conflicting thoughts that one gazed on the scene, a scene that now almost brought tears to one's eyes and anon produced a sense akin to indignation. Hundreds of people were about, none apparently seriously ill, and a few cripples still using their crutches. As they sat or stood in front of the grotto, all were reverently intent on the shrine, some counted their beads, others were saying "sotto voce" their "aves," others again were lost in contemplation: but as one watched and attempted to read the faces around the wonder grew, how? how could such a thing exist, and not only exist, but be a force in this twentieth century? and "still the wonder grew." Lost in reverie, the hours had sped, and I barely allowed myself sufficient time to get back to the station, where I found my friend beginning to get anxious lest I should miss the train. A pleasant ride brought us to Luz, and another change on to the electric tram brought us through lonely and romantic scenery to St. Sauveur, from whence the journey to Gavarnie was completed by carriage. We had scarcely got into the hotel, when a well known voice saluted us, and we found ourselves face to face with Mr. Rowland-Brown, who had already spent a fortnight in the locality. So we arrived at the "haven where we would be." [Fig. 91]

Our first day was spent on the way to the "Port de Gavarnie," *i.e.*, the Pass over into Spain, in the hope of taking *Erebia lefebvrei* [Lefèbvre's Ringlet], and in this we were not disappointed, two or three falling to each of us. *E. stygne* [Piedmont Ringlet] also was not uncommon and in beautiful condition, the most plentiful of the genus was, however, *E. tyndarus* [Swiss Brassy Ringlet], which occurred both in its type form and its var. *dromus*. Among the blues *Plebeius argus* (*aegon*, Auct.) [Silver-studded Blue] was common and shared honours as to which was the commoner with *Agriades coridon* [Chalk Hill Blue], this latter being generally of the Pyrenean form with very pale creamy underside, sometimes almost white. *Heodes virgaureae* [Scarce Copper] was taken, and I took a single specimen of the much coveted *Latiorina pyrenaica* [Spanish subspecies of the Small Mountain Ringlet]. *Urbicola comma* [Silver-spotted Skipper] was the only Hesperiid seen this day, the Argynnids were few and far between, the one species taken being *Argynnis aglaia* [Dark Green Fritillary], whilst *Pararge maera* var. *adrasta* [Spanish form of the Large Wall Brown] was also the only one of its genus that put in an appearance.

Our next day was spent on the slopes below the Piméné in search of *Erebia gorgone* [Gavarnie Ringlet]. The path up after quitting the river bed is by a series of steep zig-zags and very few insects cheered our eyes as we ascended bend after bend. *Erebia stygne* appeared now and then, and a single *Melitaea dictynna* [False Heath Fritillary] fell to my net, and when we got on to the grassy slopes, already so closely cropped by the cattle that they were poor hunting grounds for us, I took one *Coenonympha pamphilus* [Small Heath], which in the end turned out to be the only one I took, though this does not mean that we did not see it again. At last we got on to the special slopes of which Mr Rowland-Brown had told us,

Fig. 91. An Amusing Incident. Gavarnie, France (1912).
Left to right: H. Rowland-Brown. A. H. Jones. C. J. Wainwright. G. T. Bethune-Baker

and by dint of working hard we captured a nice little lot of *E. gorgone*. We were by no means satisfied, however, for as this species occurs only in the Pyrenees we were naturally anxious to get a good series, so we decided to come again after the arrival of my friend Mr. C. J. Wainwright. As we descended, a nice *Polyommatus escheri* [Escher's Blue] was enticed into my net, and also a single *Aricia medon (astrarche)* [Brown Argus]. I think I omitted to say that *E. tyndarus* var. *dromus* occurred everywhere, and also that we took a nice little series of *Erebia epiphron* [Small Mountain Ringlet] with its var. *cassiope*, the latter species flying high up with *E. gorgone*.

Our next trip, after having had another day in search of *E. lefebvrei*, was up the Val d'Ossoue where *E. manto* var. *cæcilia* [Yellow-spotted Ringlet] was to be found. In this valley insects were more plentiful than anywhere else. As we wended our way among the rocks in the early part of the path, we were much struck by several very small specimens of what we thought must be *Satyrus alcyone* [Rock Grayling], but here it was far away from all trees, disporting and sunning itself on the roads. Several evaded our endeavours at first, but finally we were both successful, and found it was *S. alcyone*, as we had first surmised, but with the underside strongly yellowish. Monsieur C. Oberthür, who was also staying at Gavarnie, and whom we had the great pleasure of meeting, told us that this was the Pyrenaean form, but the difference in habit was also remarkable. *Polyommatus escheri* in both sexes greeted us, and when we came to the bridge, over which we had to go, we again had the pleasure of taking *Latiorina pyrenaica* with *A. coridon*, *P. argus* and *Polyommatus icarus* [Common Blue]. After crossing the bridge we came into quite another lie of country, we first passed through some meadow land covered with flowers, among which the commoner of the "blues" disported themselves. I hoped to have taken some Zygaenidae [the Burnets], but they were conspicuous by their entire absence. Then we had to ascend through a wide belt of trees of all kinds, and in some of the small clearings I took a *Colias edusa* [Clouded Yellow] and a single *Pontia daplidice* [Bath White]. *Erebia euryale* [Large Ringlet] soon appeared commonly, but quite passé, so much so that it was difficult to find a decent specimen. All the way along *Parnassius apollo* [Apollo] had been in evidence, a fine large form with very large black spots. At last we came to the *E. manto* ground, along which we wandered to and fro with a fair amount of success, and were able to secure a nice, if short, series of var. *cæcilia*. . . .

After this Mr. Wainwright joined us, and we had a glorious walk to the Port d'Espagne, taking the bridle-path on the north side of the mountains. Some parts of the way were very steep, but very delightful, and as we dispersed more or less a flock of sheep sheltering from the broiling sun beneath a vast rock, we realised something of its steepness for a short distance, where we had to cling to any herbage or tufts of grass that were strong enough to hold us. Ere long, however, we found ourselves on a lovely soft green pasture, and smooth as velvet, along which we wandered until my attention was attracted by a pair of *Urbicola comma*, that were evidently courting. . . . Soon after this I saw a dark coloured blue that I could not quite make out, and ere long another came, but this time the opportunity was not lost, and I found that I had secured my first *Lampides boeticus* [Long-tailed Blue] from this locality. A few minutes more brought us to the Port de Gavarnie or the Port d'Espagne as it is sometimes called. In front of us lay Spain with its many and deeply interesting associations, its checkered history, its beautiful country – poor Spain from nearly every point of view – behind us lay "la belle France" with her marvellous history and lovely country, filled with life, and so internally and financially strong that when she wanted twelve millions the other day for one of her western railways, over thirty times the amount was subscribed for in a single day, the larger portion of this coming from its peasant proprietors. But the time had come to cease

from reveries and to find a place for lunch, the sun was hot, the wind cool. Water? Where was water? The only visible sign was a trickle across the path 100 yards away. We therefore "followed the gleam" and made our way thither. Just about fifty yards up the hillside we found its source, a little underground stream bubbling up into a wee well about eighteen inches in diameter surrounded by soft verdure as green and fresh as could be desired. Here we had our repast and promised ourselves to return to Spain at some other time, having pleasant memories of our lunch there on this day. . . . As the time wore away it became evident that not only should we not arrive at the Lac de Gaube that night, but that it would be all we should do to reach the Refuge d'Ossoue before dark, so we had to push on, passing meadows that I longed to spend an hour in, until at last the Refuge was sighted between half-past eight and nine, and then we learnt from the guide that it was a good five hours' walk to that spot and another six to Cauterets. It was along this route that we came across one of the most lovely scenes I have ever witnessed. As we rounded one of the mountain sides, suddenly we had laid open just in front of us on our right, the whole side of two mountains closely carpeted with most magnificent examples of the large purple iris, a perfect blaze of intensest colour in the brilliant sunlight. There must have been acres and acres one mass of colour — we could but stand and gaze, lost in wonder and admiration. The whole setting was perfect, words fail to express one's thoughts, the two expressions that rose to our lips were, "marvellous," "glorious" — certainly that sight will ever live in my memory. We were very thankful for the hospitality of the Refuge of the French Alpine Club, and were up at four o'clock in the morning in time to see another view of great beauty — shall I call it the "Passing of the Night?" The sky was just changing from the darkness of night to that wonderfully steely-blue that is only to be seen high up in the mountains. We were then 8,900 feet high, the stars were still visible, the silence was to be felt, and a sort of adoration came over one as gradually the dark blue softened, and yet more softened into that indescribable colour that occurs just before dawn. Then the sun lit up first one peak then another, gently creeping throughout the whole circle as the orange tinge warmed up, first this one and then its neighbour. Gradually this hue changed into palest yellow, until at last the sun showed himself in his strength, and life was renewed for another day. Having partaken of our *petit déjeûner* we passed on our way up to the Col de Vignemale, and then down over the snow, guided by the footsteps of someone who had recently come up from that side — probably two French climbers who had passed the night at the Refuge as we had done. The snow was in greater abundance than usual, and it was at least an hour to two hours before we left it quite behind us. As we passed downwards an *Erebia* foiled a hasty and ill-directed stroke, but it put me on the *qui vive*, and so later on several *E. gorge* [Silky Ringlet] were made captives, fine large specimens too, decidedly larger than any Swiss ones. A little further along a quite fresh *E. gorgone* allowed me to box him; and whilst doing this a Zygaenid flew past at a great rate, and I followed. Having tracked him down I found I had a species new to me, with a very hairy body and a central red band, it was of course *Anthrocera anthyllidis* [Pyrenean Burnet] . . . .

The next day was Sunday, and we were glad to be present in the morning at the dedication of a new little English church for Gavarnie. It was especially interesting as the foundations were laid and all was built during the fortnight we stayed at the village — of course the upper portion was all of wood. The afternoon of that Sunday will be memorable in our annals, for at *déjeûner* a hail storm of unusual violence began. In the middle of the meal, the heavens having become black with clouds, the storm suddenly broke with a torrent of hail stones bigger than marbles; the noise was so great that everyone rose from the tables to look, in five minutes the road began to flood, the gradient in front of the hotel being great, the water and stones ran down the hill to the stables in great volumes. The top lights of the hotel in the roof were perfectly riddled by the force of the hail, every animal fled for shelter, but it was not until later on that we realised the full potency of what proved to be a record-breaking storm. It lasted at Gavarnie about two hours. We had arranged to take a Sabbath-day's journey into the Cirque and at about 4.30 p.m. it cleared sufficiently for us to do so. As we approached nearer our goal we began to have some idea of what had happened. Across the path were rivulets that ordinarily would not have necessitated even lengthening our usual tread to pass over, but that had become streams to be jumped, and once or twice to be taken at more than one jump, whilst one stream had become so violent and deep, that it took us a quarter of an hour to find a ford, and even then we suffered more or less in taking it. Hail-stones as large as good-sized hen's eggs were lying about by the hundred. . . . I picked up a hailstone over $3\frac{1}{2}$ inches long by 3 inches broad and $1\frac{1}{2}$ inches thick, and when it is remembered that I did not find it until after two hours from the time it had fallen and that it had melted greatly, we realised that originally that stone must have been larger than a cricket ball, or at least fully as large. Had such a stone struck a human being on the head it must have been death. Mr. Jones sent a model of this to the Royal Meteorological Society whose Secretary informed him that it was a "record." On the Spanish side the storm was much worse, the stones being described by Mr. Wheeler, of Eastbourne, as usually the size of golf balls, whilst a very large percentage were as large as cricket balls, causing the death of many scores of sheep, and of between twenty and thirty cattle.

We had arranged to go to Argelès-Gazost the next day *en route* for home and we were not sorry to do so. There our pleasant party broke up, Mr. Jones went back to Mende to take *Erebia neoridas* [Autumn Ringlet] . . . after staying on a couple of days I returned direct home, whilst Mr. Wainwright stayed a day or two longer to "dipterise.". . .

[Bethune-Baker, G. T. 1912. A fortnight at Gavarnie. Hautes-Pyrénées. *The Entomologist's Record and Journal of Variation* 24: 150–152; 157–162].

JULY IN THE EASTERN PYRENEES

George T. Bethune-Baker, F.L.S., F.Z.S., F.E.S., Edgbaston, Birmingham. (1914)

George Thomas Bethune-Baker (1857–1944) was the son of a doctor practising in Birmingham and developed his interest in entomology at an early age. He collected extensively in Europe, especially in Switzerland and the South of France. In 1910 he was elected Vice-President of the Entomological Society of London and was President from 1913 to 1914. He was a religious man, much interested in the work of foreign missions. His main entomological writings were about the Lycaenidae. In 1927 he lost his sight in both eyes. His great collection was later bequeathed to Cambridge University.

Fig. 92. George Bethune-Baker specialized in the Lepidoptera of Switzerland and southern France.

Last year's summer holiday was spent in the Pyrénées Orientales the first fortnight being passed at Vernet-des-Bains, and the latter part of the time at the Chalet Hotel on Mount Canigou. The journey to Vernet is an easy one though long, once on the other side of the Channel the only change (if you select the best trains) is at Paris. I arrived there about 4.30 p.m. and had ample time to walk across the river to a comfortable restaurant that I knew of near the Louvre, where I got a good dinner at a reasonable price, after which I walked quietly back having plenty of leisure to catch the 7 o'clock through train, which I suppose is in reality one of the Spanish expresses. I arrived at Vernet on the morning of July 1st, and after lunch took a stroll up the hill at the back of the Hotel des Bains Mercader in the brilliant sunshine of the Mediterranean. Insects, however, were not plentiful, a few of the commoner "blues" and *Melanargia lachesis* [Iberian Marbled White] being the only species I noticed; possibly, however, this was because I had stayed and partially unpacked so that I did not start out till between 3 and 4 p.m. The following day was dull and the sky entirely overcast, nevertheless I went for the day up the St. Martin Valley and spent a pleasant hour going over the ruins and the Church of St. Martin of Canigou, the old church below the present new edifice is very interesting with its three aisles, each of which is arranged with its altar at the east end. The monks in old days certainly knew how to obtain both commanding and beautiful situations. One day I saw the Archbishop of Perpignan in the grounds (the Church of St. Martin is a country living and seat of the Archbishops of Perpignan) directing some of his men how to gather the fruit of his plane trees, he was evidently particular that they should not break the branches of the trees, and very picturesque his tall figure looked in his reddish purple cassock and cape and very broad brimmed, stiff, round hat of the same colour.

My primary object in coming to Vernet was to obtain and watch *Laeosopis roboris* [Spanish Purple Hairstreak] in one of its most abundant localities. My friend Mr. Jones had given me many details, so I had no difficulty in discovering its haunts as also those of many other species. The second day, July 3rd was brilliant though at times there was a cool breeze, and I spent it beyond the dairy and on the hill at the back. *L. roboris* was evidently just coming out, for by persistent effort I obtained about half-a-dozen flying around the ash trees and occasionally settling on some bramble that grew at the foot of the rocks just at the corner leading over the stream to the pastures beyond. They were all quite fresh, so I looked forward to obtaining a fair series before leaving. . . .

After I had passed a week's pleasant stay I returned to the hotel to dinner one evening having had a long and hard day's work — and a very hot one too — in the St. Vincent Valley, and had scarcely sat down in my accustomed place at table, when an evident Englishman and his wife were placed next to me; the meal proceeded with the usual enquiries as to the weather and the scenery of the neighbourhood, and then a chance remark at dessert revealed the fact that the newcomers were bent on some branch of natural history, and on a more minute enquiry I found that I was talking to Mr. and Mrs. C. F. Johnson, of Stockport, both of whom were bent on an entomological holiday. Notes were soon being compared and explanations as to hunting grounds given. I believe their first day was spent in the St. Vincent Valley, while I had before arranged for a longish day up the St. Martin Valley with an extension to the Col du Cheval-Mort and up to the Randais Hut. A most lovely day I had, a description of which will serve for several other shorter excursions in the same direction.

The route lies *viâ* the little village of Casteil, but there is plenty of work to be done before even that short distance is accomplished. The right side of the valley as we ascend is almost entirely under cultivation, but the left side, though cultivated, has a good deal of rocky bare land and some poor pasture on the hill sides, where insects fly freely. *Leptosia sinapis* [Wood White] was common, whilst the bright and pretty *Euchloë euphenoides* [Spanish subspecies of the Moroccan Orange Tip] was at this time rather rare. I only picked up about half-a-dozen examples on this side of Vernet, and they were not confined to definite spots but occurred singly in different localities, some in the Valley, some well above Casteil. A whitish specimen of the same genus attracted my attention and gave me a sharp race in the hope of securing a female *euphenoides*, but alas it turned out to be only *Euchloë cardamines* [Orange-tip] after all. The "blues" and "coppers" up in this direction were conspicuous by their absence, the only specimens I took being a single *Polyommatus semiargus* [Mazarine Blue] and two *Rumicia phlaeas* [Small Copper], neither of which can be called var. *eleus*, though they must have been of the summer brood. . . .

Having turned out of the St. Martin Valley and begun the ascent towards the Col du Cheval-Mort, whilst however still more or less in the branch valley, a vast bush of clematis was the rendezvous of many species. *Limenitis camilla* [White Admiral] with its graceful flight settled on the flowers and hovered over them, darting rapidly away only to return, and finally (after being admired greatly, I having had much pleasure in watching its movements) it made a home in my net and has come to live with me. Most of the specimens had, however, passed their best. Then *Brenthis* (*Argynnis*) *daphne* [Marbled Fritillary] put in an appearance, and I took several at this spot, it being the only place I took it during this trip. *Parnassius apollo* [Apollo] was here also, and fell a victim to my avidity, the specimens were by no means the large fine form one is accustomed to associate with this district. As I ascended, *Erebia stygne* [Piedmont Ringlet] became very common, all being a large fine form having broad rufous bands and large spots with prominent white centres; this is quite the finest form that I have taken, being much larger and finer than that obtained in the Hautes Pyrénées. Single specimens of both *Colias edusa* [Clouded Yellow] and *Gonepteryx rhamni* [Brimstone] were obtained, the former not being uncommon though not in good condition. *Leptosia duponcheli*

249

[Eastern Wood White] turned up twice, and one beautiful specimen of *L. sinapis* var. *diniensis*, with the wings entirely white above, was also taken. . . . On July 11th we (Mr. and Mrs. Johnson and I) took an excursion together to Ille sur Tet, a little town down in the valley of the river from which it takes its name. The town itself did not appear to have very much of interest about it, and after supplying ourselves with peaches and fruit from the market-place, we hastened on. Our way led us over the long bridge crossing the Tet, which must have been at one time a broad fine river, but is now confined to a very narrow channel, though doubtless when the snow is melting on the hills the bed may have a fair volume of water in it; it was a very hot day and we were glad of some shade on the other side of the river. Immediately on arrival there, however, a chase became necessary, for *Gonepteryx cleopatra* [Cleopatra] sped on his way in front, but was overtaken and captured after a sharp run, as also were several others of the same species. As we wandered along we noticed a little *Epinephele* that flew differently among the undergrowth of the hedges, and we soon discovered that it was *E. ida* [Southern Gatekeeper], a nice little series of both sexes fell to each of us, and *Pararge aegeria* [Speckled Wood] seemed more or less to accompany it. . . . As we ascended — for the heat of the valley made our ascent imperative — up the sides of a little water course a fine dark Satyrid, new to me, settled a yard or two out of reach. A few steps among the rocks brought me within its compass, but the balancing necessary on a steeply slanting boulder just gave it a chance and off it flew only to settle in a more inaccessible place. In its flight, however, it showed its underside for a moment, and that sight inspired the resolution to obtain the specimen if possible. Up I clambered again, and in the end perseverance was rewarded, for I returned with a lovely fresh specimen of the beautiful *Satyrus fidia* [Striped Grayling], and before the day was out a second also fell to my net; both are unusually black specimens above, whilst the underside is in sharp contrast. . . .

The following day we (the same trio) spent in the Gorges de Carença. To get there it is necessary to take the Mont Louis electric railway up the Valley of the Tet and detrain at Thuès, at the entrance to the gorge, we, however, being at the very rear of the train did not realise, amid the lovely scenery, that we had arrived there, and so we passed our destination and went on to Fontpédrouse, further up the valley. It being only three miles further on the little detour made no difference to us, nay, as a matter of fact, it added several species to our day's sport. It was a fine walk, down hill all the way. . . .

[Bethune-Baker, G. T. 1914. July in the Eastern Pyrenees. *The Entomologist's Record and Journal of Variation* **26**: 8–15].

We have been unable to discover why the Archbishop of Perpignan was collecting fruit from the monastery plane trees. We do know, however, that during the Victorian era children played a game similar to 'conkers', in which the fruit of plane trees (*Platanus* sp.) were used rather than horse-chestnuts. The lengthy stalks would have made excellent handles when lashing out at an opponent's fruit. It does, however, seem inconceivable that the Archbishop's men were collecting fruit in abundance simply to play 'conkers'. If, as seems possible, Bethune-Baker named his trees wrongly, then they could have been lime trees (*Tilia* sp.). For centuries, monks and others have used the leaves and fruit of that tree to make a health-giving infusion or tisane. In 1993 one of us (P. J. E.) followed the route taken by George Bethune-Baker. The butterflies were still there exactly as described, but the monks and their Archbishop, as well as the plane trees in the monastery garden, were nowhere to be seen. It would appear that considerable changes have taken place at the Church of St Martin during the past ninety years.

THE ENTOMOLOGIST IN WARTIME

To judge from the number of military men who have written articles for the various entomological journals, the pursuit of butterflies, moths and other insects must represent the perfect panacea for stress suffered while under enemy attack. It is surprising to find so many that were apparently able to continue the all-absorbing hobby while actually under attack, or while facing the advance of enemy troops. Long ago, in January 1878, Lieutenant Harford, carbine in hand, fought off the Natal Kaffirs in a decisive encounter during the Zulu War. In an epic account — *The Washing of the Spears* — D. R. Morris informs us that: 'He [Harford] had done well in his first action ... [However,] he had given Hamilton-Brown a scare by dropping to his hands and knees as the attack started ... When the battalion commander rushed to his side he found Harford intent on transferring a rare beetle to a small tin box.' From this we must presume that the Lieutenant knew and respected his priorities.

This interest in butterflies and other insects continued throughout both world wars. In his novel *All Quiet on the Western Front* the author Erich Remarque describes how the hero, Paul Baumer, is shot by a French sniper in the last few days of the campaign. In that last moment of time he was killed not while 'going over the top', or while leading a charge, but as he leaned out of his trench to pick up a Red Admiral.

The following articles are representative of a much larger number written by lepidopterists who could claim to have spent one or more of their summers 'in the wars'.

THE NATURALIST AT THE FRONT

To the Editor of *The Entomologist* (1915) from Henry Rowland-Brown:

The following letter was received by an entomological friend last July when the writer was in the trenches, apparently in north-eastern France in the department of Nord, Pas de Calais, or Somme. ... French entomology generally is of great interest, and it is a pleasure to those of us who perforce remain at home to know that, amid the grim realities of war, the mind of the young soldier finds relaxation in the observation, and even the collection, of natural history objects. I may add that the officer commanding a distinguished London Territorial regiment last summer gave me a cordial invitation to his quarters in the firing-line — at that time described by him as the haunt of innumerable Chalk Hill Blues — probably somewhere on the chalk hills of Upper Somme.

"France, July 27th, 1915.

"The parts of France and Belgium where we were until a short time ago were exceedingly poor collecting grounds, but now we are nearly eighty miles south of there, by means of train and 'frogging' it. The wood we are now camping out in is fine ground for all sorts of insects. The wood itself grows on a long ridge and the slopes are covered with a fine growth of wild flowers, mainly hairy St. John's wort, musk mallow, and nettle-leaved bellflower. There is not much here, however, except a few Red Admirals and Painted Ladies. It is just on the outskirts of the wood, on the hedges of bramble dividing it from the lucerne and cornfields that you see such a number of flies. First and foremost everywhere in such situations is the Silver Washed Fritillary, a close second is the Ringlet, but both of these are apparently nearly over, as they are practically all battered to pieces. I saw one specimen of the var. *valesina* and actually knocked it down, but unfortunately could not find it afterwards.

I was more fortunate with the other good thing I saw, and that was the Purple Emperor in fine condition. I have him packed up now in a box with other specimens waiting an opportunity to despatch. How did the first consignment of *galatea* [Marbled White] arrive, by the way?

"I had my doubts about the safety of such packing, and I certainly should not care to trust my *iris* to the tender mercies of the cancelling stamp. The lucerne fields I mentioned before are absolutely swarming with the Latticed Heath, rather a common thing, but I fancy rather local, so I will enclose one or two specimens with the rest. I have seen two of those huge green grasshoppers of which you mounted one specimen. I had forgotten that the blighters bite like h — l, but the first one I picked up didn't forget to remind me of the fact. Another thing that is very common here in the woods is that huge brick-red slug with the tiny remnant of a shell near its head, *testacella* I believe its name is. I have about twenty Fox Moth larvæ feeding up, one unknown larva also doing well on elm, and another that has now turned into a chrysalis. This latter by the general characteristics of the chrysalis I should say belonged to the Tussock family. The larva was a large hairy one, dark and with a series of large purplish warts along the back. The unknown larva is a most ferocious looking creature. The following is his description. Pale yellow green in colour, rather rough-looking surface, series of yellow transverse stripes on body, short horn on anal segments, two horns on front segment, and two more horns on second segment from front, head pale green, prolegs red [here follows sketch].

"In the previous village from which I sent the *galatea*, I went out one day to have a look round and found that nearly all the poplar trees were riddled with, presumably, Wood Leopard borings. I could not find any live chrysalides or larvæ, but have a couple of the pupa cases. I also found a Puss Moth larva there, and a newly emerged Poplar Hawk. Otherwise there was little of note.

"By the way, I forgot to mention that I caught one specimen of the White Admiral, but it was so badly damaged that I let it go again.

"Well, I must close now. I haven't a lot of time, and I want to write home as well. With best wishes,   FRED STONE."

[Stone, F. 1916. The Naturalist at the front. *The Entomologist* **49**: 64–65].

BUTTERFLIES IN THE TRENCHES

From the Editor of *The Entomologist* (1915):

Mr. Harrold Sims, of the Entomological Society of Montreal, writes on September 21st from Flanders: — "We have had, on the whole, wonderfully fair weather, and some species of Lepidoptera were very common, even in the trenches. Most kinds have disappeared now, though there are still some late-brood specimens of *P. brassicae, rapae, napi* [Large, Small and Green-veined Whites], *V. urticæ* [Small Tortoiseshell], *P. atalanta* [Red Admiral], *L. icarus* [Common Blue], *C. hyale* [Pale Clouded Yellow]. When we first went into the trenches, *P. megæra* [Wall] was extremely abundant, and flew about actually in the trenches and 'dug-outs.' It was quite the commonest butterfly, although all three 'whites' were very common, and in the waste land just behind the firing line I saw many other species, notably *C. hyale, C. edusa* [Clouded Yellow] (doubtful), *G. rhamni* [Brimstone] (doubtful), *urticae, io* [Peacock], *polychloros* [Large Tortoiseshell], *cardui* [Painted Lady], *atalanta, egeria* [Speckled Wood], *mæra* [Large Wall Brown], *E. tithonus* [Gatekeeper], *M. jurtina* [Meadow Brown] (doubtful),

C. pamphilus [Small Heath], *C. phlæas* [Small Copper], *L. icarus, bellargus* [Adonis Blue], *C. argiolus* [Holly Blue], *P. machaon* [Swallowtail]. I saw others but could not with any approach to certainty identify them. This was near Armentiers, but we have since been moved to quite another part of the line."

[Editor. 1915. Butterflies in the trenches. *The Entomologist* **48**: 289–290].

COLIAS HYALE NEAR FIRING LINE

From the Editor of *The Entomologist* (1915):

My son has asked me to forward the following note to you for publication: – "To one who has never met with the species before, the sight of half a dozen *Colias hyale* [Pale Clouded Yellow] on the wing together near a chalky bank on September 19th, a mile or so behind the firing line, gave great pleasure.
– F. Norton; 11th Welsh Regiment, British Expeditionary Force."

In a previous letter my son referred to the great pleasure he derived from his knowledge and love of natural history, and the relief it afforded him from the tedious monotony of some of his days of training before he proceeded on active service "somewhere in France."
– M. A. Norton; Skirbeck, Whitchurch Road, Cardiff, September 28th, 1915.

[Editor. 1915. *Colias hyale* near firing line. *The Entomologist* **48**: 289].

THE LARGE COPPER, AND OTHER BUTTERFLIES AT ST. QUENTIN

Henry Rowland-Brown, M.A., F.E.S., Harrow, Middlesex. (1917)

Henry Rowland-Brown (1865–1922) specialized in the butterflies of Central and Western Europe and his obituarist tells us that his knowledge of these 'was certainly without an equal in our country'. Educated at Rugby, where he came under the influence of the eminent entomologist the Revd F. D. Morice (Fig. 11), and University College, Oxford, he studied for the Bar. An able journalist and essay writer, he was also the author of more than one volume of poetry written under the pen-name 'Oliver Gray'. Among a number of distinctions, he was a Vice-President of the Entomological Society of London and a member of the Entomological Club. His great friend and neighbour was Sir W. S. Gilbert (of Savoy opera fame) and included in his last writings were reminiscences of their friendship, published in the *Cornhill Magazine*.

In this article Rowland-Brown (Fig. 30) reflects upon the legacy of the Great War on certain entomological hunting grounds in France.

The Allies' advance is from henceforward on ground familiar to many lepidopterists. It remains to be seen how far the awful havoc wrought by the retreating enemy, and by our own and the French guns driving him Rhinewards, will have affected the happy hunting-grounds of Aisne, Marne and Nord. St. Quentin, entomologically speaking, has a special interest for the British collector. It was supposed to be a last stronghold of a form of *Chrysophanus dispar* [Large Copper], over the identity of which much ink has been slung on both sides of the Channel — last known, I say, because when the indefatigable M. Charles Oberthür organised a search party to locate the Large Copper in the St. Quentin marshes — well, the Large Copper had disappeared, *more anglico*. There is a lively account of this expedition in fasc. iv of Lépidoptèrologie Comparée, with the usual fine figures of French (Bordeaux) and British *dispar* for comparison. The expedition failed apparently to run *dispar* to earth hereabouts, except as represented by forty specimens in a dealer's glass case. I need not enter further into the subject of differentiation by colour of the under side. Suffice it to say that the size of the largest French examples was equal to that of the largest British, and since Mr. Bethune-Baker has proved beyond doubt that var. *rutilus* co-existed with typical *dispar* in the fens of Cambridgeshire and Huntingdon, the determination by size (for sale-room purposes) of "genuine British *dispar*" is less conclusive than ever. I believe the pins are now accepted as convincing evidence, but I am sure Boisduval, for example, would not have tolerated Doubleday's short pins for a moment.

My copy of the 'Catalogue des Lépidoptères de l'Arrondissement de Saint-Quentin,' par M. Dubus, Capitaine au 87ᵉ de Ligne, published first in the 'Proceedings' of the Société Académique of that famous city, has lost its title page. I believe the first part made its appearance in the 1879 volume. However that may be, we find (p. 182), under 80. *Hippothöe* L., var. *dispar* Dup., the following interesting note: "This butterfly, which has not been found previously except in England, has been taken by M. Gronnier . . . of St. Quentin, in the Rouvray marshes. . . . It is found rather commonly in England in marshy fields in the environs of Huntingdon and Cambridge."

But I think, for "it is found," the printer is responsible, not M. Dubus, and that "*on le trouve*" should read "*on le trouva*" — which makes all the difference.

At all events, St. Quentin was thenceforward visited by Parisian and other foreign collectors — and there are plenty of St. Quentin examples to witness in their cabinets — until either the precise locality was lost, or became the secret of wisely uncommunicative individuals on the spot — or, least likely under the circumstances, the locality itself was destroyed.

Anyone familiar with the environs of St. Quentin in peace time will recognise the likeliness of the terrain for our species, the numerous streamlets falling into the river and canal, fringed with osier and willow and green with the giant dock and every manner of marsh flora; the spongy meadows, the shelving weedy clay banks admirably fortified by Nature against the too frequent incursions of the destroyer. From the military point of view these obstacles are of minor importance in the operations of modern war, but they guard the preserves of millions of tiny creatures.

Yet, curiously enough, the war has already restored the lost *dispar* to the north of France, and in localities which by now must be far beyond echoes of the Hymn of Hate. Of this I am apprised by M. René Oberthür — *ex-Armoricâ semper aliquid novi!* — who, in his last letter to me, and while our Allies were still hibernating in the trenches, informed me that several localities had been discovered during the year 1916 under the very guns of the foe, and if — as, alas! must be expected — much of the butterfly woodlands and meads of St. Quentin have been reduced to splinters and mounds of disrupted earth, it is some consolation to think these localities at least may have escaped.

One wood in particular — most favoured by lepidoptera — has no doubt suffered the common fate at the hands of the unspeakable Hun. The Bois d'Holnon, in the opening weeks of April, was about as unhealthy a spot as any of the shell-scorched forests of Picardy. This name, and that of other equally once attractive woods, appear one after another in communiqués of the French and British Commands. In Holnon both generations of *Pontia daplidice* [Bath White] found their home, with *L. sinapis* [Wood White], *T. w-album* [White-letter Hairstreak], *T. ilicis* [Ilex Hairstreak], *Z. quercûs* [Purple Hairstreak], *A. corydon* [Chalk

Hill Blue], *N. semiargus* [Mazarine Blue], *L. sibylla* [White Admiral], the great *L. populi* [Poplar Admiral], and glorious *A. iris* [Purple Emperor], while the Bois de Savy, at no great distance, contained *A. ilia* [Lesser Purple Emperor]. Holnon shared with St. Gobain the greater number of Argynnids and Melitæids, including *I. lathonia* [Queen of Spain Fritillary] and *B. ino* [Lesser Marbled Fritillary], *M. artemis* [the old name for the Marsh Fritillary] and *M. dictynna* [False Heath Fritillary]: Of the Vanessids, *A. levana* [Map Butterfly] and *E. antiopa* [Camberwell Beauty] (taken in the city gardens also); *Erebia medusa* [Woodland Ringlet] (once); *P. achine* [Woodland Brown]; and, last of all, *C. hero* [Scarce Heath]; while the Rouvray *dispar* marshes were also shared with *C. tiphon* (*davus*) [Large Heath], a rare insect in France. For moths the same wood was a very "New Forest." But I think I have said enough to convince the entomologist that the destruction of the Bois d'Holnon may have desolated one of the most fruitful localities in the north of France. I have been told that that other and larger forest east of Laon, where so many of us have hunted day and night — the forest of Samoussy — has practically disappeared; that though for more than two years and a half not a gun has been fired in this region, the Germans have razed the forest to the ground and left barely a bush to mark the site where we watched our first *Melitæa maturna* [Scarce Fritillary] poised on the privet bloom, or marked the elusive *Limenitis populi* down from his leafy heights to the little mud patch in the forest glade which was its own particular and chosen wet canteen. Never again shall we dare to bribe with a bottle of "demi-rouge" the guard of the Laon-Liart non-stop to let us down from his van at Samoussy "halte"; never again of a June night will the "all-sorts' man" trundle our paraphernalia from the aforesaid "halte" through the dense mysterious tunnels of the forest of our dreams to the little farm-house, auberge, and general store, whose presiding genius announced himself to the world — entomological and otherwise — as E. Hemmery, Représentant en Vins. I trust that he, good man, may have taken with him his *vins en gros* — if he had not handed on his inn to "Successeurs" before the storm broke. They were too good for Teuton tastes. At all events, may we see *hippothoë* again a gleaming fire among the grasses of Samoussy, and live to decide upon the spot for the nth. time the specific identity or otherwise of *aurelia* [Nickerl's Fritillary] and *athalia* [Heath Fritillary].

[Rowland-Brown, H. 1917. *Chrysophanus dispar* and other butterflies at St Quentin. *The Entomologist* **50**: 97–99].

SHOOTING LARVAE

Maj. R. Bowen Robertson, Oare Camp, Faversham, Kent. (1918)

On going my rounds of sentry visiting this morning, I heard some shooting going on in an orchard near at hand and went to investigate, and found the farmer with a shot-gun firing into the nests of *Bombyx neustria* [The Lackey]. There is a plague of these on the apple and plum trees this year, two or three nests on nearly every tree, and sometimes quite out of reach at extreme top of tree. My experience hitherto has been that they are to be found on hedgerows quite low down. The farmer told me that sometimes they use as much as 10 lb. of powder and very small shot. I suggested a mixture of paraffin and water, which might be applied with a syringe, as likely to be less damaging to the trees, but see in today's 'Times' ¹/₂ lb. of acetate of lead paste and 10 gallons of water advocated; this, of course, would kill everything that touched the leaves afterwards, such as bees, flies, etc.

[Robertson, R. B. 1918. Shooting larvæ. *The Entomologist* **51**: 162].

AN ENTOMOLOGIST AT WAR

Maj.-Gen. C. G. Lipscomb, C.B., D.S.O., Crockerton, Wiltshire. (1966)

Major-General Christopher 'Kit' Godfrey Lipscomb (1907–1982) was the distinguished Commander of the 19th Infantry Brigade and Commandant of the Senior Officers' School, Camberley. During the Second World War he led the 4th Battalion of the Somerset Light Infantry from the Normandy beaches with such distinction that he was awarded the D.S.O. and bar. It was said that under his leadership the Battalion, during exposure to months of bitter fighting, had earned the reputation of 'never having had a failure and never lost an inch of ground'.

He first developed his interest in the Lepidoptera while a schoolboy at Charterhouse, but it was not until he entered the Army that his attention turned to the serious collection of butterfly aberrations. It is said that this interest was stimulated by his friendship with those great variety hunters S. G. Castle Russell and the Revd J. N. Marcon.

Fig. 93. Major-General 'Kit' Lipscomb. He was probably the only British commanding officer to capture a Chalk Hill Blue downland for 'King and Country'. 'The place was covered in Chalk Hill Blues. I was delighted . . . it was a wonderful sight and I lost all interest in the battle and went looking for these things.'

Entomological expeditions to the Continent and beyond are commonplace nowadays and every year the Record contains accounts of collecting trips abroad conducted in safety and comfort.

My first experience of the entomological possibilities of the Continent was somewhat different. It started when I landed on the beach at Arromanches in Normandy in mid-June 1944 and finished some eighteen months later when I left Germany. Throughout this time I commanded a battalion of my Regiment, the Somerset Light Infantry, and although in war, particularly at the sharp end, one can't go looking for butterflies but must take them as they come, the opportunity for making interesting observations is always there even if the conditions are somewhat unusual.

We landed as part of a 'follow-up' Division, so that by the time we got ashore the fighting had moved some miles inland. As we marched off down a country lane, I was rather astonished to see farm workers unconcernedly going about their jobs in the fields and paying no sort of attention to the streams of vehicles and troops. I remember noticing that there had evidently been a big emergence of *A. urticae* Linn. [Small Tortoiseshell] as there were great numbers of the butterflies feeding in the clover fields near the roadside and I was fairly sure I caught a glimpse of a fine melanic variety. It was a most cheering and homely sight and my only regret was that I was not able to stop and examine them properly. Further on we passed a potato field that had recently been fought over. What was left of the potatoes was a mass of Colorado beetles, both larvae and adult insects. I had never seen this pest before and noticed that there were few leaves on the potato haulms.

Our first proper contact with the enemy was made when our Brigade was given the task of clearing the woods of Germans west of Caen and establishing ourselves on the Caen-Baron road.

These woods are divided by the deep valley of the Odon and in those days contained many blackthorn thickets amongst the oak and other deciduous trees. At one stage, while we were being heavily shelled and mortared, I was cowering in my slit trench when a lovely fresh *S. pruni* Linn. [Black Hairstreak] came and shared it with me, sitting on the newly dug earth. Later that evening, when we had gained our objective, I went round visiting the various company positions. My route took me through several clearings in the wood and I was most interested to see numbers of *A. crataegi* Linn. [Black-veined White] at rest on grass heads. The date was now 29th June and I have another very vivid recollection of this wood. Where we crossed the Odon there was a mill and the miller had in his garden several dozen rabbit hutches, housing black and white rabbits. The miller had gone but the wretched occupants of the hutches had been left behind without food or water. That same evening I had all the hutches opened and the occupants, somewhat the worse for wear, made their way down the valley, a crowd of small black and white figures hopping up and down as they vanished into the twilight. I have often wondered what is the colour pattern of the present rabbit population.

July saw a period of hard and bitter fighting while the British Army occupied the bulk of the German forces, thereby allowing the Americans on our right to start their big flanking movement, which was eventually to take them to Paris. At one stage we were in a defensive position at Fontain Etoupefour, quickly christened 'Four by Two' by the troops, the name and size of the regulation piece of flannelette used for cleaning a rifle barrel. My Headquarters were dug in the grounds of the local Chateau and close by were the remains of a battery of beehives. Most of these had already been destroyed by shelling but a few with their occupants still remained. My Second in Command, who always had an eye for the main chance, determined to acquire a supply of honey and this was done with the aid of hand smoke grenades to keep the bees quiet and with the raiders' heads protected by their camouflage face veils. The action was accomplished without a single casualty and a large quantity of excellent honeycomb provided for my Mess. After the War, I revisited the by now repaired Chateau and told the occupants the story of the honey. They were most amused.

During the second week in August the Falaise pocket was being eliminated with very heavy loss of life and equipment for the Germans. For part of this time my Brigade was in reserve for the River Noireau crossing and my battalion was centered on the village of La Villette. The Noireau flows through rugged hilly country with many limestone outcrops. A good collecting area I should think under normal conditions but now it was an unpleasant spot where heavy fighting had only just finished and the smell of dead cattle and burning houses pervaded the whole area. However, for me it had its compensations because in a rough field close to my Headquarters I found a strong colony of *C. semiargus* Rott. [Mazarine Blue]. They were flying in company with *P. icarus* Rott. [Common Blue], but the very dark blue coloration of the males and drab appearance of the females made them easy to distinguish. I was glad they had survived the fighting, particularly as they were a butterfly I had not previously seen.

On 25th August came the news that Paris had fallen to the Americans and that our Division was to force the crossing of the Seine at Vernon, some thirty miles west of the Capital.

The Seine is a big river, about 200 yards wide where we were to cross, and both the road and railway bridges had been destroyed by the retreating Germans or our own bombing. On the opposite bank the village of Vernonnet nestles at the foot of a 300 foot chalk escarpment with the Forêt de Vernon in the background. Two roads traverse the area, to Gisors to the north and to Gasny to the east. My battalion's objective, once over the river, was the high chalk downland to the west of the Gisors road. As this ground commanded all likely crossing places, it was held by the Germans in some strength and through field-glasses one could see evidence of digging.

'I was cowering in my slit trench when a lovely fresh *S. pruni* Linn. came and shared it with me,
sitting on the newly dug earth.'

There were many clumps of Hemp Agrimony growing near the river bank and during my reconnaissance for a suitable crossing place, I noticed that the flowers were being well patronised by *C. quadripunctaria*, the Jersey Tiger, now mostly worn.

The crossing, which was done that same night, proved more difficult than we had anticipated but by dawn on the 26th we had got over the river, cleared Vernonnet and were established on our objective, the high chalk down. In the village we had overrun the German Headquarters and in the process liberated a large crate of several dozen champagne with 'Reservé pour le Wehrmacht' stamped all over it. It proved to be excellent wine. During the morning I found time to examine our down in some detail and was surprised and delighted to find that amongst the debris of war left behind by the Germans *L. coridon* Poda [Chalk Hill Blue], still very fresh, was flying in numbers. I am afraid I quickly lost interest in the vacated German position and concentrated on the Coridon, particularly as I found that a proportion of the females, possibly as high as 20% were ab. *syngrapha*. I felt I had at last really captured something and celebrated it that night with the champagne so thoughtfully provided by the Germans.

Three years later in August 1947, when on a Staff College battlefield tour, I was again able to visit Vernon. This time I was better prepared and sent a number of live female ab. *syngrapha* back to the late S. G. Castle Russell, who was anxious to try breeding from them. Unfortunately, they were despatched in a heatwave and didn't survive the journey, so the genetics of this remarkable colony have still to be worked out.

On the 27th my Division was ordered to enlarge the bridgehead to the limits of the forest. By now the Germans had had time to get their second wind and we had a rather sticky time fighting our way down forest rides with the thick undergrowth of bracken and hazel bushes limiting visibility to a few yards. By evening we had reached our objective, the village of Bois

Jerome St. Ouen, and there to greet me, in the garden of the house I selected as my Headquarters, were several large *P. machaon* Linn. [Swallowtail] larvae, feeding on the carrots in the vegetable patch.

The following day we continued our advance to the village of Le Mesnil Milon and it was when we were here that we learned that the Division was temporarily to lose its transport, so that the trucks could give extra support to the Armoured thrust that was by now streaming across the Seine and was to beat all records in its dash across Belgium.

While in this truckless state I was able to find time to take stock of our surroundings. Further colonies of *L. coridon* were discovered, one locally near the village and another large one at La Roche Guyon, where Field Marshall Rommel had had his Headquarters for the battle of Normandy. Ab. *syngrapha* was present in both these colonies but not in the same frequency as at Vernonnet. The countryside round our village was delightful and it was a joy to find ourselves, for the first time, in an area comparatively untouched by the battle and with the Entente Cordiale between ourselves and the locals very much in evidence. There were many clover and lucerne fields in the district and not unnaturally all supported their quota of *C. croceus* Fourcroy and *C. hyale* Linn. [Clouded and Pale Clouded Yellows], while a brown butterfly that seemed to be particularly attached to a certain farm track was found to be *A. lathonia* Linn. [Queen of Spain Fritillary], another new insect for me. I made several expeditions to the Forêt de Vernon, which now looked most attractive, but beyond finding on the outskirts the second brood of a fritillary, which looked like *M. didyma* Esp. [Spotted Fritillary], I saw nothing of particular interest, probably because it was too late in the season. Hornets were common and on a hot sunny day could be seen in some numbers on the rough ground round the village hunting for insects on the bramble bushes and other undergrowth.

Our rest came to an end with the return of our transport and we left for the battles of Nijmegen and Arnhem on 14th September. It was now well into autumn and the entomological season was virtually over and so indeed was the campaign in N.W. Europe before butterflies appeared again.

The surrender of the German forces in the first week of May found my battalion north of Bremen, poised to advance on Bremerhaven. Heather, birch and fir trees were the dominant features of the countryside and I had already noticed several male *E. versicolor[a]*, the Kentish Glory, as they darted about amongst the birch trees.

With the War over, the pattern of our existence changed and we became involved in sorting out the mess that it had left behind. Towards the end of May the battalion was billeted in Fallersleben, some twelve miles north of Brunswick. Our task here was to assist the Control Commission to sort out and send home the great number of Russian and Polish D.P.s [displaced persons] that had been working in the Volkswagen factory in nearby Wolfsburg and elsewhere. Every day train loads of these unfortunate people were despatched to the frontier and each carriage was always decorated with branches in full leaf. Whether this was a national custom or an ingrained habit of camouflage I never discovered.

Stretching westward to Gifhorn from the factory was a splendid oak forest with rough meadowland on its southern boundary facing Fallersleben. It was a matter of a five minutes run in a jeep from my billet to this collecting ground, which proved to be a gold mine for a butterfly starved entomologist. *A. selene* Schiff. [Small Pearl-bordered Fritillary], *E. aurinia* Rott. [Marsh Fritillary], *M. cinxia* Linn. [Glanville Fritillary], *M. athalia* Rott. [Heath Fritillary] were all flying together in the fields bordering the wood and here for the first time I saw that lovely Copper, *L. hippothoë* L. [Purple-edged Copper]. *C. palaemon* Pall. [Chequered Skipper] was common on the edge of the wood and so too was *A. crataegi* Linn. It was a wonderful place and one evening when I was walking down a ride on the look out for roe deer, an old badger came snuffling towards me and almost fell over my feet before he realised I was there.

Later that summer we moved to Celle, where amongst other duties we had the unpleasant task of being responsible for the security of the male and female German guards from Belsen. I have one vivid recollection of our time at Celle and it is of a ride in a wood near the village of Lachendorf that was flanked with clumps of Hemp Agrimony. One day, as I walked down it, I found the flowers covered with several dozen *N. antiopa* Linn. [Camberwell Beauty], all as fresh as paint and obviously the result of a big local emergence. They were a remarkable sight, particularly as in the years I subsequently spent in Germany I can only recall seeing three other specimens and these all after hibernation.

[Lipscomb, C. G. 1966. An entomologist at war. *The Entomologist's Record and Journal of Variation* **78**: 121–124].

Rupert Barrington (pers. comm.) recalled a story told to him by one of Kit Lipscomb's friends — Bob Craske. Apparently they had visited Whixall Moss, Shropshire, home of the Large Heath:

> After a morning looking for ab. *cockaynei* of the Large Heath, Bob was ready for a quick sandwich. The General was not and from the back of an average-sized car produced tables and chairs the scale of which apparently challenged physical law. There was a table-cloth, cutlery, wine and a lunch of several courses — all in the middle of the bog. Bob delighted in the surreal touch that they were apparently harassed throughout the meal by a very large and aggressive chicken. The entire day was spent, at the General's insistence, on the most difficult terrain of the whole bog where regular falls and soakings were assured. 'The butterfly was just as common on the drier ground, but the thing was,' Bob would chuckle, 'you couldn't tell him anything. He'd just pull rank!'

DAY OFF FROM WAR

Meanwhile back home in Britain, entomological activities also continued despite the war. Several very important butterfly collections including those of Mr Percy M. Bright and Sir Beckwith Whitehouse came up for sale in London during the period, with firms such as Glendining & Co. (Fig. 95) and Debenham, Storr & Sons, Ltd conducting the auctions. At these events the affluent collector could wield the 'Golden Net'* to secure the object of his desire.

The following article appeared in the *Daily Sketch* newspaper in the early 1940s:

Three fighting men took a day off from the war yesterday — a fighter pilot, a naval lieutenant and an Army captain. And they went buying butterflies.

There were two prize specimens in a sale of 400 butterflies from the collection of Mr Percy Bright, of Bournemouth — and all three fighting men wanted them. But the prices were too high. A unique white Galatea [Marbled White] brought £49. An entirely black Galatea brought £41. [**]

The R.A.F. man said, "I'd have got a big kick out of one of those Galateas. But I've picked up a few specimens I shouldn't have had time to collect this summer."

---

* A euphemism for a cheque book. In 1947 Sidney Castle Russell went to Harold Smith's sale and afterwards wrote: "Brought back the gorgeous *bellargus gynandro*, the most striking I have ever seen; it needed a costly use of the 'Golden Net' to catch it." (Kershaw, 1958)

[**] These famous insects were both taken in Kent. The white one by Thomas Marshall in July 1843, between Dover and Walmer; the melanic specimen (ab. *nigra* Frohawk) by a Mr Doran in July 1871, at Lodge Hill, near Rochester.

Established 1879.   PRICE ONE PENNY   Tel.: TEMple Bar 9451

WATKINS & DONCASTER

(R. L. E. FORD, F.R.E.S., F.Z.S.)

36 STRAND, LONDON, W.C. 2.

(Adjacent to Charing Cross).

Wartime Price List No. 11   -   **ENTOMOLOGY**

BRITISH BUTTERFLIES, SET.

m. - male, f. - female.

Swallowtail	1/6d.	Large Heath ...	m. 5d., f. 8d.
Black-veined White ...	5/-	Small Heath	1½d.
Large White	2d.	Brown Hairstreak ...	6d.
Small White	1½d.	White Letter Hairstreak ...	6d.
Green-veined White ...	1½d.	Black Hairstreak	2/6d.
Orange Tip ... m. 2d., f. 3d.		Purple Hairstreak... ...	3d.
Wood White ... m. 4d., f. 8d.		Green Hairstreak	4d.
Clouded Yellow	6d.	Small Copper	1½d.
Pale Clouded Yellow m. 1/-, f. 1/6d.		Silver Studded Blue ...	2d.
Brimstone	2d.	Brown Argus	2d.
Pearl Bordered Fritillary ...	2d.	Scotch Brown Argus m. 6d., f. 9d.	
Small Pearl Bordered Fritillary	2d.	Castle Eden Argus ...	1/6d.
Dark Green Fritillary m. 2d., f. 4d.		Common Blue	1½d.
High Brown Fritillary m. 3d., f. 5d.		Clifton Blue	2d.
Silver Washed Fritillary ...	3d.	Chalk Hill Blue	1½d.
Greasy Fritillary	3d.	Holly Blue ... m. 3d., f. 4d.	
Heath Fritillary	6d.	Little Blue	3d.
Glanville Fritillary ...	4d.	Large Blue ...	2/- to 5/-
Comma	4d.	Duke of Burgundy Fritillary	3d.
Large Tortoiseshell ...	3/6d.	Grizzle Skipper	1½d.
Small Tortoiseshell ...	1½d.	Dingy Skipper	1½d.
Peacock	2d.	Small Skipper	1½d.
Red Admiral	2d.	Essex Skipper	4d.
Painted Lady	4d.	Lulworth Skipper	5d.
White Admiral	5d.	Large Skipper	1½d.
Purple Emperor	7/6d.	Silver Spotted Skipper ...	3d.
Marbled White	2d.	Chequered Skipper m. 1/-, f. 1/4d.	
Scotch Argus ... m. 5d., f. 1/3d.			
Small Ringlet ... m. 8d., f. 1/3d.		**VARIETIES**	
Speckled Wood	2d.	Edusa var helice ...	2/6d. to 5/-
Wall	2d.	Paphia var valezina ...	9d.
Grayling	2d.	C-Album var Hutchinsoni...	9d.
Meadow Brown	1½d.	Hyperanthus var caeca ...	2/6d.
Small Meadow Brown ...	1½d.	Napi, Irish, (Yellow) ...	1/-
Ringlet	2d.	Corydon, semi-Syngrapha...	9d.

SPECIAL OFFER — 50 of above selected by us, 7/6d., inc. box and postage.

We often have the following **CONTINENTAL** examples in stock :—

Camberwell Beauty 1/6d., Black-veined White 1/-, Bath White 1/-, Queen of Spain Fritillary 1/6d., Large Blue 1/-, Mazarine Blue 1/-, Large Copper 2/6d.

SPECIAL NOTICE.—The above prices do not include postage or boxes, the cost of which is extra.   We should like to have back as many boxes as possible, as we cannot replace these during the war.

When ordering by post, please state alternative choice when possible.

Printed by F. MARTIN, (H. J. Sills), 7 Bourne Road, Bexley.

Fig. 94. Wartime price list of British butterflies (*c.* 1944). Watkins & Doncaster.

Fig. 95. No. 7 Argyll Street, London, W. 1 (1938). The home of Glendining & Co., next door to the London Palladium.

The Navy man said, "I'm rather sore about those Galateas. One of them would have looked well in a frame on my cabin wall."

The auctioneer, Mr Frederick Stevenson, said, "The result of the sale — £980 — was very satisfactory."

A buyer said, "Prices were not higher than peace-time. If collections are not sold in this way it might be impossible to pay death duties on estates."

Less than two years later, these same two butterflies were sold again. In November 1943, when Sir Beckwith Whitehouse's collection was auctioned by Glendining, Captain Vivian Hewitt, a wealthy collector who had a private museum in Wales, purchased the pair for £110 — equivalent to around £3,000 today. It is interesting to compare the prices paid for these two insects with the average weekly wage at that time: a craftsman could normally expect to earn around £5–6. In Watkins & Doncaster's wartime price list (Fig. 94), a typical Marbled White was priced at just 2d.

What became of these two specimens and whether they still exist remains a mystery. It is known that Captain Hewitt later removed to the Bahamas and his collection was consigned to an outbuilding where it presumably faced a predictable fate. Hewitt also possessed eggs and skins of the great auk, according to Bernard Kettlewell (Revd A. H. Harbottle, pers. comm.).

Fortunately, both for science and posterity, F. W. Frohawk figured these two specimens in the first volume of his *Natural History of British Butterflies* (1924) and in *Varieties of British Butterflies* (1938), and a detailed account of their history is given in L. Hugh Newman's *Living with Butterflies* (1967).

PRISON CAMP ENTOMOLOGY IN THE FAR EAST, 1941–1945

T. Graham Howarth, B.E.M., F.R.E.S., F.Z.S., Muswell Hill, London, N. 10. (1949)

Thousands of miles from the theatre of war in Europe, the British and Empire Armies faced a different enemy in the tropical jungles of the Malay peninsula. On 15th February 1942 (his twenty-sixth birthday) Thomas Graham Howarth watched as General Percival carried the white flag of surrender outside the Raffles Hotel in Singapore, indicating the cessation of hostilities and the devastating and humiliating defeat of the Empire forces. So began three and a half years of life as a prisoner of war for Howarth under the watchful eyes of the Japanese. Throughout his internment he managed to pursue actively his interest in entomology whenever the opportunity arose. He was allowed to keep his copy of A. D. Imms' *A General Textbook of Entomology*. He also kept detailed records of his observations and findings (which included a moth new to science), together with drawings of larvae and

pupae, in a remarkable diary — each page of it scrutinized and censored by his guards (Plate 2). In this article we are given a unique account of entomological dedication under the most difficult of circumstances.

Towards the end of August 1941 my name was forwarded through the usual channels of the Army as a volunteer for service overseas in a Mobile Malarial Laboratory and little did I realize then how I should be caught up in the catastrophic events that changed the colour of the maps in the early part of the following year.

On September 29th seventeen hundred of us embarked at Liverpool in the "Dominion Monarch" for an unknown destination, and we did not sight land again until the 15th October, when we made our way into the port of Freetown, Sierra Leone, W. Africa. We anchored some three quarters of a mile off shore but unfortunately were not allowed shore-leave. . . . Each night we had a spectacular display of electrical storms lasting some four or five hours. During this time I toured the deck lights hoping to find a few moths but whether the climatic conditions were unsuitable or the lights not bright enough I shall never know for certain, but I rather think the latter, as I found nothing. We left after a stay of nearly a week, my only regret being that I was unable to go ashore and examine this part of tropical Africa more closely.

Our next port of call was Cape Town . . . and with a very short stop at Colombo, Ceylon, we arrived on the 29th November at our destination — Singapore!

This island is now too well known for me to waste time giving a detailed description of it, but a few very brief remarks may be of interest. Singapore Island is roughly the size and shape of the Isle of Wight, and is situated just South of the Malay peninsula and separated from the mainland by the Straits of Johore, but joined by the Johore Causeway which carries the railway and the main road from Johore Bahru to Singapore City, situated on the southern tip of the island.

My first impression of the Island was a land of brilliant green — so vivid in the bright sunlight that it almost hurt the eyes, and with a variety of tropical insects whose abundance rather startled me at first. . . .

One of the main difficulties confronting the soldier entomologist, and there are many, is that he is primarily a soldier and being such may be sent anywhere with the shortest possible notice, and for him to have a quantity of entomological equipment adding to the weight of an already overburdened kit, is seriously restricting his mobility.

For the first two weeks after my arrival I had little enough time to observe the many insects around me, let alone collect them, as I was moved to first one camp and then another, but on December the 10th I settled at Tanglin. Here at last I managed to gather enough apparatus together to begin collecting in earnest. For the most part I reared my larvae in tins wherever possible, for an emergence cage I made a collapsible affair resembling a meat-safe of muslin with two hoops of wire for supports, tied at both ends and suspended by string covered with tanglefoot. For a killing bottle I used a large sweet jar with strong ammonia (.880), and I papered all my specimens and stored them in cigar boxes or tins.

I found it possible to collect near the camp most afternoons when I was not on duty, and my favourite locality was the edge of a patch of secondary growth adjoining a coconut plantation. Places such as this are the breeding grounds of the *Culex* mosquitoes that utilize the rain-filled coconut husks for their early stages, and the first time I went there the dead quiet of the Malayan afternoon was broken by the high pitched whine of these countless pests, and I was bitten so badly that I had to retreat.

Fig. 96. T. Graham Howarth collecting butterflies on Mt. Makiling, Philippines (1973).

It was quite noticeable that between the hours of three and four o' clock in the afternoon most of the butterflies began to find resting places for the night and whereas I would see an abundance of specimens about three o' clock, soon after this none was to be seen, although on one occasion I noticed *Amathusia phidippus chersias* [a palm-king butterfly] just leaving its shelter on the underside of some palm-fronds and preparing for its evening flight.

On Boxing Day I moved once more to a new camp, this time to Reformatory Road, near the village of Bukit Timah, where I joined a Field Hygiene Section which undertook the anti-malarial work in and around all the camps on Singapore. I was allotted an area in the northern part of the island, bounded by Kranji on the western side and Nee Soon on the east, an area which took me a week to cover. I was out every day and until we were forced to leave by the approach of the Nipponese I was kept very busy at work which was not only congenial but very interesting. . . .

There are times when the more self-conscious of us feel uncomfortable, especially when armed with entomological paraphernalia we are suddenly confronted by the public; I was never more so than when I encountered the enemy, armed only with a steel helmet and a larval scoop! The Japanese eventually landed in my area and made it impossible to carry on with the field work and we retired to unprepared positions at Tanglin. While there my collection and gear was dispersed by a shell, fortunately a small one, but I managed to salvage and amalgamate it again under considerable difficulties.

On the 15th February 1942 the war was over as far as I was concerned, but a new one, a much more insidious affair, was about to begin — a war against boredom, starvation, pestilence, and death.

I remained in the Raffles Library for three or four days after the capitulation, then had to move to the huge P.O.W. camp at Changi, situated on the eastern tip of the island. Here we finally settled down and I began to collect once more. After a while I managed to get outside the perimeter fence several times a week on the pretext of helping the English Agricultural Officer who had permission to collect the natural food in the neighbourhood. This enabled me to explore and to collect whatever came my way.

During the time spent on Singapore forty-two species of Rhopalocera [butterflies] and thirty-two species of Heterocera [moths] were taken; of these I bred five species of each suborder. I took only two species of cosmopolitan distribution, namely, *Lampides boeticus* [Long-tailed Blue] and *Herse convolvuli* [Convolvulus Hawk-moth], the remainder having a purely Indo-Australian distribution. . . .

On the 16th August, just six months after capitulation, fifteen hundred of us left Changi and boarded a Japanese trooper, a converted cargo boat, the "Fukki Maru." We occupied the top section of the four holds, 375 men in each. We left Keppel Harbour on the morning of the 19th and sailed up the coast to Port St Jacques, which we reached on the 22nd. We left the next day and reached Takow, Formosa, on the 29th August, and began to unload our cargo of bauxite. Many of us were taken ashore to move coal and machinery and during the days spent at this place I saw more specimens of *Odonata* [dragonflies] than I have ever seen. The air was literally alive with them as they hawked above the river and streams near the port. I saw several species of Rhopalocera, including the common *Papilio polytes* Linn. [Great Mormon], but I was unable to catch any of them to make identification certain.

After a two weeks' stay we left for the last stage of this nightmare voyage, which proved to be the worst of all. We ran into the edge of a typhoon, dysentery and diphtheria broke out, and we finally came ashore at Fusan, Korea, feeling more dead than alive.

Korea itself is a peninsula some five hundred miles in length by two hundred miles in breadth at its widest point and is situated between the 35th and 43rd lines of latitude. The climate throughout the year belongs to the usual continental type. There is a dry cold Winter with the mercury sometimes registering forty degrees (Fahr.) of frost, a damp Spring and Autumn, and a hot Summer with the temperature often in the eighties and nineties.

The natives as a race are more like Manchurians than Japanese and belong to the peasant class. Consequently the landscape in parts is not unlike some of our English countryside with cultivated fields and low rolling pine-covered hills of reddish earth.

From the port of Fusan we travelled by rail to our camp at Jinsen (Chemulpho), a small town on the western coast about twenty miles from the capital Keijo (Seoul). I remained here for two and a half years and during this time I did all kinds of manual work. The main job the camp did was to help build an extension of the docks, a job that lasted us for the whole time we were incarcerated here. With the hard work and the outdoor life we became fined down so that to outward appearances the majority of us were a healthy bronzed crowd but having very little resistance to the ailments that beset us.

The dock area was about a mile square and enclosed by a sea-wall of granite. On the inside of this was a sunken expanse of firm sandy soil covering a subsoil of peculiar blue-grey clay. The plants growing here were mainly thistles, docks, clovers, dandelions, several large patches of a dwarf Michaelmas Daisy and a strange fern-like plant growing two to three feet high with a habit like that of the American "Tumble-weed". There was only one small alder tree about twelve feet high in this rather desolate looking place.

I have described this locality in some detail as the majority of insects taken were collected either here or in the camp garden.

Six months before the end of hostilities we were moved from Jinsen via Keijo to Konan (Hamhun) in the north-east of the peninsula, some three hundred miles south of Vladivostok. Here after our release by the Russians I was able to indulge in a bout of collecting away from the camp and the watchful eyes of our late "hosts". . . .

[In Korea] I took thirty-five species of Rhopalocera, eleven of these were represented by only single specimens and three more by only two. Some of the species were very common in the camp area and long series were taken of those that showed any variation. . . .

Unfortunately, I was unable to collect many moths, due to restrictions, but any specimens that came my way were made very welcome. A few entered the hutments at night and the remainder were either flushed from the herbage or found at rest during the day.

A total of 66 Heterocera (Macrolepidoptera) were taken, about a third of those occur or have occurred in Britain . . . .

Several larvae of a species of *Apatele* were found feeding on a Japanese flowering cherry at Jinsen (Chemulpho) on 9.7.44, and the moths . . . that were bred from these belong to an undescribed species. I therefore propose for them the name **Apatele cerasi sp. nov.** . . .

In all, the Singapore and Korean collections totalled some fifteen hundred specimens, of which there were 1115 Rhopalocera, 347 Heterocera, and nearly a hundred specimens of other orders, all of which have been presented to the British Museum. . . .

[Howarth, T. G. 1949. Prison camp entomology in the Far East, 1941/45. *Proceedings and Transactions of the South London Entomological and Natural History Society* **1949-50**: 94–110].

It was not until repatriation at the end of hostilities in late 1945 that Graham Howarth and his fellow POWs came to realize how fortunate they had been to be removed from the tropics to the more temperate climate of Korea, where there were less unpleasant diseases. At the same time, the treatment meted out to them by their captors was reasonably humane. The prisoners survived on the same meagre rations as their captors and were given hard manual work, but so long as they behaved themselves they were not ill-treated. One spring Sunday morning (a rest day) the Japanese welfare officer arranged for a party of them to go on a tour of the town for an hour or so to enjoy the many flowering cherries lining the streets in full bloom — a kindness that was greatly appreciated.

Howarth was elected a Fellow of the Royal Entomological Society of London in 1939. Prior to the Second World War he had joined the Territorial Army (RAMC) and, after hostilities began, was awarded the British Empire Medal (Mil.) for rescue work during the Blitz on London. When finally the war was over he resumed his career at the Natural History Museum, London, in the Rhopalocera section of the Department of Entomology (see also p. 275).

He was made President of the South London Entomological and Natural History Society (now the British Entomological and Natural History Society) in 1951.

In what does seem a rather appropriate and somewhat ironic twist of fate, in the mid 1950s, Howarth went on to discover and describe fourteen new taxa and one new genus within the Asiatic and the Japanese *Neozephyrus* (Hairstreaks), among the specimens in the National Collection. Through his work, Graham Howarth has become well known and respected amongst the Japanese lepidopterists; he has been made a life member of the Japanese Lepidopterological Society. Following an invitation to address their society, in 1973, he was to find himself once more a 'guest' of the Japanese, but on this occasion under somewhat better circumstances altogether.

Since his retirement in 1976 from the Museum he has maintained these links, becoming busily involved in editing many Japanese entomological manuscripts for publication.

Fig. 97. T. Graham Howarth discovered a moth new to science while a Japanese prisoner of war. He was an honoured guest at the Reunion Supper held in January 1946 by the South London Entomological and Natural History Society. He is seen here with Suguru Igarashi, from Yokohama — a leading authority on the Papilionidae (1990).

AN ENTOMOLOGICAL MOTOR TOUR IN SPAIN IN 1927

Brig.-Gen. Bertram H. Cooke, C.M.G., C.B.E., D.S.O., F.E.S.,
Datchet, Berkshire. (1928)

To those intending to visit Spain for entomological or other purposes I would give the following advice: Treat all information received beforehand from friends with caution.

When I decided to spend the spring and summer of 1927 in Spain the following were some of the warnings I was given:

1. All but the main traffic routes (which are bad) are impossible for cars.

2. It is out of the question to stay at any but the "best" hotels. At the small hotels the rooms are dirty and infested by insects; the food is bad and sanitary arrangements non-existent.

3. At the best hotels it is impossible to get food and accommodation at less than 20 to 25 pesetas a day (*i.e.* 15 to 19 shillings).

4. The towns possessing good hotels are few and far between, the distances rendering motoring most inconvenient.

5. At towns frequented by tourists (notably Granada) the importunities of guides are such as to make life scarcely worth living.

6. The climate in the south of Spain in the summer is tropical.

These warnings made me pause for reflection, and their effect was not much lessened by a visit to the Spanish Travel Bureau and the Automobile Association; indeed, at the latter institution I was advised, in order to get from Madrid to Granada, to take a circular route involving a detour of about 200 kilometres, the reason given being that nothing was known of the direct route *viâ* Manzanares and Valdepeñas.

Luckily, however, I received far more encouraging accounts from a friend who, with her daughter, had made a successful motor tour in Spain last year. Eventually I decided to take the risk, spent a week at Dinard learning to drive a car, and started off by myself on 30th March *viâ* Bordeaux, Biarritz, Burgos, Madrid and Valdepeñas to Granada, taking 10 days to do the 1707 kilometres without any unpleasant results. At Granada I was joined by General van Straubenzee, who came by sea to Gibraltar, preferring (no doubt wisely) not to trust himself to my driving until I had imbibed experience.

I may say at once that none of the adverse reports turned out to be true. The main roads in Spain can hold their own with those of any country in which I have motored on the Continent in recent years. The direct road from San Sebastian to Granada was, on the whole, excellent, with good surface except for short stretches under repair, and with easy gradients over the mountains. The road from Granada to Murcia *viâ* Guadix is also good on the whole, though there are two or three steep gradients. The roads from Cuenca to Madrid, Murcia *viâ* Albacete to Madrid, and Cuenca to Guadalajara are also excellent. Many of the by-roads are also good, though occasionally one strikes a really bad one.

As regards hotels, I spent the night sometimes in what was not much more than a large village, but always found the little hotels clean, beds comfortable, and food and wine excellent, the usual charge for complete food and lodging for the day being about 10 pesetas (7*s*.6*d*.).

Granada has the reputation of being the most expensive town in Spain, and I first arrived there at the beginning of the Easter fêtes. Yet I found a modest little hotel, where I had a good room and excellent food for 8½ pesetas a day (6*s*.4*d*.), whereas my friends who stayed at one of the tourist establishments on the Alhambra had the privilege of paying 35 pesetas a day for accommodation and food that was very little better.

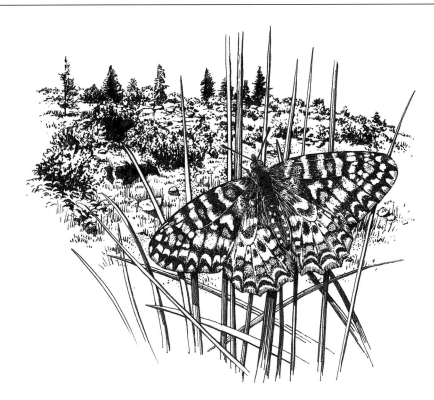

As far as guides are concerned, we were never bothered by one during our stay. Nor were we much troubled by an excess of heat. Murcia is a stuffy little town, and was distinctly hot in June, but once outside the town there was not much to complain of. As to Granada, the climate was quite delightful. The nights were always cool in July, and, with the exception of three really hot days, there was always a little cool breeze all day, though we hardly saw a cloud in the sky for weeks. We never saw a mosquito all the time we were there.

The first captures of interest were made on the 7th April — the day I left Madrid. When crossing a plateau just south of Aranjuez I noticed some white butterflies among the heather. These proved to be *Euchloë tagis* [Portuguese Dappled White] flying in considerable numbers, and on the same ground I took a very small form of *Thais rumina* [Spanish Festoon], also *Euchloë belia* [Moroccan Orange Tip], *Leucochloë bellidice* [an old name for the Bath White], *Callophrys rubi* [Green Hairstreak], *Anthocaris euphenoides* [a subspecies of the Moroccan Orange Tip] and *Gonepteryx cleopatra* [Cleopatra]. Shortly before reaching Granada on 8th April a few *Thestor ballus* [Provence Hairstreak] were flying near a stream by the roadside.

We stayed at Granada from 9th to 20th April. At that time of year the ground suitable for butterflies is rather restricted, the best locality being the slopes on the north side of the Genil Valley. Here there are a number of fields in which *Biscutella* [a crucifer] grows plentifully, and from the 10th up to the date of our departure *Zegis eupheme* v. *meridionalis* [Sooty Orange Tip] was flying in abundance. They never seemed to settle on any flowers other than *Biscutella*.

I took only one specimen of *Euchloë belemia* [Green-striped White]; possibly we were too early for it at this altitude (at about 2300 ft.). Among other species we took *Lycaena baton* v. *panoptes* [Panoptes Blue], *L. melanops* v. *algirica* [Black-eyed Blue], *Thais rumina, Melitaea phoebe* v. *occitanica* [Knapweed Fritillary] and *M. dejone* v. *nevadensis* [a form of the Provençal Fritillary]; the last two were just emerging when we left Granada. . . .

We left Granada on 20th April, halted the night at Lorca and arrived at Murcia on the 21st.

Before leaving England I had been invited by Mr. Morris Carswell, who is resident at Murcia and an ardent entomologist, to pay him a visit, and when he learnt that I was accompanied by a friend he extended the invitation to him as well. His kind hospitality made all the difference to our stay, and he personally conducted us to the collecting-grounds in the neighbourhood. Without a car, collecting from Murcia would be very difficult indeed. There is no suitable ground nearer than about 6 miles away, and the local taxi-drivers charge enormous fares outside the town. A visit to the Sierra de Espuña involves a drive of nearly 50 kilometres, and the road rises from just above sea-level at Murcia to about 4000 ft. at the highest point it reaches on the Sierra. Most of the climb is done during the last 20 kilometres or so.

With Mr. Carswell's assistance we obtained official leave to stay at the Casa Forestal in the Espuña range; this is a house built for the convenience of the visiting forest officers. The ground floor of the house is occupied by the head keeper or "guardia," and his family, and we lived with them, almost as part of the family, for two periods of ten days each, *i.e.* from 4th to 15th May and from 30th May to 8th June, and returned for a third visit from 22nd to 27th July. Early in May, Dr. A. Schmidt turned up from Budapest, accompanied by Señor de la Escalera of the Natural History Museum, Madrid.

For some reason or other the number of insects flying in the Espuña range, both as regards species and individuals, was extremely small in the spring and early summer. It is true that the weather at first was very showery and somewhat cold, but this can hardly account for the dearth. Things had improved a little by the time we paid our last visit, but even then there was a very marked difference from the abundance of butterflies which we found in the Sierra de Alfacar and around Albarracin. The few species which were really abundant in the Sierra de Espuña were *Melitaea dejone*, *Lycaena aragonensis* [Spanish Chalkhill Blue], *Lampides boeticus* [Long-tailed Blue], *Tarucus telicanus* [Lang's Short-tailed Blue], *Satyrus fidia* [Striped Grayling], *Epinephele pasiphaë* [Spanish Gatekeeper] and *Lycaena aegon* v. *hypochiona* [a form of the Silver-studded Blue]. The capture of a new species of *Zizera* (*Z. carswelli* Stempffer) [Carswell's Little Blue] went a long way to compensate us for the other deficiencies. The remainder of the period between 21st April and 15th June we spent hunting in the low hills near Murcia, which were far more productive. . . . Shortly before leaving we found by chance the very unpleasantly thorny bushes round which *Tarucus theophrastus* [Common Tiger Blue] flies. We found only a few of these bushes in one place, but they produced considerable numbers of *theophrastus* in first-rate condition.

On the 15th June, having exhausted the Espuña, and as things were coming to an end for the time being round Murcia, we drove back to Granada. We seemed fated to choose the most popular periods for our visits to this town, for as we drove into it we found all the streets decorated, and learnt that it was the first day of Corpus Christi fête, which lasts nearly a fortnight. We secured hotel accommodation with some difficulty, but the semi-religious, semi-pagan processions and the many other displays which took place during the fête are characteristics of Andalucia, that one will never forget.

We at once set to work to get permission to stay at the Casa de Forestal of the Sierra de Alfacar, and this we obtained, thanks to the kind efforts of the British Consul, Mr. Davenhill.

The road from Granada is very indifferent and exceedingly steep, but the car stood the strain on several occasions. After one or two preliminary trips we stayed at the Casa de Forestal from 1st to 7th July. The accommodation was not as good as in the Espuña, and the first night we discovered insects in our beds which we were not by way of collecting — they were not Lepidoptera. During our visits to the Sierra de Alfacar we found swarms of butterflies everywhere . . . We were unfortunately too late for *Melitaea desfontainii* [Spanish Fritillary].

We remained at Granada until 22nd July, and made a few excursions to the Sierra Nevada, during one of which I drove my car along a dreadful road to the Sierra Nevada Hotel. The last part of the journey is up a slope so steep, and with such hairpin bends, that the car refused to function until it was pushed up by General van Straubenzee and two stalwart Carabineros. We found the Nevada far less productive than the Alfacar, and we failed entirely to discover two species which we wanted, *Satyrus hippolyte* [Nevada Grayling] and *Lycaena idas* [Idas Blue].

We returned to the Sierra de Espuña on 22nd July and made a further unsuccessful search for *L. idas* up to the top of the Morron, the highest peak of the range. On the 27th we left there for Cuenca *viâ* Murcia, and Albacete. On the 28th we had our one and only serious casualty to the car. About 60 kilometres short of Cuenca a small piece of metal, which had recently been mended, gave way in the gear-box, and we had to complete the journey in a passing "diligence," leaving the car to be towed in next day. We stayed a few days in Cuenca, and made an expedition to some wooded country in the valley of the River Jucar. Having discovered that the road to Teruel was extremely bad, I decided to leave the car at Cuenca and do the journey *viâ* Caete to Teruel and Albarracin by a series of motor diligences. We left Cuenca at 4 p.m. on 1st August in a crowded vehicle and, after much bumping on a bad road, arrived at about 6 p.m. at the small village of Carboneras. Here, as it was discovered that the majority of the passengers had booked their passages, not to Cañete, but to Villora (which is on a branch road), it was decided to switch off the diligence to the latter place, leaving us with four other passengers sitting on our baggage by the roadside. We managed to get a scratch meal, and at about 10.30 p.m. a dilapidated Ford car arrived, into which the seven of us had to pack ourselves. A passenger crouched on the dashboard on either side, clinging on like monkeys, and the baggage was tied to the bonnet of the car with indifferent string. Somehow we arrived at Cañete without loss or mishap at about 12.30 a.m., and spent the rest of the night (somewhat restlessly!) in the primitive village "posada." Next morning we were off again in another vehicle, and once more changed at Torre Baja, finally reaching Teruel at mid-day. After lunch we again started in a small motor 'bus for Albarracin. After going about 15 kilometres the driver discovered he had no water in the radiator, so we all got out and sat for an hour and a half by the roadside while he walked with a can to the nearest cottage (about 4 kilometres) to fetch water. We finally reached Albarracin at about 7 p.m., and found humble but fairly comfortable quarters at the Hospederia de Manuel Moreno for 8 pesetas a day, all included. We remained here from the 3rd to the 10th August, and thoroughly enjoyed our stay.

The contrast between this fertile and wooded country and the burnt-up and rather sterile surroundings of Andalucia and Murcia is very marked, and we found the change most welcome. An old acquaintance of mine, Herr Karl Predota, a Viennese collector whom I had known in Vienna in 1920, has spent the last three seasons collecting at Albarracin. He is known to all the local inhabitants as "Don Carlos," and he at once took us under his wing and escorted us to all the best collecting-grounds.

We now began to feel the want of the car, as the main roads from Albarracin are fairly good, and the distances to Tramascastilla, Noguera and Bronchales are considerable. However, we managed to hire the only local car at some expense on two occasions, and did the rest of our journeys on foot. We took all the species which we had expected to find at this time of the year . . .

270

E. zapateri [Zapater's Ringlet] was only just emerging at the Puerto de Bronchales when we left, but we got a series of males and two females at the Puerto de Losilla. We took *L. caelestissima* [Azure Chalk-hill Blue] only at one spot, just above the village of Noguera, but they had only just emerged and we got a series in first-class condition. Herr Predota took a beautiful female of the same brilliant blue as the male, and I secured a female in which the lower half of the left fore wing is of the male colour. *S. prieuri* [Southern Hermit] was fairly plentiful, especially females, on the south side of the Vega Valley; we also took a number near Santa Croche, including a few ab. *uhagonis*.

On the 11th August we returned to Cuenca by the same route (less the Ford car episode), packed our things in my car, and started on our return journey to France. On the 15th, after crossing the Somosierra range, I took a number of *Chrysophanus virgaureae* v. *miegii* [Spanish form of the Purple-edged Copper], and *Argynnis paphia* [Silver-washed Fritillary] was also flying here in very worn condition. We joined the main road from Madrid to France at Guadalajara, in which pleasant little town we spent a night, and for the rest of the journey, which was quite uneventful, we followed the same route as in the spring, arriving at Dinard on 23rd August.

The great interest, as regards collecting in Spain, lies in the fact that nearly every species has a local form differing (often considerably) from those occurring in other countries, and that certain African species and races inhabit southern Spain. On the other hand, the number of species of butterflies is more limited than in the countries of Central Europe, whole genera, such as the Erebias, being represented by only a few species. . . .

[Cooke, B. H. 1928. An entomological motor tour in Spain in 1927. *The Entomologist* **61**: 154–159; 176–182; 197–202].

This enthusiastic account by Brigadier-General Bertram Hewett Hunter Cooke of his motorized butterfly collecting tour in Spain, published in *The Entomologist*, is followed by a further thirteen pages, in which he described the butterflies he encountered.

THREE MONTHS' BUTTERFLY COLLECTING IN GREECE

Brig.-Gen. Casimar H. C. van Straubenzee, C.B., C.B.E., London, S. W. 3. (1932)

At 5 p.m. on April 17th, 1931, the Simplon-Orient Express landed me, after an uneventful and rather tedious journey of 78 hours from London, at Bralo (the station for Delphi), on the main line from Nisch to Athens. Here, much to the amusement of the French attendant of the sleeping-car I had just quitted, I was tumultuously received by three rival motor-car proprietors, each with a retinue of sympathisers, and each, so far as I, being ignorant of modern Greek, could gather, claiming to be the chosen agent for my conveyance to Delphi. Fortunately a Greek engineer with a knowledge of German happened to be on the platform, and he, having grasped the situation, very kindly extricated me from it, re-assembled my scattered baggage, which had been forcibly borne off piecemeal to the rival cars, and soon he and I were speeding on the way to Delphi in the motor 'bus. For this only dr. 100 per passenger plus a little extra for the baggage is charged, as against dr. 500 for a car to oneself, so the saving is considerable.

Delphi was reached about 7.30 p.m., and I was soon installed in the room I had booked at the Grand Hotel d'Apollon Pythien, which is by no means so imposing as its name. The food, however, was excellent, and the staff most attentive, notably the interpreter. My bed-room was soon supplied with the extra table and chest of drawers asked for to supplement its originally somewhat meagre furniture, and I settled down to a very pleasant month's stay, marred only occasionally by the tramp of tourists, arriving or departing, sometimes in the small hours, on the bare boards of the bedrooms and corridors. Tourists of all nationalities, but mostly American and English, are numerous in the spring months, and during my stay the hotel was generally full, so it is advisable to book rooms well in advance. The charge *en pension* was dr. 220 daily. The following morning broke cold and wet, but cleared about 11.30, when I sallied forth to a collecting-ground, only a quarter of an hour's walk from the hotel, which eventually, so far as my experience went, proved the best in the neighbourhood. To reach it one goes about a mile down the main road towards Bralo, to the point where a small stream of water, emerging from a deep cleft in the red cliffs on the left, flows down to the road. On the left is a path which runs for about twenty paces alongside the stream and bends left-handed away from it, and winds, between the cliff and the ruins, back in the direction of Delphi. The first two or three hundred yards of this path produced in my case the best results, but butterflies were to be found on the other paths radiating from it, and on the banks on either side. On this ground I took, on April 18th, several *Pieris ergane* [Mountain Small White], four *P. krueperi* [Krueper's Small White], five *Anthocaris damone* [Eastern Orange Tip] and one or two *A. gruneri* [Gruner's Orange Tip], all fresh, besides commoner insects.

April 19th was a very fine, bright day, and I found *A. gruneri* females much more numerous, especially near the stream, taking about a dozen. Otherwise results were much about the same as the previous day, and continued to be so till the 23rd, when I walked towards Parnassus. This involves a steep ascent of about an hour up a good path, which brings one out on what may be described as relatively a plateau, more or less undulating, and intersected by shallow ravines. Now for the first time one sees the snow-clad peak of Mt. Parnassus in the far distance. My guide who had worked on the Panama Canal and spoke quite good English, or rather American, told me it was ten hours' march away.

Continuing our advance, the path led us, half a mile or less further on, into a shallow ravine or dry watercourse with a stony bottom, and sides covered in places with low scrub. Here *Zerynthia polyxena* [Southern Festoon] and a small race of *Argynnis lathonia* [Queen of Spain Fritillary] were common and fresh, and there were a few male *A. gruneri*, but beyond these I saw little of interest. One continued to find these species up to, and in diminishing numbers for a few hundred yards beyond, a spring of excellent water which gushes out of the bank above the path at a point about a mile or so from where the latter debouches on the plateau. After refreshing ourselves, we continued our walk for a further two or three miles, but as we progressed we found the paucity of butterflies became ever more and more marked, till eventually even the *A. lathonia*, which had persisted longer than any of the other species, ceased to appear. This confirms the experience recorded by Staudinger, of Dr. Grueper, in 1865, that "on the barren plateau of Parnassus hardly anything was to be found." The limit of our walk was a second spring, with a lake lying, as far as I remember, about a quarter of a mile to the right front of our line of advance. Here we lunched and were joined by a patriarchal looking Greek on a donkey, the only person we had seen since leaving the first spring. My guide told me that the old man was well over eighty, and was, with the exception of his son, the only permanent resident on the plateau. In that case he was a living testimony to the salubrity of the climate. I was told that a month or so later vast flocks of sheep would be brought up to the plateau to graze, and that the sheep-dogs then became troublesome, if not actually dangerous, to the passing stranger.

I paid two further visits to the plateau on May 4th and 6th, when I found both species and individuals more numerous. Among those taken were *Melitaea trivia* [Lesser Spotted

Fritillary] and *Carcharodus orientalis* [Oriental Marbled Skipper] on the way up, and on the plateau itself *P. ergane* and three specimens of a small form of *Lycaena semiargus* [Mazarine Blue], resembling *montana* M.-D., and lacking any trace of the orange markings on the underside distinctive of *parnassia* Stgr.

On April 29th, on the low ground, I took the first *Papilio alexanor* [Southern Swallowtail], presumably var. *maccabaeus* Stgr., though I can see little to distinguish it from the type. From now onwards this species became fairly numerous, though, as usual, by no means easy to catch. I also took, on the same day, a blue pronounced by Capt. Hemming to be *L. vicrama* Moore [Eastern Baton Blue], the only individual of that or any *baton*-like species that I saw at Delphi.

On May 14th, which was the last day on which I collected at Delphi, *M. trivia* had become common and *P. alexanor* fairly so, but *P. krueperi* was getting rarer (though I did get three fresh specimens), and *A. damone* and *A. gruneri* had completely disappeared. I found, as have other collectors, that the females of these two last-named species are very difficult to get, and, despite assiduous search, I only succeeded in taking five of the former and four of the latter. Delphi in the spring is by no means a land of perpetual sunshine, and on five days of my stay collecting was rendered useless by persistently dull or wet weather.

On May 15th I left by car for Itea *en route* for Kalavryta. At Itea I chartered a motor-boat, at a cost of dr. 650, for the passage across the Gulf of Corinth, which took me three hours. About 11 a.m. the rising breeze made the sea decidedly choppy, as the boatmen told me it always does about mid-day, so the indifferent sailor making the crossing in a small boat such as ours may find it advisable to start in the early morning. Presumably because there is no landing place at Diakofto, our boat was beached in a sandy cove about a mile from the railway station, to which the boatmen carried my luggage along the line, which runs all along the southern coast of the Gulf to Patras.

Quite a good meal is obtainable at Diakofto Station, but on this occasion I had no time for one, as my train was almost due to start up the little mountain railway to Kalavryta, which I reached about two hours later. Through the interpreter at Delphi, who wrote in Greek (neither of the two hotel proprietors I had to do with could read any other languages), a room was booked for me at the Hotel Anesis. I had been under the erroneous impression that there was only one hotel at Kalavryta, but discovered on the following morning that there was a second, the Hotel Khelmos, larger and outwardly more attractive and also possibly quieter, as it lies on the outskirts of the town. Had I foreseen what, towards the close of my stay, when the Kalavryta season was in full swing, I should have to endure, up to the small hours of the morning, from four to five gramophones and loud-speakers in my immediate neighbourhood, I should probably have shifted to the Khelmos forthwith. As it was I remained at the Anesis for the seven weeks of my stay, and found it very clean and cheap. It came to about 8s. daily, wine and all.

For my first day's collecting, on May 16th, I went along the railway-line below Kalavryta, which runs on the right bank of a small river. This latter is spanned by two bridges, the first about one, and the second about two and a half, miles below the town, by either of which the path following the left bank may be reached. I occasionally tried this path later on, but found that I generally got better results on the railway. On this occasion I found very little flying, but took four *Lycaena helena* [subspecies of the Mazarine Blue], which, however, was by no means numerous. I found it far commoner on the following day about half an hour's walk above Kalavryta in the open spaces in the scrub bordering the path to Sondena, but many were worn.

May 23rd was distinguished by my taking a single specimen of *Lycaena bavius* [Bavius Blue] on the left-bank path below Kalavryta at a point about half-way between the first and second bridges. This experience was repeated on the 27th, when I took two (one badly damaged and released) on the railway line almost immediately opposite to the spot on the other bank where I had taken the first. So far as I have been able to ascertain, this species is new to the Kalavryta district, if not to Greece. Between May 16th and 25th I took a male and two female *Cupido sebrus* [syn. Osiris Blue] among the bushes on the left of the Sondena path half an hour's walk above Kalavryta. I may have seen others on the wing, but mistaken them for *L. helena,* which, as stated before, was common there.

On May 31st I netted my first *Colias aurorina heldreichi* [Greek Clouded Yellow] only some thirty-five minutes' walk from the town, in a small ravine on the upper path to Mt. Khelmos. I never saw another in this locality, or indeed till ten days later, when I found one of its flight places on the Cherokobus plateau some thousands of feet higher up, near the tree line, and just below the easternmost peak of Mt. Khelmos. Here, on June 11th, I saw about half a dozen males, but found the species ever more and more numerous at each visit, till June 24th, when I took 12 females, and it might be described as abundant, as also, to an even greater degree, was *Parnassius mnemosyne athene* [Greek form of the Clouded Apollo].

On a little strip of track a short distance beyond where the path from Sondena debouches on the plateau, 14 *Lycaena anteros* [Blue Argus], some rather worn, were taken between June 14th and 24th. The best way to reach Cherokobus is by the path from Sondena, which the traveller from Kalavryta will find turning sharp off to his left as he nears the ridge overlooking Sondena. After I got to know my way, I used to take a short cut to the left up the dry watercourse. . . . Here at the end of June and the beginning of July there is still a little water flowing, and on patches of damp sand and mud may be found *Lycaena sephirus* [Zephyr Blue] and *L. admetus* [Anomalous Blue] in large numbers, while *L. meleager*

[Meleager's Blue] and a race of *L. escheri* [Escher's Blue] appearing to correspond to Seitz's description of *dalmatica* Spr. were occasionally to be taken. It was here, too, that on June 28th and 30th, I was fortunate enough to take over 30 *Hesperia phlomidis* [Persian Skipper], all newly emerged. I occasionally took odd ones higher up the hill, but the watercourse seemed to be their headquarters.

It had been my intention to remain in Greece until the end of July, but a late season compelled me to stay on in Kalavryta till in early July, the heat, in spite of 2500 ft. elevation, became so unbearable that on the 9th of that month I left for Patras, and thence in a Yugo-Slav steamer up the Adriatic to Fiume on my way home.

In conclusion, and especially as that hitherto unsolved mystery, the disappearance of Mr. Cockrane, which caused much comment at the time, happened the day after my arrival at Delphi, I feel impelled to add that I never met with anything but the greatest kindness and civility from everybody I came across on my rambles. The country people were nearly always ready for a chat, but my ignorance of Greek unfortunately cramped my efforts at social intercourse except with those, by no means few in numbers, who had learned a limited amount of English while working in the U.S.A. English, indeed, seemed the most generally understood foreign tongue in the parts of Greece I visited. French, apart from the ordinary salutations, I only heard spoken by two people — one of my boatmen when crossing the Gulf, and a girl on the railway-line at Kalavryta. As for German, I found nobody who responded to that language except the engineer mentioned at the beginning of this article and Dr. Karantonis and his charming wife, a German lady, the kindly companionship of both of whom relieved for me the tedium of many a long evening in Kalavryta.

[Straubenzee, van, C. H. C. 1932. Three months' butterfly collecting in Greece. *The Entomologist* **65**: 154–159].

COLLECTING LEPIDOPTERA IN THE SOUTH OF FRANCE
IN 1950 AND 1951

T. Graham Howarth, B.E.M., F.R.E.S., F.Z.S., Arkley, Hertfordshire. (1952)

Thomas Graham Howarth (b. 1916) was a Senior Scientific Officer in the Department of Entomology, British Museum (Natural History) until his retirement in 1976. He described two British butterfly subspecies: *Hipparchia semele hibernica* — the Grayling which occurs throughout Ireland (except on the Burren, in Co. Clare); and *Pararge aegeria insula* — the Speckled Wood found on the Isles of Scilly. His book *South's British Butterflies* (1973) was an extensive revision and rewrite of the classic by Richard South: *The Butterflies of the British Isles* (1906) — a work that, together with its two companion volumes on the British moths, underwent numerous editions and which were described by Norman D. Riley as 'the best of their kind ever produced'.

Early in 1950 I was asked to make a collecting trip to the Alpes Maritimes and Basses Alpes in order to obtain certain high altitude butterflies for a private collector.

I realized immediately that much work might be done which would prove of interest if I could collect Heterocera [moths] for the [Natural History] Museum at the same time, and after an agreement was reached between the various parties concerned I was very fortunate in having one of the prototypes of the Robinson Mercury Vapour trap placed at my disposal for the whole time abroad. . . .

The road from Nice to St. Martin Vesubie runs due west for a short way until it reaches the Var valley where it turns inland and follows the river northwards to the high mountains. At the junction of the Vesubie River, a tributary of the Var, the road divides and we followed the river through its chasms and gorges to the north-east, climbing all the way amidst magnificent scenery towards the Italian border. Before reaching this, the river divides again into two tributaries, the Fenestre and Boreon and the village of St. Martin Vesubie is situated at the junction of these two streams at about 3000 ft. above sea-level. Beyond the town the road continues to climb sharply in a series of zigzags from the village up the lower slopes of the Balme de la Frema, a mountain 7100 ft. high, finally reaching the top of a pass at 5000 ft. and descending on the other side to the little village of St. Dalmas and Valdeblore.

The Colmiane Hotel, where we stayed, is situated just below the crest of the pass in extensive pine forests. Within a few hundred yards of the back of the hotel there is a small valley, the Combe de la Colmiane, which runs nearly at right angles to the road. This was filled to overflowing with an amazing assortment of flowering plants including lucerne, clovers, vetches, scabious, *Lotus corniculatus* [bird's-foot-trefoil], orchids by the hundred, alpine lilies, lavender and gooseberry bushes, heather and a host of others. When I saw this place I realized what a great pity it was that I should be unable to use the trap here as it was too far from the Hotel.

I had written to the hotel about their electricity supply and having found out about it I went prepared for all eventualities or so I thought. The proprietor was most helpful and allowed me to run my 100 yard flex from an outhouse down towards the valley at the rear of the hotel to a wide space on a mule track. I wired up and plugged in and all was well. I retired to bed the first evening early so that I should be ready for the morrow and I had just reached my room when — "Phut" — out went the lights. I was called immediately and on descending to the outhouse was met by a cloud of tarry wood-smoke and fumes from the transformer box. Fortunately there was no actual blaze but only a great deal of smouldering which was soon dealt with. I am certainly no electrician but it appears that the current was not the right sort and using the transformer as a resistance had heated it up unduly until the windings had begun to smoulder in their wooden box. Subsequently I used an ordinary 150 watt bulb in the trap until an electrician came to stay at the hotel and on his advice we placed two 50 watt bulbs in series which acted quite successfully as a choke for the M.V. bulb although the light did not seem so bright as usual.

The day following our arrival broke clear and fine and after seeing to the trap and having a light breakfast I set off up the Balme making my way along a mule track which winds its way through the pine forests that cover the lower slopes of the mountain. I was fortunate in meeting a local shepherd boy who showed me the way as the path divides in several places and it is quite likely that I should have ended up on the wrong side of the mountain with no access to the summit had I not met him. However we plodded on up the rough track, climbing about 1000 ft. per hour.

Many species of Rhopalocera [butterflies] were flying near the path. The large Satyrid, *Satyrus hermione* L. [Woodland Grayling] could be seen flitting from tree-trunk to tree-trunk, and seeming to prefer a dark surface on which to rest, as several times this insect was quite fearless and would actually settle on my black net or on my trousers. They did not appear to do this as so many *Lycaenidae* do, in order to feed, as their tongues were not uncoiled and they appeared quite content to rest for as long as I cared to remain stationary. *Maculinea arion* L. [Large Blue] was occasionally seen in company with many of the commoner

Satyridae and *Lycaenidae. Erebia ceto* Hb. [Almond-eyed Ringlet], *Cyaniris semiargus* Rott. [Mazarine Blue], *Lysandra escheri* Hb. [Escher's Blue], *L. bellargus* Rott. [Adonis Blue], and *Polyommatus icarus* Rott. [Common Blue] were numerous, while the little yellow moths *Isturgia limbaria* Fab. [Frosted Yellow] and *Pseudopanthera macularia* L. [Speckled Yellow] could be seen flying about the broom bushes that grow in profusion on these slopes.

After about an hour's climb we came to the tree line and emerged quite abruptly onto the grassy slopes which cover the upper parts of these mountains. Up here were many species flitting about, but they were mostly those that I had seen lower down. I was on the lookout for five species while I was here, namely *Pontia callidice* Esp., [Peak White], *Euchloë simplonia* Frey. [Mountain Dappled White], *Euphydryas cynthia* Hb. [Cynthia's Fritillary], *Erebia gorgophone* now named *aethiopellus* ssp. *mediterranea* Warren [False Mnestra's Ringlet] and *Oeneis aëllo* Hb. [Alpine Grayling] and during the morning and afternoon of this first day I saw no sign of any of them but took several examples of *Erebia epiphron* Knoch [Small Mountain Ringlet] and *pandrose* Bork [Dewy Ringlet]. I explored the summit of the Balme and then went along the ridge or Col to the slopes of Mt. Peppouri which rises another 1000 ft. higher than the former.

On the 27th and 28th I climbed to the summit again and while there I managed to catch my first *callidice*. This species is one of the most difficult I have ever had to catch. It flies in rather the same erratic manner as a male *croceus* [Clouded Yellow], low and very fast over the roughest ground and if it were not for the fact that it likes to make the tops of the mountains, and I do mean the very tops, its playground it would be very nearly impossible to catch. As it was, after watching these insects flying around, I was able to see that they made fairly regular flight-tracks amongst the rocks and herbage of the summit and by stationing myself near these tracks I found that I at least could make a stroke at them and I considered myself lucky in capturing eight specimens in two hours.

Callidice was not the only species flying around the summit. Three or four specimens of *Papilio machaon* L. [Swallowtail] were cavorting about and resting on the warm stones and rough herbage, with *Aglais urticae* L [Small Tortoishell], *Pararge megera* L [Wall] and an occasional *Colias phicomone* Esp. [Mountain Clouded Yellow], and that lovely Copper *Heodes alciphron* Rott. [Purple-shot Copper] could be found at rest on the small patches of thyme that were just coming into flower. These patches, scattered over the mountain side above the tree line and lower down along the path, gave very good collecting and it was delightful and exciting to see as many as a dozen butterflies of four or five different species at rest on a small plant no bigger than a tea-plate and with care it was possible to examine and box any specimen that was required. In this way I took a fair series of the Theclid — *Strymon spini* Schiff. [Blue-spot Hairstreak], a species which I saw nowhere else except on these thyme patches.

Near the summit on the second day in a rocky gully on the eastern side of the Balme I saw two or three specimens of a small white butterfly flying rapidly up and down the mountain side. After a hectic and exhausting chase I succeeded in taking a specimen which proved to be one of my specific quarries *Euchloë ausonia simplonia* Frey. This species, which is rather like a female *cardamines* [Orange-tip] in appearance but with more angular wings and a greater expanse, seems confined to these slopes above the tree line and never seems to descend below 6000 ft. It is a difficult species to catch due to its erratic flight, its shyness and the terrain of its home. . . .

I searched in vain for *Euphydryas cynthia* for several days but finally located it near the Col already mentioned at about 7000 ft. This attractive "Fritillary", which resembles *E. aurinia*

Rott. [Marsh Fritillary] in its female, is much more sexually dimorphic than our British species in having a beautiful brown, black and white barred male. On climbing higher a day or so later I found the butterfly in hundreds. The sexes were equally common and in the high wind and during cloudy weather it was easy to find pairs *in cop.* and at rest in the grass tufts. . . .

In 1950 I made it a practice to visit the Combe de la Colmiane every other day so as to have a rest from mountaineering, but this was not possible in 1951 as the weather was so uncertain that it was imperative to climb the Balme every morning in order to prove to one's conscience that there was still nothing to be found above the tree line. As so often happens in these mountains a day which dawns bright and clear will be clouded over, often by ten o' clock, so an early start is essential to arrive at the collecting ground before the clouds begin to gather around the peaks. In the Combe there was an abundance of insect life, the Lepidoptera taking a major part in this diverse population. . . . *Papilio machaon* L., *Pontia daplidice* L. [Bath White], *Aporia crataegi* L. [Black-veined White], *Leptidea sinapis* L. [Wood White], *Colias croceus* Fourc., *C. hyale* L. [Pale Clouded Yellow], *C. australis* Ver. [Berger's Clouded Yellow], *Melitaea cinxia* L. [Glanville Fritillary], *Issoria lathonia* L. [Queen of Spain Fritillary], *Cyaniris semiargus* Rott. and *Maculinea arion* L. were all here in company with *Zygaena purpuralis* Brün. [Transparent Burnet] and *achilleae* Esp. [Slender Scotch Burnet] thrown in for fair measure.

Representatives of the genus *Zygaena* were abundant in the valley and I found it a profitable practice to pay the Combe a quiet visit in the evening when the 'Burnets' were not so active . . . I think it is indicative of the abundance and popularity of this Genus that the French entomologists with whom I collected more often than not devoted themselves entirely to the Rhopalocera, Zygaenidae and *Procris* [Foresters].

I might mention here that they have a field technique quite unlike our own, of nipping their specimens and papering them on the spot. To do this they carry a small pair of stamp-pattern forceps on a thong on the wrist and a small size wooden store-box with a simple canvas pocket covering half of one side for carrying empty papers and with a canvas strap attached to the two opposite side edges to act as a shoulder sling. When the box is stood on its hinged edge and half opened it can be seen that inside there is a sheet of stout material covering the lower half of the side which is actually the bottom of the box which acts as an inner pocket and prevents the papered specimens falling out when the box is opened while being carried. On returning home the papers, or 'papillottes' as they are called, are dropped into a large killing bottle and then later removed and labelled to await relaxing and setting.

The Frenchmen were quite as intrigued with my glass-bottomed boxes as I was with their 'papillottes'. Their method is very much quicker than ours, for an expert and dexterous operator can catch and paper as many as four or five hundred specimens in a day and of course it entails only carrying a light-weight store-box compared with a haversack and numerous nests of boxes which become more bulky and more awkward as they are un-nested.

During the hours of darkness the moth trap worked well and it was quite usual to find over four hundred 'Macros' in it in the morning and these and the 'Micros' would take me well over an hour to sort over. To digress for a moment I had better mention here and now that the insects were not all killed but were anaesthetized and only those wanted were kept. The mercury vapour light as a form of insect capture is here to stay and quite apart from the moral and aesthetic principles involved, and no matter what some people say, it has proved

beyond a shadow of doubt, that, *used intelligently,* and this I italicize, it can do and has done more to show how little we knew, before its introduction, of the real status of our insect populations. It has given and is likely to continue to do so, countless hours of enjoyment and excitement to those of us who use it. But nevertheless it is an extremely powerful instrument and care should be taken to see that its use is for the pursuit of knowledge rather than as the means to amassing long series of local and rare insects. . . .

I was surprised and very excited on the 26th June, 1950 to find in the trap a male specimen of *Hydrillula palustris* Hb. and on subsequent nights three more specimens were taken in the trap. The life history of *palustris,* the Marsh Moth, remained a mystery for many years until finally solved by Edelsten, who bred it for the first time in England in 1941 from larvae collected in Hunts. (1944, *Entom.,* **77**: 49 and 65, Plates II and III). For most the capture of a single male in a season was considered 'good going' as *palustris* is a moth of retiring habits and is very erratic in its appearance at the light. The female has been found in the wild state only on two or three occasions. I was surprised by the difference of this alpine locality at 5000 ft. in a pine forest compared with English localities. Admittedly I have seen *P. machaon* L. on the Balme at 7100 ft., while in England it favours the fenlands as does *palustris,* so the latter is not by any means the only species with this queer distribution. Consequently when I returned to the Colmiane in 1951 I had high hopes of being able to find out a little more of the habits of this interesting insect. This time I went equipped with one of the new fluorescent battery operated tubes instead of the trap so that I should be more mobile and therefore more likely to locate the actual breeding grounds and flight places of *palustris,* as I felt that the four specimens taken in 1950 were only stragglers from the main colony. The most obvious place to begin my search was the little meadow-like valley — the Combe de la Colmiane near the Hotel. We visited this on the 19th June, a week earlier than 1950, and as soon as the light was switched on a male fluttered up to it soon followed by another. In all we took six specimens in the hour, three came to the light and three were caught flying just on the borders of the pine forest and meadow. No other insects were seen or came to the lamp. We searched diligently for a female here the next evening after dark but only succeeded in taking four or five males which came to the light while we were walking about.

On the 21st we went down again. This time just at sunset. The temperature was 60°F., there was a clear sky and an imperceptible wind from the S.W. At ten minutes past seven I saw what few, if any, Lepidopterists have seen, which was three or four male *palustris* flying at once. At one period I had six specimens in my net awaiting boxing. Several of these were worth keeping but they were all boxed and those not wanted were released later. At 7.19 a male was observed flying and for ten minutes was followed in the hopes that it might lead to a virgin female, as Edelsten had found that males of this species assemble readily to a newly emerged female, but it was lost. Later I saw a male dive into the herbage. I watched it for three or four minutes as it wandered about and rested. It then began to fly and it was followed continuously for forty minutes, it then dived into the grass again (not in the same place) and this time was lost. This spot was searched thoroughly but nothing could be found. While the moth was in flight it quartered a small area of the valley perhaps half an acre in extent. It flew gently and rather undulatingly from side to side of the valley at about one to three feet from the ground sometimes gently bumping into grass and flower stems and occasionally running up these for a short distance before continuing on its way at the speed of about a slow walking pace.

We searched during the day, in the evening and after dark for a female but could find no trace of this elusive creature. Having drawn a blank when it would seem that conditions were propitious with the males flying freely I am forced to the conclusion that female *palustris* very rarely fly and only when weather conditions are absolutely suitable, and that they crawl about amongst the low herbage and only venture up the stems a short way possibly for the purpose of pairing. In the South of France as over here *palustris* flies on evenings when no other moth is on the wing. . . .

[Howarth, T. G. 1951–52. Collecting Lepidoptera in the South of France in 1950 and 1951. *Proceedings and Transactions of the British Entomological and Natural History Society* **1951–52**: 55–65].

A little over half a century later, some of the Cynthia's Fritillary (*Euphydryas cynthia*) aberrations that Howarth caught on these two trips were featured in the *British Journal of Entomology and Natural History* (2004).

CHAPTER SIX

'WELL, MR HOLMES, WHAT DO YOU MAKE OF THESE?' – A CABINET OF ENTOMOLOGICAL CURIOSITIES

'A small fly or moth had fluttered across our path, and in an instant Stapleton was rushing with extraordinary energy and speed in pursuit of it. To my dismay the creature flew straight for the great Mire, but my acquaintance never paused for an instant, bounding from tuft to tuft behind it, his green net waving in the air.'

Sir Arthur Conan Doyle, *The Hound of the Baskervilles* (1902)

'Among the first Aurelians was one James Leman, a silk pattern designer, who was said by friends to possess a "curious cabinet" of insects.'

(Anon. *c.*1738)

ON 29th DECEMBER 1944 THE BBC broadcast a talk by Sir Compton Mackenzie and Moray McLaren. After regaling the listeners with fishing tales from the riverbank, their conversation turned to butterfly hunting.

> 'There is one butterfly that is really carnivorous,' said Sir Compton.
> 'I don't believe it,' replied McLaren.
> 'Oh, yes. Or rather the caterpillar is. And it's a very remarkable business because it has only been discovered within the last twenty years. This butterfly is called the Large Blue — I forget the Latin name — and it frequents the chalky downs in Hampshire and Sussex and the caterpillars feed on thyme — "I know a bank whereon the wild thyme grows". As a boy I have often found caterpillars of the Large Blue, and have taken them home and fed them dutifully on thyme, hoping they would turn into chrysalis. But they never did; they always died. And they died on everybody. Until someone whose name I have disgracefully forgotten, and to whom, if he happens to be listening, I apologise, discovered that the caterpillar of the Large Blue tires of its vegetarian diet and leaves the banks of thyme and crawls along until it meets a wood ant. When it does it then puts itself in a queer hunched position and oozes a drop of honey dew. Other ants arrive and the party grows merry. Finally the caterpillar is gathered up by the company of rather intoxicated ants and carried off to their nest — like another Persephone or Proserpina. . . .'
> 'Is that really a true story?' asked Moray McLaren. 'Yes, it really is,' replied Sir Compton.

We were fascinated to hear this account of the early life of the Large Blue with all its errors and inaccuracies. Apart from an eighteenth-century record from Winchester, there is no evidence that the Large Blue ever frequented the 'chalky downs in Hampshire and Sussex' — at least not during the past 250 years. The caterpillars do not associate with *wood ants* and whereas individual ants of certain other species carry the young larvae down into the nest, we can find no record that a larva was ever carried off by a 'company of rather intoxicated ants'. At the same time we found the comment by Sir Compton Mackenzie that he had 'often found caterpillars of the Large Blue' quite extraordinary. Apart from these and several other inaccuracies, the broadcast was full of other curious things. Listeners were told that four Red Admirals had been 'trained' to alight on a hand and accept honey. And on another occasion, Sir Compton, searching for a book in his library, 'found' a Camberwell Beauty sitting on his desk. Could these just be fishermen's tales? If not, they would certainly merit inclusion in this chapter that contains a 'cabinet of entomological curiosities'.

THE MYSTERIOUS CASE OF PARSON GREENE'S SILVER TROWEL

Eric W. Classey, F.R.E.S., Feltham, Middlesex. (1950)

In the year 1857 the Rev. Joseph Greene, M.A., of immortal fame, published a treatise on "Pupa Digging".

The paper was published in that august journal, the "Zoologist", and there is evidence that it caused a considerable stir in entomological circles.

In "THE SUBSTITUTE; Or, Entomological Exchange Facilitator, and Entomologist's Fire-side Companion" for Saturday, January 17, 1857 the following letter was printed:

TESTIMONIAL TO THE REV. JOSEPH GREENE, M.A.

It is proposed to present to the Rev. Joseph Greene, M.A., a Silver Trowel, as a small mark of gratitude and esteem for his very valuable and detailed information on the subject of "Pupa Digging" published in the January number of the "Zoologist" and for the highly important service he has by this means rendered to the Science of Entomology. All gentlemen of the net who sincerely desire to join in the acknowledgment of the same, are requested to communicate their intentions to the Rev. J. Johnson, Denby Parsonage, near Huddersfield, as soon as possible.

Two weeks later, on Jan. 31st. 1857, a Mr. C. J. Cox of Fordwich House, Fordwich, seconded the proposal in a lengthy letter to the "Substitute".

With the issue of Saturday, February 7th, it became obvious that an "underground movement" was in being; Edward Newman forwarded three letters to the Editor, one from himself to the Editor, a copy of one he had written to the Rev. J. Greene and one he had had, in reply, from the Rev. Gentleman. They are worth quoting in extenso:

TESTIMONIAL TO THE REV. JOSEPH GREENE

Mr. Newman to the Editor of "The Substitute"
9, Devonshire Street, Bishopsgate.
Jan. 24, 1857.

Sir,

On reading the Rev. Job Johnson's suggestion in "The Substitute" (p. 155) for a testimonial to the Rev. Joseph Greene, an idea occured to me which will be better explained by the following correspondence, which I have Mr. Greene's full permission to print and publish.

My object in addressing this correspondence to you is to obtain, through the medium of "The Substitute", Mr. Johnson's public consent to my attempting to carry out his design in an altered form, the entire merit of the idea resting with him.

Yours most truly,
Edward Newman.

To the Editor of "The Substitute"

Mr. Newman to the Rev. Joseph Greene
London. Jan. 22, 1857.

My dear Sir,

Fully participating as I do in the sentiment conveyed in the Rev. J. Johnson's proposition in "The Substitute", I still take the liberty of inquiring directly of yourself whether the presentation of a silver trowel be really the best mode of expressing to an entomologist the sentiment of gratitude for his literary services.

My own idea is that a complete copy of Guenée, Fischer, or some other standard European work on Lepidoptera would be more appropriate.

Fig. 98. Eric W. Classey (b. 1916), magistrate, lepidopterist and entomological bookseller. He is pictured here with Michael Salmon (b. 1935). (1988)

I would also take the liberty of suggesting a London recipient of subscriptions, and the name of the universally esteemed President of the Entomological Society occurs to me, as in all respects, the most desirable.

Believe me, my dear Sir,
Very truly yours.
Edward Newman.

Rev. J. Greene. M.A. & C.

The Rev. Joseph Greene to Mr Newman
Playford. Jan. 23. 1857.

My dear Sir,

The proposition to present me with some testimonial in consideration of my paper on "Pupa Digging" published in the "Zoologist", was wholly unexpected by me. I can truly add that it does not appear to me to merit such a token of approval. At the same time, it would be idle in me to deny that such an expression of approbation emanating from my brother entomologists would be in the highest degree gratifying and acceptable.

In your letter you state that, in your opinion, a copy of Guenée's work on the European Lepidoptera would be a more appropriate testimonial than that originally suggested by the Rev. J. Johnson will not deem me either ungracious or ungrateful when I say that I cordially concur in that suggestion.

Fig. 99. Revd Joseph Greene left Ireland to practise as a clergyman in England. An admired and respected lepidopterist, his colleagues proposed that he should be presented with a silver trowel in recognition of his pupa-digging exploits.

With regard to your concluding proposal I must leave it entirely in your hands, at the same time requesting you to tender my sincere thanks to the (as you justly term him) universally respected President of the Entomological Society, should he kindly consent to undertake the office alluded to.

Believe me, my dear Sir,

Very sincerely yours,

Joseph Greene.

E. Newman Esq., F. L S. & C.

Immediately following this correspondence is printed the following curious "letter":

TESTIMONIAL TO THE HON. J. PATIENT

It is proposed to present to the Hon. J. Patient, of Oil-cum-Honey, one pound weight of solid gold pins, as a small but pointed testimonial of the value set upon his services in the distribution of rare foreign insects in Britain. It is thought that no better form for the expression of the opinion of his entomological brethren could be found than that of the instruments by which so many victims were fixed; and it is presumed that the gift will prove of eminent service to the distributor of such priceless beauties at so cheap a rate. All who wish thus to join in testifying their sense of such disinterested exertions are requested to communicate their intention to R. E. Laxe and R. E. Pinne, Members of the Setting Committee, Dupe Street, Cheetham.

The following week (Feb. 14th) a less oblique criticism was published from an anonymous contributor signing himself "Crito":

> Permit me to remark that I altogether object, upon principle, to the proposed testimonial to the Rev. J. Greene.
>
> No one can be more sensible of the value of Mr. Greene's labours in entomology than myself, but if you once resolve to present pieces of plate to the authors of papers in our periodicals, where are you going to begin and where to end?
>
> Among the writers on Entomology how many are there who have fairly earned such a mark of distinction! but who ever thought of repaying literary fame by silver candlesticks or candelabra. Surely the proposition is ill-judged.

The next issue of the "Substitute" contains a letter from the Rev. J. Johnson, the originator of the idea, which seems to hint that things were not going as well as they might and that there was a chance that the whole scheme might have to be abandoned:

. . . I have in hand some subscriptions, some promised, and other communications on the subject. If the matter drop through, notice to that effect will be forwarded to you for publication, and subscription returned. If a more suitable mark of respect to Mr. Greene from his fellow entomologists can be suggested and carried into effect, I shall be most glad, and resign my part without a murmur. One word more I may be allowed to say, viz., that many more costly and larger gifts than a "Trowel" were thought of, but this seemed to be more appropriate, and might be worthy a place over the cabinet, and in the study of the Rev. gentleman.

J. Johnson.

Denby Parsonage,

Huddersfield;

January 31. 1857.

The heavy guns were brought up on Sat. February 28th 1857 by the Rev. P. H. Newman of Woodbridge Road, Guildford. who writes as follows:—

The Testimonial to the Rev. J. Greene;

Sir,

When it is proposed to confer honour upon any person not wholly undeserving of it, the "ayes" are pretty sure to carry the day; for if there be any who dissent from the proposition, the feeling that it would be ungracious to appear to detract from acknowledged merit generally stops their mouths. Now, Sir, one of the features which characterises the present state of society is a rage for testimonials. Any one who has been supposed to do his duty, or to confer benefit on a greater or less portion of his fellow-creatures, must needs be presented with a testimonial. Even were this literally the case, — were the most deserving men always selected, — will you allow me to suggest that the principle is an utterly wrong one. It is part and parcel of that system of doing good, and being good, for the sake of reward, which is the bane of so much of our secular and theological teaching now-a-days. And yet virtue, in whatever line, is surely its own reward. Surely no testimonial ever conveyed a pleasure equal to the conscious pride of having done good and helped others, and being indebted to no man. There are many periods in a man's life in which he has good reason to exclaim, "Save me from my friends!" Those who get up testimonials on every possible occasion little think how often they give real pain to those whom they delight to honour. . . . I do not entirely depreciate the custom of testimonials; in certain cases they are right and proper. But is the present case one in point? Here is a patient and accurate naturalist who has specially turned his attention to a much neglected method of collecting insects; he has thus obtained many rarities, and splendid specimens for his own cabinet: his liberality in distributing his duplicates has gained him the good word of every entomologist. He has also done what every one ought to do under similar circumstances; he has published a full description of his modus operandi. By this, no doubt, hundreds of collectors will make great profit; what special benefit will accrue to Science remains to be seen. Now, has not this gentleman's discovery been its own reward? He has the satisfaction of knowing that he has helped others. Why alloy that satisfaction with anything that can diminish the feeling of independence, or impose that of obligation? And again, how does this case differ from those who of late years originated the various "dodges" of sugar, sallow and ivy blossoms, street lamps, and the many other new methods of taking insects? Why should pupa-digging be specially honoured above all these. But surely, Sir, testimonials in connection with scientific objects should be given, at all events, first of all to those who have materially aided the progress of scientific truth; to those whose labours have added the most to our acquaintance with the real domestic history of the various works of Creation. One could easily mention many such names; but they are quiet unobtrusive ones; hardly thought of by "the 'many" who care little for science and the common good, but much for what immediately affects their own individual interests. Suffer me to add that I have not the slightest acquaintance of any kind with any persons to whom I have alluded. I fear that I may have trodden on many a "corn", if so, I humbly beg pardon of the possessors of these uncomfortable excrescences.

Rev. P. H. Newman,
Woodbridge Road,
Guildford.

After this follows silence, absolute and blanketting silence.

Did Parson Greene receive his silver trowel, if so where is it preserved?

If the proposal ended in failure, where was it chronicled and what happened to the subscriptions already received?

I should like to think that Parson Greene did receive his trowel and that, one day, it will be unearthed and preserved for posterity on a plush cushion, in a glass case, in the library of the Royal Entomological Society.

If anyone can throw any further light on this fascinating subject I should very much like to hear of it.

[Classey, E. W. 1950. The mysterious case of Parson Greene's silver trowel. *Entomologist's Gazette* **1**: 32–36].

Fig. 100. P. B. M. Allan's personal pupa-digging implement.

TWO PUPAE OF *SATURNIA* IN ONE COCOON

To the Editor, *The Entomological Magazine* (May 1835) from A. Edmunds, jun., of Park Place, Worcester:

The following singular fact perhaps might not be deemed unworthy of insertion in your valuable magazine. A lady, whose name is Eginton, residing near Worcester, had a very fine larva of *Saturnia pavonia minor* [Emperor Moth] brought to her, which shortly afterwards formed its cocoon, and from its extraordinary size, she entertained great expectations of a very fine specimen to adorn her cabinet the following spring; but to her great astonishment there emerged therefrom a *male* and a *female* of the species in great perfection. A few days afterwards I called upon the lady, and witnessed this most singular fact, and made such inquiry as to be fully satisfied that no other insect of the kind, in either state, could have gained admission into the box where the larvæ [*sic*] had been deposited to undergo its transformation.

With the lady's kind permission I have thought fit to mention her name, who can, if needful, corroborate this very singular and extraordinary vagary of nature, as I am quite disposed to think that many Entomologists will imagine some mistake must have been made, or else perhaps doubt or disbelieve the circumstance altogether; and really I must be candid enough to remark, that had I not been an eye-witness thereto, I should be much inclined to dispute the truth myself. I have been an Entomologist, and have collected diligently for upwards of thirteen years, and have known very singular occurrences, such as hermaphrodites of the order *Sphingites*, and some instances of Lepidopterous insects with five wings; others, where circular and rather large holes have occurred in the anterior wings, though the specimens have been quite perfect in every other respect; but an instance like the foregoing is, I think, of very unusual occurrence.

[Edmunds, A. jun. 1835. *The Entomological Magazine* **3**: 206–207].

To the Editor, *The Entomological Magazine* (February 1836) from Thomas Marshall of Birmingham:

Sir, — The Entomological Magazine of July last (No.12) contains a somewhat circumstantial statement of the "singular fact," of a perfect male and female of *Saturnia pavonia-minor* being produced from a single "very fine larva," to the great astonishment of their possessor. I then took for granted that more would be said upon the subject of so surprising a phenomenon; but time has rolled on — two more Fire-flies have been suffered to enlighten the land — but not a ray has fallen upon the "singular fact." Of course, therefore, it is considered to be sufficiently clear, and should not be doubted. Unfortunately, however, all have not equally comprehensive minds, and my attention having recently been recalled to the subject by an application from a young friend for my opinion as to how such a wonder could be accounted for, I found myself somewhat posed. A doubt of the occurrence was not to be entertained, when it was recollected under what auspices it was introduced to the world. On referring to the original, I see that it is entitled "Two pupæ of *Saturnia* in one cocoon," as if two animals had, for economy's sake, sheltered under one blanket, which would have been natural enough; but this is not borne out by the context, whence I suspect that the Editor, like myself, did not fully comprehend the account. The statement itself is entirely at variance with its title. It expressly affirms that the cocoon was formed by *one* very fine larva, and that from it emerged a male and female of the species in great perfection. The relator witnessed the "most singular fact," having called upon the possessor a few days afterwards, and "made such inquiry as to be fully satisfied that no other insect of the kind, in either state, could have gained admission into the box where the larvæ (? larva) had been deposited to undergo its transformation." Here all is clear and intelligible: a single larva formed its cocoon, and two moths emerged from it. Now, although we are bound to believe that which is put forth in the Magazine, gravely, and without comment, or even a single ! (which surely implies that it is almost a matter of course, as when a really wonderful thing is given three notes of admiration can be afforded; see Vol. 1. p. 318,) yet I think we have a right to request that you will endeavour to obtain some more particulars, to enable dull brains, like mine, to comprehend it. Had the larva two heads, and two sets of legs, or only one of each? Is it known whether the division took place when the larva changed to pupæ, or when the pupa changed to moths? Is the cocoon preserved? Has it been opened? Does it contain one or two exuviæ? If one, what is its appearance? generally the head, eyes, antennæ, wings, feet, and segments of the abdomen may be traced on the skin of the pupa. How are they arranged here? If the possessor cannot answer these questions, pray do try to induce some of your learned friends to give us a plausible, probable, or even possible theory, that we may have some ground for our faith. My old-fashioned prejudices have said that the successive changes in the larva, and from larva to pupa, and from pupa to imago, are but as the casting off of so many garments, within which the imago was from the first encased, every part in its appropriate place, as I have often fancied I could see in the Lepidopterous pupæ. — Are these mere fancies? Does the larva contain merely an homogeneous pulp, which, if it be but sufficiently abundant, may be elaborated into two flies instead of one? If not, then how are we to suppose that the two animals were disposed in the one skin? Were they placed head to tail, or side by side, or one within the other? Had the last been the case, one would think the inner one would have burst the other when making its escape — they must therefore have been severally contained within the caterpillar's skin. Had it a double set of spiracula, or how could breathing be carried on by both? Must it have had two mouths, or could one communicate with two alimentary canals? Is it probable — but so many questions suggest themselves that I shall tire your patience; and, as I am sure you know all that I would ask, I will conclude by again begging that you will, by some means or other, gain further information on so very interesting a subject.

[Marshall, T. 1836. *The Entomological Magazine* 3: 511–512].

Thomas Marshall's letter provoked the following response from Edward Newman, the Editor. Reading it, one is inclined to think that it is not quite the reply that Marshall really wanted.

Mr. Marshall, at page 511 of the last volume, is somewhat severe on the editor of the Fire-fly, for not expressing his doubt or disbelief of the statement made by Mr. Edmonds [*sic*] of Worcester, touching the production of two moths from one caterpillar. Without expressing a decided opinion on the subject, we should like to call Mr. Marshall's attention to the fact, that the same assertion had been previously made by at least half a dozen different authors of respectability, among whom we may mention Kirby and Spence. Mr. Dale, in the Magazine of Natural History, asserts that he reared *Arctia Menthrasti* [*sic: Spilosoma menthastri* — White Ermine], and six of *Ophion Vinulæ* [a parasitic ichneumon wasp], from a pupa of *Cerura Vinula* [Puss Moth]. This is far more extraordinary; for supposing the six Ophions to be the natural parasites of the *Cerura* caterpillar, then from whence came the *Arctia Menthrasti*? Was that insect really produced from a portion of the caterpillar of the puss moth? We believe neither the editor of the Magazine of Natural History, nor any of his correspondents, ever expressed a doubt of this "curious fact," as Mr. Dale very appropriately calls it. Another correspondent of Mr. Loudon's excellent and scientific periodical roundly asserts, that the "tail of the caterpillar becomes the head of the butterfly: this is as remarkable as if it stood thus: "the great toe of the boy becomes the nose of the man." We still would not dispute the question; we should only conclude that our researches into insect anatomy had been too shallow to develop the fact, which this insect anatomist had by almost superhuman skill and elaborate investigation discovered. The real name of this extraordinary genius, we believe, has not yet transpired; nor do we hear that he is at present publishing his researches: we venture to predict, that when they are fully received by entomologists, the works of Straus-Durckheim, Herold, Lyonnet, Dufour, and Audouin, will become waste paper.

[Editor. 1836. *The Entomological Magazine* 4: 84].

LOCUSTS ON A BALLOON

W. Robinson, Grantham, Lincolnshire. (1873)

On Saturday evening last, about half-past eight, a balloon descended in a field about a mile from my house, and being near at the time I was on the spot almost as soon as the car touched the ground, and was immediately surprised (as was the aëronaut) to find a large quantity of locusts flying about all round the balloon; and on further inspection we found the balloon had a great many of the insects clinging to it, and a number remained on it till it was rolled up, some apparently dead from the effects of the gas escaping. No locusts have been heard of this summer in this neighbourhood. The balloon had come from Nottingham, about twenty-five miles from here in a straight line. The evening was beautiful, with a slight wind, from a little south of west. — *W. Robinson; Grantham*; [from a letter published in the] '*Field*,' *Aug. 2, 1873.*

(I know not whether Mr Robinson is an entomologist; if so it would be interesting to know the technical name of the locusts found on the balloon. In the market-gardens about

London, *Acherontia atropos* [Death's-head Hawk-moth] is the locust; on the heaths of Surrey, *Gryllotalpa vulgaris* [Mole Cricket] bears that name. The great death's-head larva is not very likely to be found 'up in a balloon;' still it would be pleasant for entomologists to know what the species really was. — *Edward Newman*).

[Robinson, W. 1873. Locusts on a balloon. *The Entomologist* **6**: 525].

EXTRAORDINARY MIGRATION OF THE PAINTED LADY

Francis Buchanan White, M.D., Perth, Perthshire. (1872)

My friend, Colonel Drummond Hay, of Seggiedon, Perthshire, has furnished me with the following account of a great flight of *Pyrameis cardui* that he once witnessed, which I think should be recorded.

"It was, as far as I recollect, in the early part of the summer of 1842, while stationed at Vido, a small island in the harbour of Corfu, that an extraordinary flight of the Painted Lady Butterfly took place. The first part of the column reached the island about 9 o'clock in the morning, and continued steadily to advance in rolling masses of many thousands for

upwards of three hours. Though the density of the column was at no time very great, yet it appeared to extend in breadth as far as one could see, having the appearance of black drifting snow, if I may so call it. By one o'clock the flight had completely passed: the wind at the time was blowing fresh from the south-east. In the afternoon, on sailing up the channel of Corfu, the traces of the passage of the flight were very evident, from the quantities of dead butterflies which floated on the surface of the water; and, for days afterwards, they were to be seen drifting into the various bays in the island of Corfu. I did not hear whether this flight had been observed on the Continent; but, as they appeared to be taking the direction of the coast of Italy, they would, in all probability, strike the land in the vicinity of Otranto."

[White, F. Buchanan 1872. Extraordinary migration of *Pyrameis cardui. Entomologist's Monthly Magazine* **9**: 149].

BUTTERFLIES AT SEA

From the Editor, *Entomologist's Monthly Magazine*:

In the 'Abhandlungen vom naturwissenchaftlichen Vereine zu Bremen,' . . . Herr F. Buchenau notices the occurrence of swarms of *Pieris brassicae* [Large White] at sea, off the mouth of the Weser. In the middle of July, 1872, he made a sea-excursion on board a fishing boat from Bremerhaven. So long as the boat was in the river, or at its mouth, only an occasional 'cabbage-white' was to be seen crossing the river, and soon disappearing. But, when once out at sea, the boat was enveloped in a swarm of these butterflies, so thick as to resemble a snow-storm. The weather was hot, and the surface of the sea undisturbed by any wind. Many of the insects were to be seen posing themselves with erect wings on the surface, others were to be seen lying flat on it, as if dead, but flew away rapidly if disturbed. They were accompanied by Dragon-flies (*Æschna* sp.) which evidently preyed upon them, and also by small flies and ichneumons. . . .

[EDS. 1872–73. Butterflies at sea. *Entomologist's Monthly Magazine* 9: 246].

During his memorable five years aboard *HMS Beagle*, from 1831 to 1836, Charles Darwin (1809–1882) was aware of the numbers of insects the 'good little vessel' encountered off the coast of Argentina and recorded his observations:

. . . Several times when the ship has been some miles off the mouth of the Plata, and at other times when off the shores of Northern Patagonia, we have been surrounded by insects. One evening, when we were about ten miles from the Bay of San Blas, vast numbers of butterflies, in bands or flocks of countless myriads, extended as far as the eye could range. Even by the aid of a telescope it was not possible to see the space free from butterflies. The seamen cried out "it was snowing butterflies," and such in fact was the appearance. More species than one were present, but the main part belonged to a kind very similar to, but not identical with, the common English *Colias edusa* [Clouded Yellow]. . . .

[Darwin, C. 1839. *A Naturalist's Voyage Round The World. Journal Of Researches Into The Natural History And Geology Of The Countries Visited During The Voyage Round The World Of H.M.S. 'Beagle' Under Command Of Captain Fitz Roy, R.N.* London, John Murray].

There are numerous other accounts of butterflies being encountered at sea, but few are as extraordinary as that recounted by J. S. Walker in 1873:

Ever since we left Tunis, all along the Malta Channel, and upwards to Italy, the sea was covered with large brown butterflies, moths of all sizes, and dragon-flies, evidently just dead, as they had not been long in the water. For four or five days we sailed through many miles of water without finding any diminution in their number, and we began to ask ourselves the question whether they could have been a provision of Nature for the sustenance of birds during their passage.'

[Walker, J. S. 1873. Insects at sea. *The Entomologist* 6: 457].

NOTE FROM THE DIARY OF A LIGHTHOUSE KEEPER

John Cordeaux. (1884)

Under the date of June 30th, Mr. Owen Boyle, of the Larigard lighthouse, reports: "A skylark, followed by a string of bees. The plaintive cries of this poor bird first attracted my attention; it flew so close that I almost caught it; it was closely pursued by a large number of bees, and in its fright took to the water, followed by its pursuers. When last seen it was making for the Essex coast."

[Cordeaux, J. 1884. *Report on the Migration of Birds*. London].

In 1910 *The Entomologist* reported that the Migration Committee of the British Ornithologists' Club had twice recorded the Death's-head Hawk-moth (*Acherontia atropos*) at the Kentish Knock Lighthouse (on 27th May 1905 and 15th September 1909). As this light-vessel is situated well out, off the mouth of the Thames, and is about thirty-five miles from the nearest points of the Essex and Kent coasts, they asked: 'Were these true over-sea migrants?'

MOTHS SETTLING ON WATER

Henry Rowland-Brown, M.A., F.E.S., Stanmore, Middlesex. (1887)

. . . Perhaps it may be of interest to relate that while watching the lake of St. Moritz I was surprised to notice the movements of a certain Geometer, very common in the adjacent pine woods. It apparently took great pleasure in the water, and hundreds of them might be seen dipping like swallows upon the surface. Several, however, ventured yet farther, and lay with their wings extended almost on the water, but apparently found no difficulty in directing their flight upward when disturbed in their bath.

[Rowland Brown, H. 1887. Moths settling on water. *The Entomologist* **20**: 283].

PAINTED LADIES AT NIGHT

Russell James, Highgate, London, N. (1915)

The queerest experience of the night was with a butterfly — *Pyrameis cardui* [Painted Lady]. Each night I saw *P. cardui* very conspicuously at rest on the gorse along this lane, and was interested to note that certain bushes were favoured night after night, probably by the same individuals. On the last night as I passed along to the *craccae* [Scarce Blackneck] ground at 10.30 p.m. there were three *P. cardui* at intervals of about twenty yards. Upon my return two hours later I looked for them and found the first one gone. The second was where I had left it, but what was my astonishment at finding the third one paired, doubtless with the first specimen.

There is no possibility of error in this fact, as in each case the particular position of the specimen was known to me exactly from observation of previous nights. *Cardui*'s habit of flying late into the dusk is familiar to me, but even assuming that my strong light had unsettled them at 10.30, such a proceeding as this is, as far as I know, quite without parallel. It would be interesting to hear if others have had a similar experience.

[James, R. 1915. Lepidopterological notes for 1914. *The Entomologist's Record and Journal of Variation* **27**: 1–7].

THE STORY OF A FRAUD

Dr Edward A. Cockayne, M.A. D.M., F.R.C.P., F.R.E.S., Tring, Hertfordshire. (1952)

Professor Theodore Dru Alison Cockerell (1862–1948) (Fig. 101) was born at Norwood, South London and educated at various private schools as well as The Middlesex Hospital Medical School. He was later appointed Professor of Zoology at the University of Colorado in 1912. The author of a number of important papers on fossil insects, he was widely regarded as the foremost insect palaeontologist of his time. His paper 'On the Variation of Insects', published in 1889, is an important contribution to the study of aberrational forms.

Fig. 101. Professor Theodore Cockerell, the celebrated expert on fossil insects.

In 1889, in *The Entomologist* (22: 176), he described a remarkable female variety of the Clouded Yellow (*Colias croceus*) — ab. *duplex* — in which the forewings were both of *helice* colouring (the creamy form of the female), but the hindwings normal orange *croceus*; or specimens with the left wings *croceus* orange colouring and the right wings *helice* colour. The specimens that he applied this name to had been illustrated in colour by Edward A. Fitch (1878)* and, some sixty years later, were copied by F. W. Frohawk in his *Varieties of British Butterflies* (1938).

In 1952 Dr E. A. Cockayne re-examined these two specimens which were now in the Rothschild Collection and in doing so discovered that an attempt had been made to deceive collectors.

On the coloured plate, [accompanying Fitch's paper] fig. 5, has the forewings *helice* and the hindwings *croceus* and is Mr. P. H. Harper's female variety taken near Enfield, Middlesex, in 1877, and fig. 11 has the left side *croceus* female and the right side *helice*, and is Mr. W. P. Weston's curious specimen taken at Finchley, Middlesex, 7th August 1876.

Two similar specimens are figured by Frohawk (*Varieties of British Butterflies*, 1938, Pl. 3, figs. 2 and 3). Fig. 2 is described as "Hermaphrodite captured at Finchley, Middlesex, 7.8.1876. R. side ab. *pallida* [= *helice*], L. side *croceus*. Rothschild Collection". Fig. 3 is described as "captured by H. Edwards, 7.2.1878, in the W. of England. Purchased by W. P. Weston. Upper wings ab. *pallida*, hindwings *croceus*. Rothschild Collection". Both specimens are at Tring [Rothschild Museum] and when I first saw them they were set high on continental pins. The specimen with the right side *helice* and the left side *croceus* has a label saying "Weston's coll. Finchley, Middlesex, 7.8.1876", and this agrees with the data given by Fitch for the one on his Pl. 1, fig. 11, but I do not think it is the original label. It is female on both sides and Frohawk's description of it as a hermaphrodite is incorrect. When Mr. A. L. Goodson re-set it in the English style it fell into two parts in the relaxing tin. The fraud had been carried out very cleverly; a cut had been made through the thorax of a *helice* and a *croceus* in such a way that the two parts fitted exactly when gummed together.

The specimen with the forewings *helice* and the hindwings *croceus* has a label on it signed by W. Hawker Smith saying that when it was re-set it was found to be artificial and that it was examined by Dr. [Karl] Jordan. There are two other labels, one in copper-plate handwriting says "W. of England, 1877", the other says "West of England, 1877. Purchased W. P. Weston of H. Edwards, Feb. 7, 1878".

* *Entomologist*, 11: 52, pl. 1.

If Frohawk had read the labels he would have learnt that it was a fraud and would not have figured it. Apart from this he has copied the one label incorrectly. It was bought in February and not caught at that time of the year. The locality on both labels is different from that given by Fitch for the specimen figured by him Pl. 1, fig. 5, and Fitch does not say that it was bought by W. P. Weston from H. Edwards in February, 1878. The one he figured was in W. H. Harper's collection and the Harper collection was not sold until 1884. When Mr. Goodson relaxed it in order to re-set it it fell into two parts again.

It seems to me unlikely that the specimens figured by Fitch were frauds. According to him one was caught in 1876 and the other in 1877. If the labels are correct there was little time for fraud before they were figured in 1878, and they were at that time in different collections. It is, however, possible that someone manufactured the two insects and sold each to a different collector after having supplied it with a fictitious data label, but it is more probable that someone perpetrated the frauds at a later date and copied Fitch's plate. If so it is surprising that the label on one agrees with that given by Fitch, whereas that on the other does not agree.

If the specimens figured by Fitch were genuine and these in the Rothschild Collection are copies of them, the genuine ones may still exist in some collection. If anyone has seen them and knows where they are, I should like to be informed. There seems to be no hope of solving the mystery in any other way.

[Cockayne, E. A. 1952. *Colias croceus* Fourcroy ab. *duplex* Cockerell. The story of a fraud. *The Entomologist's Record and Journal of Variation* **64**: 193–194].

Unfortunately, as a consequence of these discoveries, Cockerell's aberrational name is no longer valid (see Plate 1).

'A TELEGRAM FROM CANTERBURY' — THE KENTISH BUCCANEERS

Fraudulent dealing in entomology is thankfully rare. Miriam Rothschild (1995), in her Presidential Address to the Royal Entomological Society of London in 1994, said that:

> In Oxford, we used to say that when a lecturer became so incompetent that few if any students attended his classes, he retired into a resentful coma glorified by the title of research. This never applies to true entomologists — because they are basically naturalists not scientists. They do not use insects merely as tools — they just find them irresistible. Naturalists usually live to a ripe old age, because they take endless long, slow walks (no pernicious jogging), with their minds fixed on the agreeably green present, getting rid of their aggression with the net and killing bottle. . . .
>
> I looked up the 40 odd cases of serious misconduct recorded for scientists by Broad & Wade (1983), and found no entomologists among them. These authors consider that fame and fortune are the two principle objectives of fraudulent scientists.

Fame and fortune certainly motivated a few villains with an interest in butterflies. During the mid-nineteenth century, the heyday of collecting, the extraordinary enthusiasm of thousands of butterfly collectors was soured by the activities of a small minority of crooked dealers. Clearly motivated by thoughts of fame and fortune, these bounty hunters

Fig. 102. Edward Newman, the distinguished editor of *The Entomologist*, which he founded in 1840.

invaded the ordered world of lepidopterists, duping the unsuspecting collector with a combination of intrigue and falsehood.

At first the surreptitious importation of Continental 'rarities' for their breeding and subsequent release went largely unnoticed. With their headquarters in Canterbury, these dealers soon became known as the 'Kentish Buccaneers'. George Parry was probably the most important 'buccaneer' and he found that London collectors were only too ready to part with their money in exchange for 'British' specimens of rare migrant species. He knew that a telegram to selected and unsuspecting collectors would bring them hurrying down to Kent — and little did his victims know that the 'rarities' they were about to find had either been recently spirited away from the Continent, or else had just emerged in the breeding cages of Parry and his colleagues at Canterbury. A masterly account of these buccaneers was given by P. B. M. Allan (1943), who wrote: 'Across the Channel these insects might be as common as sparrows and cheap as ha'pence: that was not the point. Did they but succeed in crossing the water they were worth, in London, much more than their weight in gold. It was a great discovery . . .'

In 1868, Parry wrote to tell Edward Newman, editor of *The Entomologist*, that he had netted no less than thirteen *Argynnis lathonia* (Queen of Spain Fritillary) near Dover Castle. 'He should have remembered that it was an unlucky number,' wrote Allan. And Parry's letter certainly made Newman suspicious, for in the October edition of his magazine he wrote: 'An account of the capture of thirteen Lathonias near Canterbury has been received, but is declined.' This did not deter Parry however, who, in 1872, was at it again. A second letter to Newman boldly stated that:

> I have sent a specimen of Lathonia alive for you to see, one of four which I took yesterday, August 4th, at Swarling Downs, the same place where I took the species in 1868, which appeared to have been doubted by many. I took the four specimens off the viper's bugloss, all in about five minutes: it was mizzling rain at the time.

P. B. M. Allan then takes up the story again:

> Fortune favours the brave. It also favours artists such as Mr. Parry, for artist he assuredly was. 1872 proved to be a *lathonia* year in other places besides Canterbury. The mid-Victorian years were a period of great collecting activity; there were eager searchers after lepidoptera in all parts of the kingdom; Kent no less than other counties was scoured by brothers of the net and sugaring-tin. No less than 25 *lathonia* were reported (many of them twice) from the South Coast during August and September. This abundance, while it did

nothing to abate the market value of 'British' (caught) *lathonia* gave the stamp of 'authenticity' to those which emerged in the breeding cages at Canterbury. *Daplidice* (Bath White) and *antiopa* (Camberwell Beauty) also flew across the Channel that year and here too G. Parry was by no means behindhand with his butterfly-net.

Although Edward Newman was suspicious that 'something was going on', he continued to publish a number of highly dubious reports made by Kentish buccaneers and others. It was not until 1873 that Parry made an undoubted mistake. He 'discovered' the Niobe Fritillary (*Argynnis niobe*) in Kent and foolishly sent living specimens not only to Newman but to the distinguished lepidopterist Henry Doubleday as well. Pretending that he didn't recognize the species, Parry asked for an identification. Newman thought the specimen sent to him was a High Brown Fritillary (*Argynnis adippe*), but Doubleday immediately recognized his specimen as *A. niobe* and wrote at once to *The Entomologist* (23rd August):

> Mr. Parry of Canterbury sent me two specimens of an *Argynnis*, to name one of them, which he said he had sent alive to my friend Edward Newman. They are females of Argynnis Niobe, — the typical variety, with the spots on the underside

Fig. 103. Niobe Fritillary (*Argynnis niobe*) 'taken' by George Parry the 'Kentish buccaneer' at Dover, Kent in 1875.

> silvery. I know nothing of their history beyond the statement of Mr. Parry, — that he took them twenty miles from Canterbury. Being a sub-alpine species on the Continent, and a native of Sweden, its occurrence in this country might be looked for in the northern counties of England and Scotland rather than in Kent.

With this comment, Parry should have heard alarm bells. In fact, he probably did for he wrote no more on the subject of Kentish *niobe* for the next two years. Figure 103 shows a specimen of *Argynnis niobe* allegedly caught by George Parry in Kent.

The Kentish buccaneers soon turned their attention to rare moths as well as butterflies. Parry (1872) claimed to have found *Catocala fraxini* (Blue Underwing) 'about three miles from Canterbury', and then added for good measure 'This is the third specimen I have taken in the same wood during the last few years.' Other rare moths were quick to put in an appearance in the Canterbury area — and Parry was equally quick to announce their capture:

> A fine specimen of *Leucania l-album* (L-album Wainscot) was taken at Pine Wood, Settlebourne, by Mr. E. Edney, a collector, on Tuesday, the 24th of September. I took one myself at sugar last evening, Saturday, in the same place. It was very windy when both were taken — in the same wood where my brother took the only known specimen three years ago, which Dr. Harper had: and singularly enough I took *Catocala Fraxini* in the same wood the same year; so also I have this year.

Several years later, in 1875, Parry was at it yet again. *Blepharita satura* (Beautiful Arches) was said to have turned up at sugar, on Braborne Downs, and Parry wasted no time in publishing his 'finding'. He added, perhaps cunningly, that 'Since then Mr. Edney, a collector here, has taken two more, which I now possess, at the same place.' And so it went on! Did 'Mr Edney' really exist, or was he really just a creation of George Parry . . .?

In 1874 a Mr W. Wigan of 8, Wincheap, Canterbury, appears in print for the first time. It is of interest to find that he lived not far from Church Street where George Parry resided. His letter to *The Entomologist* asked for identification of a large fritillary caught by him 'on a very hilly inaccessible spot near here'. Like Parry, Wigan also sent two specimens by the same post to Henry Doubleday. Edward Newman published Doubleday's reply in which he confirmed that the pair of specimens he had received were *Argynnis niobe* and that 'I have no doubt whatever that these two specimens were captured in Kent; they could not have been obtained from the Continent alive in such dry weather as we have had lately.' In a second letter he wrote: 'The butterflies are most certainly Niobe, and quite distinct from Adippe and Aglaia. The moment I opened the box I saw what they were, without looking at the under sides.'

Newman then asked Wigan for further information as to their capture and for a pair of specimens that could be figured in his magazine. P. B. M. Allan suggested that Messrs Parry and Wigan might be one and the same person and that Wigan, Parry's *alter ego*, might have been employed to further Parry's earlier 'discoveries'. Perhaps in anticipation of such comments and to allay any suspicion, Wigan replied saying that he had spoken to Parry of his capture and it transpired that both of them had taken *niobe* at 'the same spot, (I may add, there is no collusion between us, only we both possess the knowledge of this locality) . . .'

In a reply to Newman's request for further information Wigan elaborated a little more, informing him that the specimens were 'taken' in a hilly district between Wye and Ashford in Kent:

> The locality is a huge rent, caused at some remote time by a convulsion of Nature, with almost perpendicular sides, and covered with long grass, amidst which peep out the flowers of the wild heart's-ease, which grow here in great profusion. Upon these steepy slopes, where an alpen-stock would not be despised by any but an entomologist, fly Aglaia, but not Niobe. At the bottom of this trough, which is no more than a few yards wide, grows a kind of rush, and there, within a confined area, is to be found Niobe, — and very few, alas, indeed.

By now, Henry Doubleday had become really concerned by the continued reporting of *A. niobe* from Kent. In a letter to *The Entomologist* (1873) he suggested that:

> Having had the opportunity of examining a considerable number of specimens of some of our rarer Lepidoptera which had been sold as British, nearly all of which proved to be re-set Continental specimens, I unhesitatingly say that I believe a very large majority of the specimens of Daplidice, Lathonia . . . which now exist in collections of professedly British Lepidoptera, are in reality Continental . . . It is now almost impossible to say what insects are really British, as living pupæ of various species are regularly obtained from France and Germany; and the fact of an insect being exhibited alive is no proof of its British origin — living butterflies and moths can be easily obtained from the Continent by post.

This letter from one of the most respected and eminent lepidopterists in Britain certainly appeared to undermine the enthusiasm of George Parry, W. Wigan and other 'Kentish' colleagues. Perhaps aware that their credibility was fast waning their fraudulent activities started to slow down, although Parry again claimed to have 'found' *A. niobe* in 1874. Then, in 1875, a Mr W. J. Mercer took things to an absurd extreme by announcing that he had taken a specimen of the Arran Brown (*Erebia ligea*) at Margate in Kent. This certainly would not have fooled serious lepidopterists who knew well that the Arran Brown was a montane species and most unlikely to appear at a seaside resort! Or, as Allan so wryly put it, 'the mountain fastnesses of that salubrious watering-place'. The death-knell of the buccaneers had been clearly sounded.

Edward Newman died in 1876, and with this the Kentish buccaneers lost a 'friend' who was apparently prepared to accept and occasionally publish some of their more outrageous records in the journal that he had edited. It was now impossible for them to continue reporting their 'discoveries' in *The Entomologist*. Shortly before Newman's death, however, G. B. Corbin (1876) wrote to him:

> If I mistake it not, it was stated in the 'Entomologist' at the time of the occurrence of Argynnis Niobe, that a pair were to be figured in its pages; but the non-appearance of these portraits seems to point to the fact that some doubt existed as to the thoroughly British origin of the specimens in question. Did such a doubt exist?

Edward Newman was quick to reply:

> I am much obliged to Mr. Corbin for these enquiries. I cannot believe in the Kentish captures of these two species [the other being *Cnethocampa pityocampa* — the Pine Processionary] . . . When I penned the paragraph to which Mr. Corbin alludes I certainly intended to figure Argynnis Niobe as British; but the specimens in my possession on further information proved so questionable that I postponed the drawing and engraving *sine die*. I have received records of twenty-six specimens of Daplidice and a round dozen of Podalirius [Scarce Swallowtail], which I suppress for the same reason.

[Allan, P. B. M. (1937). *Talking of Moths* (from Chapter VII: 'The Kentish Buccaneers')].

Although the activities of the Kentish buccaneers slowly petered out, the entomological literature of the past one hundred years still contains occasional reports of fraudulent deeds.

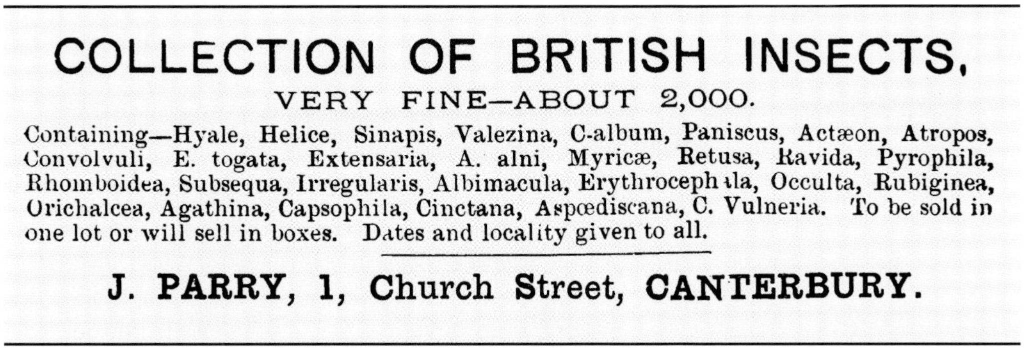

Fig. 104. Advertisement from *The Entomologist's Record and Journal of Variation* (1893).

THE STATE OF THE UNION

L. Hugh Newman, F.R.E.S., F.R.H.S. Bexley, Kent. (1946)

Leonard Hugh Newman (1909–1993), the son of L. W. Newman (p. 379), was known to generations of schoolboys as the owner of the famous Butterfly Farm at Bexley, Kent. His interest in butterflies and moths first developed in childhood. Within a year of leaving Bembridge School he was elected a Fellow of the Royal Entomological Society, and had published his first article on butterflies.

Fig. 105. L. Hugh Newman (*left*). 'All my life I have been surrounded by butterflies or talk of butterflies.' The white-haired gentleman is L. W. Newman; a young, bespectacled R. L. E. Ford is in the background. The photo (*c.* 1932) shows the fennel plantation at the Butterfly Farm where several thousand Swallowtails were raised each year. The exceedingly rare melanic form of this beautiful butterfly, which had appeared amongst the stock a couple of years earlier, first came to their attention in an indignant letter from a schoolboy customer complaining bitterly about the 'nasty black thing' which had emerged from his chrysalis — and wanting his money back! He was generously recompensed with a cheque for £7 and a pair of normal specimens for his collection.

The period between the wars witnessed a gradual change in the Farm's clientele; the wealthy private collector specializing in obscure moths and other such rarities was being replaced by a different and much younger type of enthusiast. The increasing popularity of natural history as part of the school curriculum ensured sufficient funding for the purchase

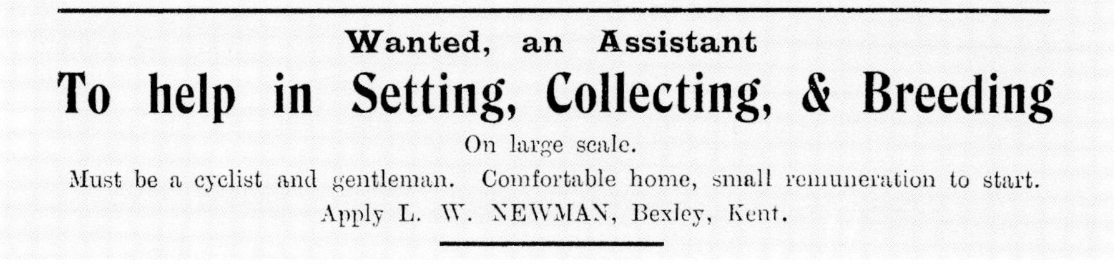

Fig. 106. Advertisement from *The Entomologist's Record and Journal of Variation* (1902).

Fig. 107. End of an era. These late Victorian buildings at 41–42 Salisbury Road, Bexley, Kent had been the home of The Butterfly Farm since 1894. Much of the livestock was bred in the lantern-roofed greenhouse constructed around 1910. When L. Hugh Newman retired in 1966 the premises were sold for redevelopment. (*c.* 1968)

of study material. When he took over the running of the business in 1941, Hugh Newman soon realized that the Farm's survival would depend on its ability to supply a growing demand from both schools and pupils for the more common, showy British and foreign species. It was a policy which although lamented by older customers made financial sense.

He was an accomplished writer and broadcaster and did much to promote natural history, in particular the Lepidoptera, to the younger generation, writing over a score of books on the subject. After the Second World War he appeared regularly on the successful BBC radio programme 'Nature Parliament' which he had devised in collaboration with fellow panel members Derek McCulloch ('Uncle Mac') and Peter Scott. James Fisher joined the team later on.

In the following short article Hugh Newman describes an extraordinary pairing between two different species.

Every year I breed many hundred *P. machaon* [Swallowtail] in my greenhouses. The weather during most of June was so bad that insects would not fly in the field or breed in captivity. Although I had nearly eighty *P. machaon* alive at one time, I only succeeded in obtaining four pairings during a gleam of sun late one afternoon in early June. As a desperate measure I introduced a system of flood-lighting in some of my cages with at least one most curious result. At night the same cages are used for pairing the various hawk moths that we also breed every year, and the day following the introduction of artificial "sunlight" a male *P. machaon* paired with a *S. populi* [Poplar Hawk]. I watched them for more than a quarter of an hour — all my staff witnessed the extraordinary event, and two outsiders, one a well-known entomologist, and so there was no doubt about it and I did not dream the event! I rather wish I had bottled the pair, as by after tea they had parted company. It was only then that I noticed the Poplar hawk was also a male, making the union even more extraordinary.

[Newman, L. H. 1946. A mixed pairing — *Papilio machaon* x *Smerinthus populi. The Entomologist* **79**: 244].

The remarkable event described by Hugh Newman is not unique. During August 2003 Pat and Peter Gardner came across the most unusual spectacle on Old Winchester Hill, Hampshire, of a male Silver-spotted Skipper and a female Silver-Y moth in copula. They photographed this phenonomen for posterity (Fig. 108). In the same year that Newman reported his discovery, a pairing between a female Marbled White and a male Meadow Brown was observed near Bideford, Devon by E. W. W. Durant.

Fig. 108. A remarkable pairing between a butterfly and moth: female Silver Y (*Autographa gamma*) and a male Silver-spotted Skipper (*Hesperia comma*) (2003).

In 1956 Ronald Demuth described another misalliance that occurred in the wild:

While walking on Haresfield Beacon, Gloucestershire, in the last sunshine of Whit-Monday, 21st May, I saw a sight unique in my experience; the mating of a butterfly with a moth. The butterfly, the male, was a Dingy Skipper (*Erynnis tages* L.) and the moth, the female, was the Burnet Companion (*Euclidia glyphica* L.). The mating had taken place on a dandelion flower-head and the butterfly had almost covered the moth with its wings. Both remained perfectly quiet while I examined them, and to show that it was no casual affair, remained paired when I transferred them to a pill box. Unfortunately, I had no camera with me and, hoping to preserve an example of such a misalliance I put them in a killing bottle, where they separated.

I take it that scent played no part and that it was simply a case of mistaken identity, there being a very considerable resemblance between the upper wings of the two species, in colour, size, and in markings. On the other hand, it may simply have been the Bank Holiday spirit!

[Demuth, R. P. 1956. An unusual pairing. *The Entomologist's Record and Journal of Variation* **68**: 191–192].

Opposite is another example of cross-specific pairing, captured on camera here by Richard Revels at Waresley in Cambridgeshire; the same combination was also observed in 1997 at Daventry in Northamptonshire (Williams, 1998). Except for what is believed to be the natural hybrid ab. *polonus* Zeller (Plate 1), a pairing between the Chalk Hill Blue and Adonis Blue, wild pairings such as these, between our native butterfly species, do not produce offspring.

Fig. 109. Male Meadow Brown (*Maniola jurtina*) and female Gatekeeper (*Pyronia tithonus*) in copula (*c.* late 1980s).

ON BECOMING 1000

Philip B. M. Allan, M.A., M.B.E. (1946)

Throughout this book we have drawn liberally from the vast literary wealth contained within *The Entomologist*, founded in 1840 by Edward Newman, and *The Entomologist's Record and Journal of Variation*, founded in 1890 by James W. Tutt. Both publications are discussed in a highly informative and entertaining article, 'On Becoming 1000', by P. B. M. Allan (1946) in which he charted the mixed fortunes of various entomological magazines and journals that made their debut in the nineteenth century. He explained how *The Entomologist's Record and Journal of Variation* had come into being. Allan wrote that in Tutt's opinion journals such as *The Entomologist*, of which Richard South had now become the editor, did '"good work in the more strictly scientific and descriptive branches of the subject in that part relating to Foreign Entomology" . . . he had founded '*The Record*' solely "in order to supply a Magazine devoted entirely to the wants of British Entomologists, restricted to their own fauna, and such parts of Foreign Entomology as aid them in the thorough understanding of the British species."' He went further and stated that: '"Owing to the general absence of interest among British entomologists in descriptions of purely foreign species, and the gradual tendency of our old magazines to fill up their pages with such matter, utterly useless to the British collector, *The Entomologist's Record* . . . was started, with the aim of supplying its readers with material of utility and interest to them."' As Allan remarked: 'Tutt was nothing if not forthright.' And he was clearly not convinced that Tutt's action had been purely altruistic:

. . . The real reason lay somewhat deeper. Tutt and South had never seen eye to eye. They had quarrelled — in print — in 1887, when South had alleged, in the pages of *The Entomologist*, that certain varieties of Lycaenid butterflies were 'hybrids.' . . . They quarrelled at Entomological Society meetings, they quarrelled at South London meetings, they quarrelled at City of London meetings, they damned one another behind each other's backs. Their temperaments were so fundamentally incompatible that they could hardly meet without quarrelling. Then came the news that South was to edit the chief entomological magazine of this country. Tutt would be debarred from its pages — he would never risk having a contribution returned to him with a printed slip, and by South of all people! This was the last straw. . . . He gathered his supporters round him and decided to take action immediately. On April 15, 1890, he published the first number of *The Entomologist's Record and Journal of Variation*. The wrapper announced that it was "Edited by J. W. Tutt, F. E. S." No reference committee for him. . . .

[Allan, P. B. M. 1946. On becoming 1000. *The Entomologist* **79**: 195–208].

Whilst *The Entomologist* had ceased publication in 1997, *The Entomologist's Record*, the *Entomologist's Gazette* and the *Entomologist's Monthly Magazine* still continue to appear regularly. In 'On becoming 1000' Allan referred to a particular talent of Henry Guard Knaggs:

Knaggs had a natural genius for inventing gadgets, mostly futile, and conceived the idea of assisting collectors by designing a pasteboard butterfly which flapped its wings when a string was pulled from a "hide." It was all very well to lure *Ornithoptera* [bird-wing butterflies] from the tree-tops by such means: but British butterflies! Not surprisingly then when Richard South subsequently printed (with truly remarkable diagrams) Knaggs' description of his mechanical butterfly in *The Entomologist*, Tutt could not resist the temptation. . . .

In a vituperative onslaught Tutt vilified Knaggs' invention, contemptuously referring to both gentlemen as 'Whitechapel bird-catchers'.

SUGGESTIONS FOR DECOYING BUTTERFLIES

Henry G. Knaggs M.D., F.L.S., Camden Road, London, N.W. (1893)

Dr Henry Guard Knaggs (Fig. 39) was so impressed by the possibility of luring butterflies to the net by mechanical decoys that he set to work and devised a complicated apparatus with strings and springs that would do just this. The 'wings' of his decoy could be moved by cords manipulated by the collector, who was exhorted to conceal himself nearby. Knaggs suggested using the finest 'water cord' such as that used in fishing tackle, and advised that 'the pulling at which will produce a close imitation of the movements of the living insect'. Having attracted the specimen, the collector merely had to pull on 'the thick cord' for the net to be activated. He went further and even suggested the positioning of 'an artificial flower, mounted on wire and of the colour of the species sought, in front of the decoy'. The entire concept (Fig. 111) is rather reminiscent of the comic fantasies of the eccentric cartoonist W. Heath Robinson (Fig. 110).

Then having retired to the place of concealment with the two cords, pull remittingly at the thin one to work the decoy, and bide your time. Should the species wanted catch sight of the bait, it will probably make for it, and hover over it for a few moments. Now is your chance, let fly with the thick cord, hurry up, don't be excited, secure the prize, reset the net, and when you get home, write off to the 'Entomologist,' and tell us all about it.

Fig. 110. 'A new method of studying night-flying Lepidoptera.' W. Heath Robinson.

I have satisfied myself that the *modus operandi* is quite practicable, that the apparatus will work effectively, and that butterflies will "tumble into it"; my apparatus was set on our grass plot, and our first attempt with a white paper decoy met with no success to speak of; but I recollected that there were the remains of a white butterfly captured last year by one of my grandchildren; I managed to find these, pasted them on to the decoy frame, and, being rather out of spirits with my previous failure, gave the cords to my attendant to work; in less than a minute he missed a splendid chance — had time enough to pull the cord half a dozen times, but left it till too late. And so I reset the trap, and took up the reins myself, and in less than another minute — Swish, whack! and mechanical decoying was a *fait accompli* so far as *P. rapae* [Small White] was concerned. I did set the trap again, but before I could get to my hiding-place our kitten came upon the scene, and being used to playing with string, inadvertently let the thing off, which so astonished it that it gave a big buck-jump, and went scampering down the garden with — oh! such a tail! After that I drew the stumps, and at once set to work to finish this paper. . . .

[Knaggs, H. G. 1893. Suggestions for decoying butterflies. *The Entomologist* **26**: 154–157; 180–182; 207–210].

Perhaps Knaggs' invention was not so fanciful after all. Other members of the Pieridae (the Whites and the Yellows) seemed to be equally susceptible to artificial attractants, as demonstrated in the next article.

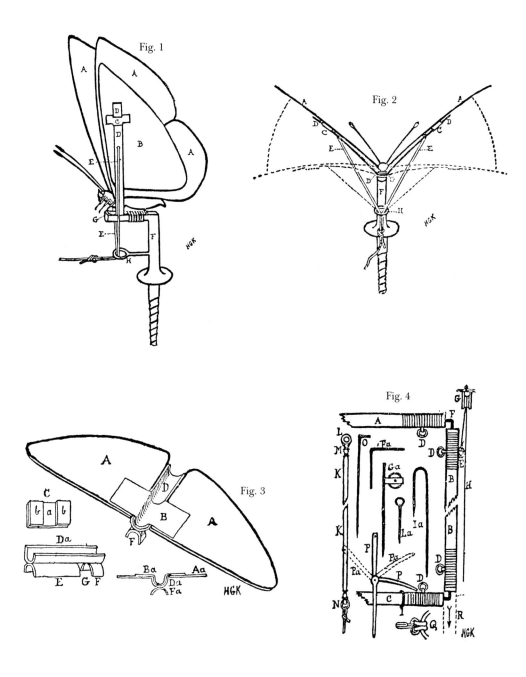

Fig. 111. Dr Henry Guard Knaggs' apparatus for decoying butterflies. He 'had a natural genius for inventing gadgets, mostly futile'.

PERCEPTION OF THE BRIMSTONE AT FAULT

Albert Müller, South Norwood, London, S. E. (1873)

On Easter Monday a little incident occurred, which may be worth mentioning in these days, when at last some systematic attention begins to be paid to the faculties of the lower animals. While plodding along a dusty highroad in this neighbourhood, a ♂ *G. rhamni* [Brimstone] rapidly passed me on the wing. A few yards further on, it suddenly arrested its straight flight and began to wheel round an object lying in the dust, which, on coming up, I found to be a crumpled-up ball of rose-coloured tissue paper. My arrival frightened the butterfly and it continued its headlong career, but, scarcely had I left the spot, when doubling on its track, it rushed back and repeated the circling round the paper, descending repeatedly to within about an inch of it, but without actually settling. This time I watched its proceedings from a convenient distance without disturbing it. After a few minutes' bird's-eye view, the insect seemed to have made up its mind, that there are such things in the world

as rose-coloured balls without the perfume and nectar of the rose; so away it went and so did I. But imagine my astonishment to see it fly steadily a few hundred yards ahead, and then suddenly return to the ball, over which it again performed similar aerial evolutions, till a band of noisy excursionists made the place too hot for it to stay, much to my inward regret, as I had made up my mind to wait and see how long the deception would last.

[Müller, A. 1873. Perception of *Gonepteryx rhamni* at fault. *Entomologist's Monthly Magazine* **10**: 20].

THE FLAVOUR OF CATERPILLARS

George W. Kirkaldy, F.E.S. (1900)

George Willis Kirkaldy (1873–1910) was born in Clapham and educated at the City of London School. He was elected a Fellow of the Entomological Society of London in 1893. In 1903 he emigrated to Hawaii to work for the Department of Agriculture and Forestry at Honolulu. Soon afterwards he unfortunately suffered a severe riding accident, breaking a leg in five places. It necessitated two operations as the bones failed to unite properly. A third operation carried out during a holiday visit to San Francisco also failed; he only survived five days.

"De La Lande — the celebrated astronomer," says d'Isjonvalle, "often supped with me on Saturdays, and found nothing more to his liking than to eat caterpillars and spiders when in season. As my room opened directly on to a fine garden, he easily found the wherewithal to satisfy his first hunger; but as Madame d'Isjonvalle likes to do things well, she used to collect some during the afternoon, to offer him on his arrival. As I always declined my share of this relish, I can only trust to hearsay for the difference in flavour between a spider and a caterpillar. The first, says our astronomer, has a nutty taste, the second a taste exactly like that of a stone-fruit." (A. Daguin, in 'Le Naturaliste,' 1899, p. 25).

[Kirkaldy, G. W. 1900. The flavour of caterpillars. *The Entomologist* **33**: 87].

Fig. 112. George W. Kirkaldy was interested in the Hemiptera. He strongly believed in the 'rule of priority', and 'rigidly objected to orthographic emendation being admitted on any plea whatever. Strict priority without exception of any kind was the predominant note in all his nomenclatorial work.' (*The Entomologist*, 1910)

SHERLOCK HOLMES, ENTOMOLOGIST

John A. Hollier, Minehead, Somerset. (1989)

In 1881, in the chemical laboratory of Bart's, Sherlock Holmes met Dr John Watson and uttered the words "You have been in Afghanistan, I perceive." Thus began one of the best known partnerships in literature, chronicled in four novels and 56 short stories.*

The career of Holmes spans some 30 years, and coincides with the period of the great entomological collectors, and the Victorian Naturalists. It might be expected that something of this would find its way into the stories which describe Holmes' cases, but one must remember that there is no mention of cricket, even though Conan Doyle was very fond of the game and even played for the MCC on a number of occasions (Shaw, 1985). The student of entomology is more fortunate however, two entomologists are involved in his cases (if one discounts Jethro Rucastle's son who showed "quite remarkable talent in planning the capture of mice, little birds and insects" and was adept at killing cockroaches with a slipper (*The Copper Beeches: Adventures*) as an entomologist proper).

Nathan Garrideb, described as a "crazy boob of a bug collector" by Killer Evans (*The Three Garridebs: Case Book*) was a harmless if eccentric man who spent all his time in his rooms with "cupboards and cabinets all round, crowded with specimens, geological and anatomical. Cases of butterflies and moths flanked each side of the entrance." Unfortunately for him there was another collection in the room, known only to Evans, hence the involvement of Holmes.

The other entomologist was rather more interesting; none other than the dastardly Stapleton *alias* Vandeleur *alias* Baskerville (*The Hound of the Baskervilles*). This man had lived in Costa Rica and Yorkshire before moving to Dartmoor, had acquired a name as a "recognised authority" according to the BM, and had described at least one new species. One of the rooms of his house was "fashioned into a small museum, the walls were lined by

* Conan Doyle placed many of these stories with magazines [e.g. *The Strand*], but the references here are to the collected stories as published by Penguin.

305

a number of glasstopped cases full of (his) collection of butterflies and moths". Stapleton considered his collection "the most complete one in the South-west of England." Stapleton was never without a butterfly net and when Watson first met him he was in hot pursuit of a specimen of "*cyclopides*". I can only suppose that this was the Chequered Skipper, given as *Cyclopides* (*Carterocephalus*) *palaemon* by South (1941), the only reference to the name I can find. If the identification is correct this certainly extends the range of this woodland species considerably [and its period of emergence too: the story is set in the late autumn!].

Holmes expected to have him "fluttering in our net as helpless as one of his own butterflies. A pin, a cork and a card, and we add him to the Baker Street collection." In the end Dartmoor got there first.

Three cases of Holmes' include real invertebrates. The case of the Lion's Mane (*Case Book*) is told in full, the villain of the piece being a jellyfish identified as *Cyanea capillata*. Williams (1951) has already pointed out that *C. capillata* is not really poisonous enough to fit the bill and suggests *C. arctica* as the culprit. The other two cases: the "repulsive story of the red leech and the terrible case of Crosby the banker" (*The Golden Pince-Nez: Return*) and the case of "Isadora Persano, the well known journalist and duellist, who was found stark staring mad with a matchbox in front of him which contained a remarkable worm, said to be unknown to science" (*The Problem of Thor Bridge: Case Book*) are only mentioned in passing, though both sound intriguing. I must take issue with Trevor Hall (1971) when in the course of an entertaining discussion of the Persano case he suggests that the term "unknown to science" implies a belief in the supernatural. Holmes meant of course that it was an as yet undescribed form, and probably added a scientific description to his long list of publications. This quibble in no way affects the rest of Hall's argument, with which I am inclined to agree.

Other real invertebrates mentioned include "the scorpions and the centipedes" which inhabit the old fort at Agra, and the "beetles" which the naturalist Mr Sherman's snake kept down (*The Sign of Four*).

Invertebrates are also used in metaphor and simile. Given the large number of stories Watson is very restrained in his use of detective story clichés such as spiders-and-flies (*The Five Orange Pips: Adventures, The Norwood Builder; The Final Problem: Memoirs*) and "she wouldn't kill a fly" (*The Problem of Thor Bridge: Case Book*). In Black Peter (*Return*) Inspector Hopkins produced the colourful (if inaccurate) phrase "he was pinned like a beetle to a card" to describe the body which was suspended from the wall by a harpoon, and added that the scene of the crime "was droning like a harmonium with the flies and bluebottles". Watson himself compared Dr Mortimer's fingers to "agile and restless" insect antennae (*The Hound of the Baskervilles*) and the ruined Kitty Winter told Holmes that the evil Baron Grunner "collects women, and takes pride in his collection, as some men collect butterflies and moths" (*The Illustrious Client: Case Book*).

Watson always presented Holmes as an emotionless reasoning machine, uninterested in anything but his cases; the introduction to The Cardboard Box (*His Last Bow*) is a case in point "everybody was out of town, and I yearned for the glades of the New Forest or the shingle of Southsea. . . . as to my companion, neither the country nor the sea presented the slightest attraction to him. He loved to lie in the very centre of five millions of people . . .". Such indeed was the image Holmes liked to promote, but his suggestion of a walk in the "beautiful woods" around Forest Row (one of the last remnants of the great Weald Forest) to "give a few hours to the birds and the flowers" (*Black Peter: Return*) gives the game away. Although Holmes claimed to despise knowledge which took up space in his memory without helping him in his chosen career (even protesting ignorance of the Copernican theory *A Study in Scarlet*), once again he is misleading Watson. His references to the role of natural enemies in the control of oyster populations (*The Case of the Dying Detective: His Last Bow*) show him to be up-to-date with contemporary theory, as well as convincing Watson that he is delirious.

When he retired it was to a cottage in rural Sussex, and there Holmes became an entomologist in earnest. In His Last Bow (*His Last Bow*) (set in 1914) Holmes was engaged in feeding the German master-spy Von Bork false information. At their last meeting Holmes, with Watson in attendance took Von Bork a supposed book of Navy Signals. It was none other than the "magnum opus of his latter years", the *Practical Handbook of Bee Culture, with Some Observations on the Segregation of the Queen.*

REFERENCES

Hall, T. (1971) *The Late Mr Sherlock Holmes.* Duckworth. London.

Shaw, S. (1935) *Sherlock Holmes and the 1902 Fifth Test.* Allen. London.

South (1941) *The Butterflies of the British Isles.* (new ed.) Warne. London.

Williams (1951) *Catalogue of the Sherlock Holmes Exhibition.* pp. 23–4.

[Titles abbreviated in the article: *The Adventures of Sherlock Holmes; The Case Book of Sherlock Holmes; The Memoirs of Sherlock Holmes; The Return of Sherlock Holmes.*]

[Hollier, J. A. 1989. Sherlock Holmes, entomologist. *Bulletin of the Amateur Entomologists' Society* **48**:107–109].

THE PURPLE EMPEROR IN HAMPSHIRE

G. Heseltine, Lymington, Hampshire. (1888)

In August, 1887, whilst driving in a dog-cart from Christchurch, I saw *Apatura iris* [Purple Emperor] flying along the hedge of a bare roadside. I immediately gave the reins to a friend who was in the cart with me, and pursued it with the dog-cart whip, and through a piece of luck I managed to hit the under wing above the upper, and so disabled it enough to capture it. It was a fine male specimen, and not in the least damaged with the novel way of capturing butterflies.

[Heseltine, G. 1888. *Apatura iris* in Hants. *The Entomologist* **21**: 209–210].

TAKING THE PURPLE EMPEROR BY HAND

Francis C. Woodforde, B.A., F.E.S., Market Drayton, Salop. (1903)

On July 12th I returned to the New Forest and tried sugar once, about the 16th, on a warm, cloudy, nice-seeming night, with a most disappointing result, the only insect that came to sugar being one *Hydrocampa nymphaealis* [Beautiful China Mark] — not a single noctuid . . . . One day I saw three *Apatura iris* [Purple Emperor], one of which sat on the ground within two yards of me, but when I tried to catch it, it pleaded successfully a previous engagement. It was a female, but on another day I got a nice male which an old woman had caught in her hands sitting on a flower in her garden and, which, strange to say, she had but slightly damaged.

[Woodforde, F. C. 1903. Fifty years ago. (From *The Entomologist's Record* of 1903). Taking *Apatura iris* L. by hand. *The Entomologist's Record and Journal of Variation* **66**: 88.].

This record of the Purple Emperor being caught by hand is not the first. In 1888 Alfred Russel Wallace and his wife were walking through the Forest of Dean:

We were walking on a broad path in the wood when on the ground before me, with wings expanded, I saw, for the first time in my life, a living Purple Emperor! I just stopped my wife from walking over it, then knelt down, & gently touching the tips of the wings with my outstretched fingers, made him raise them for an instant & then neatly caught him between fingers & thumb, pinned him in my hat and took him home safely for Willie.

[Raby, P. 2001. *Alfred Russel Wallace. A Life.* Pimlico, London — p. 251].

THE HIBERNATION OF THE MARSH FRITILLARY

Harold Dodsworth Ford, Thursby Vicarage, Carlisle. (1928)

I wrote a short note which appeared in last November's number of this magazine, in which I hazarded the suggestion that the larvae of *Melitaea aurinia* [Marsh Fritillary] are capable of sustaining intermittent periods of submersion while hibernating. I was led to make this suggestion owing to the fact that in more than one locality in this district the larvae are to be found on ground which I have frequently seen flooded during the winter. In September last I marked a small patch of ground, not more than 40 yards square, on which the nests of the larvae were spun up in some numbers. I visited the place at intervals during the winter and found that it was flooded several times and was always very swampy, so much so, in fact, that I was able to get on to the ground only during the hard frost in December. I was hardly surprised therefore when I searched the marked portion carefully in March, but could find no

nests, the ground being quite wet at the root of the herbage, which is of some length. However, about April 20th I found larvae in moderate numbers on this marked piece of ground. They were almost without exception near its centre, and there I also found the remains of a nest consisting of a few threads of silk, in which were entangled a few cast skins, the nest being spun very low down, at the roots of the herbage. I made a careful search of the drier portion of the field, but could find no larvae on that part, and although the devil's bit grows freely there, I have never found nests on that portion. Possibly, therefore, a few nests survived the exceptional floods of last winter, but the result of my experiment, if it can be called an experiment, merely amounts so far to this, that larvae were found in the spring on a marked piece of ground on which were a considerable number of nests in September, which was flooded several times during the winter, while I have had no evidence of larvae on other parts of the field. But the experiment is quite uncontrolled, and I propose if it be possible to establish a double control next autumn (*a*) by marking a number of individual nests on that part of the ground which is subject to flooding, and keeping them under regular observation, (*b*) by taking some nests home and subjecting them to occasional and varying periods of immersion. I am aware that these larvae are also found in dry situations; friends have informed me that they have even been found spun up in heather and on hill sides. Here, however, they appear to prefer the dampest localities; I have personal experience of five such localities, two of which are often flooded, but I have not found the nests on dry ground in this district.

[Ford, H. D. 1928. The hibernation of *Melitaea aurinia*. *The Entomologist* **61**: 188–189].

NEWSPAPER ENTOMOLOGY

From the *Western Morning News* (1886):

In these days of School Boards and cheap science classes it is hardly credible that any person could be found to pen the following paragraph, cut from the 'Western Morning News' of March 31st, 1886, and dated Capetown, March 10th. The italics are our correspondent's, who, in sending this literary curiosity, added, "This is reversing the natural order of things with a vengeance." "From Durban it is reported that much alarm has been caused in the Camperdown district by the scourge of armies of caterpillars which have appeared amongst the forage crops. One army extends a mile and a half deep, and has swept over about seventy acres of fine forage; another, comprising many millions, has eaten every bit of forage in one district; and the two armies are on the eve of joining, when it is feared that more damage will be done than the pest caused in 1878. *It makes its appearance in the form of a small moth, in a few days it sheds its wings, becoming a caterpillar, and in a week it lays eggs, each caterpillar producing two hundred.* They blacken the fields as they move about voraciously eating; and in one place forty acres of forage were reduced to stubble."

[Editor, 1886. Newspaper entomology. *The Entomologist* **19**: 140].

From the *Bristol Mercury* (1833):

On Sunday, as Mr. William Ferris, of Pennywell Lane, was in his garden, about eleven o'clock in the forenoon, millions of insects, of the caterpillar species, forming quite a cloud, which darkened the air, passed over him from west to east.'!!! ED.

[Editor, 1833. Rather extraordinary. *The Entomological Magazine* **1**: 317–318].

From *The Examiner*, 25th November 1905:

A convolvulus or hawk moth, just captured at Hartford, Cheshire, has been presented to the Northwich Museum. The hawk moth is nocturnal, and lives upon smaller moths. It measures four inches from tip to tip of wings.

[Grensted, L. W. 1957. Entomology rampant. *Entomologist's Monthly Magazine* **94**: 13].

It is interesting to note that even as long ago as 1833 the news media were quite unable to report events accurately.

SUSPENDED ANIMATION IN A MOTH

Col. Charles F. Cowan, Tring, Herts. (1965)

On 6th February 1964 at Devizes an Early Grey, *Xylocampa areola*, was noticed on the trunk of a Cherry Tree which I visited daily to check my max./min. thermometer. The site was exposed, on the southern slope of Roundway Hill, altitude 500 ft. The weather for the next month was frigid with biting south and west winds, and sleet alternating with fog or driving drizzle. Daily, and often at night, I visited this moth, which remained on the trunk for five weeks till 12th March. I once thought I had lost it, but found it had moved round the trunk, probably for better shelter. It moved about six times in all, within a span of nine inches between the south and west sides of the trunk.

The minimum night temperature rose above zero for the first time on 4th March, and remained then between 5° and 8 °C, so I hope its disappearance was voluntary and not inside a sparrow.

[Cowan, C. F. 1965. Suspended animation in a moth. *The Entomologist* **77**: 113].

INCREDIBLE MASSES OF LARVAE

Edward Hopley, Regents Park, London. (1865)

Edward William John Hopley (1816–1869) (Fig. 126) intended to follow the profession of medicine and was articled to a surgeon in Brighton, but then relinquished this to become an artist. In 1867 'he was attacked by an insidious renal disease, of a kind that has hitherto baffled all medical skill, and though he retained his habitual happiness of disposition up to the last, he knew that, sooner or later, he must succumb to its ravages'. He died at the relatively early age of fifty-three, yet 'only a short time before his death he had occupied himself with a re-arrangement of his collection in a new cabinet'.

Fully a mile from the Loughton Station, on the left hand side of the road to Epping, upon somewhat lower ground than the surrounding forest, stands a spacious grove of trees of considerable size, chiefly beech, oak and hornbeam, forming a densely canopied wood of several acres.

Approaching its skirts, last May, I was astonished to observe what appeared to be long lines of cobwebs enshrouding every tree, but crossing and re-crossing each other at angles, in length and arrangement unlike those of the *Arachnida*.

Penetrating still further into the covert, and using my beating-stick to displace these shreds of webbing, it was soon apparent that their silky lines *depended* from the branches, swinging even more multitudinously beneath and within the grove than on its confines. I presently perceived that the web had seemingly captured nothing but a small larva,* — thousands and millions of

* The larva of *Cheimatobia brumata* [Winter Moth].

310

which, wherever the eye turned, were, with their peculiar wriggle, actively occupied in hauling, crawling, twining, winding, and enshrining one another in mid-air, in such a vague, hopeless tangle as no description can realize. And these countless acrobats I found thus suspended, literally from every *limb* in this very considerable and stately plantation; and it was a little gale of a few hours previous which had enabled these grand trees to shake them from their crowns.

Soon, as I could look about, on the ground were noticeable little masses of what seemed to be ladies' muslin handkerchiefs, which, on closer inspection, proved to be colonies of these creatures who had seized upon some unfortunate fern-plants in despair of re-gaining their more lofty thrones, and which, in an hour or two, they had stripped to mere skeletons. Then, to my amazement, I discovered the entire ground itself positively thick with caterpillars, moving hopelessly everywhere, over one another, and the fallen last year's leaves, — not more numerous than themselves, — searching, and finding not; while, amidst the profound silence, the strange ticking sound of their little claspers on the dry, dead foliage, fell perpetually upon the ear like the gentle and plentiful pattering of a summer shower. There it would seem to be their fate to die of starvation, by countless millions, in the very bosom of plenty, their own strugglings and contortions their sufficient bondage!

I found no serviceable breeze for *my* purposes, on escaping from a spot which had enabled me to notice at once more organised life than I had ever before seen at one glance. On garments, hair, flesh, — over my eyes, my ears, my nostrils, and down my neck, crawling, crawling, crawling, had I brought them away; and infinite was the picking, plucking, and displacing of what, had I remained long enough, would probably for once in my life have attired me in silk, if not in fine linen.

It was inexpressibly saddening to see these heaps of "butterflies in embryo" annihilating one another through the very plenitude of the abundant life there sacrificed in this huge "struggle for existence."

The next morning I found a couple of them alive in my bed, and gave them a chance by dropping them from the casement to some shrubs below.

[Hopley, E. 1865. Incredible masses of larvae. *Entomologist's Monthly Magazine* **1**: 243–244].

MASS MOVEMENT OF CABBAGE WHITE BUTTERFLIES

Brig.-Gen. J. B. G. Tulloch, C.B., C.M.G., Abergavenny, Monmouthshire. (1940)

The year 1940 was remarkable in many ways. It began with one of the most severe winters on record. This was followed by week after week of continuous winds from the N.W., N., and N.E. This produced a series of closely following droughts. These droughts produced fine, clear weather. The weather helped to produce and keep alive more butterflies than I have ever seen in England during any previous summer. . . .

On July 14 I went up a narrow wooded ravine on the south side of the Sugar-loaf Mountain (1955 ft.) which lies three miles north-north-west of Abergavenny. . . . On reaching a clearing at 1000-ft. level I sat down to see what butterflies were about, and soon found that a mass movement of *P. brassicae* and *P. rapae* [Large and Small Whites] was in progress. All these insects were coming over a shoulder of the hill, 1300 ft., from the N.E. On arriving at the clearing the butterflies turned due south and went down the centre of the ravine, flying low over the scrub oaks. They passed at the rate of three or four to the minute, and rather lazily. This was at 3.30 pm. In the stream came a solitary *Colias croceus* [Clouded Yellow]. Now this gave a clue to where the movements began. For ten miles north of the direction from which the "whites" were coming there is an endless succession of mountains and narrow valleys, covered at the top with bracken, and on the sides with thick undergrowth. There is no "cabbage white" territory there. But well east of the Black Mountains and the Sugar Loaf, running from Abergavenny towards Hereford, there is a cultivated valley in which there are acres of market gardens and cabbages. Also in that valley and one and a half miles due east from where I saw *croceus* there is a rough field where it can be found, if at all. This field is at the 400 ft. level. It therefore seemed to me that the *brassicae, rapae* and the *croceus* had come out from the Abergavenny-Hereford valley, flown west and climbed 900 ft., then turned S.W. over the ridge, turned south again down the ravine and therefore back towards Abergavenny, again one and a half miles down the hillside.

After a while I followed the insects back to my house, which lies at the bottom of, and the entrance to the ravine. The stream continued over my garden walls and hedges, and straight over the house. Those that came to the house all appeared to pass up the same drain-pipe, so much so that I called to members of my household to come out and watch "butterflies trying to emulate cat-burglars!" After passing over the house or close by the sides, the insects went steadily on over a belt of trees down towards the town of Abergavenny. During the night what I had expected happened. The barometer dropped, rain began, and next day the wind was east, which all showed that a small cyclonic depression had passed to the south of Abergavenny. The day following the wind was back in the N.W.

On August 4 the same thing happened all over again. Barometer 29.70, falling; temperature 70°, inclined to be thundery. Wind south. This time I was at a point three miles south of Abergavenny. The movement was from the N.N.E. from the direction of cabbage fields, two miles away. The butterflies went over trees and woods as before. Insects passed at a rate of five or six a minute. No other butterflies were affected, the edges of the woods swarming with *Vanessa io* [Peacock] and *P. comma* [*c-album*? – Comma]. The movement was, in general, down the river Usk, the valley at the spot where I was being about one mile broad. . . . The result of the two mass movements as described was to leave the Abergavenny district alive with *brassicae* and *rapae*, and many gardens and allotments had their cabbage crops ruined. The former outnumbered the latter by 3 to 1. But during the whole of the summer the *brassicae* females have outnumbered the males by 4 to 1. I checked this many times quite easily because the lavender hedges and Buddleias in my garden were a seething mass of "white" butterflies, which made observations very easy. What causes mass movements of butterflies? My own opinion, based on personal observations in several parts of the world, is that these so-called "migrations" are not migrations in the sense of bird and animal movements, which have to do with feeding or breeding, but are mass movements due to atmospheric disturbances. . . .

[Tulloch, J. B. 1940. Mass movement of *Pieris brassicae* and *P. rapae. The Entomologist* 74: 32–35].

The Editor did not think too highly of Brigadier-General Tulloch's theory as to the cause of these mass movements of various butterflies. His note following the article states: 'An ingenious theory; but that *Danaus plexippus* [The Monarch] migrates, in the true sense of the word, in North America, is an established fact.'

Butterfly migration has been recognized since early times. One of the earliest references is that of Thomas Mouffet (1590), who wrote: 'Wert thou as strong as Milo or Hercules and wert fenced or guarded about with a host of giants for force and valour, remember that such an army was put to the worst by an army of butterflyes, flying in troops in the air, in the year 1104, and they hid the light of the sun like a cloud.'

CABBAGE WHITE BUTTERFLIES EATEN BY A CAT

Charles Mosley, Huddersfield, Yorkshire. (1926)

Is the fact of any consequence that a cat should develop a liking for Pierids? Last summer a young kitten in my house became quite an adept at catching white butterflies, principally the large one (*Pieris brassicae*) [Large White], but less frequently the smaller ones also. Almost invariably it would eat its captures with an apparent relish, after having toyed with them for some minutes as cats do with mice. This year she has again exercised the same trait. Is it usual? I have never known a similar case before.

[Mosley, C. 1926. Pierids eaten by a cat. *The Entomologist* **59**: 254].

LONG-TAILED FIELD MOUSE EATING PEACOCK BUTTERFLIES

James E. Campbell-Taylor, F.R.E.S., Combe Martin, Devon. (1946)

In the autumn of 1939 I caught a number of *Vanessa atalanta* L. [Red Admiral], *Nymphalis io* L. [Peacock] and *Aglais urticae* L. [Small Tortoiseshell] (the two latter species mainly as a check) with the intention of hibernating the *atalanta*. I put them all into a large room in the side of a bungalow, built on a steep slope, so that the room was, as it were, in the side of a hill facing south-east and under the habitable part of the bungalow, with no light in it, save that which filtered through the door, rough walls and beams overhead. I had previously made some attempt to hibernate *atalanta* in cages with no success. Here in more spacious and and natural surroundings (a sort of outhouse) I thought I might succeeded, but the experiment was again unsuccessful. On two occasions only have I ever found *V. atalanta* hibernating in the wild.

On going into the room in February, 1940, to see how matters stood, I found several *io* hanging from the beams, and also some *urticae* on the walls, head downwards, but no *atalanta*; they had all disappeared! They could not possibly have escaped from the room. However, on the floor were the two fore-wings of a red admiral! Whilst I stood wondering what had become of them, I saw a long-tailed field mouse (*Apodemus sylvaticus* L.) come out of a deep crevice with something in its mouth, which proved to be a 'peacock.' The mouse had its back to me, and did not appear to see me. I froze and watched. It proceeded to bite off the wings, and then to eat the body. After which I think it saw me, for it quickly scuttled off to the crevice. I wondered if that was where my red admirals had gone!

Later in the spring, four peacocks and three tortoiseshells returned to activity. I let them out.

[Campbell-Taylor, J. E. 1946. Long-tailed field mouse (*Apodemus sylvaticus* L.) eating *Nymphalis io* L. (Lep., Nymphalidae). *Entomologist's Monthly Magazine* **82**: 65].

IZAAK WALTON – ENTOMOLOGIST, NOT JUST FISHERMAN

Peter J. Edwards, M.R.C.G.P., F.R.E.S., Dinton, Buckinghamshire. (1993)

Four hundred years ago this year on 9th August Izaak Walton, England's most famous fisherman, was born. The fishing fraternity, of which I count myself one, are celebrating the event with two fairs at Chatsworth and Broadlands. Walton's fame undoubtedly rests on his well-known book *The Compleat Angler*, probably the most famous of all fishing books, which sits on most fishermen's bookshelves, and probably, like mine, remains unread. This is unfair as it is quite fascinating to read, as I have now discovered that Izaak Walton was, like many other fishermen after him, a keen Entomologist. . . .

In the chapter headed "The Third Day" he discusses the various sorts of trout of which he says there are "Several kinds considered but by few men; for they go under the general name of Trouts" — even in the sixteen fifties fishermen then, like Entomologists now, were concerned by regional variations. "Nay, the Royal Society has published lately that there be thirty and three kinds of spiders; and yet all, for all I know, go under the general name of Spider". There is little doubt that this rather testy remark is referring to Martin Lister's first paper on spiders published in the *Philosophical Transactions of the Royal Society*. This indeed includes a list of 33 spiders as well as three harvestmen and a red mite. This list he later increased to 38 for his great *Tractus*. All this erudition about Lister comes, of course, from the recent translation from the Latin of Lister's work, published and partly translated by Basil Harley — a fascinating book even for the non-Arachnologist.

During the chapter "The Fourth Day", Walton talks about baits for the trout. The third type of bait is flies — "Too many for me to name or for you to remember". He then adds delightfully that "The little living creatures with which the sun and summers adorn and beautify the river banks and meadows for the recreation and contemplation of us anglers" — and Entomologists too!

He discusses the various shapes of caterpillars. "Some are horned in the head, some in the tail, some have none". Some have a motion "not unlike the waves of the sea". He describes what I take to be pre-pupating wanderings of an ermine moth caterpillar in a way that cannot be bettered and calls him a Palmer or Pilgrim Worm. "He will not content himself . . . with any certain place of abode . . . but will boldly and disorderly wander up and down and not endure to be kept to a diet or fixt to one particular place". I like the thought of a bold and disorderly caterpillar. It was not until 1758 that Linnaeus called the White Ermine *lubricipeda* "swift of foot", presumably for the same reason.

He then goes on to describe two caterpillars which take his fancy and without doubt these are the Privet hawkmoth (*Sphinx ligustri*) and the Puss moth (*Cerura vinula*). The *ligustri* "was found on a privet hedge" and was as "big as a small peascod". It was put in a box with some privet "on which I saw it feed as sharply as a dog gnaws a bone", but sadly it died after five or six days "by some neglect of the keeper of it".

The *vinula* larva impressed him "his eyes black as jet; his forehead purple; his feet and hinder parts green; his tail two forked and black", and towards winter "come to be covered over with a strange shell or crust, called an aurelia; and so lives a kind of dead life, without eating all winter". This must be a very early use of the term aurelia for a pupa (I have used Walton's Fifth Edition of *The Compleat Angler*, published in 1676; the book was first published in 1653.)

There are several mentions of other flies in use for fishing including the May-fly and the Oak-fly (?) and the whole book is full of descriptions of wildlife observed and on occasions, wildly inaccurate. So join me in remembering an old fisherman who loved the countryside so very long ago.

[Edwards, P. J. 1993. Izaak Walton — entomologist, not just fisherman. *Bulletin of the Amateur Entomologists' Society* **52**: 281–282].

GREAT ABUNDANCE OF THE SMALL WHITE

Thomas J. Bold, Longbenton, Northumberland. (1869)

On the 24th of August [1869], immense numbers of *Pieris rapae* [Small White] suddenly appeared here, filling every garden with their swarms. On the 25th, they were still more numerous, and continued so until the 28th, when we had a storm of wind and rain, with a great fall of temperature, since which they have been much less abundant. Thousands were slain by the gardeners, some of whom were heard to say that for the first time in their lives they had done a day's work in entomology. I examined some scores of the killed, and all were, without exception, the small white, *Pieris rapae*.

[Bold, T. J. 1869. Great abundance of *Pieris rapae. Entomologist's Monthly Magazine* 6: 171].

THE DARK GREEN FRITILLARY AND
GREEN-VEINED WHITE FLYING OUT TO SEA

Professor John W. Heslop Harrison, King's College, Newcastle upon Tyne, Northumberland. (1939)

Lying on the south side of the Isle of Rhum is a veritable suntrap near Papadil; here, on the thyme-clad slopes, many unexpected species of Lepidoptera occur. To investigate these we made a journey by sea in early August, 1938, and after a series of minor incidents, managed to land. Our work was well repaid, but on our attempting to regain the boat, more difficulties arose. In attempting to solve these I worked my way some way out to sea by means of a ladder used to bridge the gaps between detached rocks. While indulging in the acrobatics which such a feat necessitated, I was surprised at the numbers of specimens of *Argynnis aglaia*

[Dark Green Fritillary] which dashed past me out to sea. Some of these, after a series of gyrations, soon returned to land, but a few sped far across the water and were lost to view. On the rocky islet of Longay, where colonies of *Pieris napi* [Green-veined White] exist, I have seen similar flights made by that insect. Careful watch, however, revealed the fact that, no matter how far over the sea the insect proceeded, or how protracted the flight, it invariably returned to the cove, or rock-ledge, supporting its food-plant. The possible bearing of the latter observations (which I have repeated elsewhere) on statements concerning alleged "immigrations" of this butterfly I leave for the consideration and appreciation of others. They become more important when due weight is attached to the fact that at many points in the British Isles are to be found *P. napi* colonies depending solely on *Cochlearia officinalis* [common scurvygrass] growing on rocks and cliffs along the sea coast.

[Harrison, J. W. Heslop 1939. *Argynnis aglaia* and *Pieris napi* flying out to sea. *The Entomologist* **72**: 59].

HERESY MOST FOUL

An Old Moth-Hunter. (1938)

I have got a bee in my bonnet. To the orthodox it is a ridiculous bee — nearly as stupid as those spelling ones which lately attacked, and stung, the B.B.C. It is this.

I hold that the scales on the wings of a lepidopteron, being attached to the wings by means of pedicels which fit into sockets in the wing membrane (Imms) [*], cannot be blown off by the wind. Puff I never so hard through a glass tube not one scale can I remove from the wings of a living insect. I allege that not any wind known to Aeolus — not Boreas, Aquilo, Auster, Notus, Eurus, Africus — let alone Zephyrus; neither tempest, hurricane, tornado, nor typhoon — can detach scales from a lepidopteron's wings so long as that insect remains in the air.

It follows, therefore, that a Bath White, or a Queen of Spain Fritillary, or a Long-tailed Blue, or a Clifden Nonpareil, which crosses the Channel or North Sea shortly after its eclosion, will arrive in England or Scotland, or wherever it first settles, in identically the same condition as that in which it left its native shores.

This hypothesis, of course, is heresy most foul, and it has all the weight of AUTHORITY against it. Time and again, in all the classic works on British lepidoptera, in the pages of *The Entomologist,* the *Entomologist's Monthly Magazine,* the "*Record,*" the Proceedings of all the Entomological Societies, one comes across the orthodox statement — that a migrant which is in perfect condition, as fresh as paint, must, *de ipso facto*, have emerged from the pupa not very far away — must, in fact, be an Englishman (or Scotsman) born and bred. "Its fine condition," says Barrett (*Entomologist's mon. Mag.* **25**: 180) "forbids the idea that it can have *flown* any very great distance" (the italics are his own). And so say, and continue to say, all true brethren of the butterfly net and sugaring tin.

Mr F. W. Frohawk has no doubts whatever on this subject. Again and again in his *Complete Book of British Butterflies* he proclaims his orthodoxy. "There is not the slightest doubt that several have been British born, as examples have been taken in perfectly fresh condition" (p. 99); "These were in the finest possible condition and had evidently bred in his garden" (p. 199); "Many of the specimens taken have been in very perfect condition, apparently freshly emerged" (p. 313); and so on.

[*] A. D. Imms, *A General Textbook of Entomology*

Why, then, should I, an insignificant person whose opinions are of no interest whatever to anybody, make myself ridiculous by proclaiming this preposterous heresy?

The answer is just this — that I have been reading *The Migration of Butterflies* by Mr C. B. Williams [1930] for the *n*th time. And every time I read it my heresy swells within my bosom. "Practically nothing is known," says this very wise writer, "of the conditions or period of time in which butterflies get 'worn' or 'rubbed'; and any conclusion drawn from such evidence is unreliable in the extreme. I have captured specimens of *V. cardui* [Painted Lady] migrating through Cairo that were practically perfect, and yet it was impossible to believe that they had bred within four hundred miles. In the migration of *B. severina* [African Common White] . . . in 1928, the majority of the specimens were in almost perfect condition . . . Yet there is reason to believe that they had flown many hundreds of miles, and all from the same spot, as there is no known large area in the vicinity which contains their foodplant . . . Grossbeck notes that *A. argillacea* [The Cotton Worm] in 'fresh condition' was taken in New York in . . . 1911, yet the nearest cotton field was four hundred miles away and no other foodplant is known." Moreover in 1887 this same moth, *A. argillacea*, swarmed "fresh and unrubbed" at Ottawa — some 200 miles north of New York and 600 miles from its nearest foodplant. No wonder that the French moths which I have been taking at my sugar, fifty miles from the coast, this year are as fresh as though they had come straight out of a bandbox.

It is no use you quoting *"quot homines, tot sententiae"* at me. Even less shall I be moved if you remind me that Satan can quote Scripture for his needs. Either the scales of a lepidopteron's wings can be blown off during a sea voyage or they cannot.

I will go still further — as well will I be hanged for a sheep as a lamb. I will assert that unless a lepidopteron hits up against something *en route* it can travel miles and miles *overland* without parting with a single scale.

Are there any on my side? Or do I stand alone? If I do, my head is — so far — bloody but unbowed. Though the might of the big battalions be arrayed against me, though I be gnashed upon by all those who cherish immaculate specimens of rarities whose value depends on native origin, I shall continue to say (though it be in an undertone) "bosh!" whenever, in print, the freshness of an insect is adduced "in proof" of recent and local eclosion.

[An Old Moth-hunter [Allan, P. B. M.], 1938. Heresy most foul. *The Entomologist's Record and Journal of Variation* **50**: 157–159].

WAS THE LARGE COPPER EVER AN IRISH INSECT?

Raymond F. Haynes, Dorking, Surrey. (1958)

The recent notes on the former distribution of *Lycaena dispar* Haw. [Large Copper] in England and the appeal for old records, prompts me to draw readers' attention to what may come as a surprise to many people: The possibility that *L. dispar* was once an inhabitant of Ireland.

What evidence is there for this statement? Unfortunately Donovan's Catalogue of the Macro-Lepidoptera of Ireland [1936] omits all reference to the butterfly, so I would like to put before everyone's attention such information as I have been able to derive from other sources.

It may not be generally known that an attempt was made to introduce *L. dispar rutilus* into Ireland. Full details were described in a long article which appeared in the *Proceedings of the Entomological Society of London*, Vol. 4 (1929). Briefly the story was as follows: An apparently successful effort to establish *L. dispar rutilus* into Southern Ireland was attempted by Capt. E. B. Purefoy in 1913. The site for the experiment was a snipe bog and the surrounding

Fig. 113. Edwin Birchall, the peripatetic Yorkshireman who specialized in the Irish Lepidoptera. Possessed of an extremely genial and buoyant disposition, he liked to argue theological matters. The bad health he suffered during his last years was said to be as a consequence of a fall down the cliffs of Howth, Co. Dublin while collecting.

terrain, in the vicinity of Greenfields, Co. Tipperary. The ground was cleared and the foodplant (*Rumex hydrolapathum*) [water dock] was introduced from England. Larvae of *rutilus* were sent by Herr H. Rangnow from a locality near Berlin out of which only some eight imagines were bred and released.

In May 1914, Capt. Purefoy went to Berlin and visited the marshes where *rutilus* occurred. Some 700 larvae were brought back to Greenfields and kept under nets as many of the caterpillars were parasitised. About 400 imagines were later bred and released to form the fore-runners of a fairly thriving colony. This colony was apparently still flourishing in 1928 but according to Mr. B. P. Beirne, writing in *The Entomologist*, Vol. 75, 1942, p. 82, the locality was not visited after that year (1928), and without any attempt in the way of clearance of undergrowth it is highly doubtful if the Large Coppers held their own.

An artificial introduction, however, into a country, does not constitute a native species; so it is necessary to search old books for obscure references. Quite by chance in 1956 I was given a copy of the *Proceedings of the Natural History Society of Dublin* for the Session 1865-66, Vol.5. Pt. I, and on page 20 appears an interesting account about Irish Lepidoptera by Mr. W. A. Andrews, V.P. The section relating to *L. dispar* reads thus:

"Some years since, when botanizing in the County of Kerry, at the south-eastern extremity of Castlemaine Harbour, and while collecting *Bartsia viscosa* [yellow viscid bartsia], where extensive marshes stretch towards Milltown, Mr. Andrews noticed a swift-flying insect, which he attempted to capture. From its size and brilliancy of colour, he was satisfied that it could be no other but the Large Copper Butterfly (*Lycaena dispar*). Having no net, and the drains being wide, it escaped. Although at one time this insect was plentiful in the fenny districts of England, yet drainage has so altered the features of the country, that it had disappeared from those localities that were accessible to collectors. There is no reason to suppose, where such favourable districts present themselves as the south-western part of this country, that that insect, as well as others equally rare, may not be met. Already many rare instances of zoology have been recorded from these localities, and therefore the inference is strong that equally striking facts of interest may yet be noticed."

Mr. B. P. Beirne, writing in *The Entomologist* (see above), criticises Mr. Andrews' records as being unreliable. After nearly a century, it is impossible to corroborate such an old record but as a matter of interest it was Mr. Andrews who first recorded *Gonepteryx rhamni* Linn. [Brimstone] as an Irish insect and doubts were expressed for nearly twenty years before another entomologist, Mr. Edwin Birchall, confirmed the record by taking specimens himself. This Milltown locality, to the best of my knowledge, was never visited by any other collectors. I have read all or nearly all of Birchall's writings about Irish entomology and he certainly didn't collect there; neither did Kane at a later date.

The remote possibility, therefore, exists that if Mr. Andrews' identification all those years ago was correct, *L. dispar* once inhabited that part of south-west Ireland. Whether it still does so is extremely dubious.

[Haynes, R. F. 1958. Was the Large Copper ever an Irish insect? *The Entomologist's Record and Journal of Variation* **70**: 150–151].

Edwin Birchall (1819–1884) was originally from Liverpool and was one of the first lepidopterists to explore Ireland, making several trips to Killarney, Galway and Wicklow. In 1866 his 'Catalogue of The Lepidoptera of Ireland' was published in the *Proceedings of the Natural History Society of Dublin*. He eventually moved to Douglas in the Isle of Man where, in 1879, he became the first President of the Isle of Man Natural History & Antiquarian Society.

COLLECTING IN NORTH DEVON

Richard South, F.E.S., St. John's Wood, London, N. W. (1881)

As far as I can learn, there are few resident collectors of insects in the whole district of North Devonshire. In a note from a gentleman at the United Services College, Westward Ho! I am informed they have a Natural History Society in that establishment, some of the members of which are aspiring entomologists. At Barnstaple I understood there were two gentlemen of that town who had collections of Lepidoptera; but I only met with one of them, and he was good enough to show me his collection, which consisted mainly of butterflies, and they were strong in the commoner species of the genus *Vanessa*. The insects were set and arranged more in accordance with individual fancy than scientific requirements. In his collection was a curious example of *Acherontia atropos* [Death's-head Hawk-moth], which at once caught the eye, and appeared familiar and yet strange. A closer inspection instantly revealed the cause of my imperfect recognition. *Atropos* was before me certainly, but, having lost its own hind wings, a pair of the posterior wings of *Papilio machaon* [Swallowtail] had been substituted; hence my momentary mystification. This "hybrid" was referred to in a recent law case by its manufacturer as "*Acherontia atropo-papilio-machaon*." . . .

[South, R. 1881. Collecting in North Devon. *The Entomologist* **14**: 202–205].

Fig. 114. Richard South, the distinguished author of *The Butterflies of the British Isles* which remained in print for over sixty years — an indispensable handbook for several generations of British lepidopterists.

Richard South was twice President of the South London Entomological and Natural History Society (1885 and 1896). It was formed in 1872 and was later to become the British Entomological and Natural History Society, in 1968. Field meetings have always been an important part of the Society's entomological calendar, and in Fig. 115 a relaxed South can be seen enjoying one of these events in May 1900.

SILVER-STRIPED HAWK-MOTH IN A BOOK-CASE

Sydney Webb, Dover, Kent. (1895)

An enclosed book-case is scarcely the locality that we should exploit for hawk moths, although strange entomological captures have, from time to time, been recorded, as, for instance, the *Catocala fraxini* [Blue Underwing], found in the last throes of death upon a mantle-piece of an empty room in an empty house. On Tuesday last, Mr. W. Fenn, of this town, upon raising a horizontal-lying book in the situation named, discovered it to be pressing down a fine female specimen of *C. celerio* [Silver-striped Hawk-moth], which was dead, but not yet stiff, and only very slightly injured on the thorax. The finder has liberally added it to my collection.

[Webb, Sydney. 1895. *Chœrocampa celerio* in a book-case. *The Entomologist's Record and Journal of Variation* **7**: 62–63].

F. M. B. Carr.   N. D. Warne.   S. W. Kemp.
G. E. Browne.   A. Cant.   S. R. Ashby.   W. West. R. A. Adkin. E. B. Carr.   R. Ficklin.
                                                                          T. A. Chapman.   W. H. MacGee.
        J. H. Carpenter. W. J. Lucas. S. Edwards.   H. S. Fremlin.   R. Adkin.   A. Ficklin.
            E. J. Crow.   H. J. Turner. R. South.   W. J. Ashdown.

Fig. 115. Field meeting of the South London Entomological and Natural History Society (May 1900). In 1884 the Society had moved its meetings to a room at the Pride of St. George's Coffee Tavern and Restaurant, 60 Blackman Street, Borough, S. E. According to Edward Step F.L.S., Treasurer at the time, 'this was the most distinctly entomological place we have occupied, as our orthopterists could always rely upon getting a series of the small cockroach, *Blatta germanica*, in all stages climbing the walls of the meeting room'.

SOUNDS PRODUCED BY THE FEATHERED GOTHIC

Capt. B. Blaydes Thompson, London, E.C. (1894)

The following extract from a letter recently received by me from Mr. J. T. Fountain of Birmingham, relates a curious observation on the above subject, made by that gentleman last year, when sugaring on the borders of Epping Forest, not far from Ponders End. "Whilst visiting the sugar, we had to keep crossing the corner of a meadow. I carried the lamp, and my son the net; suddenly I heard a slight sound near my feet — 'nick,' 'nick' — as if someone had touched the edges of two knives together. Turning the light in the direction of the sound, I saw a moth flying over the grass, which my son captured, and which proved to be *N. popularis* [*Tholera decimalis* — Feathered Gothic]. During the two evenings we spent there, this incident recurred 23 times; on every occasion but one, whenever we heard the sound, we netted a moth; on the exceptional occasion, not seeing any insect flying, we went down on our knees, and discovered a freshly-emerged specimen sitting on a grass stem. I do not know how the moth could produce the sound, but every time we heard the latter, the moth was in evidence. Not a single *N. popularis* came to sugar, but they were more

numerous near two gate posts that were sugared, as if the scent had attracted them." It will be interesting to learn whether any other entomologist has observed the same phenomenon.

[Blaydes Thompson, B. 1894. Sound produced by *Neuronia popularis*. *The Entomologist's Record and Journal of Variation* **5**: 148–149].

WARNING SOUND EMITTED BY THE PEACOCK BUTTERFLY

Charles M. Beadnell, Surgeon Rear-Admiral, R.N. (ret.), F.Z.S., Egham, Surrey. (1939)

On December 13th, whilst I was moving some wood that had been lying for months beside the south wall of my garage, I saw on the ground a Peacock butterfly that had apparently selected this sheltered site for its hibernation. I was very astonished to hear, coming from the butterfly, a slight hissing noise that was easily audible even from my erect position. Scarcely believing my ears, I put down the wood I had in my arms and bent over the butterfly to observe it more closely. At once its wings were opened and shut, and the hissing noise was repeated. I say "hissing", but perhaps the sound produced by uttering a prolonged "hith" would more correctly describe it. Indeed, it resembled, though, of course, very much softer, the sound sometimes made by a goose on the approach of a dog. Waiting until it closed its wings I cautiously picked it up, and taking it into the house placed it on a table. The creature made no attempt to fly away, but opened its wings and repeated the sound every time I moved my hand within its range of vision. To make assurance doubly sure I called my wife to listen, and she exclaimed: "It must be hurt, it's making such a queer noise." . . . I suggest, by way of explanation, that during the summer months the butterfly on the approach of danger takes instantly to flight and, as every lover of Nature knows, its zigzag motion on the wing affords it excellent protection from man or bird. When hibernating, however, the animal is sluggish because of the cold and the general lowering of its vitality; hence, to warn off enemies under these conditions it falls back upon a *noli me tangere* gesture, which undoubtedly would possess an obvious survival value for the species.

[Beadnell, C. M. 1939. Warning sound emitted by the Peacock butterfly. *The Entomologist* **72**: 45].

Rear-Admiral Beadnell's article was the signal for other articles to appear on the same subject. G. D. Rowley (1939) informed readers of *The Entomologist* that:

> With regard to the warning "hiss" or rustling sound emitted by *Nymphalis io* . . . I would like to add that during the summer of last year I kept several of this species [Peacock] under observation in an outdoor cage, and noted that on my approach on almost any cold morning, the whole lot would commence slowly opening and shutting their wings and uttering at the same time this peculiar

rustling or hissing sound. This only happened on cold days or during hibernation when disturbed, and is probably used to ward off enemies when the butterfly is in a state of semi-daze and incapable of flying away.

E. J. Salisbury (1940) reported yet another example in the *Entomologist's Monthly Magazine*:

In December last, when my gardener and I were moving some logs from a woodstack, one near the base was seen to bear a hibernating Peacock butterfly. So we placed this log carefully to one side where it was in bright sunshine. Almost immediately our attention was recalled to it owing to the production of a hissing sound which can best be described as something between that produced by an angry cat and the hissing of a disturbed snake. The volume of the sound was also not dissimilar. I could not at first credit that so loud a noise was being produced by the insect, but it was soon apparent that the sound accompanied the movements of the butterfly's wings, which partially opened and closed in a manner similar to that when sunning itself normally.

This phenomenon in fact had been noticed years before. In *The Complete Book of British Butterflies* (1934) F. W. Frohawk reported that Mr A. B. Farn had once discovered a large assemblage of Peacocks in a tree:

Thinking it might be a likely place for hibernating butterflies, he happened to look in and immediately noticed a hissing sound, not unlike the hiss of a snake, produced by the large number of butterflies rubbing their wings together; a habit peculiar to the Vanessidae. The noise is made by the sudden expansion of the wings, causing the inner margin of the fore wing to rub against the costal margin of the hind wing, this resulting in a chafing, stridulous sound.

Albert Brydges Farn (1841–1921) was born in Hackney, Middlesex and is credited by Colonel Sidney Kershaw (1956) as being '"the Father of the Var-hunters". By proving that *all* species varied, even the Cabbage White, he opened up a vast field of enjoyment and research for posterity'. Through his own endeavours, both in the field and by acquisition, he amassed one of the finest collections of butterfly aberrations, many of which were figured by Frohawk.

Kershaw described him as a 'tall man with magnificent shoulders ... Farn's charm, generosity, love of practical joking, quick temper, sense of humour, combined with resentment of any slight or injury, real or imaginary, (and a complete incapacity to forgive or forget such a slight) made Farn ... a complex mass of conflicting emotions ... He had no Laodiceans amongst his friends and enemies: you either loved or hated him (either being warmly returned).' He was happy to let anyone view his collection if they were generally interested, rather than because it was deemed 'the right thing to do'.

Fig. 116. Albert Brydges Farn. 'On one occasion, returning home after inspecting a pair of "reputed British" Spurge Hawks offered by a collector and rejecting their data as insufficient, on reaching Mount Nod he found a freshly emerged *C. euphorbiae* [Spurge Hawk-moth] clinging to his front door-knob!'

A certain lady badgered Farn every time she saw him to show her his collection. At last in desperation he did so, and at the end of two and a half hours' hard work for the old man, she remarked: "Oh, Mr. Farn! What a lot of pins!" Farn's reply was: "Had I known earlier what would have interested you most, I could have shown you boxes and boxes of pins without troubling you to look through so many drawers to see them". To this the lady replied effusively: "Oh! No trouble at all, I assure you!"

Although Farn studied for the medical profession, it is not known whether he passed the necessary exams; he certainly never practised as a doctor. He maintained his interest in the field of medicine, latterly working for the Local Government Board as Vaccine Controller.

A year before Farn reached the age limit the L.G.B. wished him to retire at once, as his work was being transferred; this meant that he could not qualify for a full pension. This did not suit A.B.F. and for about a year he travelled up to his office as usual by the 8.5 a.m., read his Times, and came home again by the 5.23 p.m., continuing this manoeuvre until he earned his full pension!

A considerable and timely legacy allowed him to indulge in his interests throughout most of his life; besides collecting, these included billiards and shooting. In shooting over

dogs on the Gravesend marshes, he is reputed to have bagged 176 snipe with as many cartridges. In many ways he epitomised the Victorian and Edwardian collector, and it is believed he inspired the cover illustration for *The Text Book of British Butterflies and Moths* (1913) by L. W. Newman and H. A. Leeds (Fig. 12).

AN EXHIBITION OF INSECTS

Every year the British Entomological and Natural History Society stage their major entomological exhibition in London at which members are invited to present collections made during the current season. In the nineteenth century even larger exhibitions were organized, and they attracted considerable attention in the popular press. One such, held in 1887, came in for some very mixed criticism.

From the *Echo*, 8th December 1877:

On Thursday and yesterday an interesting exhibition drew together a large number of people at the Church Room, George Street, Grosvenor Square. This was the fifth annual exhibition of the West London Entomological Society. There were many very excellent collections on the tables, of which some cases of rare moths and butterflies are specially worthy of mention. In one of these there was a hermaphrodite specimen of *Anthocaris cardamines* [Orange-tip]. It was noticeable that the efforts of the exhibitors seemed all directed to but few orders of the vast insect world. The *Lepidoptera* (butterflies and moths), of course, predominated over everything else put together, but we could not see any good purpose served by many of the collections containing numerous specimens — sometimes even scores — of the same species of insect. A very large proportion of the insects was unnamed, a defect which efforts should be made to rectify in a future exhibition. Next to the *Lepidoptera* came some good collections of *Coleoptera* (beetles), and almost the only other order represented was that of the *Hymenoptera* (bees, wasps, &c.), to which a few cases were devoted. There were some cases of well-preserved caterpillars, including that of the Lobster Moth (*Stauropus fagi*). In many of the collections of Lepidoptera the absurd fashion was adopted of arranging the insects in patterns regardless of their connection by species or family. Thus a beehive, an anchor, stars and crosses were figured — certainly very artistically — but they were of no value from a scientific point of view. In but very few instances was the life history of any particular insect worked out by the exhibition of specimens in all the stages of its growth.

The organizers of this exhibition could not have forecast the tone of this newspaper review which, one month later, was enhanced by further criticism from the editors of the *Entomologist's Monthly Magazine*:

(We cordially endorse the foregoing remarks. It is surely time that such trivial employment as making designs in the form of a "bee-hive, an anchor, stars and crosses," with insects should cease, or, at any rate, should not be deemed entomological work, nor be patronised by an Entomological Society. Such things only excite the pity of scientific men and the ridicule of others, extending not only to the makers, but also to entomology itself. We earnestly hope the officials of our useful local Entomological Societies will discourage to the utmost exhibitions of this nature. An ample field for the investigation of the natural history of insects, as well as the examination of their structure, still remains to be occupied, and collectors would do good service if they turned their attention in these directions — EDS).

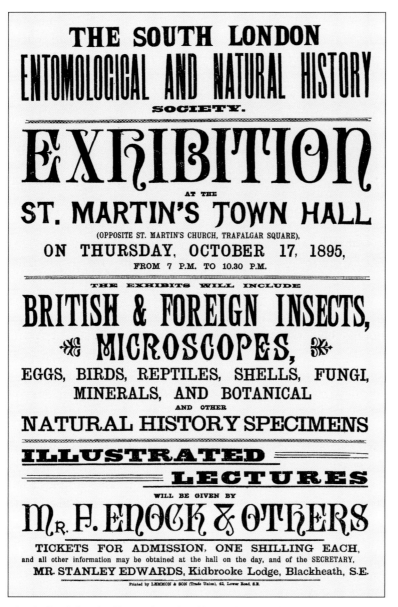

Fig. 117. Poster for the South London Entomological and Natural History Society's Exhibition in 1895. Their First Great National Entomological Exhibition, held in 1878 at the Royal Aquarium, Westminster, proved somewhat controversial. Whilst some of its members warmly supported it, others thought it undignified for a scientific body to be mixed up with music-hall turns —'Zazel the Renowned' — and side-shows. Recrimination and resignations followed.

Although the editors of the *Entomologist's Monthly Magazine* condemned the exhibition of 'pictures' composed of butterflies in various ornamental shapes, one distinguished reader of that magazine expressed a contrary view:

In the last number of the *Entomologist's Monthly Magazine* appears an address from the Committee of the "West-London Entomological Society," protesting against the severity of some of the remarks made in that Magazine on their recent exhibition of insects, &c. To this address the editors append a foot-note, from which I make the following extract, "We repeat that 'such things only excite the pity of scientific men, and the ridicule of others.' The manufacture of 'pictures' only represents so much time thrown away." I not only deny this latter statement but I assert the exact converse. I *assume* that the "pictures" are the collections and handiwork of *poor* and *ignorant* men — of men in a humble station of life, whether in town or country — I assume, also, that humble and "unscientific" though they be, they are, nevertheless, capable of appreciating beauty, form, colour, and ornament. Am I then to be told it is "a waste of time" for these poor men, on one of their rare holidays, to go and catch "butterflies," or, after a hard day's work, to walk miles into the woods, and spend the night there (as I have known them do) in search of "moths"? This, I think, will scarcely be maintained. But then the subsequent "arrangement" of their spoils! The "geometrical" and "fantastic" pictures! How are they to know better? To whom or to what are they to apply for information. Is there any *harm* in such a picture on the wall of a poor man's room? Which is the more "ridiculous," such a picture, or that of whole "rows" of rare species in the wealthy collector's cabinet. What do the vast majority of these latter know or care about "science"? Why! many of them have not even the credit — which belongs, at any rate, to the poor man — of collecting their own specimens! . . . For thirty years I have been a "collector," and during that period I have visited, in a collecting sense, many of our manufacturing towns, as Sheffield, Manchester, &c., and also many country places. Whenever, during those visits, I have seen a "butterfly picture," I can honestly and conscientiously say that I have seen it with unalloyed pleasure. In such cases, whether seen in the labourer's cottage or the mechanic's shop, I can always say with much confidence, "this man at any rate loves the fields and the woods more than the public house and the beer shop." But the Editors urge farther that it is not merely a waste of time, but that it involves the "needless destruction of myriads of beautiful insects." Surely this cannot be intended as a *serious* argument. I might take exception to the somewhat exaggerated estimate of "myriads" of insects, but let that pass. Whether we count them by thousands or tens of thousands, the Editors must know that the whole of them, in the ordinary course of nature, perish in a few weeks, whether captured or not, and with the exception of a few hibernating specimens, vanish as completely as if they had never existed. Why not, then, preserve these "beautiful" insects to be a "joy for ever." If fantastically and unscientifically arranged, why not? "*Non cuivis contingit adire Corinthum.*"

[Greene, J. 1878. 'Butterfly pictures.' *Entomologist's Monthly Magazine* **14**: 261–262].

The Reverend Joseph Greene M.A. (1824–1906) was the author of the celebrated entomological article 'On pupa digging', which was published in *The Zoologist* (1857). He also wrote a very popular book, *The Insect Hunter's Companion* (1863). After graduating at Durham University he served as a parish priest in Derbyshire before removing to Halton in Buckinghamshire. Although a 'shy, retiring man', he was said to exaggerate some of his entomological findings. On one occasion he claimed to have dug up a thousand pupae of the moth *Orthosia incerta* (Clouded Drab). To have done this, P. B. M. Allan (1937) had calculated, would have meant that Greene worked five hours a day for five months!

Although the editors published Mr Greene's letter and admitted that the 'comparison drawn by our correspondent is a very just one' in respect of the self-taken specimens of the hard-working mechanic as opposed to the rich man's purchased 'rarities', they criticized the First Great National Entomological Exhibition, held two months later, in the strongest terms. 'Devoid as this exhibition was of true scientific interest, almost the only result we can expect is an increase of mere butterfly — and beetle-butchers, of whom too many already exist.'

ANALYSIS OF LEPIDOPTERA EATEN BY BATS

John Manwaring Baines, Hastings Museum, East Sussex. (1939)

On the night of August 5, 1939, a number of Dark Arches (*monoglypha* Hufn.) were attracted to light at a bungalow in Little Common near Bexhill. This is a species which is reinforced by immigration and it is thought that these specimens were immigrants. They were attacked by bats believed to be the Common Pipistrelle (*Vespertilio pipistrellus* Schr.), which is very common in that locality, but this could not be confirmed definitely. A careful search was made below the windows and a number of fragments recovered. With the exception of one right fore wing of a Brown-line Bright-eye (*conigera* F.) in very good condition, all the remains belonged to *monoglypha*. There were nine left fore wings, of which five were without the hind wings, and four had the hind wings attached. Of the latter, one had the head and first pair of legs as well, and three had the head only. Of the seven right fore wings, two had the hind wings (one of which had the head only, and one the head and first pair of legs), and five had no hind wings (one with the head and four without it). In addition, there were three separate left hind wings and five right hind wings, one head with fore legs attached and two separate legs. Despite a long search no further remains could be found, having either been blown away or removed by the bats, when they ate the bodies. The disjecta membra were sorted into eight heads, nine left and seven right fore wings, seven left and seven right hind wings, thus accounting for at least nine specimens. These were examined to see if any light could be thrown on the method of attack. Instances of sudden dives by the Long-eared Bat (Entom., **72**: 190) showed that the bat hovered before making its attack, and that each of these attacks was successful.

Single wings	18
Fore and hind wings . . .	6
Fore and hind wings and head . .	4
Fore and hind wings, head and legs .	2
Bodies only	0

From this it appears that the bat or bats attacked their prey from behind while the moths were fluttering up and down the window-pane attracted by the light, and that in four out of the nine or more moths, the body had been seized at an angle so that all the wings of one side as well as the head were left in one piece. In six cases all the wings of one side had been left. Four attacks had been made from the left and two from the right. This was to a certain extent confirmed by experiment. A pair of V-shaped pliers approximating as closely as possible to the bat's mouth proved unwieldy, and a pair of entomological forceps were substituted. Sudden darts, resembling as much as possible those made by bats, were made at the only moths available, *monoglypha* and *pronuba* L. [Large Yellow Underwing]. It was noticed that when these were fluttering up and down a window-pane their bodies were generally at right-angles to the glass in a vertical plane, though inclined horizontally. Thus any attack in a vertical plane had almost certainly to be made at an angle. It was extremely difficult to get immediately behind the body, where such an attack by a bat might be expected to shear off all the wings at one time, and leave no fore and hind wings attached. It was also very clear that the bat must have been able to regulate the depth of its dive very accurately, for none of the eight heads was damaged by concussion with the glass, which was constantly happening in the experiments. In addition, as each dive was invariably successful on the occasion referred to above, each must have been made at a greater speed than could be conveniently reproduced by the human hand and forceps.

[Manwaring Baines, J. 1939. Analysis of Lepidoptera eaten by bats. *The Entomologist* **73**: 139–140].

NOTE ON DROWNING IN LEPIDOPTEROUS LARVAE

Dr Thomas A. Chapman, M.D., F.E.S., Reigate, Surrey. (1904)

I suppose few lepidopterists have been without the experience that larvæ placed on a branch of the food plant in water, are very apt to avail themselves of any oversight in the arrangements, and to crawl down into the water and get drowned.

When this happens, it most frequently occurs that the larva is asphyxiated when it has crawled about a couple of inches beneath the water, it may then fall off and sink, or remain clinging to the twig till it dies.

My observations of this occurrence led me to use this means of producing anaesthesia in any larvæ I wanted to have quiescent for examination or experiment, as I found that a few minutes under water produced a death-like stillness, which, if not prolonged, was completely recovered from, without any apparent ill-effect, whilst the use of chloroform or any anæsthetic of that sort seemed to produce intense discomfort and usually sickness in nearly all cases, and in fact was seriously damaging, and prejudiced the chance of rearing them.

I have treated a good many larvæ in this way, and few required more than a few minutes' submersion, and none more than a quarter of an hour to become quietly asleep.

I was much astonished last autumn to meet with a remarkable exception. On October 21st I found a *Tortrix* [a micro-moth] larva, which was, I have no doubt, that of *D. petiverella*, in a stem of *Achillea millefolium* [yarrow]; I dropped it into water, and it sank to the bottom. Twenty hours later, on the 22nd, it lay quiet at the bottom of the water, but when touched proved to be quite lively and active. On the 23rd, after forty-eight hours' immersion, when touched it moved freely, but a little sluggishly, and seemed a little swollen. (Many larvæ imbibe water (by endosmosis?) when immersed, and swell up very much, they may recover (in some species only?) after this has made some progress.) I took it out and left it out two hours, it was then quite active and seemed normal; I then re-immersed it.

The next day, the 24th, after twenty-four hours' immersion, it seemed quite well; on the 25th (forty-eight hours under water), it seemed quite lively; 26th, still quite active after seventy-two hours' continuous immersion. On the 27th, ninety-six hours' immersion, is rather distended, and apparently dead; removed it from the water, and in ninety minutes after it had shrunk perceptibly, and moved when touched. On the 28th, after being out of the water twenty-four hours, it seemed quite well and active, but after twenty-two hours re-immersion it appeared to be dead, and though removed from the water did not recover. I imagine removal from its food plant had more to do with killing it than the immersion.

I have not since had an opportunity of experimenting with any internal-feeding larva to test the question, but it seems probable that the possibility of being overwhelmed by sap or other moisture in its burrow, has been provided against by this great power of resistance to drowning, to which most Lepidopterous larvæ rapidly succumb.

[Chapman, T. A. 1904. Note on drowning in lepidopterous larvae. *Entomologist's Monthly Magazine* **40**: 81–82].

It has been shown apparently conclusively that some larvae are able to withstand the effects of submersion during long periods of hibernation. As long ago as 1834, William Bree, the entomological Rector of Polebrook, in Northamptonshire, published a letter on this subject from Adrian H. Haworth. It concerned the Large Copper:

> It so happened that the following winter proved to be a very wet one, and the entire tract of land where the Coppers had been found was completely inundated, and actually lay under water for a considerable time. The entomologists deemed that the flood would certainly destroy the Coppers, and that the race would become extinct in that part of the country. The next summer, however, the butterflies were found again on the very same spot, as plentifully as before.

More recently, in 1928, Captain E. Bagwell Purefoy investigated the flooding at Woodwalton Fen, where the Large Copper had recently been re-introduced after an absence of almost seventy years. The Royal Entomological Society of London reported his findings in 1929*:

> The water in Woodwalton Fen reached a depth of over four feet, and many storms swept it, raising great waves, which swept away many dead docks [water dock — *Rumex hydrolapathum*], leaves and stems and all loose material. January 6th, 1928, was the date of the worst storm. On that occasion more than forty of the large poplars that form a screen along the east flank of the fen were snapped off by the wind, and the waves striking the embankment on the far side of the canal threw up spray to a height of over eight feet. It seemed quite certain that any larvae that had crawled up stems in search of safety must have been annihilated by this terrific weather.

Capt. Purefoy revisited the fen during the spring of 1928:

> The next and most important visit was made on April 13th, by which date it was judged that the larvae, should any have survived, would have just commenced to make their characteristic little 'windows' in the young dock leaves. It was a strenuous search, the plants themselves being mostly hidden under rubbish or slime, but it was not an unfruitful one, several very small larvae, still clothed in their brown winter coats, coming to light. The highly interesting and important fact was established on this occasion, that a certain number of the larvae could sleep out long periods with as much as three or four feet of water over them.

THE GHOST MOTH AND A 'WILL-O'-THE-WISP'

Dr Kenneth G. Blair, D.Sc., F.R.E.S., Freshwater, Isle of Wight. (1922)

In his Presidential Address to the South London Entomological and Natural History Society in 1922, Dr Kenneth Gloyne Blair (1882–1952) discussed early theories as to the nature and aetiology of the 'phenomenon known variously as Will-o'-the-Wisp, Jack-o'-Lantern or Ignis Fatuus, etc.'. He then put forward his own theory, stating boldly that he was 'practically certain' that the Ghost Moth (*Hepialus humuli*) was the true source of the popular legend.

* 1929. Report of the Committee appointed by the Entomological Society of London for the Protection of British Lepidoptera. *Proceedings of the Entomological Society of London* 4: 53–68.

It is of interest to note that the *Oxford Dictionary* defines Ignis Fatuus as being 'A phosphorescent light seen hovering or flitting over marshy ground, and supposed to be due to the spontaneous combustion of an inflammable gas (phosphuretted hydrogen) derived from decaying organic matter'. The definition continues: 'It seems to have been formerly a common phenomenon, but is now exceedingly rare. When approached the Ignis Fatuus appears to recede and finally to vanish, sometimes re-appearing in another direction. This led to the notion that it was the work of a mischievous sprite intentionally leading benighted travellers astray.'

Collins English Dictionary, on the other hand, defines the phenomenon as 'a pale flame or phosphorescence sometimes seen over marshy ground at night. It is believed to be due to the spontaneous combustion of methane or other hydrocarbons originating from decomposing organic matter'. Although this definition appears to agree with that of the *Oxford Dictionary*, it is wrong in suggesting that methane might be the gas responsible: methane is stable and not given to spontaneous combustion. Phosphine, or phosphuretted hydrogen, is a much more likely candidate.

The *Shorter Oxford Dictionary on Historical Principles* (1973) defines Will-o'-the-wisp quite differently. It is apparently 'a thing (rarely a person) that deludes or misleads by means of a fugitive appearance' or 'An Alga, *Nostoc commune*, so called from the inexplicable suddenness of its appearance in 1866'.

. . . There is, however, another theoretical cause not mentioned in the *Oxford Dictionary*, and so far as I am aware not generally considered nowadays, though as we shall see later very generally accepted a century or so ago, and that is that the appearance is due to a light-giving insect hovering or flitting about. Such an explanation would, I think, be most obvious and probable were it not for the difficulty of accounting for the luminous insect. . . .

The belief that the Will-o'-the-Wisp is caused by some flying insect apparently dates back at least to the time of Bacon [*c.* 1214–1292] who calls it the *Flying-Gloworm* . . . "In *Italy*, and the Hotter Countreys, there is a flie they call *Lucciole*, that shineth as the Gloworm doth, and it may be is the *Flying-Gloworm*; but that flie is chiefly upon *Fens* and *Marshes*. . . ."

Probably the best known direct observation in support of the 'luminous insect' theory of the Will-o'-the-Wisp is that given by Kirby and Spence [1826], related by the Rev. Dr. Sutton of Norwich. A farmer [Mr Simpringham], of Ickleton, Cambridgeshire, "brought to him a mole cricket (*Gryllotalpa vulgaris*, Latr.), and told him that one of his people, seeing a Jack-o'-Lantern, pursued it and knocked it down, when it proved to be this insect, and the identical specimen shown to him."

As to the accuracy of this observation I shall have something to say later.

Another account of the actual capture of a Will-o'-the-Wisp is recorded by Mr. J. Main (1837, *Annals of Natural History* (New Series, 1: 548). He relates how "travelling by coach through Dedham Vale someone in the company mentioned that it was famous for Will-o'-the-Wisps seen dancing about on nights. His companion, a farmer, immediately exclaimed that all the world was mistaken with respect to this delusive light, for, said he, 'it is nothing but a fly,' and related how he once saw one hovering over the backs of some cattle he was driving and struck it down with his stick. He picked it up, but its light was extinguished, and it appeared exactly like a Moggy-long-legs' (? *Tipula*.) [? Crane-fly]." . . .

In a paper read before the Linnaean [*sic*] Society in 1830* Richard Chambers . . . quotes an observation of his friend Thomas Stothard who said: "As I was returning from Plymouth early

* 1837, *Annals of Nat. History* (New Series, 1: 353).

in June, 1821, having travelled all the preceding day and night, and had passed Blandford early in the morning, considerably before sunrise, when objects were just distinguishable, I saw what was new to me, and which fixed all my attention, for the short time allowed to observe it while mounted on the outside of the coach, passing at the usual rate of 7 or 8 miles an hour. On my right hand, and the side on which I was placed, at the distance of 40 or 50 paces, appeared an irregular light, bounding or rising to the height of three or four feet over some heathy shrubs which covered the high and marshy ground spreading to a great extent: amongst these it sank and reappeared with a motion somewhat between flying and leaping . . . . The experienced coachman pronounced it to be a Will-o'-the-Wisp." Mr. Stothard was of the opinion that the supposed Ignis Fatuus was a Mole Cricket, bringing a specimen from his cabinet and pointing to the structure of the wings in proof of this conclusion; for it could not fly high nor long together; the habitat of the *Gryllotalpa* being the same as where this luminous appearance is usually seen is another coincidence. . . .

Fig. 118. Dr Kenneth Blair was 'practically certain' that the Ghost Moth was the true source of the Will-o'-the-Wisp legend. His name is commemorated in the three moths he introduced to the British list.

Dr Blair dismissed this theory and suggested that Mr Stothard's conclusion was probably influenced by the account in Kirby and Spence's *An Introduction to Entomology* (1826). He went further and suggested that Dr Sutton's labourer 'after knocking down his Will-o'-the-Wisp could not at first find it, and groping among the herbage found what he at once assumed to be the creature he was seeking, but that the Mole Cricket thus found had no connection whatever with the Will-o'-the-Wisp'. He continued:

Now destructive criticism is all very well, but, you may ask, have I anything more likely to suggest in place of the Mole Cricket? I think we are justified in assuming a luminous insect, or apparently luminous insect, to be the cause of the apparitions we have so far considered. Also I fail to find any satisfactory explanation of a truly luminous insect capable of producing this kind of appearance; but "apparently luminous insect;" I think that gives us a clue. Many of you lepidopterists when out dusking or later on a June evening have no doubt seen the appearance of a shining luminous object hovering in one spot for a time, then moving off to repeat the motions a few yards away, then off again, and then disappearing altogether, only to appear again a few moments later. You know it at once to be a male Ghost Swift Moth displaying his attractions in the hope of finding a mate. But would the average countryman know it for such? Would it not appear to him as indeed a pale light hovering over the herbage? *You* have heard of the Will-o'-the-Wisp perhaps, and know it to be caused by the spontaneous ignition of marsh gas given off by the decomposition of organic substances, so that there is no connection in *your* minds between it and the Ghost Swift; but *he* sees this pale hovering light and has heard his father or his grandfather describe the Will-o'-the-Wisp; and the identity of the two is obvious. Then when he knocks it down, it falls back downwards, or with only the underside of the wings exposed, and in the darkness is practically invisible. No wonder then that when he finds an extraordinary looking animal like a Mole Cricket he at once jumps to the conclusion that that was what he knocked down.

It is well to bear in mind, too, the traditional appearance of the Will-o'-the-Wisp; it is described as a 'phosphorescent' light, *i.e.*, it does not look like an actual flame, but is a pale shining luminosity suggesting phosphorescence, which is exactly the appearance of the male Ghost Swift.

That the Ghost Swift is the substantial basis of this class of phenomena appears to some extent to be confirmed by the following paragraph that appeared in the *Westminster Review* in October, 1832 (reprinted in the *Ent.* Mag., 1833, p. 216).

"*Ignis Fatuus.* This appearance has been strongly surmised to be a luminous insect. It is many years since the similarity of its motion was observed to that of an insect avoiding pursuit. A subsequent examiner has stated that he approached one near enough to see distinctly the form of an insect with wings like a dragon-fly. Two or three years ago an anonymous article in a country paper announced that some person in digging up the mud of an old pond had discovered two creatures which he surmised to be the insects in question, and which he described as looking like crayfish with wings. The entomologist who can ascertain the fact by securing an *Ignis Fatuus* in a bottle will have drawn a tooth from the jaws of superstition and human suffering."

The editor asks, is the insect in question the Mole Cricket? But the description of 'an insect with wings like a dragon-fly' seems clearly to indicate the Ghost Swift, for the two pairs of long narrow wings, the hinder pair free from the fore pair, are very much the shape

of the wings of a dragon-fly, and the shining white wings of the male Ghost Swift are the only ones that would be clearly discernible in the dark. . . .

Hearing that I was interested in this subject the late Mr. Benjamin Harrison of Ightham, Kent, was good enough to send me one of his old notebooks drawing my attention to an entry which I will quote *in extenso*: —

Met Bridger the butcher, who formerly resided on the confines of Woolmer Forest.

He said: — "Did you see Old Will of the Wisp?"

I replied: — "Once, in passing a boggy spot near Brasted late at night, I fancied I saw a faint light over the water, but it was impossible to approach near."

"Well then, I have; and not only seen Old Will, but caught him!"

"Oh! how was that?"

"Well, I'll tell you. Me and a friend had been to a cricket match and stayed late. It were about midsummer, and as we were passing a boggy spot in Woolmer Forest we saw a lot of lights dancing up and down, and I said, 'There's Old Will of the Wisp.' Presently the trackway led us close by the outside of the bog and we saw a lot more of the light. We were both on horses, and seeing the light get close to my mate, who was in front, I shouted out 'Here he comes, Strike at un with your whip.' He did so, and hit un too, and in a minute his horse's mane was all alight, as it were. We stopped and examined, and saw lots of little lights all entangled in the mane; and so it kept on until we put our horses in the stable, where the light became stronger. 'Wait a bit' I said, 'let me go and get something to catch un in.' I went indoors and got a tumbler, and came back and shook the mane over the glass, and then covered it with my hand, and took it indoors. We found a lot of little gnats something like the flies on the hops only bigger, and kept until the next day, and their little tails all shone like little glowworms. There was about twelve or thirteen of them, and we showed to lots of our neighbours the next day, and they shone a little the next night, but not so bright." (30th October, 1888.)

Dr Blair presented a number of other extraordinary theories that had been put forward to account for the Will-o'-the-wisp phenomenon:

Yet another explanation is offered by Mr. R. J. W. Purdy, in the *Transactions of the Norfolk and Norwich Naturalists' Society*, vol. viii. (ante), p. 547. The light was first seen on February 3rd, 1907, moving horizontally backwards and forwards over a distance of several hundred yards. It rose in the air to the height of forty feet or more, then descended again, and went through the same evolution many times. . . .

On December 1st of the same year, and many subsequent dates, it was seen again, and observed to alight on the ground and disappear in a plantation. Seen within a few yards it had two intensely bright spots on its head, and was uttering the quickly repeated 'Chuck, Chuck' of the White Owl.

The author expresses the belief that most of the tales respecting "Will-o'-the-Wisp," "Corpse Candles," and "Lantern-Men," are the result of occasional luminosity assumed by birds of nocturnal habits that frequently fly over marshy ground in search of prey. This luminosity is probably accounted for by the feathers being smeared with putrescent matter from the hollow trees or other cavities in which the birds pass the day.

He ended his Presidential Address by returning to the widely accepted origin of the phenomenon:

We also see that the popular explanation of the mystery, '*viz.* — the spontaneous ignition of marsh gas evolved from decaying organic matter, though supported by definite scientific observations relates not to the Will-o'-the-Wisp, but to a very different phenomenon that should be designated by a different name, such as 'Marsh Lights' or 'Marsh Fires.' If we ask how it is that this explanation is now so widely received at the expense of the older and once very popular theory of the insect origin of the light, I can only suggest that it is because of its scientific foundation in contrast with the unsatisfactory and unconvincing nature of the evidence for the latter, and consequently, since it was the only explanation in the field that was in any way satisfactory, the fact that phenomena of very different character were involved has continued to be overlooked.

That the Ghost Swift Moth is the true source of the popular legend of the Will-o'-the-Wisp is in my opinion practically certain, since it is the *only* simple and natural solution of the luminous insect theory. It is of course possible that the mystery of the luminous insect may not be so simple as I contend, that it *may* depend on some rare instance of an insect becoming luminous owing to pathological causes, but the probabilities against such a supposition are immense. At the same time that the simplicity of the Ghost Swift theory is a very strong point in its favour, in some ways this very simplicity militates against it, for if that be the true explanation of the Will-o'-the-Wisp how is it that it has not been proved to be so beyond question long ago? Probably because the testimony of a few sturdy countrymen, who had convinced themselves that it was nothing but a fly, a "Moggy-long-legs," was insufficient to outweigh the very circumstantial evidence of the marsh gas explanation that appealed so much more forcefully to the theoretical scientist; and because with the spread of the study of entomology the Ghost Moth has become more generally known for what it is, and its association with the Will-o'-the-Wisp either not recognised or ridiculed. . . .

[Blair, K. G. 1922. Presidential Address. *Proceedings of the South London Entomological and Natural History Society* **1921–1922**: 9–29].

Claude Morley was obviously not a subscriber to the idea that birds were the source of the mystery. In *The Entomologist* (1911) he wrote:

Since Spence wrote Letter xxv. of the 'Introduction to Entomology,' we can recall no claim made to *ignes fatui* as an entomological subject. He distinctly states, however, his expectation that luminous insects would be discovered to be the explanation of the phenomenon, and regards the phosphureted hydrogen theory as impracticable on account of the light's erratic and local movements in a high, steady breeze. Personally, we have (with Wailes) vaguely supposed it to be "the spontaneous ignition of gaseous particles" given off by decaying vegetable matter. But the only person who has ever "knocked down" a will-o'-the-wisp — at Ickleton, Cambs, in 1780 — found *Gryllotalpa*! A recent writer in 'Country Life' brings forward a very different explanation, pointing out that Linné probably named the barn-owl *Strix flammea* on account of the occasional luminosity of its breast feathers, caused (thinks Lydekker) by "their plumage having come into contact with phosphorescent bacteria developed in the decaying wood of their nesting resorts." But jack-o'-lanterns are not found in farmyards, and even a Cambridge yokel of 1780 knew a barn-owl from a mole-cricket!

[Morley, C. 1911. By the way. *The Entomologist* 44: 297–298].

WILL-O'-THE-WISP

Philip B. M. Allan, M.A., M.B.E., Bishop's Stortford, Hertfordshire. (1965)

Forty-three years after Dr Blair addressed the 'South-London' about the possible nature of Will-o'-the-wisps, P. B. M. Allan wrote a lengthy article for *The Entomologist's Record* on the same subject. Curiously, Allan made no reference to Blair's paper at all. In the 1890s, while staying in the New Forest, he actually witnessed the phenomenon known as Will-o'-the-wisp.

Fig. 119. P. B. M. Allan M.B.E. The 'Old Moth-Hunter' (1958).

. . . I was passing over the open ground at the lower end of King's Garn enclosure when I saw a light crossing my path a few yards ahead of me. It was moving about as fast as a man running slowly but I saw nobody although it was not yet dark enough to prevent me seeing a man fifty yards away. Of course, there were no electric torches in those days and the light could only have been — as I thought — the flame of a match. When the light was a little distance away it suddenly dived to the ground — just as though the match, as I supposed it to be, had been thrown down. Still I did not see anybody. It was a little eerie and I expect I quickened my pace.

The more I thought about it the more puzzled I became. When a man lights his pipe out of doors he stands still and, having lit his pipe, throws down the match; he does not run with the lighted match in his hand. Also I was certain I could have seen a man had there been one present. Moreover, what would a man have been doing at late dusk *crossing* the path and going over the rough ground which led to nowhere? A poacher going to set a snare in the plantation? Then why did he advertise his presence by shining a light for twenty or thirty yards? So, not wishing to invite a more or less — probably less — polite reflection on my veracity I said nothing about the matter to anyone.

Both Dr Blair and Philip Allan investigated the history of Will-o'-the-wisp in considerable detail. Allan tells us that John Ray's learned colleague and travelling companion, Francis Willughby (1635–1672), studied the *Ignes fatui* in England:

> [He] came to the conclusion that so far from being evil sprites (as was popularly supposed) these phenomena were neither more nor less than luminous insects; and as the only luminous insect with which he was acquainted in England was *Lampyris noctiluca* Linn. [Glow-worm] he not unnaturally identified the *Ignis fatuus* with the glow-worm. . . . Unfortunately, Willughby did not pursue the matter farther . . .

In 1830 the Revd William Derham F.R.S. challenged Willughby's theory. He read a paper before the Royal Society in which he asserted that Will-o'-the-wisps were not insects but vapours. Derham's description of his own meeting with this phenomenon is recorded by Allan:

His own observations he made at a place in a valley between rocky hills . . . in some boggy ground near the bottom of those hills. Where, seeing one in a calm, dark night, with gentle approaches he got up within 2 or 3 yards of it, and viewed it with all possible care. He found it frisking about a dead thistle growing in a field, till a small motion of the air made it skip to another place, and thence to another, and another.

It is now about 55 years since he saw this phenomenon, but he had as fresh and perfect an idea of it as if was but a few days. And as he took it then, so he is of the same opinion now, that it was a fired vapour. The male glow-worm Mr. D. knows emit their shining light as they fly; by which means they discover and woo the females: but he never observed them fly together in so great numbers as to make a light equal to an *ignis fatuus*. And he was so near that had it been the shining of glow-worms he must have seen it in little distinct spots of light; but it was one continuous body of light.

Allan went on to ask:

How an *Ignis fatuus* "frisking about a dead thistle" and skipping from one place to another could be reconciled with a vapour the Reverend observer did not relate, and indeed his succeeding words militated against his own theory. "They are most frequent in watery and morassy ground . . . They are continually in motion, but this motion is various and uncertain. Sometimes they disappear of a sudden, and appear again in an instant in some other places. Commonly they keep hovering about 6 feet from the ground . . . In general these lights are great friends to brooks and rivers, being frequently observed along their banks."

Allan dismissed the 'vapour theory' at once. 'There are three indisputable facts — indisputable because they are based on certain fundamental physical laws which prevail on this earth — which rule out, quite definitely, any supposition that the *Ignis fatuus* is an ignited gas.' He went on to explain what he meant before coming to the same hypothesis as Dr Blair: a Will-o'-the-wisp or *Ignis fatuus* is an insect, not gaseous ignition. And his favoured insect was the Mole Cricket. Allan quoted Gilbert White, of Selborne: '. . . when mole-crickets fly, they move *cursu ondoso*, rising and falling in curves', and adds: 'Note how exactly this describes the flight of almost all the observed *Ignes fatui*.'

He ended his extraordinary article with a lament:

At the end of the last century mole-crickets used to inhabit a small bog in the woods near Bramshaw in the New Forest, within a few hundred yards of the place where I saw my — as I believe — *Ignis fatuus*. . . . It was quite a small bog, not, I think, much more than half an acre in extent, and like many of the New Forest — and other — bogs it was not a place which one would try to walk across. But it was well sprinkled with little hillocks, like conical molehills covered with turf, and these were firm enough to stand on. They were also the 'warrens' of the mole-crickets, and if you stooped and dug the fingers of both hands well into the base of one of these hillocks and, with a sudden effort, wrenched it up entire, you would find that the hillock was traversed by burrows large enough to emit a finger. . . .

The inhabitants of these burrows could be taken only in the evening; presumably they slept down in their warrens by day. But if you approached a hillock, as delicately as Agag — for the mole-cricket, like most other insects, is extremely sensitive to vibrations — at dusk, and tore it up with great suddenness, it was odds on that you would expose a *Gryllotalpa* . . .

And now that I have investigated the *Ignis fatuus* and have read all about Farmer Simpringham and the rest I am too old to revisit that bog. Dearly would I like to go there on an evening in May or June, with a camp-stool and a butterfly-net, and sit there quietly smoking my pipe until a Will-o'-the-wisp appeared.

[Allan, P. B. M. 1965. Will-o'-the-Wisp. *The Entomologist's Record and Journal of Variation* 77: 252–259; 273–280].

A KESTREL CATCHING BUTTERFLIES

Wilfred Parkinson Curtis, Poole, Dorset. (1903)

. . . On the 13th July, 1901, I was in company with my brother, Mr. E. Harker Curtis, on the top of Ballard Down, Swanage, catching butterflies. The species noticed were mostly *Melanargia galatea* [Marbled White], *Argynnis aglaia* [Dark Green Fritillary], *Hipparchia semele* [Grayling], *H. tithonus* [Gatekeeper], and *H. janira* [Meadow Brown]. Whilst thus engaged, a kestrel (*Falco tinnunculus*) was observed hawking about and hovering over the long grass, every once now and then dropping like a stone to the ground, remaining a second or two and then rising again. These movements attracted my attention, so my brother and I lay down in the grass to watch the bird. After some time I remarked to my brother that the bird did not appear to get much, as it never rose with a mouse or a lizard, and it certainly did not remain on the ground long enough to eat either. Presently the bird dropped close to a furze

bush, and I crept up to the bush and looked over the top. The kestrel jumped and flew off, leaving a half-eaten *Argynnis aglaia* on the ground. Then I followed the bird and examined the places where it went down, and found almost every time either the mutilated remains of a *M. galatea* or of an *A. aglaia*. It seemed to have least difficulty in catching *galatea*, as, finding what it was doing, I watched it very closely and saw it miss several of the wily *aglaia*. The bird waited until the insect pitched, and then pounced down on it, and, having regard to the fact that the females were busy depositing ova, the percentage of the females killed must have been very large. I found by counting that the bird caught about thirty-six specimens in an hour, and it was hard at it for at least five hours, that is to say, the whole time I was present; and when I left, the bird was still hawking about. I have seen a kestrel at the same place on many occasions since, and similarly occupied. The bird certainly did not seem to bother itself about me, as I could have captured it in my net had I been so disposed, since it allowed me to approach within a couple of yards or so. . . .

[Curtis, W. Parkinson, 1903. Kestrel destroying butterflies. *The Entomologist* **36**: 68].

Wilfred Parkinson Curtis (1878–1968) was one of the great Dorset naturalists. He was born in Poole, and was a lawyer by profession and practised in Bournemouth. He was also an accomplished artist, photographer and horticulturalist. He 'started to collect seriously in 1893', and in 1934 published the first part of his valuable 'A List of the Lepidoptera of Dorset', with a second part in 1947. 'He knew and worked with all the late Victorian and early 20th century entomologists both within and outside the County.' (Thomas, J, & Webb, N. 1984). Recalling his friendship with the Rector of Bloxworth (see p. 12), Curtis wrote: 'I knew the Revd O. Pickard-Cambridge nearly all my life and his memory was phenomenally accurate.'

CHAPTER SEVEN

SOME 'GENTLEMEN OF THE NET' –
AND A RANNOCH SPRAWLER

'A little nonsense, now and then,
Is relished by the wisest men.'

Ernest A. Elliot, 1896

WITH THE OPENING YEARS of the twenty-first century, butterfly collecting appears to be a hobby in serious decline. Today there are perhaps five hundred serious collectors – and if this figure is disputed, then certainly less than one thousand. One hundred and fifty years ago, the figure was probably twenty to thirty times this. What has happened? The rise of the conservation movement, from its roots in the 1920s, has led to changing attitudes and the perhaps unfortunate insistence that butterfly collecting might be cruel, morally wrong, or even downright unspeakable. With this in mind it is of more than passing interest that the Victorian directory of entomologists published by Henry T. Stainton in the 1850s included an extraordinary number of clergymen, many of whom would appear to have spent most of their leisure hours net in hand, or busily arranging specimens in the vicarage cabinet. Clearly those gentlemen were not too worried about the morality of butterfly collecting.

W. S. Coleman (see p. 377) was another mid-Victorian lepidopterist. He published a little volume – *British Butterflies* (1860) – in which he attempted to justify the collecting and killing of butterflies as a worthy pursuit. After telling us that butterflies had never been known to sting or bite, he went on to show that insects could not and did not feel pain. 'Plenty of striking instances of this are on record,' he wrote:

> I have seen a wasp that had been snipped in two, afterwards regale himself
> with avidity upon some red syrup, which, as he imbibed, gathered into a large
> ruby bead just behind the wings (where the stomach should have been); but
> really the creature's pleasure seemed to be only augmented by the change in
> his anatomy, because he could drink ten times his ordinary fill of sweets,
> without, of course, getting any the fuller. I could almost fancy a scientific
> epicure envying the insect his ever fresh appetite and gastronomic capabilities.

Coleman went even further: 'I think few will deny that man enjoys a vested right to make use of any of the inferior animals, even to the taking of their life, if the so doing ministers to his own well-being or pleasure, and practically every one assumes this right in one way or another.' It is at this point that we part company with Mr Coleman and leave it for others to contest the moral argument.

Before this volume is brought to a close we have put together a final selection of entomological notes and observations. In this chapter we look at cyanide as a killing agent, the plight of Russian entomologists and the identity of a certain Dr 'Hammersmith'. We also note that the wing patterns of some butterflies and moths resemble human faces, and learn that one moth uses rabbit-burrows as a place of safety. There is still a great deal more to learn about our native Lepidoptera, and with this thought we bid farewell to our fellow 'gentlemen of the net'.

A PROFILE OF THE HUMAN FACE IS OBSERVABLE UPON THE UPPER SIDE OF THE PRIMARY WINGS OF THE FEMALE CLOUDED YELLOW . . .

Revd William T. Bree, Allesley Rectory, Leicester. (1834)

Fig. 120. Clouded Yellow (*Colias croceus*): forewings show profile of a human face.

It is observed, in vol. i. p. 518. of the *Entomological Magazine* [1833], "that on the reverse of Hippárchia Janìra [Meadow Brown] may be traced a very tolerably defined profile, in some specimens no very bad likeness, of the Lord Chancellor Brougham." This is not very evident in the specimens I have examined. A much stronger resemblance of the human profile (I do not say portrait of the Chancellor) is exhibited on the upper side of the primary wings of the female of Còlias Edùsa [Clouded Yellow]. In some specimens, which, I need hardly observe, vary very much, the face is so conspicuous, as at once to catch the eye of the beholder on the first inspection of the insect. The black spot towards the centre of the wing forms the eye of the profile; the profile itself being yellow upon a black ground, and fronting the tip of the wing.

[Bree, W. T. 1834. A profile of the human face is observable upon the upper side of the primary wings of Còlias Edùsa, female. A profile of Chancellor Brougham is observable on the reverse of Hippárchia Janìra. *Magazine of Natural History* 7: 262–263].

Examination of the undersides of almost one hundred specimens of the Meadow Brown has failed to convince us, as it had the Revd William Bree too, that the patterning represents a conspicuous profile of Henry Brougham (Fig. 121), Lord Chancellor and 1st Baron Brougham and Vaux (1778–1868). A distinguished lawyer and noted polymath, he founded the University of London. And, in a very famous court case, he secured a settlement of £50,000 a year for Queen Caroline following her divorce from George IV. He was also well known for his long-term relationship with the famous courtesan Harriette Wilson.

Fig. 121. Henry Brougham was responsible for establishing Cannes as a health resort for the rich and famous. In 1834 while en route to Italy to winter in Nice he found the border with France closed due to cholera restrictions. Forced to turn back, he stopped overnight in the fishing village of Cannes on the Côte d'Azur. Enchanted by the scenery and climate he remained there and had a villa built for himself. His influence was such that very soon other members of the British aristocracy were following his example.

Examination of 300 Clouded Yellows, however, revealed that in a small number we could detect a passable likeness to a profile of the human face. Whether or not this also resembles the profile of the Lord Chancellor remains uncertain. What is certain, however, is the fact that he designed a carriage (brougham) that was named after him.

Henry Tibbats Stainton (1822–1892), perhaps the doyen of the Victorian lepidopterists, was a wealthy man who devoted most of his time to entomology. His collected correspondence (and he was a prolific correspondent) is housed in the Entomology Library of the Natural History Museum in London. Included among the papers is a receipt for the new brougham carriage he purchased in 1872. Complete with brass lamps, it cost him £198–10s (Fig. 122).

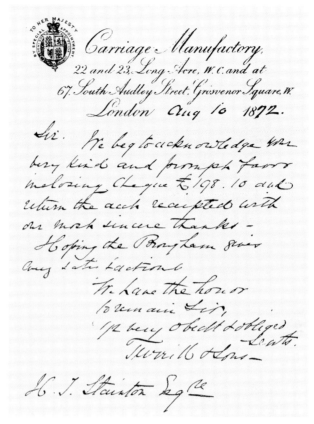

Fig. 122. Receipt for Henry Stainton's brougham carriage; complete with brass headlamps it cost £198 10s.

Fig. 123. Mother Shipton (*Callistege mi*): forewings show profile of a witch's face.

Another insect to carry the outline of a human profile is the Mother Shipton (*Callistege mi*). Mother Shipton (1488–*c*.1560) was thought to be an English witch and prophetess who, so it was claimed, was carried off by the devil and bore him an imp. The forewings of the moth reveal a striking pattern resembling the witch's face.

MODE OF KILLING INSECTS

James F. Stephens, South Lambeth, London. (1835)

"What a cruel practice!" frequently exclaims the spectator, when he beholds an entomologist's box, in which a fine *Bombus* [Bumble-bee], or other lively insect, is impaled upon a pin, and whose futile exertions to extricate itself produce the semblance of agonized writhings. My present object, however, is not to moot the broad question of insect feeling, but to quiet the apprehension of those humane individuals whose fine sympathies are called into action by a practice (as above alluded to) which savours more of cruelty than humanity. You will perhaps, therefore, Mr. Editor, allow me to mention an expeditious, certain, and not unpleasant mode of destroying vitality in the little objects of our research — a plan communicated to me by my friend F. Wood Esq.; one which, from having recently tried its effect, I can safely recommend for adoption; and may be resorted to in almost every situation, unaccompanied by the danger attendant upon employing the active poisons, — such as the nitric, oxalic, or prussic acids, which are frequently used, — the inconvenience resulting from the change of colour in the species when sulphur, &c. is employed, — or the smell from tobacco, &c.

The plan is simply this: — Take three or four juicy leaves (the younger the better, with, if a more powerful effect is required, a small portion of the tip of the stalk) of the common laurel; break or cut them into small pieces, and crush them quickly between two stones,[a] in a thin piece of paper, screw up the produce in the latter, with as little exposure to the air as can be avoided, and fix the mass by a pin in a corner of the collecting box in which the living insects are to be previously placed; keep the box closely shut, and in about five minutes every specimen will have expired. It is necessary that the external air should be excluded, otherwise the fumes of prussic acid, which are evolved from the crushed leaves, will become too much attenuated to affect the respiratory organs of the insects, and the latter will partially revive if too speedily exposed to the vivifying influence of a purer atmosphere. I have tried the experiment rather extensively upon insects of various families: *Bombi* and *Helophili* [hoverflies] die very rapidly in less than two minutes, and without any struggling, as is the case when heat, &c. is applied; and moths, in a state of repose, expire without a single previous motion: consequently the process I have recommended is most admirably adapted for killing the larger *Lepidoptera* almost immediately upon their capture, and thus fine specimens may be conveyed home uninjured. I yesterday killed a gigantic *Epeira diadema* [Diadem Spider] in less than half a minute; and a specimen of *Helops cæruleus* [Tenebrionid beetle], with one or two fresh-captured *Philonthi* [Rove beetles], at liberty in the box, were also dead when it was opened. I therefore strongly recommend the above process to the notice of the practical entomologist, as being, from its convenience, better adapted for general application than any hitherto proposed.

[Stephens, J. F. 1835. Mode of killing insects. *The Entomological Magazine* 2: 436–437].

This letter to the Editor of *The Entomological Magazine* effectively introduced the laurel leaf killing bottle, which was then widely used by generations of amateur collectors and schoolboys for almost one hundred years. The advantage of using laurel leaves was that it appeared to delay or minimize the effects of *rigor mortis*, so that specimens could be set shortly after being killed. Although ether had been used by entomologists in France as early as 1827, it antedated the use of such killing agents as chloroform (1842) and potassium cyanide (1854). The most widely used killing agents today are ammonia and ethyl acetate.

EFFECT OF CYANIDE UPON COLOUR

Charles G. Barrett, Pembroke. (1884)

A very curious case of artificial colouring in a butterfly has been sent me by a friend. He says that the specimen, a male *Gonopteryx rhamni* [Brimstone], was placed in a spare cyanide bottle, and left undisturbed for two years; but that, at some intermediate time, the stopper was tampered with and not properly replaced, so that air was introduced. The result is, that the butterfly is richly coloured with crimson along the costal area, and partially round the margins of the fore-wings, and has large blotches of the same on the hind-wings. Indeed the

---

[a] At home a mortar may be employed.

only portion of the wings which is left entirely of the usual brimstone colour is that portion which, in *G. Cleopatra* [Cleopatra], *is clouded with crimson.*

[Barrett, C. G. 1884. Effect of cyanide upon colour. *Entomologist's Monthly Magazine* **21**: 23].

F. W. Frohawk, in his *Varieties of British Butterflies* (1938, Pl. 48), figures a similar specimen of the Brimstone, which was caught by Mrs R. I. Iremonger in April 1920. It was apparently resting on Virginia creeper in her garden at Langford, Bristol, and 'she caught it because of its unusual colouring, as it reminded her of an autumn leaf'. That a living specimen might possess this remarkable colouring suggests that the role of cyanide in the production of Barrett's aberrant specimen remains speculative; there are two further specimens of this unusual aberration in the Natural History Museum. In 1922 Frohawk, however, did report a possible association with cyanide exposure when he stated that 'certain species, especially *G. rhamni* and both *C. edusa* and *C. hyale* [Clouded and Pale Clouded Yellow], are very liable to become blotched with crimson and otherwise discoloured, and if left for any considerable time in the cyanide bottle only a small proportion of their original colour will remain'. In spite of this, Frank Littlewood, a lepidopterist from the Lake District, strongly supported the use of cyanide as it appeared to promote relaxation from *rigor mortis* thus enabling the collector to set his specimens under improved circumstances.

Of all the killing agents used by collectors, potassium cyanide was the most deadly. It was first used for killing insects in 1854, and lepidopterists continued to use it for the next one hundred years. Fifty years ago, a cyanide killing bottle could be purchased from most chemists for a few shillings and thousands came to be used by schoolboy and adult collectors alike. Despite their widespread use we have been quite unable to find evidence that there was any increase in morbidity or mortality amongst collectors using potassium cyanide. Indeed, they appeared to be more at risk when pricking the thorax of a specimen with strong oxalic acid!

In the next piece, Frank Littlewood discusses the merits of cyanide versus other killing agents.

KILLING BUTTERFLIES AND MOTHS WITH CYANIDE

Frank Littlewood, Kendal, Cumberland. (1922)

I do not think that it is known — at any rate I have never seen the fact referred to in any book or journal I have ever read — that a butterfly or moth killed in the cyanide bottle (half an hour in a strong bottle will ensure death, although no harm accrues if left in longer) and then simply pinned or laid loose in a tin box (an empty tobacco tin will do) quite *dry* and without any *relaxing* agent whatever, will, *of its own accord,* in the space of about forty-eight hours (for an insect of average size, like *Pieris rapae* [Small White]) return to its original natural flexible condition. A shorter period (say twenty-four hours) will suffice for small insects, whilst an *extra* day or even two days may be necessary for the largest moths. The tin may be kept in the ordinary sitting-room temperature. The same thing happens, of course, if specimens are left *in* the killing bottle for an equal period of time, but it is only this season that I discovered that the happy result might be obtained in the above more convenient way, without the necessity of encumbering oneself with a number of reserve killing bottles. Cyanide of potassium is one of the best all-round killing methods, almost its only drawback being the "rigor" that it causes, and which renders immediate setting impossible. The above hint may enable even a busy collector to use cyanide more freely, as it is an easy matter to put each day's killing into a separate resting-tin and to affix the date. If, when the insects *have* arrived at the proper setting condition, it is not convenient to set them, I use a laurel leaf tin, which is admirable for *keeping* them relaxed, though apparently not at all necessary for bringing them to that state in the first instance. In any case, the shorter time any specimen is exposed to cyanide or laurel, or to any other killing or relaxing agent, the less likely are its colours to be injured. . . .

The late Mr. J. W. Tutt condemned cyanide because he found that it necessitated keeping the insects a week longer on the setting-boards. This was due, I believe, to his method of using it, viz. attempting to set the specimen as soon as it was dead. Many collectors try to anticipate the rigor in this way with insects they breed or bring home alive, but I have never been able to consider it a good method. For after even half-an-hour's exposure in the bottle (the bare safe minimum for the bulk of things) a certain amount of rigidity is apparent — far too much for really good and rapid setting. And although the specimen may then be set, the rigor will still carry on for the full time, and will be followed by the inevitable period of relaxation. Which means that the insect is occupying valuable board-space under false pretences, for it does not begin to dry, really, until the fifth or sixth day! . . .

I do not wish any reader to infer that I place no value on the laurel-leaf relaxing box. On the contrary, I consider it one of the most useful items of the collector's outfit. But it is not necessary for the relaxation of an insect that has been killed in the cyanide bottle. Its principal use, with me, is to preserve the relaxation (spontaneously produced) until such time as it is convenient to set one's specimens. And this it will do, for weeks if necessary, with many of the moths, but caution must be exercised when entrusting butterflies to its action. Furthermore, for the relaxation of old insects, I do not think laurel leaves, or the ready-made mixture from a laurel base supplied by one enterprising dealer, can be equalled.

[Littlewood, F. 1922. Killing with cyanide. *The Entomologist* **55**: 260; **56**: 90–92].

MOTHS AND RABBIT-BURROWS

In his article entitled 'Protective Resemblance' (1913) C. W. Colthrup had discussed the association of moths and rabbit-burrows. He said of The Annulet moth (*Gnophos obscuratus*): 'I am well aware of the habit of this moth in the New Forest, where the earth is dark and the moth dark also. If the dark coloration is "protective," why is it that the moth hides itself in a rabbit-burrow?' Although the question attracted a short answer from A. Bacot, this failed to clear the air. It merely encouraged Mr Colthrup to report sundry other observations.

Letter from A. Bacot, F.E.S. of Loughton, Essex:

Gnophos obscuraria [*G. obscuratus*] and rabbit-burrows.— I am wondering if Mr. Colthrup's remarks *re Gnophos obscuraria* and rabbit-burrows . . . covers a case of association that has hitherto escaped notice. I have frequently noticed the partiality of this species for *bare soil* in chalk districts, but the suggested restriction to rabbit-warrens is outside my experience. Possibly the habit is a local one and limited to the dark form alone.

[Bacot, A. 1913. *Gnophos obscuraria* and rabbit-burrows. *The Entomologist's Record and Journal of Variation* **25**: 282].

Reply by C. W. Colthrup of East Dulwich Grove, London:

With regard to Mr. Bacot's query *re G. obscuraria*, I may say that on a slope of the Downs at Eastbourne, where there are no rabbit-burrows, this insect rests on the bare soil, etc. . . .

but on other parts of the South Downs where there are rabbit-burrows, it rests in them. It is possible some may be found outside, but I have not done so.

The method employed by the New Forest collectors to get the insect (which I have worked well elsewhere) is to take a "swish" made of one or two long twigs, rattle them at the mouth of the burrow, and net the insects as they fly out.

After all, this habit of hiding away in dark places is not so unusual with moths as is generally supposed, and I feel pretty sure that those found on fences and tree trunks are in most cases the exceptions.

On the Crumbles, at Eastbourne, a large expanse of bare shingle with only a few wooden posts, *Xylophasia monoglypha* (*polyodon*) [Dark Arches] sometimes swarms at sugar, yet if you examine these posts the next day you will be lucky if you find a single specimen of *X. monoglypha* at rest on them, yet they would harmonize very well with the old wood. Where do they go? I believe down in the shingle.

At the beginning of last July in a small outhouse in our garden, a specimen of *Mania maura* [Old Lady] was found at rest, and day by day the number increased till one morning there were seventeen. The moths went out for their flight at night, and returned through five triangular openings at the top of the door, the base of the triangles being only three inches. Individual moths could be recognised by certain marks. They continued to resort to the shed after I left London at the end of July for my holidays.

[Colthrup, C. W. 1913. *Gnophos obscuraria* and rabbit-burrows. *The Entomologist's Record and Journal of Variation* **25**: 282–283].

THE DEATH'S-HEAD HAWK-MOTH

'When *A. atropos* is on the wing, therefore, shut your doors and windows, lest he bring war, pestilence and hunger to you and yours. And see that you have electric light.' (Allan, 1937).

VITALITY OF THE DEATH'S-HEAD HAWK-MOTH

Annie Dows, Boston, Lincolnshire. (1881)

I have to record a most extraordinary instance of vitality in the case of a fine *Acherontia atropos* [Death's-head Hawk-moth], which I captured last autumn. Upon my first taking it, it emitted a shrill cry, which continued without ceasing until I put it in my killing-box. This box is a close-fitting tin one, with a false bottom of perforated zinc. Being a large moth I dropped thirteen or fourteen drops of chloroform into the box, and kept it close between two and a half and three hours, at the expiration of which time, on opening the box, the chloroform was unpleasantly strong, and the moth to all appearance dead. I cut it open, eviscerated it, stuffed it with cotton-wool, and put it on the setting-board. To my astonishment, on inspecting it the following morning, it was quite lively, and, had the pin through the thorax not been a very strong one, would have liberated itself. I killed it by soaking it in benzoline, which, by-the-bye, I find the quickest and cheapest mode for all moths, and one doing them no damage.

(We doubt whether the method of killing Lepidoptera recommended by our correspondent is the best; some of the older systems are less likely to damage the specimens, — the vapour of ammonia for instance. — ED.)

[Dows, A. 1881. Vitality of *Acherontia atropos*. *The Entomologist* **14**: 114–115].

The next two articles include another instance of the seemingly indestructible nature of this particular species and the irrational reaction that this spectacular family of moths — the Sphingidae — often engenders in the unenlightened.

From *The Entomologist's Record*, March 1918:

In the *Naturalist* for December [1917] still other *Agrius convolvuli* [Convolvulus Hawk-moth] are reported to have turned up in the North. The advent of this and other large moths is often attended with remarkable incidents. Mr. W. J. Clarke says, "I was attending the funeral of an old friend at the cemetery, and an old lady in the company suddenly made a furious onslaught with her umbrella upon some object in the grass. Presently one of the grave-diggers went to her help, and assisted in hammering with his spade the object of her attentions. After the funeral was over I went to the spot to see what they had been killing, expecting to find a frog or a toad, but instead I found the battered remains of a Convolvulus Hawk Moth. The grave-digger was standing by, and when I stooped to pick it up he hastily exclaimed, "Deaen't touch it, it's a hoss-teng." I had some difficulty in persuading the man that the object of his attentions was after all but a harmless moth." Mr Clarke goes on to give an incident which is too good not to be repeated. "A Death's Head Moth had flown upon the deck of a Scarborough fishing boat while out at sea. The crew viewed the intruder with great dread, and turned the hose on it, washing it into a corner, where, half dead, it was transfixed to the deck by a daring member of the crew, armed with a hammer and big wire nail. To make it additionally secure a fish box was turned over it, and so it arrived in port, where I saw it shortly afterwards, still alive in spite of its ill-usage."

[Anon. 1918. Current notes and short notices. *The Entomologist's Record and Journal of Variation* **30**: 54].

SUPERSTITION REGARDING THE DEATH'S-HEAD HAWK-MOTH

Revd John Hellins, Exeter, Devon. (1886)

The Revd John Hellins (1829–1887) was Chaplain to the Devon County Prison, and before that an Assistant Master at Exeter Grammar School. He is largely remembered for his collaboration with William Buckler (1814–1884) (Fig. 128) in tracing the life histories of a number of British Lepidoptera. Volume 1 of Buckler's *The Larvae of the British Butterflies and Moths* (1886) contains a valuable appendix compiled by the Revd Hellins. He died at the relatively early age of fifty-eight from erysipelas.

The following story is given me by a friend residing at Teignmouth, who has heard it more than once from the principal actor (or sufferer) in it; and it is by no means a story of ancient days:

A fine specimen of *Acherontia Atropos* [Death's-head Hawk-moth] had been caught by a sailor on board ship out at sea, and brought ashore and given by him to a youngster, who being fond of curiosities received it as a great prize, and in his pride displayed it on the wall in his mother's room in a case specially made for it. Some time after the young man fell ill, and, during his illness, an old woman, who had officiated as nurse in his early days, and took an especial interest in him, paid his mother a visit of condolence, and unfortunately cast eyes on the "Death's Head." The cause of the illness was seen at once! "No wonder your son has fallen ill! and he'll never be well again as long as *that* thing is in the house."

Of course she had plenty of instances to relate of the horrible danger of neglecting her warnings, till the mother in alarm promised to throw the unlucky thing away. But that was

not enough, it must be burnt; nothing else would avert the impending evils — and into the fire it went. And before long the unfortunate curiosity-lover recovered his health — only to find that the good ladies' affectionate care had robbed him of his greatest treasure!

[Hellins, J. 1886. Superstition regarding *Acherontia atropos. Entomologist's Monthly Magazine* **22**: 212].

PECULIAR ODOUR EMITTED BY THE DEATH'S-HEAD HAWK-MOTH

Christopher G. Hall, Deal, Kent. (1883)

Has anybody noticed the remarkable odour sent forth by *A. atropos* [Death's-head Hawk-moth] when handled in the imago state? I have had a good opportunity of observing the insect lately, as it has been commoner than usual, three or four being taken on the same evening. As I had some brought to me in a very bad condition, I kept them alive for some days in order to witness their peculiarity of stridulation. Although I believe the exact manner in which this sound is produced has never been satisfactorily discovered, it is too well-known to need comment, but I find that upon pressing the sides of the thorax it also emits a peculiar odour, resembling musk more than anything else; this occurred with all the specimens I examined.

(Mr. A. H. Swinton says " a yellow fan or fascicle of hairs, rising perpendicularly from a fold at either side of the anterior part of the abdomen, emits a pungent scent of jessamine" (*Entomologist's Monthly Magazine* **13**: 219) — E. A. F.)

[Hall, C. G. 1883. Peculiar odour emitted by *Acherontia atropos. The Entomologist* **16**: 14–15].

THE MOTH

Herbert George Wells. (1895)

Most of the articles, notes, and letters included in this volume are concerned with 'facts'; many proved beyond reasonable doubt — others disputed or even fanciful. To balance these we have included the following short story by H. G. Wells, in which an entomologist comes to be haunted by a moth; a moth which at first appears to be new to science, but later materializes as the ghost of his nemesis — arch-rival Professor Pawkins. Incidentally, some readers may see similarities in the relationship between Hapley and Pawkins in the story and that of those two eminent Victorian lepidopterists Richard South and James W. Tutt in real life (p. 301).

Probably you have heard of Hapley — not W. T. Hapley, the son, but the celebrated Hapley, the Hapley of *Periplaneta hapliia*, Hapley the entomologist.

If so you know at least of the great feud between Hapley and Professor Pawkins, though certain of its consequences may be new to you. For those who have not, a word or two of explanation is necessary, which the idle reader may go over with a glancing eye if his indolence so incline him.

It is amazing how very widely diffused is the ignorance of such really important matters as this Hapley–Pawkins feud. Those epoch-making controversies, again, that have convulsed the Geological Society are, I verily believe, almost entirely unknown outside the fellowship of that body. I have heard men of fair general education even refer to the great scenes at these meetings as vestry-meeting squabbles. Yet the great hate of the English and Scotch geologists has lasted now half a century, and has 'left deep and abundant marks upon the body of the science'. And this Hapley–Pawkins business, though perhaps a more personal affair, stirred passions as profound, if not profounder. Your common man has no conception of the zeal that animates a scientific investigator, the fury of contradiction you can arouse in him. It is the *odium theologicum* in a new form. There are men, for instance, who would gladly burn Sir Ray Lankester at Smithfield for his treatment of the Mollusca in the Encyclopaedia. That fantastic extension of the Cephalopods to cover the Pteropods . . . But I wander from Hapley and Pawkins.

It began years and years ago with a revision of the Microlepidoptera (whatever these may be) by Pawkins, in which he extinguished a new species created by Hapley. Hapley, who was always quarrelsome, replied by a stinging impeachment of the entire classification of Pawkins.* Pawkins in his 'Rejoinder'** suggested that Hapley's microscope was as defective as his power of observation, and called him an 'irresponsible meddler' — Hapley was not a professor at that time. Hapley in his retort,† spoke of 'blundering collectors', and described, as if inadvertently, Pawkin's revision as a 'miracle of ineptitude'. It was war to the knife. However, it would scarcely interest the reader to detail how these two great men quarrelled, and how the split between them widened until from the Microlepidoptera they were at war upon every open question in entomology. There were memorable occasions. At times the Royal Entomological Society meetings resembled nothing so much as the Chamber of

---

* 'Remarks on a Recent Revision of Microlepidoptera'. *Quart. Journ. Entomological Soc.,* 1863.

** 'Rejoinder to Certain Remarks', *Ibid.* 1 64.

† 'Further Remarks'. etc. *Ibid.*

Deputies. On the whole, I fancy Pawkins was nearer the truth than Hapley. But Hapley was skilful with his rhetoric, had a turn for ridicule rare in a scientific man, was endowed with vast energy, and had a fine sense of injury in the matter of the extinguished species; while Pawkins was a man of dull presence, prosy of speech, in shape not unlike a water-barrel, over-conscientious with testimonials, and suspected of jobbing museum appointments. So the young men gathered round Hapley and applauded him. It was a long struggle, vicious from the beginning and growing at last to pitiless antagonism. The successive turns of fortune, now an advantage to one side and now to another — now Hapley tormented by some success of Pawkins, and now Pawkins outshone by Hapley, belong rather to the history of entomology than to this story.

But in 1891 Pawkins, whose health had been bad for some time, published some work upon the 'mesoblast' of the Death's-Head Moth. What the mesoblast of the Death's-Head Moth may be does not matter a rap in this story. But the work was far below his usual standard, and gave Hapley an opening he had coveted for years. He must have worked night and day to make the most of his advantage.

In an elaborate critique he rent Pawkins to tatters — one can fancy the man's disordered black hair, and his queer dark eyes flashing as he went for his antagonist — and Pawkins made a reply, halting, ineffectual, with painful gaps of silence, and yet malignant. There was no mistaking his will to wound Hapley, nor his incapacity to do it. But few of those who heard him — I was absent from the meeting — realised how ill the man was.

Hapley got his opponent down, and meant to finish him. He followed with a brutal attack upon Pawkins, in the form of a paper upon the development of moths in general, a paper showing evidence of an extraordinary amount of labour, couched in a violently controversial tone. Violent as it was, an editorial note witnesses that it was modified. It must have covered Pawkins with shame and confusion of face. It left no loophole; it was murderous in argument, and utterly contemptuous in tone; an awful thing for the declining years of a man's career.

The world of entomologists waited breathlessly for the rejoinder from Pawkins. He would try one, for Pawkins had always been game. But when it came it surprised them. For the rejoinder of Pawkins was to catch influenza, proceed to pneumonia, and die.

It was perhaps as effectual a reply as he could make under the circumstances, and largely turned the current of feeling against Hapley. The very people who had most gleefully cheered on those gladiators became serious at the consequence. There could be no reasonable doubt the fret of the defeat had contributed to the death of Pawkins. There was a limit even to scientific controversy, said serious people. Another crushing attack was already in the press and appeared on the day before the funeral. I don't think Hapley exerted himself to stop it. People remembered how Hapley had hounded down his rival and forgot that rival's defects. Scathing satire reads ill over fresh mould. The thing provoked comment in the daily papers. It was that made me think you had probably heard of Hapley and this controversy. But, as I have already remarked, scientific workers live very much in a world of their own; half the people, I dare say, who go along Piccadilly to the Academy every year could not tell you where the learned societies abide. Many even think that research is a kind of happy-family cage in which all kinds of men lie down together in peace.

In his private thoughts Hapley could not forgive Pawkins for dying. In the first place, it was a mean dodge to escape the absolute pulverisation Hapley had in hand for him, and in the second, it left Hapley's mind with a queer gap in it. For twenty years he had worked hard, sometimes far into the night, and seven days a week, with microscope, scalpel, collecting-net, and pen, and almost entirely with reference to Pawkins. The European reputation he had won had come as an incident in that great antipathy. He had gradually worked up to a climax in this last controversy. It had killed Pawkins, but it had also thrown Hapley out of gear, so to speak, and his doctor advised him to give up work for a time, and rest. So Hapley went down into a quiet village in Kent, and thought day and night of Pawkins and good things it was now impossible to say about him.

At last Hapley began to realise in what direction the preoccupation tended. He determined to make a fight for it, and started by trying to read novels. But he could not get his mind off Pawkins, white in the face and making his last speech — every sentence a beautiful opening for Hapley. He turned to fiction — and found it had no grip on him. He read the 'Island Nights' Entertainments' until his 'sense of causation' was shocked beyond endurance by the Bottle Imp. Then he went to Kipling, and found he 'proved nothing' besides being irreverent and vulgar. These scientific people have their limitations. Then unhappily he tried Besant's 'Inner House', and the opening chapter set his mind upon learned societies and Pawkins at once.

So Hapley turned to chess, and found it a little more soothing. He soon mastered the moves and the chief gambits and commoner closing positions, and began to beat the Vicar. But then the cylindrical contours of the opposite king began to resemble Pawkins standing up and gasping ineffectually against checkmate, and Hapley decided to give up chess.

Perhaps the study of some new branch of science would after all be better diversion. The best rest is change of occupation. Hapley determined to plunge at diatoms, and had one of his smaller microscopes and Halibut's monograph sent down from London. He thought that perhaps if he could get up a vigorous quarrel with Halibut, he might be able to begin life afresh and forget Pawkins. And very soon he was hard at work in his habitual strenuous fashion at these microscopic denizens of the wayside pool.

It was on the third day of the diatoms that Hapley became aware of a novel addition to the local fauna. He was working late at the microscope, and the only light in the room was the brilliant little lamp with the special form of green shade. Like all experienced microscopists, he kept both eyes open. It is the only way to avoid excessive fatigue. One eye was over the instrument, and bright and distinct before that was the circular field of the microscope, across which a brown diatom was slowly moving. With the other eye Hapley saw, as it were, without seeing. He was only dimly conscious of the brass side of the instrument, the illuminated part of the tablecloth, a sheet of note-paper, the foot of the lamp, and the darkened room beyond.

Suddenly his attention drifted from one eye to the other. The tablecloth was of the material called tapestry by shopmen, and rather brightly coloured. The pattern was in gold, with a small amount of crimson and pale blue upon a greyish ground. At one point the pattern seemed displaced, and there was a vibrating movement of the colours at this point.

Hapley suddenly moved his head back and looked with both eyes. His mouth fell open with astonishment.

It was a large moth or butterfly; its wings spread in butterfly fashion!

It was strange it should be in the room at all, for the windows were closed. Strange that it should not have attracted his attention when fluttering to its present position. Strange that it should match the tablecloth. Stranger far that to him, Hapley, the great entomologist, it was altogether unknown. There was no delusion. It was crawling slowly towards the foot of the lamp.

'New Genus, by heavens! And in England!' said Hapley, staring.

Then he suddenly thought of Pawkins. Nothing would have maddened Pawkins more . . . and Pawkins was dead!

Something about the head and body of the insect became singularly suggestive of Pawkins, just as the chess king had been.

'Confound Pawkins!' said Hapley. 'But I must catch this.' And looking round him for some means of capturing the moth, he rose slowly out of his chair. Suddenly the insect rose, struck the edge of the lampshade — Hapley heard the 'ping' — and vanished into the shadow.

In a moment Hapley had whipped off the shade, so that the whole room was illuminated. The thing had disappeared, but soon his practised eye detected it upon the wall-paper near the door. He went towards it poising the lampshade for capture. Before he was within striking distance, however, it had risen and was fluttering round the room. After the fashion of its kind, it flew with sudden starts and turns, seeming to vanish here and reappear there. Once Hapley struck, and missed; then again.

The third time he hit his microscope. The instrument swayed, struck and overturned the lamp, and fell noisily upon the floor. The lamp turned over on the table and, very luckily, went out. Hapley was left in the dark. With a start he felt the strange moth blunder into his face.

It was maddening. He had no lights. If he opened the door of the room the thing would get away. In the darkness he saw Pawkins quite distinctly laughing at him. Pawkins had ever an oily laugh. He swore furiously and stamped his foot on the floor.

There was a timid rapping at the door.

Then it opened, perhaps a foot, and very slowly. The alarmed face of the landlady appeared behind a pink candle flame; she wore a nightcap over her grey hair and had some purple garment over her shoulders. 'What *was* that fearful smash?' she said. 'Has anything — ' The strange moth appeared fluttering about the chink of the door. 'Shut that door!' said Hapley, and suddenly rushed at her.

The door slammed hastily. Hapley was left alone in the dark. Then in the pause he heard his landlady scuttle upstairs, lock her door, and drag something heavy across the room and put against it.

It became evident to Hapley that his conduct and appearance had been strange and alarming. Confound the moth! and Pawkins! However, it was a pity to lose the moth now. He felt his way into the hall and found the matches, after sending his hat down upon the floor with a noise like a drum. With the lighted candle he returned to the sitting-room. No moth was to be seen. Yet once for a moment it seemed that the thing was fluttering round his head. Hapley very suddenly decided to give up the moth and go to bed. But he was excited. All night long his sleep was broken by dreams of the moth, Pawkins, and his landlady. Twice in the night he turned out and soused his head in cold water.

One thing was very clear to him. His landlady could not possibly understand about the strange moth, especially as he had failed to catch it. No one but an entomologist would understand quite how he felt. She was probably frightened at his behaviour, and yet he failed to see how he could explain it. He decided to say nothing further about the events of last night. After breakfast he saw her in her garden, and decided to go out and talk to reassure her. He talked to her about beans and potatoes, bees, caterpillars, and the price of fruit. She replied in her usual manner, but she looked at him a little suspiciously, and kept walking as he walked, so that there was always a bed of flowers, or a row of beans, or something of the sort, between them. After a while he began to feel singularly irritated at this, and, to conceal his vexation, went indoors and presently went out for a walk.

The moth, or butterfly, trailing an odd flavour of Pawkins with it, kept coming into that walk though he did his best to keep his mind off it. Once he saw it quite distinctly, with its wings flattened out, upon the old stone wall that runs along the west edge of the park, but going up to it he found it was only two lumps of grey and yellow lichen. 'This,' said Hapley, 'is the reverse of mimicry. Instead of a butterfly looking like a stone, here is a stone looking like a butterfly!' Once something hovered and fluttered round his head, but by an effort of will he drove that impression out of his mind again.

In the afternoon Hapley called upon the Vicar, and argued with him upon theological questions. They sat in the little arbour covered with briar, and smoked as they wrangled. 'Look at that moth!' said Hapley, suddenly, pointing to the edge of the wooden table.

'Where?' said the Vicar.

'You don't see a moth on the edge of the table there?' said Hapley.

'Certainly not,' said the Vicar.

Hapley was thunderstruck. He gasped. The Vicar was staring at him. Clearly the man saw nothing. 'The eye of faith is no better than the eye of science,' said Hapley awkwardly.

'I don't see your point,' said the Vicar, thinking it was part of the argument.

That night Hapley found the moth crawling over his counterpane. He sat on the edge of the bed in his shirt-sleeves and reasoned with himself. Was it pure hallucination? He knew he was slipping, and he battled for his sanity with the same silent energy he had formerly displayed against Pawkins. So persistent is mental habit that he felt as if it were still a

Hapley looked at the moth. 'It was not at all dream-like but perfectly clear and solid-looking in the candle-light.'

struggle with Pawkins. He was well versed in psychology. He knew that such visual illusions do come as a result of mental strain. But the point was, he did not only *see* the moth, he had heard it when it touched the edge of the lampshade and afterwards when it hit against the wall, and he had felt it strike his face in the dark.

He looked at it. It was not at all dream-like but perfectly clear and solid-looking in the candle-light. He saw the hairy body and the short feathery antennae, the jointed legs, even a place where the down was rubbed from the wing. He suddenly felt angry with himself for being afraid of a little insect.

His landlady had got the servant to sleep with her that night, because she was afraid to be alone. In addition she had locked the door and put the chest of drawers against it. They listened and talked in whispers after they had gone to bed, but nothing occurred to alarm them. About eleven they had ventured to put the candle out and had both dozed off to sleep. They woke with a start, and sat up in bed, listening in the darkness.

Then they heard slippered feet going to and fro in Hapley's room. A chair was overturned and there was a violent dab at the wall. Then a china mantel ornament smashed upon the fender. Suddenly the door of the room opened, and they heard him upon the landing. They clung to one another, listening. He seemed to be dancing up the staircase. Now he would go down three or four steps quickly, then up again, then hurry down into the hall. They heard the umbrella-stand go over, and the fanlight break. Then the bolt shot and the chain rattled. He was opening the door.

They hurried to the window. It was a dim grey night; an almost unbroken sheet of watery cloud was sweeping across the moon, and the hedge and trees in front of the house were black against the pale roadway. They saw Hapley, looking like a ghost in his shirt and white trousers, running to and fro in the road and beating the air. Now he would stop, now he would dart very rapidly at something invisible, now he would move upon it with stealthy strides. At last he went out of sight up the road towards the down. Then while they argued who should go down and lock the door, he returned. He was walking very fast, and he came straight into the house, closed the door carefully, and went quietly up to his bedroom. Then everything was silent.

'Mrs Colville,' said Hapley, calling down the staircase next morning, 'I hope I did not alarm you last night.'

'You may well ask that!' said Mrs Colville.

'The fact is, I am a sleep-walker, and the last two nights I have been without my sleeping mixture. There is nothing to be alarmed about, really. I am sorry I made such an ass of myself. I will go over the down to Shoreham, and get some stuff to make me sleep soundly. I ought to have done that yesterday.'

But half-way over the down, by the chalk pits, the moth came upon Hapley again. He went on, trying to keep his mind upon chess problems, but it was no good. The thing fluttered into his face, and he struck at it with his hat in self-defence. Then rage, the old rage — the rage he had so often felt against Pawkins — came upon him again. He went on, leaping and striking at the eddying insect. Suddenly he trod on nothing, and fell headlong.

There was a gap in his sensations, and Hapley found himself sitting on the heap of flints in front of the opening of the chalk-pits, with a leg twisted back under him. The strange moth was still fluttering round his head. He struck at it with his hand, and turning his head saw two men approaching him. One was the village doctor. It occurred to Hapley that this was lucky. Then it came into his mind with extraordinary vividness that no one would ever be able to see the strange moth except himself, and that it behoved him to keep silent about it.

Late that night, however, after his broken leg was set, he was feverish and forgot his self-restraint. He was lying flat on his bed, and he began to run his eyes round the room to see if the moth was still about. He tried not to do this, but it was no good. He soon caught sight of the thing resting close to his hand, by the night-light, on the green tablecloth. The wings quivered. With a sudden wave of anger he smote at it with his fist, and the nurse woke up with a shriek. He had missed it.

'That moth!' he said; and then: 'It was fancy. Nothing!'

All the time he could see quite clearly the insect going round the cornice and darting across the room, and he could also see that the nurse saw nothing of it and looked at him strangely. He must keep himself in hand. He knew he was a lost man if he did not keep himself in hand. But as the night waned the fever grew upon him, and the very dread he had of seeing the moth made him see it. About five, just as the dawn was grey, he tried to get out of bed and catch it, though his leg was afire with pain. The nurse had to struggle with him.

On account of this, they tied him down to the bed. At this the moth grew bolder, and once he felt it settle in his hair. Then, because he struck out violently with his arms, they tied these also. At this the moth came and crawled over his face, and Hapley wept, swore, screamed, prayed for them to take it off him, unavailingly.

The doctor was a blockhead, a just-qualified general practitioner, and quite ignorant of mental science. He simply said there was no moth. Had he possessed the wit, he might still perhaps have saved Hapley from his fate by entering into his delusion, and covering his face with gauze as he prayed might be done. But, as I say, the doctor was a blockhead; and until the leg was healed Hapley was kept tied to his bed, with the imaginary moth crawling over him. It never left him while he was awake and it grew to a monster in his dreams. While he was awake he longed for sleep, and from sleep he awoke screaming.

So now Hapley is spending the remainder of his days in a padded room, worried by a moth that no one else can see. The asylum doctor calls it hallucination; but Hapley, when he is in his easier mood and can talk, says it is the ghost of Pawkins, and consequently a unique specimen and well worth the trouble of catching.

[Wells, H. G. 1895 (28th March). *The Moth*. Pall Mall Gazette].

EXTRAORDINARY ABUNDANCE OF
THE YELLOW UNDERWING

John T. Carrington, F.L.S., Royal Aquarium, Westminster, London, S. W. (1881)

John Thomas Carrington (1846–1908) was educated at a private school at Mottram, Cheshire, and then afterwards, in Dublin. Although he originally studied for the medical profession, after extensive travels in North and South America and Africa he finally chose journalism as a profession. When Edward Newman died in 1876, Carrington was then appointed editor of *The Entomologist*, 'a position he occupied with ability and tact until its purchase by the late Mr. Henry Leech in 1890' (C.A.B., 1908). He was also one of the departmental (Natural History) editors of *The Field* for many years.

In 1878 he took a leading part in organizing and managing the National Entomological Exhibition at the Westminster Aquarium, 'at which the finest representative collection of

British Entomology ever brought together was exhibited to the public'. An all-round naturalist, with interests in British conchology, botany and ornithology, as well as entomology, he had the distinction of capturing in September 1896 the only known British specimen of the Antirrhinum Brocade (*Calophasia platyptera*) near Brighton, an area he loved to explore. And for those fortunate enough to have accompanied him on one of his many excursions: 'His knowledge . . . so freely afforded, his carefully planned routes, and above all his genial manner and the genuine pleasure he showed in pointing out some new feature or rare specimen, rendered them ever to be remembered.'

He retired to Combe Martin, North Devon, where he took a great interest in the proposed reopening of the famous silver mines.

Fig. 124. John Carrington F.R.S. was appointed Naturalist to the Royal Aquarium, Westminster, where 'in its "palmy days", entomologists of all kinds foregathered at the pleasant evenings over which he presided'. He wrote a detailed series of articles on Wicken Fen, Darenth, the New Forest and other 'good spots for butterflies' especially for beginners.

During a short visit in the Isle of Wight, at the end of last month [June], I observed *Triphæna pronuba* [Large Yellow Underwing] everywhere I went in the most extraordinary abundance. In Daishe's Hotel, Shanklin, they were swept from the hall and passages each morning by

scores, where they had been attracted by light. As the train passed through the country they rose in numbers from the herbage by the railway side. While walking from Ventnor to Sandrock Hotel, by the cliffs, they were flying in abundance during the hot sunshine.

[Carrington, J. T. 1881. Extraordinary abundance of *Triphæna pronuba*. *The Entomologist* 14: 180].

THE ENTOMOLOGICAL SOCIETY OF LONDON

In 1856 The Entomological Society of London tried a number of schemes to attract new members. On one occasion the readership of *The Entomologist's Weekly Intelligencer* was introduced to members of the Committee in an imaginary scene which attempted to depict a typical meeting of the Society. In the following letters an equally imaginary pair of novitiates attempt to become members.

Letter to the Editor, *The Entomologist's Weekly Intelligencer* from FELIX (8th July 1856):

Sir, — Will you kindly inform me (through the 'Intelligencer') what the annual amount of subscription is, and the course I should pursue to be made a member of the Entomological Society. I attended the meeting of the 7th inst., and was very much delighted.

Letter to the Editor, *The Entomologist's Weekly Intelligencer* from INFELIX (8th July 1856):

Sir, — I am very sorry to see represented in the 'Intelligencer' how easy it is to introduce oneself into the company of entomologists. I presented myself for the third time on Monday last, making sure, after the invitation put forth in the 'Intelligencer,' that I should succeed; but, no; I was doomed to disappointment.

The first time that I presented myself I was told that I could not get admission without being introduced, and as I knew no one there I was obliged to go back home.

The second time I went, which was last March, I saw Mr. Foxcroft, whom I knew; I told him that I wished to see the Society's rooms, and he went upstairs to see if there was any one there that would introduce me, I being a stranger there. Mr. F. told a person high in the Society that he had a friend who wished to see the rooms: "Oh! have you," says the party; but never said bring him up, which Mr. F. could not do without permission: so I waited at the entrance about an hour without being able to meet any one that I knew to take me up. So I was disappointed again.

Having been out collecting, and having taken one or two insects which I knew were scarce, but did not know the Latin names, and having bred a tiger moth, a phenomenon, I thought I would try again. I proceeded to the second floor as directed, and I heard someone speaking, so I thought I would wait until they were done and then go in: presently out comes a figure, that evidently had no love for insects, to know what I wanted. I told her that I was waiting to go into the room: she asked me if I had a card. I said "no, I had come there through seeing an invitation in the 'Intelligencer.' " She said the meeting was private, and that I could not go in without an order, and that the meeting was almost over: this was at half-past eight o'clock, so that it must be a short meeting to begin at eight and be done at half-past. I think it would be better if you had a person "in livery and brass" to give information when required.

Letter from the Editor, *The Entomologist's Weekly Intelligencer*:

We cannot help moralising upon the above two very different letters. FELIX, we believe, was as much a stranger as INFELIX; but the *happy* man attended the meeting and enjoyed it. It occurs to us that FELIX must have opened the door and walked in nothing daunted, but that INFELIX stopped outside the door nervously listening, and so was suspected of being there for no good purpose. We can only recommend INFELIX to try again, and if still afraid to come in to send the following letter: —

Dear Sir, — I am outside the door: could you or some friend of yours introduce me as a visitor to the Meeting.

Yours truly,

A.B.

Fig. 125. Henry Tibbats Stainton F.R.S. held open house on Wednesday evenings when anyone, expert or tyro, could inspect his library and collections.

Reply from Henry T. Stainton:

In reply to FELIX'S enquiry we beg to state that the annual subscription to the Entomological Society is one guinea. *Members* pay in addition an admission fee of two guineas. *Subscribers* pay no admission fee, but are not eligible to office in the Society. If FELIX aspires to the President's chair at some future day, we recommend him to become a MEMBER.

INFELIX recommends we should have a porter in livery: just at the present we do not see exactly who could be selected for that office: the Curator has just assumed the Secretaryship, otherwise we might perhaps have thought of combining the Curator and Porter in one person. But the idea of Mr. Janson [Honorary Secretary of the Entomological Society] in the role of a Bank beadle . . .

[1856. The Entomological Society. *The Entomologist's Weekly Intelligencer* **1**: 134-135].

THE RANNOCH SPRAWLER

From the meeting of the Entomological Society – Monday, 5th May 1856:

Mr. S. Stevens exhibited the specimen of this insect [*Petasia nubeculosa* — Rannoch Sprawler] sent him by Mr. Foxcroft . . . and read a letter from Mr. Foxcroft explaining the mode in which this and other specimens had been captured. The plan was as follows: — the insects were found at rest high up the trunks of the *birches*; in the woods at Rannoch the little [tree-] creeper was always busily employed running up and down the trees looking for insects, and when the creeper came to so large an insect as *nubeculosa*, it appeared to be

rather frightened, flapping its wings and giving a sort of scream. Mr. Foxcroft then made a noise by beating the tree with a long stick, and the bird flew away, and then Mr. Foxcroft proceeded to climb the tree in search of the *Petasia*; by this means he had already collected nearly one for each of his subscribers. On one occasion, after climbing a birch tree to a height of 40 feet, he found it a false alarm, as the insect which had attracted the attention of the bird was only *Ceropacha flavicornis* [Yellow Horned]!

[1856. Editor. Entomological Society notes. *Petasia nubeculosa. The Entomologist's Weekly Intelligencer* **1**: 45–46].

THE SPORTSMAN AND THE ENTOMOLOGIST

Anon. (1856)

The ex-member for West Gloucestershire, while not otherwise engaged, is harmlessly occupied in sending to the 'Field' newspaper reminiscences of his sporting life, from which we take the following rather amusing adventure: —

Not many years ago, during a beautiful afternoon in the month of August or September (at this moment I forget which), I was aware in one of the royal forests of a fat buck. This buck was very shy, and, like all deer the moment they are worth killing, he had taken to hide in a thick wood, only diverging from it to feed at dusk in the evening, by such paths as he knew would, for the time being, give him the command or the wind of any ambushed rifle that might be ready for his destruction. The wilder the animal of chase, the more beauty there is in his attainment; and I, of course, became doubly anxious to procure this venison. Oh! that forest, that wild and graceful forest! how I have haunted its woods and its heaths, and furze brakes, and in its solitude never felt myself alone! In the wood of which this buck had become almost the sole tenant, there was a sweet grassy ride that he was very fond of. The wind favoured the position I wished to take; so, creeping under cover at a spot which commanded the game either way, and not a hundred yards from the open forest, I lay concealed, ear and eye on the alert for anything worthy of observation, and in the hope of some "shadow" to herald "the coming event."

My watch for the wary buck continued, when (as the lengthened shadows told me that the sun was far down in the west, and the evening was beautifully still) my attention of course became concentrated on the business of the hour. "Hark!" 'tis the startled note of a blackbird, sprung by something of which it is afraid. This is no deer; but it may be a fox. I trust in all that is good that no man's footsteps hitherward come. Such, indeed, were the thoughts that entered my head, and such my aspirations. All then for a time remained silent; and I settled in my own mind that a fox had disturbed the blackbird. Hark! again, the gentle rustle of a bough; and presently the sharp shake of its leafy end, as if a buck, whose horns were forward and hardened, had hit a twig beyond the reach of his mouth, to bring its verdure lower down, that he may browse upon it. A dead silence, a little rustle, and a shake again on the same spot, just at the corner of the open forest, but still quite within the cover. "It must be the buck, and can be nothing else." A bough of the copse wood then leaned toward and into the woodland glade, but flew back; it had evidently bent down from some pressure from within. "It's the buck; so here goes!" Cautiously and steadily, with stealthy motion, avoiding all jerk and sudden movement, the rifle rose to my eye, and kept its level at the spot where every instant I expected to see the buck's head. The bough bent again, the leaves rustled still more, and in the same place. "It can only be the buck at browse; and now I have the view." A dull surface appears in the middle of the bush, the hue of a deer's neck, and it moves up and down; yet (perverseness personified) I can neither see ears, nor horns, nor eyes, nor anything to guide me to spine or brain. Shall I shoot at a venture? Caution, from long experience, as well as habit, whispered "No." "Well," I thought to myself, "I have seen old women select the moment when horses are coming in to cross a racecourse: I have seen, man, woman, and child, where you least expect to find them; and though I know this can't be anything but a buck, for the love of heaven I will not pull the trigger." "Now for his heart!" and I dared hardly breathe, lest my finger should touch the light trigger. The boughs then burst wide, and out came a buck — an old buck too — but such a buck, that I would

Fig. 126. Edward W. J. Hopley (1816–1869).

Fig. 127. Revd Francis M. Bennoch Carr (1858–1930).

Fig. 128. William Buckler (1814–1884).

Fig. 129. Professor James J. F. Xavier King (1855–1933).

Some 'Gentlemen of the Net' — Style and Costume

rather have died than made venison of! *It was a man* — a benign-looking brisk old man, in a dun-coloured wide-awake hat, and drabbish dress all over, in Pickwickian cut and fashion, even to shorts and ankle-gaiters, which only just met his very well-made calves.

"Good God, sir," I exclaimed, bursting out of the bushes on his startled view, "you very nearly lost your life, and beguiled me into murder."

"Sir," exclaimed the elderly gentleman, in no small alarm, "why, how and wherefore so?"

"Simply thus; you have been personating a buck in and about the bush so long, that my arm has been aching in holding my rifle at the level of your body, the trigger so light that had I sneezed I must have shot you."

"Dear me, sir," he replied. "I will instantly betake myself out of harm's way," and, so saying, disappeared round the corner, and left me most thankful that I had done no murder.

My search for the buck that evening was useless; and on meeting the keeper at a given spot I asked him who this old gentleman was.

"A Flapper," he replied, in the most business-like and concise way.

"A Flapper!" I rejoined in astonishment, thinking it a very odd definition of the respectable old gentleman I had just seen. "What the devil do you mean by a 'Flapper?' "

"One of the gentlemen, sir, what comes down to the inn here a catching of insects. Lord, sir, they think as much of a fly or a grub as we do of the best buck in the forest; and goes out by night, too, as well as by day, a rubbing old bark of trees with sugar."

"Oh, ho," I remarked to myself, "the Entomological Society." Long time and success to them and their research; may every man with a rifle, in forest or woodland, be as sure of his buck as I have been, before he pulls the trigger.

[Anon. 1856. The sportsman and the entomologist. *The Substitute* No. 6: 58–60].

HINTS TO YOUNG COLLECTORS

Two Old Hands. (1856)

As well as teaching the young collector how to obtain insects, it may not be out of place to make reference to some of the usages of old collectors, which, if observed, will prove of benefit and comfort both to himself and others. If a collector goes to a tree to look for insects, it is usual to consider that tree HIS till he has left it; it not being deemed handsome conduct to go and pick insects off a tree that another is examining. When a tree or trees have been sugared, no one with a proper sense of justice would think of going to POACH on such a tree or trees for insects, general usage conceding the right of all trees sugared to him who has taken the trouble of sugaring. If an insect is started, or first seen, by an entomologist, and he has to give chace, he does not expect others to join in the pursuit; but, if this happens, he never dreams of the pill-boxing of the capture by some other person with quicker legs than sense of right and wrong. That these things may happen thoughtlessly, or for want of knowing better, there is no doubt, and for this reason we deem it worth while to dedicate to the subject these few lines of advice. For we are convinced that few among the many young gentlemen who have latterly taken up the net would wish to lay themselves open to the suspicion of being unjust or greedy, or of being possessed of so little delicacy of feeling as to prefer keeping an insect to retaining the good opinion of a brother collector. There are very few experienced entomologists who will not impart their knowledge with the greatest pleasure to the tyro in a science which has afforded so much pleasure and happiness to themselves; but rudeness or selfishness speedily alienates this warm feeling of sympathy, and when too late the young amateur finds he has lost both friendship and knowledge. In our time we have given away hundreds of insects, and hope to do the same again, but never one to a greedy collector.

[Two Old Hands. 1856. Hints to young collectors. *The Entomologist's Weekly Intelligencer* 1: 150].

PORTRAIT-PAINTING

Henry Tibbats Stainton, Lewisham, London, S. E. (1857)

During the summer months, now that the collectors and observers of the TINEINA are so vastly on the increase, scarcely a day passes without our receiving from some useful correspondent some larva which we had not seen before, or with the habits of which we were not thoroughly conversant. Of course it is no great labour to us to describe these novelties as fast as they make their appearance on our writing-table; but then, over and above describing them, we wish to have their portraits taken: now the correct portraiture of a minute larva is a work which requires skill, patience, and *time*; they cannot yet be photographed in half a second, — they cannot be drawn in half-an-hour. Here then we have a difficulty!

We have succeeded in rousing not merely the collectors of this country, but those of Europe: during the last month larvæ have come to us from Frankfort-on-the-Maine, from Glogau, from Lyon, from Ratisbon and from Zurich. A simultaneous arrival of larvæ from several quarters upsets all our arrangements; one pair of hands cannot depict their physiognomies whilst they remain in the flesh. Caterpillars, especially after a three days' journey from the Continent, *won't wait*; they must be done at once. But, why should it be restricted to one pair of

Fig. 130. Henry Tibbats Stainton. He vigorously advocated entomology as an improving hobby for schoolboys.

hands? why, as the collectors and observers of these insects increase, should there not be a proportionate increase of their portrait-painters? The portrait-painting of larvæ of MICRO-LEPIDOPTERA is a branch of the profession which is yet in its infancy; but it is a branch not unattended with difficulty. No one could take to it entirely as a means of living, because during the winter the work is *nil*, or nearly so. It can only therefore be followed as an adjunct to a more regular artistic employment.

We should be glad to hear from artists (residing in the neighbourhood of London) between the ages of 20 and 30, who may be willing to devote some of their summer hours to this minute and microscopic work, in which larvæ one-eighth of an inch in length have to be expanded to bulky individuals as big as one's finger. There will be no great lack of occupation of this sort for those who are disposed to throw their hearts into the work, and as for several years the stream of larvæ will be on a *crescendo* scale we have no doubt that an active worker might earn from £30 to £50 a-year by the portrait-painting of larvæ. But we must premise that those individuals who are afflicted with the bump of unpunctuality had better not reply to this appeal, for when Mrs. Gamp said, "I can't abear to wait, I do assure you. To wotever place I goes, I sticks to this one mortar, 'I'm easy pleased; it is but little as I wants, but I must have that little of the best, and to the minnit when the clock strikes, else we do not part as I could wish, but bearin' malice in our arts,' " she showed forth as graphically as her peculiar style of diction would permit the virtues of punctuality, and the inconveniences attendant on a contrary habit.

[Stainton, H. T. 1857. Portrait-painting. *The Entomologist's Weekly Intelligencer* 2: 113–114].

As a direct result of Henry Stainton's appeal, William Buckler, who had trained at the Royal Academy and was an enthusiastic amateur entomologist, applied for the post of illustrator of the thirteen volumes of Stainton's *The Natural History of the Tineina* (1855–1873). He worked on this for almost three years and during that time delineated 120 figures of larvae, leaf-mines and food-plants. He then went on to produce his *magnum opus*: *The Larvae of the British Butterflies and Moths* (1886–1901), which was published posthumously by the Ray Society. In this work he figured 850 species with almost 5000 watercolour drawings.

A BLACKNECK IN A RAILWAY CARRIAGE

J. F. Moon, Ryde, Isle of Wight. (1858)

On the 19th ult., I took near Botley, a fine specimen of this insect [Blackneck], which was drawn into the carriage window by the draught, and fell exhausted on the seat opposite to me.

[Moon, J. F. 1858. *Toxocampa pastinum* in a railway carriage. *The Entomologist's Weekly Intelligencer* 4: 117].

THE CRIMSON SPECKLED FOOTMAN

The Crimson Speckled Footman is a very rare and beautiful day-flying moth. It belongs to the family of moths known as 'footmen', so called as they seem to stand stiffly to attention with wings folded when at rest. It migrates freely and was first recorded from Hampshire in 1818, since when it has been extremely sporadic in its appearance. There were, however, some thirty records in 1871, about ten in 1923 and another forty in 1961. But many years may pass without specimens being reported. 1892 was a remarkable year for this moth and the entomological journals were full of reports of specimens seen or captured across the South of England. Some of these reports were of unusual interest.

Southsea. — "Let those laugh who win." This old proverb was well exemplified at the review on Southsea Common on Wednesday, May 25th, when a number of persons

indulged in a good laugh at seeing a man — Mr. W. H. Mackett, head-master of St. Matthew's School, Gosport, and an ardent entomologist — rush after what appeared to be a very dilapidated specimen of a small common white butterfly, but which turned out to be one of the rarest of British moths, *viz.*, the crimson-speckled (*Deiopeia pulchella*), and which is consequently of great interest and value. In Newman's standard work on this branch of entomology, the number of British specimens is limited to about three; and Morris reports about the same number. This "good thing" of entomologists was caught in the thickest part of the crowd during the "march past," and must have passed thousands of persons during its peregrinations. — *Evening Mail*, May 27, 1892.

[Mackett, W. H. 1892. *Deiopeia pulchella*. *The Entomologist* **25**: 166].

Dover. — This afternoon, May 28th, 1892, Miss Emden, eldest daughter of one of my near neighbours, and taking a keen interest in natural history, came and awoke me from a sound sleep, stretched at full-length on my lawn, to say that she had caught such a pretty moth for me. My reply, in a semi-somnolent condition, was, "Oh, where is it?" when forth came a very much-crumpled handkerchief, with the captive secured in one corner. I expected to find that great rarity *filipendulae* [Six-spot Burnet] in a somewhat shiny and nude condition. However, I was most agreeably surprised, on opening the receptacle, to find a beautiful fresh female *D. pulchella*, and in very good condition, considering the manner in which it had been captured and conveyed to me. When the insect first attracted her attention it flew up and settled at a short distance off; after a few ineffectual attempts she finally captured it under a light cap she was wearing, and eventually transferred it to the handkerchief. I was soon awake, in fact wide awake enough to take it indoors to more secure quarters.

[Williams, J. T. 1892. *Deiopeia pulchella*. *The Entomologist* **25**: 167].

Shorncliffe Camp, near Dover: A ♀ specimen of the Crimson Speckled Footman (*Deiopeia pulchella*), in fine condition, was taken by my groom on the Camp on May 29th. Oddly enough he found it in the midst of bricks and mortar where extensive building operations are in progress.

[Partridge, C. E. 1892. *Deiopeia pulchella* at Shorncliffe. *Entomologist's Monthly Magazine* **28**: 191].

Bournemouth, Hampshire: On October 6th, 1876, my pupils and I were fortunate enough to take two fine specimens of *Deiopeia pulchella* on the moorland between Bournemouth and Christchurch, now known as Southborn-on-Sea; and on the same date, in the same locality, there is a record of the capture of five specimens by the Rev. E. Brackenbury, of this town, and his pupils [1876. *Entomologist*, 9: 258]. Since that time I have been in the habit of visiting the locality annually two or three times a year with the hope of finding more of this rarity, but each time failed to turn the species up again. The operations of the "brick and mortar" speculation in this neighbourhood have been so extensive and continuous of late years that my hopes (at one time well grounded) of the permanent establishment of *D. pulchella* in the locality were with each succeeding year becoming fainter and fainter. I have, however, a strange fascination for the spot where a rarity has once been captured, and, led by this, I again visited the old ground on October 7th and spent a couple of hours, with my usual success, nil! When about to return home, however, my little dog dashed past me in pursuit of a rabbit, and rushing in among some ferns, started a pale-looking insect, which I instantly netted, and found to be *D. pulchella*. While engaged in bottling my prize some children came up, and to satisfy their curiosity I showed them my capture, when one of them said, "Harry has a butterfly like that"; and sure enough, to my surprise, in an old mustard-tin the little fellow actually had a living specimen of *D. pulchella*, with sundry still more lively grasshoppers, etc., all boxed off the moor within the previous hour. They had no net or other apparatus, and, as far as I could learn, they found the *D. pulchella* at rest on the ferns. I at once struck a bargain for the "butterfly", leaving them in possession of the grasshoppers, which seemed equally appreciated by them. On examination I was glad to find the insect had sustained little damage from either the handling of its juvenile captors or from the ill-assorted fellow-prisoners.

[McRae, W. 1885. *Deiopeia pulchella* in Hampshire. *The Entomologist* **18**: 298–299].

A PUGNACIOUS PURPLE HAIRSTREAK

Charles Healy, Haggerstone, London. (1858)

Whilst examining the 'Bishop's Paling,' one day last July, my attention was drawn to a battle between *Thecla Quercus* [Purple Hairstreak] and a wasp: I was surprised to see the undaunted pluck of *T. Quercus*; he repeatedly charged the wasp in the most furious manner, — he never attempted to fly away, but stuck to his opponent with bull-dog courage: the scene

presented the appearance of a miniature cock-fight. At length the wasp altered his tactics, and as *T. Quercus* made a charge, with wings erect, he dodged on one side, and whipped off a portion of his wings; this trick he repeated until poor *Quercus's* wings were half destroyed, and seeing that he would shortly fall a victim to his cunning opponent, I captured him, and now have him in my cabinet.

[Healy, C. 1858. A pugnacious *Quercus*. *The Entomologist's Weekly Intelligencer* 4: 20].

Some years ago we witnessed another epic insect battle — this time between a wasp and a Devil's Coach-horse beetle (*Staphylinus olens*). In this particular conflict the wasp came off worse as the beetle, with some considerable ingenuity, contrived to remove both its antennae.

A HUMBUG

From an American newspaper (1858):

Professor Adams, of Amherst College, was a great entomologist, and had the largest collection of insects that was ever accumulated by any private individual in this country, since the days of Noah. Some wicked students thought to quiz the old gentleman, and, with a great deal of care and labour, succeeded in manufacturing a nondescript insect, by taking the body of a beetle and gluing to it the legs of a grasshopper, the wings of a butterfly, and the horns of a dragonfly. With this new style of bug, they proceeded to the study of the Professor, and told him that one of their number had found a strange animal which they were unable to classify, and requested him to aid them in defining its position. The Professor put on his spectacles, and after examining the specimen carefully, said, "Well, young gentlemen, this is a curious bug; I am inclined to think it is what naturalists call a '*Humbug!*'"

[1858. *The Entomologist's Weekly Intelligencer* 4: 72].

ENTOMOLOGY AND THE POST OFFICE

There have always been problems concerning the sending of set specimens of butterflies and moths by post, and their extreme fragility militates against casual transmission. In 1858, however, the most contentious problem appeared to be the high cost of sending entomological parcels. The fact that postal charges in Prussia were lower than those in Britain was enough to stir the 'bulldog spirit' in an editorial reply.

To the Editor, *The Entomologist's Weekly Intelligencer*, from George Gascoyne, Newark (22nd May 1858):

Sir, — I am desirous to draw your attention, and that of your readers, to the great hardship to which naturalists, and especially entomologists, are subject in the transmission of specimens by post. Box and wrapper, cotton wool and cork, food plant and specimens, are all charged at the "letter rate" of two pence per ounce; yet the lawyer can send his parchments, the merchant his documents, the tradesman his patterns, the printer his books, all for a penny the four ounces, or one-eighth of the charge to naturalists; thus "trade is encouraged," as it is termed, while science is (to use a mild word) overlooked.

Can nothing be done to remedy this?

The poor entomologist, now a numerous class, particularly feels the burden. Why should not "specimens only" be sent as cheaply as "printed matter" or "patterns?" Knowledge derived from Nature herself is surely as valuable as that from books, and the same facilities for diffusing it ought to be afforded.

We have a man of enlarged and liberal views in the secretary to the Post Office, Mr Rowland Hill, and if the case were clearly, but concisely, laid before him, doubtless it would have his favourable consideration.

What, sir, would be the best course to adopt — deputation, memorial or letters? I might suggest that the London gentlemen might know how to manage these matters better than us provincials.

[Gascoyne, G. 1858. Heavy postage rates on entomological parcels. *The Entomologist's Weekly Intelligencer* 4: 68–69].

PARCEL POSTAGE

Our readers will be glad to hear that a Committee appointed by the Society of Arts to consider the above subject, have reported in favour of a uniform rate for parcels sent by post, similar to the present book-postage of *4d* per lb. We trust the matter will now be pressed upon the Treasury till this boon to the naturalists of this country is conceded. In Prussia small parcels have long been carried by the post at very low rates, and it is not fitting that we should lag behind any part of the Continent.

[The Editor. 1858. Parcel postage. *The Entomologist's Weekly Intelligencer* 4: 152].

Judging from an earlier letter to the '*Intelligencer*' dated 9th August 1856, Mr Gascoyne's indignation over the postage rates may have been somewhat academic, bearing in mind other Post Office practices at the time. Under the title 'How the Post-office breaks our boxes' Mr Arthur Naish of Bristol reported that 'a lady staying here lately, who is connected with one of the London receiving houses, tells me that the men who collect the letters, if the bag happens to be pretty full, jump upon them and push them in with their feet'.

At least one entomologist had sought to educate 'the father of the modern post office' in ways to avoid accidental damage. This helpful hint appeared in the '*Intelligencer*' in 1856, under the title 'Parchment labels for posting boxes':

I have had many letters enquiring how I manage my boxes, as "we cannot make out how to attach the parchment." Now, to save trouble, will you insert the following description of it: — Glue or fasten securely to the inside of the cover of the box a piece of parchment (sufficiently large to stick on the address, and postage stamp), which must project from the end of the box: on the top and bottom of the box, write in large letters, 'Please stamp on the parchment.' And *be sure* to stick the pins well into the cork, and all specimens with large bodies should have pins put across the abdomen, for one loose body will destroy a box of insects. I have written to Rowland Hill, asking him to issue orders to all clerks that they must stamp only on the labels of such boxes: he says "he will give it early attention." If so, then we are safe in sending by post by this plan, for I have had many, and only two have had the contents injured, these bore the post-marks Birmingham and Glasgow. — E. S. Norcombe, *Heavitree, Exeter; August 4*, 1856.

In spite of the direct approach to Rowland Hill, things did not improve. A number of other entomologists were quick to voice their feelings about the postal service and an acrimonious correspondence developed.

THE POST OFFICE

J. S. Dell, Devonport, Devon. (1859)

To the Editor of *The Entomologist's Weekly Intelligencer*, from J. S. Dell, Devonport (8th August 1859):

Sir, — The cruel mortification of the incipient, as well as other entomologists, when they find their best hopes of a valuable addition to their cabinets frustrated by the folly of others, is my best apology for troubling you with these observations. These remarks are forced on me in consequence of the utter carelessness and unfeeling recklessness — I should more properly say the fiendish wantonness — of the Post-Office officials.

The annual sacrifice of species to that shrine of Moloch, the Post Office, must be fearful to contemplate, and I am afraid that unless some means are adopted to check the evil, we shall be debarred from sending the species that occur in different counties one to another, and the interchange must cease. Is there no redress for this destruction? I am asked. I refer the question to your better judgment, and ask, "Is there no redress?"

I have, during the past three months, forwarded a great number of boxes to different parts of the country, and fully one-fourth of that number arrived crushed. I have now by me nine boxes that I have received crushed, three of which deserve their fate, being only card-board; the others are what any one would call pretty fair, and, with ordinary care, would have come safe. I forwarded a box under four ounces to Ulverstone last week, made in the strongest manner possible, well-padded, bound over with black, and labelled; it would bear any amount of pressure, and any one would have thought it impossible to break it; but lo! it arrived smashed to pieces, and all its contents spoiled. I also lately received a box, under three ounces, containing specimens of *Erebia Cassiope* [Small Mountain Ringlet] *Polyommatus Arion* [Large Blue]; the box was so strong that it had only started in one corner, but the contents were done for: the pins had stood nobly in the cork, but there they were — the thorax and perhaps one wing, perhaps two, standing to the pin, the other parts scattered about.

"It is high time," says one of my correspondents, "for the entomologists of England to endeavour to obtain compensation from the Post Office for the gross neglect and carelessness of its officials. I would that there was any chance of doing so, but I am afraid it would be of no avail. If, by publicity in the 'Intelligencer,' it could by some means reach the right quarter, I should feel happy. I hope you will excuse this long epistle, but I feel warmly on the subject, and would willingly lend a hand to anything that could be done.

[Dell, D. S. 1859. The Post Office. *The Entomologist's Weekly Intelligencer* 6: 167–168].

Nowadays, it is perhaps easy to overlook the importance of the Post Office as an adjunct to collecting in the mid-nineteenth century. With limited leisure time, money and transport, many early collectors found that the only means of enhancing their cabinets was through the exchange of surplus or local insects with other like-minded individuals, or perhaps by subscription (Fig. 132). The regular Exchange column of the 'Intelligencer' was the perfect medium for such transactions. However, even if parcels did eventually arrive intact, having survived the best endeavours of the Post Office to deliver them otherwise, the contents themselves could still prove to be something of an unknown entity. Further disappointment often lay ahead as confirmed by the following two letters, the first of which appeared in *The Entomologist's Weekly Intelligencer* under the heading: "Exchange is no robbery" — OLD SAYING. "Robbery is no exchange" — NEW SAYING.

To the Editor of *The Entomologist's Weekly Intelligencer*, from H. G. Knaggs, M.D., Camden Town, N.W. (11th April 1859):

Sir, — Now that the season has commenced, a few remarks on the present "Exchange" system may not be out of place.

It is a slur upon our Science that there are men amongst us who apply the principle of "All fair in love and war" to Entomology, — that the ends justify the means, — men, for whom the phrase "Rem honesti si possis, sed rem," might be conveniently shortened to "rem" alone, since honesty or honour have *no* part in their transactions. One cannot but pity the greedy mind, which, for the sake of a few insects, postage-stamps or boxes, will sacrifice reputation (if it have it), or all chances of ever getting it (if it have it not), — to say nothing of conscience, when present.

Fig. 131. Dealers' advertisements from *The Entomologist's Record and Journal of Variation*: (a) 1892; (b), (c), (d) 1896; (e) 1902. William Watkin's business was run from a place called The Villa Sphinx — named after the hawk-moth. With the all-pervading smell of moth balls, it was soon popularly known as 'The Villa Stinks'.

Regrettably, not all dealers could claim to have aspired to L. W. Newman's ethical standards. In 'The "Trade" in the 'Nineties' P. B. M. Allan commented on Edmonds' speciality of 'supplying genuine British insects bred from Continental stock' (these 'British Species' included the Small Lappet, Dusky Hook-tip, Water Betony, Three-humped and White Prominents, and Lunar Double-stripe). 'The year 1891 seems to have been a remarkable one at Windsor, where Mr. Edmonds had his "nurseries," Allan observed. 'In addition to the above rarities he was so lucky as to find, in his own breeding-ground, a whole brood of Oleander Hawkmoths — so many in fact that he was able to offer them to his customers at only three shillings apiece. Nothing succeeds like success, and Mr. Edmonds was successful for many years. It was in fact not for nothing that he was purveyor to the Royal Family.'

Allan added that 'Head of Scarborough also had his strong suits': in 1891 he was offering the White Prominent, Pine Hawk-moth, and Rosy and Blue Underwings. 'But "many of the rare species can only be supplied when ordered in advance". Which perhaps was quite reasonable; naturally it took a little time for these desirable species to acquire British nationality, per Her Majesty's Post Office.'

NATURALISTS' SUPPLY STORES,
31, PARK STREET, WINDSOR.
Proprietor, E. EDMONDS, Naturalist.
Manufacturer of Entomological Apparatus and Cabinets to the Royal Family and Eton College.
SPECIALITY—(Lepidoptera) Ova, Larvæ and Pupæ.
Breeding Grounds: The "Quaker's Garden," King's Road (adjoining Long Walk, Windsor Great Park), and also at "The Nursery," Osborne Road, Windsor.
Price Lists are issued about the 1st and 15th of each month and (by special arrangement with the printer) are Printed and Posted the same day. On receipt of 1s., every List issued for one year will be sent free.

(No connection with any other firm in Great Britain)

31, PARK STREET, WINDSOR (5 doors from Great Park Gates).

(a)

OVA, LARVÆ, AND PUPÆ.
The Largest Breeder of Lepidoptera in the British Isles is
H. W HEAD, Entomologist,
SCARBOROUGH.

Full List of Ova, Larvae, and Pupae, also Lepidoptera, Apparatus, Cabinets, etc., sent on application.
Many Rare British Species and Good Varieties for Sale.

(b)

WILLIAM WATKINS,
ENTOMOLOGIST,
EASTBOURNE.

Healthy Caterpillars, scarce British species from growing Food Plant.
CHRYSALIDES ALL THE YEAR ROUND. LIST, STAMP
Exotic Butterflies, new collections arriving almost daily.
Prices to suit all Buyers. Set or Unset. 6000 Species.
Selections on Approval. Collections Purchased.
New Priced Catalogue of Lepidoptera. 6,000 Species (80 pp.)
6d. post free (returned to purchasers).

(c)

WILLIAM FARREN, Naturalist.

Well authenticated Birds' Skins, Nests and Eggs.
British and Foreign Lepidoptera.

ENTOMOLOGICAL AND GENERAL APPARATUS. BIRDS, MAMMALS, FISH, Etc., PRESERVED AND MOUNTED.

BRITISH AND FOREIGN LEPIDOPTERA, BIRDS' SKINS, Etc., BOUGHT OR EXCHANGED.

Special Attention to Orders for Rare and Local British Lepidoptera.

14, MARKET PASSAGE, CAMBRIDGE.

(d)

OVA, LARVÆ AND PUPÆ.
Large stock all the year round. Finest quality.
GENUINE BRITISH ONLY STOCKED.
Price list free.
Lepidoptera reared from the ova to Pupæ or Imagines on commission.
For terms, etc., apply
L. W. NEWMAN, Bexley, Kent.

(e)

Some have been unjustly — others hastily — accused; now and then the accuser has been the culprit; not unfrequently the perpetration of a swindle has gone unpunished, while others have deservedly gained for themselves an unenviable and lasting notoriety.

My chief object in writing this letter is that the victims of these black sheep may no longer, from a feeling of modesty or timidity, be backward in denouncing men who do not deserve the name of entomologists. Barterers or sharp customers we cannot deal with, — they have a right to be so, if they please, — but swindlers it is a matter of common honesty to the public at large to expose. These lines may make a few enemies, but they will lose me no friends.

Trusting that this may have the effect of removing that delicacy which always prevents our coming forward on such occasions.

This was followed by another letter on the same subject.

To the Editor of *The Entomologist's Weekly Intelligencer*, from W. D. Crotch, Weston-Super-Mare. (7th April 1859):

Sir, — I receive four boxes of insects, rare, bred for the cabinet; I open them successively, and in No. 1 find the insects pinned with the finest possible weapon, leaving a margin of about three-eighths of an inch above for the fingers and one-eighth of an inch below for the cork; consequently in inserting my prize beneath the label, so long a mere unmeaning symbol, down slips the pin into a paper-hidden vacuity in the cork, and my digits are driven into the thorax of *Petasia nubeculosa* [Rannoch Sprawler], at the same time that his legs are crushed against the cork. In no very satisfactory mood the remaining contents of the box are transferred to the mouldy perils of the relaxer to be re-pinned.

Now for No. 2. What beauties! But what a marvellous curve their wings have, like those of a partridge, — very suitable to that bird, and perhaps to *Cerastis vaccinii* [The Chestnut], but scarcely appropriate to *Plusia bractea* [Gold Spangle]; also what singular striæ are on the wings of those *Thecla W-album* [White-letter Hairstreak], — "Set with thread for a *Leucographa* [White-marked]!" and I am not likely to lose my bet.

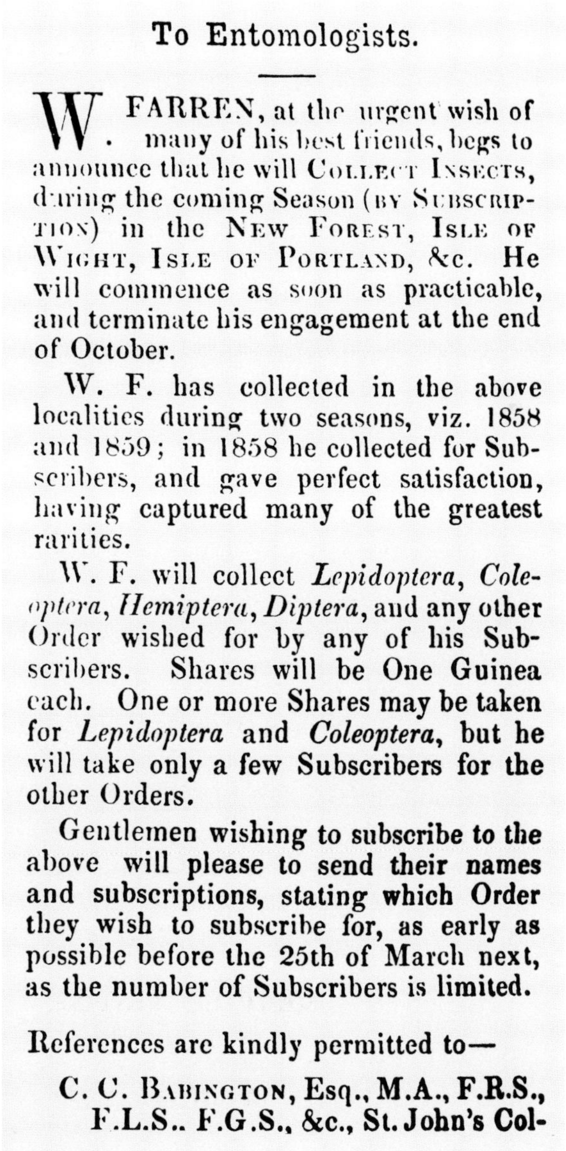

To Entomologists.

W. FARREN, at the urgent wish of many of his best friends, begs to announce that he will COLLECT INSECTS, during the coming Season (BY SUBSCRIPTION) in the NEW FOREST, ISLE OF WIGHT, ISLE OF PORTLAND, &c. He will commence as soon as practicable, and terminate his engagement at the end of October.

W. F. has collected in the above localities during two seasons, viz. 1858 and 1859; in 1858 he collected for Subscribers, and gave perfect satisfaction, having captured many of the greatest rarities.

W. F. will collect *Lepidoptera, Coleoptera, Hemiptera, Diptera,* and any other Order wished for by any of his Subscribers. Shares will be One Guinea each. One or more Shares may be taken for *Lepidoptera* and *Coleoptera,* but he will take only a few Subscribers for the other Orders.

Gentlemen wishing to subscribe to the above will please to send their names and subscriptions, stating which Order they wish to subscribe for, as early as possible before the 25th of March next, as the number of Subscribers is limited.

References are kindly permitted to—

C. C. BABINGTON, Esq., M.A., F.R.S., F.L.S., F.G.S., &c., St. John's Col-

Fig. 132. Dealer's 'dodge'. Advertisement from *The Entomologist's Weekly Intelligencer* (1860). William Farren (1836–1887) was one of the early members of the Cambridge Entomological Society.

No. 3 is a tremendous box — fourpence additional to pay. "Open sesame," and "Oh! Skewers and pancakes!" here is *Miana expolita* [Least Minor] on a spit fit for the eye of Polyphemus, and *Calocampa vetusta* [Red Sword-grass] with his wings on a dead level, as if set by a theodolite and artificial horizon. Those who have not seen a Continental cabinet, can better afford to go into raptures on the subject than those who have, and to their transports I leave them. We do not ask our Continental co-operators to change their mode and habits, nor do I think the "Long-Pin Club" at home will do more than cause an infinite amount of subsequent relaxing, — at first to their correspondents and afterwards to themselves.

Rather hopelessly I now revert to No. 4, a box of no pretensions, but within, each specimen has an allowance of a full half-inch (of pin) beneath, and nearly the same above, but the plyers (bent) can be applied beneath, and thus all danger for the fingers is avoided. No marks appear on the wings, which are variously inclined, to correspond, in some degree at least, with the natural curvature. [The article finishes with some tips on setting, recommending the use of card-braces for securing the wings.]

Despite these attendant problems, the trade continued to flourish. In an article entitled "'The Trade' in the 'Nineties", in *The Entomologist's Record* (1957), P. B. M. Allan, writing about this 'home trade' in insects, mentions that in the last decade of the nineteenth century 346 collectors and 25 live-stock dealers (in addition to some of the apparatus dealers) were advertising in the "Exchanges and Wants" pages of the '*Record*' (Fig. 131), which also had an active 'exchange club' in operation. However, by 1950 the corresponding figures had dropped to 26 and 4, which was no doubt, in part, a reflection of the unprecedented social and economic changes that had taken place in the previous half-century.

THE EXCHANGE CLUB

James W. Tutt, F.E.S., Blackheath, London S. E. (1896)

In 1890 James Tutt formed the 'Record Exchange Club', which introduced the novel idea of 'exchange baskets' whereby fellow members could exchange specimens. Several years later, following renewed interest in the scheme, he wrote an article in *The Entomologist's Record* explaining how it worked.

. . . Each member has his own box in the basket into which he puts his *Duplicates*. He selects from the other boxes his *Desiderata*, enters in a book that travels with the basket what he sends, and signs for what he takes out. He, therefore, need take out no damaged specimens, and such get returned to their owners. He can, by selecting a few of his wants from each box, obtain an excellent exchange from other collectors with whom individually he would probably fail to effect one. A does not want B's insects, B does not want C's, and C does not want A's — but C wants B's insects, B wants A's, and A wants C's, hence an exchange is effected, and with ten members in a basket this indirect system becomes much more valuable. A provincial collector can send specimens to be named. He can also make enquiries of other members, which will be answered in the note book. The member will see local forms of various species of which he did not know the existence, and so on.

The Rules are arranged for mutual protection and advantage.

They are —

1. That the "Record Exchange Club" be instituted for such subscribers to the *Entomologist's Record* as can set insects well, and fulfil the other rules of the club.

2. That each member send only fine insects, with data attached (or entered in the book); that he initial all insects taken from other boxes; and carefully fill up the Table mentioned in Rule 3. [Very common species, unless very variable, are not admissible].

3. That each member fill up on each round the Table providing for the following:— (1) The entry of the number of insects returned in his own box, and the entry in the book of the names of an equal number of fresh insects to make up for those returned. (2) The entry of the number of insects taken from other boxes, and the entry of the names of an equal number of insects which he places in his own box (and 20 per cent. extra for a working surplus).

4. That no member takes insects from other boxes until he has removed all insects returned to him from his own, and substituted an equal number of fresh specimens likely to prove useful to members.

5. That no member keep the basket for more than three clear days. If from home the member must leave instructions as to forwarding. [For this purpose each member must provide himself with a list of the names and addresses of all members in his Basket, and a list showing the order of each Basket will be printed in each number of the *Ent. Record*. Members must also publish notices, &c., through the *Record*, as the Editor can undertake no personal correspondence.]

6. That each member send, at once, to the Editor of *The Entom. Record* a postcard announcing the arrival of the Basket from Mr. —, and its despatch to Mr. —.

7. That each member shall carefully re-pack every box that he opens, to prevent damage, and shall also make himself responsible for the sufficiency of the packing in the Basket when it leaves him.

8. That the admission of members be in the hands of the Editor, who will satisfy himself, as far as possible, of the suitability of the candidates for membership, and who will provide a box as vacancies occur. That no member leave the club whilst indebted to the other members.

9. That each member pay an entrance fee of 1s. 3d. towards the general expenses of providing boxes, basket, &c., for each Basket of which he becomes a member.

10. That notes of general interest published in the Note Book may be printed in the *Ent. Record*.

The Exchange Club started as far back as February, 1890, so that its long life and present vitality show that it is appreciated by the members. Personally, I find that it has been of the greatest benefit to me, and such work as is attached thereto has been largely a labour of love. The flagrant abuse by occasional individual members of Rules 2 and 5, and the carelessness of other (usually excellent) members to satisfy Rule 6, have given the greatest amount of trouble and anxiety, but otherwise there can be no doubt the system has proved a great success.

[Tutt, J. W. 1896. Notes on collecting, etc. The Exchange Club. *The Entomologist's Record and Journal of Variation* 7: 61–62].

STRIDULATION IN THE GARDEN TIGER

Edward Lovett, Croydon, Surrey. (1881)

While examining a specimen of *Arctia caja* this morning I permitted it to walk up my hand. During the act of crawling it suddenly and several times uttered a sound as loud as, and similar to that produced by, the death's-head (*Acherontia atropos*). So remarkable was the noise that my brother, who was in the room at the time, left his work and came over to see what caused it. I have never seen any notice of stridulation in this species, and should be glad to know if any of your correspondents have made a similar observation.

[Lovett, E. 1881. Stridulation in *Arctia caja*. *The Entomologist* 14: 178].

A DITTY

'TWAS one p.m.: I sorely wished
  My appetite were blunter:
Five hours since my last meal was dished!
  I met a bad bug-hunter.

He gave me food, he gave me drink:
  His air was gay and frisky:
The food was sandwiches, I think:
  The drink, I know, was whisky.

I liked his commissariat:
  I did not like his manner:
He wore a large and airy hat:
  He waved a red bandana.

The dust it blew: his coat so brown
  Was powdered like a miller:
I took my cap and brushed him down:
  He'd caught a black Sibylla.

I smoothed his hair: I tied his tie:
  His boots with treacle painted:
I asked him for his butterfly:
  He gave it up — and fainted.

His nose I smote: his nose it bled:
  My ears with joy were ringing:
He oped his eyes, and as I fled
  I heard him softly singing.

"I creep all day along the down:
  I crawl through copses shady:
Take here a dusky Meadow-Brown,
  And there a Painted-Lady."

'Twas five p.m.: I sipped my tea:
  My appetite grew blunter:
"Sibylla black belongs to me!
  Bless, bless that bad bug-hunter."

G. M. A. Hewett.

[Hewett, G. M. A. 1894. A Ditty. *The Entomologist's Record and Journal of Variation* **6**: 22].

NOTE ON THE ODOUR OF THE CONVOLVULUS HAWK-MOTH

Dr Henry Guard Knaggs, Kentish Town, London. (1869)

Early last September, my cousin (who resides some half-mile from hence) showed me a live male *convolvuli* [Convolvulus Hawk-moth] which had been picked up on his door step by a boy. The creature had evidently flown at the light over the door, and had been stunned by coming sharply in contact with the glass. On handling it, I noticed that the odour of musk (as observed by Mr. Hellins in a previous communication to the Magazine) was strongly perceptible. The sequel is curious: — After keeping it covered over with an inverted tumbler for three or four days, my cousin removed the thing from its prison, believing it to be dead or nearly so. When the gas was lighted up the same evening, however, the family were suddenly surprised by the great moth taking wing, flying at the light, and eventually immolating itself in the flame.

[Guard Knaggs, H. 1869. Note on the odour of *Sphinx convolvuli*. *Entomologist's Monthly Magazine* **6**: 166].

PUSHING THE BOAT OUT

Lepidopterists always seem to be trespassing on private land, and many tales have been told of adventures with gamekeepers, police constables and irate landowners. In Chapter Two, a couple of Court cases were heard where the offence of trespass had brought entomological defendants before the bench. It appears that in each case the moth hunters came off best. Although few lepidopterists have ever failed to convince landowners, police and other dignitaries of their not unreasonable activities, we have included the following two anecdotes one of which shows that some moth hunters did sail very close to the wind. The individuals involved in these minor adventures were James W. Tutt and John W. Douglas, two of the great characters of Victorian entomology.

From: 'THE HUMMING-BIRD AT HOME'

James W. Tutt, F.E.S., Blackheath, London, S. E. (1894)

. . . But I wander onwards, and passing the Coastguard Station, I sit down at the foot of a post with a board nailed to it. I studiously forbear to look at such boards during my wanderings and I am soon interested in watching the habits of some little moths which rest on the ground at the roots of the grass at my feet. There are literally thousands, hurrying and scuttling in all directions as I disturb them. Whilst observing these atoms (with the wings expanded they are not much more than a quarter of an inch across) I am startled by the sight of a large black dog. I try to make friends with it, but this is not easy so I go on with my observations. Presently I become aware that the dog has a companion. A rough, shock-headed individual with leathern gaiters and a large stick suggests a member of a fraternity with which I have long been familiar. "What are you doing here?" "Observing," I reply in my most dulcet tones, for I have long since learned that if one wishes to study Nature one must get permission from the ignorant. "Well, don't you know you're a trespassin'?" "I was not aware of the fact," I reply, "but I've been told in the course of my life that I am a good many things." "Can't you see that board?" "No," say I, keeping my eyes fixed well away to sea. "Don't suppose you can there; look behind you," he says angrily. Things begin to look queer, so I raise myself, place my back against the post, and then steadily look to the north. Still keeping my back to the post I move round it and look to the east, then to the south, and then to the west, and when I have finished the four points of the compass, I drop into my original position just as he yells out, "Over your head, you fool." I look up, and remark that the gulls must be young ones as they are brown. "Brown be hanged," he says, "what do you take me for?" "A shepherd, without doubt," I remark, "your peaceful manner proclaims as much." Then, purple with rage, he explodes: — "I'm darned! I'm darned if ever I saw anything like it. The cheek of a darned Londoner makes my hair rise. Here's a fellow as sticks his back up agin a post, shuffles round it with his back still agin it, and then says he can't see it. Well I'm darned!" The situation is now decidedly ominous; the dog begins to growl, when a woman appears on the scene. "Why don't you come in to tea?" she says to him. He looks dangerous, and I turn to the woman and say, "I'm fearfully thirsty; do you mind making me a cup of tea?" at the same time paying her in advance. "No I don't, sir," she replies, looking at the coin with satisfaction; and then I turn to him and begin talking at a tangent about fowls, rabbits, &c. He is moody at first, but by the time we have had a cup of tea we are sworn friends, and I have rarely been to the sandhills since without availing myself of the hospitality of that good man whose temper I ruffled. . . .

[Tutt, J. W. 1894. *Random Recollections of Woodland, Fen and Hill.* Ed.2, pp. 52–53].

SEASONABLE NOTES – GAMEKEEPERS

John W. Douglas, Lee, London S. E. (1859)

In the "merrie month of May" the entomologist is annually reminded that, however harmless and peaceable he may believe his occupation to be, he is still looked upon by one

Fig. 133. John Douglas (1814–1905). Known as 'Jolly Douglas', he was the prolific composer of doggerel verse celebrating entomological friends and events (see pages 14 and 84).

class of men as worse than a rogue and a vagabond. Gamekeepers have a horror of collectors, and now, when the hearts of others are opened and softened by the genial influences of the season, his whole nature becomes more indurated than usual, and he nerves himself to do battle with everything that moves through a wood, because it may disturb the game. "I'd rather see any mortal thing than you fly-catchers," said one of these feudal retainers once to me, "'cause you gives us more trouble nor any other kind o' warmint." I attempted to show him that, in the paths of the wood, I could do no more harm than himself; in fact, not so much, as my weapons did not explode. "That's all stuff," said he, "the birds is used to me and a gun; but they're frightened at one o' them ere flappers o' yourn." He saw things from a different point of view, and I might as well have argued with him on the matter as with a milestone at a distance.

Once I remember crossing a field in a wood, and when about half way over the keeper issued from a copse on the other side and advanced to meet me.

"Hollo there!" shouted he, before he came near me. I waited till I should be on closer terms, and then he resumed the conversation with, "How did you get in here?" To which I meekly replied, "In the proper way — through the gate." "Then did you not see the notice?" "No." Collectors never do see such things. Well, then, he would tell me that it said "All trespassers would be prosecuted and all dogs would be shot." Of course I was dreadfully alarmed, not knowing which of the two punishments was to be my fate, nor whether one was worse than the other; but after a little "soft sawder" I was allowed to retreat unhurt.

In another wood, where I had permission to go, I was accosted by the keeper, and he condescended to explain to me that the last year there was very little game, and he had told his master that it was "all along o' them fly-catchers, and there never would be no game as long as he let them come, for he knowed they stole the eggs as well as frightened the birds off their nestes."

Now we all know that the impulse with collectors is so strong that they do not, as a rule, hesitate to go wherever their game inhabits, and so they do not wonder that they are treated as trespassers. There is no help for it; if they will go, of course they must pay the penalty. There are, however, some woods where access is free to all, and a few where admission may be had for the asking; and it is the duty of all to take care that no damage is done by their operations. I have been disgusted with the sight of trees and bushes mutilated by the thrashing they had received from heedless collectors, such damage being entirely unnecessary and indefensible, and provocative, on the part of their owners or their keepers, of retaliatory measures, which often fall, not upon the doers of the mischief, but upon innocent persons. This seasonable note, therefore, to have a care in beating, will, I trust, not be without its effect in restraining the ardour of young entomologists in the use of the beating-stick, and inducing them to keep in the paths in woods, which are far better for beating than in the cover.

[Douglas, J. W. 1859. Gamekeepers. *The Entomologist's Weekly Intelligencer* **6**: 62–63].

ABUNDANCE OF THE VAPOURER IN LONDON

Vincent R. Perkins, Pimlico, London, S. W. (1881)

Without fear of contradiction the Vapourer Moth may be said to be the commonest in town, go where you will up street, down street, or "all round the square." For some weeks to come you will be sure to see the little brown gentleman dancing about, ziczacing in the sunshine both morning and afternoon. Although the insect is so common, I would call attention to the extraordinary number of larvæ which have appeared this season in London. Persons walking up "The Mall," for instance, can hardly fail to have observed the condition of the lime-trees in that avenue, more especially from Buckingham Palace to Marlborough House. Some few are quite denuded of leaves, only the skeletons and midribs being left; many have large boughs served in the same way, and looking up at these boughs defoliated by the innumerable jaws that have been at work upon them we can soon see the cocoons of this moth, not one here and there, but in regular clusters, so abundant are they. The thorns in the park, too, have been almost as badly served. In passing along the Mall this morning I observed numbers of cocoons spun up on the bark of the plane-trees, and here and there a female had covered them with her eggs; while many were crawling about the stems of the trees.

[Perkins, V. R. 1881. Abundance of *Orgyia antiqua* in London. *The Entomologist* **14**: 178–179].

DR 'HAMMERSMITH' IS STILL ALIVE

From the Editor, the *Entomologist's Monthly Magazine*:

Since 1834, and until recently, there appeared in the list of Honorary Members of the Entomological Society of London, the name of Hammerschmidt of Vienna, who published many valuable memoirs, especially on gall insects, and entomological anatomy and physiology. During the troublous times in Austria about the year 1848, this gentleman seemed to disappear from the scientific world; and about six years since, as no information could be obtained as to his being still alive, the name was erased, and the place filled up. Within the last month, the Society has been somewhat startled at receiving from Paris a card bearing the name of "Dr. Abdullah Bey, Chevalier de l'ordre du Medjedié, Lt. Colonel et Médecin d'Etat-Major, Constantinople," and adding that he was formerly known as Dr. Hammerschmidt, of Vienna. Thus an enigma has to be solved. Being reasonably supposed to be dead, his position as Honorary Member was cancelled, and another gentleman (we do not say more worthily) occupies it. Which of the twain is now entitled to the honour?

[Editor. 1867. Hammerschmidt redivivus. *Entomologist's Monthly Magazine* **4**: 43].

THE WORM AND THE BUTTERFLY

Alfred Sich, Chiswick, London, W. (1911)

A friend of mine, Mr. Crickmay, noticed one day this summer a white butterfly, which had settled on the lawn, to be in difficulties. Being of an inquiring turn of mind he made investigations to ascertain the cause of the trouble. He discovered that an earthworm had seized the butterfly by the hindwings and was attempting to drag it down into its burrow. I imagine that the lawn had been sprinkled and the wet grass had attracted to its surface the butterfly from above and the worm from beneath. The latter taking the closed hindwings of the butterfly for a leaf, had attempted to gain possession. I have not previously heard of such an occurrence.

[Sich, A. 1911. The worm and the butterfly. *The Entomologist's Record and Journal of Variation* **23**: 274].

WHAT HAPPENS TO OUR BUTTERFLIES AND MOTHS?

From the moment that butterflies and moths leave the chrysalis, death is the only certainty. Some will live for a few days, others for a few months, and some for rather longer — but in the end all will die. Death in the natural world is usually a very private affair and rarely observed, but in the following two articles the final moments of a butterfly and moth are brought to our attention.

DEATH OF A BUTTERFLY

Peter Michael, Aldershot, Hampshire. (1951)

In the fitful October sunshine I watched a belated *Pieris brassicae* [Large White] — a female — alight on a cabbage leaf. It landed rather uncertainly, for it had come, not to oviposit but to die. Slowly the wings canted over until the insect lay almost flat on its side. I picked it up: the legs waved feebly. Gently I replaced it on the leaf, and within a matter of seconds it had expired. Soon the fragile body would be gone – blown by the wind, shrivelled or devoured.

Death, even when not violent, usually comes quite suddenly to the insect: disposal follows almost as swiftly. Often enough, we see the tiny ova laid; we may watch the larvae hatching from the eggs, pupae yielding up their transformed contents. Birth, growth, metamorphosis we are permitted to study relatively often and fairly easily; but death, except when violent, is mostly hidden from human eyes. Even the corpse is seen but seldom, for nature has tidy ways and her scavengers are legion.

[Michael, P. 1951. Death of a butterfly. *Bulletin of the Amateur Entomologists' Society* **10**: 84].

DEATH OF A MOTH

Edward A. Sadler, West Tisted, Hampshire. (1968)

On the afternoon of August 11, whilst attending a corn field being harvested on this estate, a geometer was noted flying towards me along the hedge by which I was standing, slowly losing height as it approached. It landed on a fallen branch at my feet, where it fanned its wings out and downwards beneath the body and around the twig, and then fell on its back. I had by this time recognised the moth as a male *Hydriomena furcata* Thunb. [July Highflyer] and on picking it up, realised that it was not feigning death but had indeed died, an event I had never previously observed in the wild among lepidoptera, and one which, though no doubt commonplace, has probably seldom been witnessed. The moth in question was very worn, but otherwise undamaged.

[Sadler, E. A. 1968. Death of a moth. *The Entomologist's Record and Journal of Variation* **80**: 283].

A FACT!

Revd John Hellins, Exeter, Devon. (1870)

A reverend acquaintance of mine, who dabbles in moth-catching, has confided to me his belief that the little "silver-fish" (*Lepisma*) is *the larva of Alucita polydactyla* [*A. hexadactyla* – the Twenty-plume Moth], and its food is the paper on the walls of his bed-room! The "fish" swarms on his walls — the moths swarm in his windows: the connection is clear, and I have had to give in, beaten by my friend's invincible — stupidity.

[Hellins, J. 1870. A fact! *Entomologist's Monthly Magazine* **7**: 162].

WHAT BUTTERFLIES NEVER DO

William S. Coleman, Bayswater, London. (1860)

William Stephen Coleman (1829–1904) was born in Horsham, the son of a physician. A keen naturalist from youth, he wrote *Our Woodlands, Heaths, and Hedges* (1859) and *British Butterflies* (1860). Both of these ran to several editions. He was an accomplished artist and book illustrator, and among a number of other commissions he designed the heading of *The Field* newspaper. He illustrated *British Ferns and their Allies* (1861) by Thomas Moore and *The Common Moths of England* (1870) by the Revd John G. Wood.

Among the *negative* attributes of butterflies, I may state positively, that *no butterfly whatever can either sting or bite in the least degree*; and from their total harmlessness towards the person of man, conjoined with their outward attractiveness, they merit and enjoy an exemption from those feelings of dread and disgust that attach to many, or, I may say, to almost all other tribes of insects; even to their equally harmless near relatives the larger moths. At least, it has never been my misfortune to meet with a person weak-minded enough to be afraid of a butterfly, though I have seen some exhibit symptoms of the greatest terror at the proximity of a large Hawk-moth, and some of the thick-bodied common moths — "Match-owlets," the country folk call them.

Once, also, I listened to the grave recital — by a classical scholar too — of a murderous onslaught made by a Privet Hawk-moth on the neck of a lady, and how it "*bit a piece clean out.*" Of course I attempted to prove, by what seemed to me very fair logic, that the moth, having neither teeth nor even any mouth capable of opening, but only a weak hollow tongue to suck honey through, was utterly incapable of biting or inflicting any wound whatever. But, as is usual in such cases, my entomological theory went for nothing in face of the gentleman's knock-down battery of *facts — ocular* facts; he had *seen* the *moth*, and he had *seen* the *wound*: surely, there was proof enough for me, or any one else. So, I suppose, he steadfastly believes to this day, that the moth was a truculent, bloodthirsty monster; whilst I still presume to believe, that if any wound was caused at the moment in question, it was by the nails of the lady attacked, or her friends, in clutching frantically at the terrific intruder; who, poor fellow, might have been pardoned for mistaking the fair neck for one of his favourite flowers (a *lily*, perhaps), while the utmost harm he contemplated was to pilfer a sip of nectar from the lips he doubtless took for rosebuds.

[Coleman, W. S. 1860. *British Butterflies*. George Routledge & Sons, London].

A NEW BUTTERFLY NET

Frederick W. Frohawk, F.E.S., M.B.O.U., Croydon, Surrey. (1903)

I have recently had the pleasure of putting to practical test a very ingenious net invented and sold by Rowland Ward, Ltd., 166, Piccadilly, which collectors will find of great convenience. It forms an admirable walking stick when not in use, which contains the ring of the net formed of two portions that can be instantly pulled out of the stick (after unscrewing the knob forming the handle), and an ordinary net bag run on the ring-canes; the ends can then be quickly fitted together, when a small stay is slipped into place at the base, and a net of 5 ft. circumference is ready for use. The great advantage of the invention is that the collector can always carry with him a very serviceable net, which can be adjusted rapidly and as quickly put out of sight, as the modest collector does not care to brandish a large net before the gaze of the uninitiated.

[Frohawk, F. W. 1903. A new butterfly net. *The Entomologist* 36: 191].

How successful this net proved to be is not known. Its design is reminiscent of the earlier umbrella net invented in the 1850s by the London dealer T. Cooke & Son, originally of 513, New Oxford Street. Although more expensive than a conventional ring net, it indeed proved to be very popular and was still being advertised in dealers' catalogues up until the First World War (Fig. 60). In British Butterflies W. S. Coleman touched upon a potential inherent design flaw:

Some entomologists, nervously sensitive to public opinion, are, however, somewhat shy of sporting these umbrella nets, for should rain perchance come down while he is on the road, the villagers may be astonished at the insane spectacle of a man scuttling along through the torrent and getting drenched through, while he carries a good-looking umbrella carefully under his arm for fear it should get wet; and if, on the other hand, the weather be fine, the carrying [of] such a protective would seem an equally eccentric whim. But only the very thin-skinned would be driven from the use of a good weapon by such a harmless contingency as I have supposed.

Fig. 134. The umbrella net – 'rather less than the length of the collector's arm', and let into it was a circular piece 'in the manner of my grandmother's cap'. (H. Guard Knaggs, 1869)

Unfortunately, very few examples of any of the early types of nets appear to have survived; the particular umbrella net in Fig. 134 once belonged to L. W. Newman and is now in The Simpson Collection of Entomological Memorabilia.

Leonard Woods Newman (1873–1949) founded his 'butterfly farm' in 1894 in Bexley, Kent. Although not the first of its kind – that honour going to H. W. Head of Scarborough (see Fig. 131) – his was certainly to become the best known and was usually referred to as *the* Butterfly Farm. His entomological knowledge and business integrity quickly won him the respect of the well-known collectors of the period and were a welcome change from the nefarious activities previously perpetrated by some of the earlier commercial dealers. A full and fascinating account of the history of the

Figs 135 and 136. Leonard Woods Newman, 'who endowed commercial entomology with worth and honour . . . He was unsurpassed as a collector and as a breeder . . . he had the eyes of an eagle, the energy of a dynamo, and the luck of the devil!' (L. Hugh Newman, 1967)

farm is given in *Living with Butterflies* by L. Hugh Newman. An article by Brian Gardiner about the Newmans in *The Entomologist's Record* (1993) included a contemporary account that originally appeared in 1915 of the working of the farm in its early days. Interestingly, it shows that conservation, often considered a fairly recent concern, was being both thought of and practised at the turn of the previous century.

PROFUSION OF THE SILVER-Y

John T. Carrington, F.L.S., Royal Aquarium, Westminster, London, S. W. (1879)

The sandhills and neighbourhood of the sea on the Essex coast are this August infested by a multitude of the moths of *Plusia gamma* [Silver-Y]. So large are the numbers that they almost pass description. It is no uncommon thing to see ten to twenty specimens fighting with one another to get at a single thistle-flower, to the exclusion of all other insects.

[Carrington, J. T. 1879. Profusion of *Plusia gamma*. *The Entomologist* 12: 223].

EXTRAORDINARY ABUNDANCE OF THE SILVER-Y

Joseph Anderson, junior, Chichester, Sussex. (1879)

In the August number of the 'Entomologist' [1879. **12**: 194], Mr. Fitch, in a very instructive article, has given some details respecting certain enemies to our pea crops, which did much injury in the spring of this year. And now another army of depredators has come forth to the attack, for our farmers — at least those of this district — have been ruefully lamenting the havoc committed by immense numbers of the larvæ of *Plusia gamma* [Silver-Y], whole fields of peas being well-nigh stripped bare of the leaves by them, thus arresting of necessity the subsequent development of the peas in the pods. I collected on the 5th of August a quantity of the larvæ, which were then nearly full-fed. In the course of three or four days they spun their cocoons and turned into pupæ; the perfect insects emerging on the 14th, so that the pupa state lasted but the short time of six or seven days. The thrushes (*Turdus musicus*), which are this year unusually numerous, congregated in the fields in large flocks; doubtless fed sumptuously every day on the larvæ, which they must have considerably diminished. As an instance of the ignorance of many agriculturalists on questions connected with Natural History, and their stupid inability to discriminate betwixt their friends and foes, I may mention that, because they found the thrushes at the peas, some attributed the mischief to "them rascally birds," and were for "shooting them all off." The imagines of *Plusia gamma* are now swarming in every direction, and fly from the flowers and hedges more like bees than moths. They are equally abundant by day as by night; anything like this profusion I never remember. . . .

[Anderson, J. jun. 1879. Extraordinary abundance of *Plusia gamma*. *The Entomologist* **12**: 222–223].

A MOTH CHASED BY SPARROWS

Edwin G. Bayford, Barnsley, Yorkshire. (1931)

The following observations, made about 7.30 p.m. (summer time) on July 20th, are not without interest, and may merit a permanent record.

A Noctuid moth about the size of the common 'yellow underwing' (*Triphaena pronuba*) was flying about nine or ten feet from the ground, when a sparrow darted after it, but failed to catch it, and returned to the spout of an adjacent building. Another sparrow took up the chase, with the same result. In all, five sparrows chased it, separately; at no time were two engaged together. The moth seemed to elude them without effort and without increasing speed, mounting higher and higher until it was lost to sight. The whole affair might have been a game governed by set rules, judging by the way the sparrows returned to their perches after failing to catch the moth, a fresh competitor coming forward immediately.

[Bayford, E. G. 1931. A moth chased by sparrows. *The Entomologist* **67**: 252].

THE FATE OF RUSSIAN ENTOMOLOGISTS

In the *Entomologist's Monthly Magazine* (1921), under the title 'Some news of the Russian entomologists', there is the following editorial comment:

> After an interval of several years authentic news regarding the fate of certain Russian entomologists has recently reached this country. It appears that a great number of them died during those years from different causes, mostly from typhus and several from starvation. The Russian Entomological Society has lost about 50 of its Fellows, amongst them several very prominent men. . . .

The editorial listed some of the deceased and went on to mention that no scientific papers or books published since 1915 had reached Russian entomologists, and that the low currency exchange rate precluded their being able to afford to purchase them. They requested British colleagues' help in contributing back numbers of magazines, books and separate reprints of papers for their library. 'Every publication, however small, will be accepted with the sincerest gratitude and read with the greatest interest by those of our colleagues who are starving, not physically only, but mentally as well.'

Shortly after this news was published, the magazine canvassed help in the form of books and original papers. Around this time, *The Entomologist* (1923) launched an appeal for financial assistance.

THE DISTRESS OF RUSSIAN ENTOMOLOGISTS

At a recent meeting of the Entomological Society of London, the sum of 20 dollars was voted by the Society, and another 20 dollars subscribed among the Fellows, to send a remittance of food and clothing to the President of the Russian Entomological Society, Andrei Petrovich Semenov-Tian-Shansky, Hon. F.E.S., who is living under distressful conditions in Petrograd; yet in spite of this, and of his rapidly failing eyesight, he is continuing to carry on his entomological work.

The Russian Entomological Society, under his guidance and encouraged by his devotion and enthusiasm, is also carrying on its labours; in the face of innumerable difficulties the members have succeeded in producing their Review, copies of which have reached England. The splendid work done by this school of Entomologists is, perhaps, not well enough known in Britain, except to specialists, but it is almost to them alone that we owe our present knowledge, which is considerable, of the immensely rich, interesting and important fauna of Central Asia, Siberia and the Caucasus. Yet these men can scarcely keep body and soul together, and many have families to support, while few can buy the clothing which is urgently needed. This state of affairs must seriously prejudice the efficiency of their scientific work and thus hinder the progress of Entomology.

In order to help them, a small committee has been formed, with the object of collecting funds and remitting them to the Russian Entomological Society, to be employed as their

Council thinks fit, in aiding the members in need either with food or clothing. Moderate sums of money can now be remitted to Petrograd or Moscow. This committee consists of Mr. Arthur Dicksee, Mr. B. P. Uvarov, at the Natural History Museum, and Dr. Burr. Any sympathiser is requested to communicate with either of these, preferably enclosing a remittance, however small, for a few shillings will to-day buy millions of roubles, and will help a Russian colleague to carry on the struggle and his scientific work for the benefit of the Science which we all love.

All British entomologists who enjoy happier conditions cannot but feel the greatest sympathy for their Russian brethren under these pitiable circumstances, especially those who have connections by correspondence, friendship, or scientific relationship, above all, those who have at any time enjoyed the famous and lavish hospitality of that generous people, and probably many will welcome an opportunity of contributing to their assistance, to help them tide over until better days.

ARTHUR DICKSEE, 7, Duke Street, St James's, S.W.1.
B. P. UVAROV, Natural History Museum, Cromwell Road, S.W.7.
MALCOLM BURR, United University Club, Pall Mall East, S.W.1.
[1923. *The Entomologist* **56**: 99].

AN ENTIRE PARISH TURNED ENTOMOLOGISTS

To the Editor of *The Entomologist's Weekly Intelligencer*, **from W. H. Harwood, Colchester (11th April 1859) :**

Sir: — The following paragraph, from the 'Essex Standard' will account for my extraordinary heading: —

"*St. Peter's Church.* — The satisfaction felt at the recent restoration of this church has been damped by a very singular circumstance: the whole of the new sittings in the body of the church are found to be infested with myriads of minute insects, which have somewhat puzzled our local naturalists; but Dr. Becker, a German medical practitioner, pronounces them to be of the class connected with cutaneous diseases. They are supposed to have originated from uncovering the vaults and human bones, in the process of lowering the floor of the church; and at present no remedy has been suggested short of removing the fittings and covering the floor with a coating of concrete. The celebration of Divine service has necessarily been suspended, and the use of St. Mary's Church has again been obtained for evening service, as during the progress of the alterations."

I enclose you a few specimens, and if you could throw any light on the subject I am sure, for one, I should be very much obliged. Dr. Becker informs me that he considers the "animal" in question to be the *Acarus dermanyssiformis* of Ehrenberg and Donué.

(The insects [*sic*] are decidedly an *Acarus*, but what species and what are its habits we cannot say; but no doubt the insect is connected with the new fittings themselves, and has nothing whatever to do with the process of uncovering the vaults; we have, however, forwarded specimens to an entomologist, who may perhaps be able to throw more light on the subject — Editor).

[Harwood, W. H. 1859. An entire parish turned entomologists. *The Entomologist's Weekly Intelligencer* **6**: 29].

AN ENTOMOLOGIST'S DREAM

——

I dreamt one night, as I was sleeping,
    Lying upon my bed,
That hornets, butterflies and beetles,
    Were buzzing round my head;
That they had come to ask their rights,
    Whom I had once impaled on spikes.

The horrid troop flew round my head,
    Each armed with a shining pin,
And screamed to one another
    To thrust it deeply in;
"For he," they said, "us once did slay,
    Now, now, has come the vengeance day!"

Each brandishing aloft his spear,
    Came cruelly rushing on;
Some buzzed around my aching head,
    Some leaped the bed upon;
One deeply drove his spear in me,
    I woke, and found it was a — *flea!*

V. W.

[V. W. 1858. An Entomologist's Dream. *The Entomologist's Weekly Intelligencer* **4**: 78].

ON THE VALUE OF RARE BRITISH LEPIDOPTERA

Revd Joseph Greene, M.A., F.E.S. Bristol, Gloucestershire. (1896)

In the April number of the *Entomologist's Record* is an article signed "John Bull," in which I think I recognise the hand. Be this so or not, I wish to express my most cordial approval of every part of it.

I have long since ceased to care for "Rarities," so-called, and have removed from my small collection such species as *Pachetra leucophaea* [Feathered Ear], *Ennomos autumnaria* [Large Thorn], and others. I have noticed that after a sale, you, and others, have remarked that such and such a collection (or certain rare insects in them) went for comparatively nothing — assigning as the reason the absence of any "history" of it, or its contents, such as "labels," "locality," "from whom received, etc." But of what value is such a history? What is to prevent a collector or dealer from attaching such a label, or locality or name, to any insect that he thinks worth the trouble? In these days of importation — of eggs, pupæ, etc. — of what value is the declaration —honest or dishonest — that the insect was bred by self, on such a day, and in such a locality? I would not accept as a gift any rarity or novelty captured during the last thirty years. The donor, whether amateur or dealer, may be absolutely honest, but — "Quis custodiet custodes?" How is he to prove that he himself is not the victim of a fraud? As to "dealers," I have bought for many years insects from Messrs. Harwood, W. and T. Salvage, but they know that I never buy a rarity. My experience goes back to a period when the "dealers" as such were almost unknown. When it began (*i.e.*, the business) it spread by leaps and bounds, and speedily produced such men as Parry, Button — "et id genus omne." I crossed the Channel (in 1869) in the same steamer as a dealer, who triumphantly showed me *D. compta* [Varied Coronet] on his setting boards! I observed a discrete silence. Very shortly afterwards it was proved beyond dispute that he had brought foreign pupae with him from London so as to emerge at Howth. But the most bare-faced fraud of all was the attempt to palm off three specimens of *Gluphisia crenata* [Dusky Marbled Brown] as having been taken at Howth! Now the food of *G. crenata* is strictly confined to poplar. The island of Howth is about the last place in the world to take *G. crenata*. I know Howth as well as I know my own house, and can safely affirm that there has never been a poplar tree in it — at any rate, not up to the time when this fraud was attempted. *Per contra*, I must speak in very high terms of Harwood of Colchester. I have known him well for many years. Of course, strictly speaking, he is a dealer, but far superior in every way to the average specimen, and, as he is well-known, I am sure your readers will agree with me. It does not affect me much, for, as I have already said, I have long since ceased to feel any interest in "British" (?) rarities, and confine myself to varieties, and interesting or unusual forms of common things. I have, of course, some rarities, but they belong to a bye-gone age. Some, as *Laelia caenosa* [Reed Tussock], *Agrotis subrosea* [Rosy Marsh Moth], *Phibalapteryx polygrammata* [The Many-lined], and others, I owe to my old and generous friend, the late H. Doubleday; and others to my own efforts, as *Aporia crataegi* [Black-veined White], *Polyommatus acis* (*Nomiades semiargus*) [Mazarine Blue], *Lycaena arion* [Large Blue], *Gluphisia crenata*, etc. I feel sure that (financially) all labels, localities, etc., are utterly valueless, for the reason already given.

[Greene, J. 1896. On the value of rare British Lepidoptera. *The Entomologist's Record and Journal of Variation* **8**: 33–34].

Those collectors who were willing to pay high prices for unusual forms of our indigenous species were not without their critics. In 1907 J. W. Tutt attended a sale of Lepidoptera at Steven's Auction Rooms in Covent Garden. He was appalled at the inflated prices paid for varieties of common species and he sought to castigate those who, in his opinion, had wasted their money.

GOOSEBERRIES AT STEVENS'

James W. Tutt, F.E.S., Blackheath, London, S. E. (1907)

We never saw such a jam of "gooseberries" as at Stevens' rooms on October 22nd . . . . when Mr. Raynor's collection was sold. Nor were there wanting samples of the gooseberry fool, mellowed though they were by some of that cream, which regards these fine aberrations as matters of scientific interest, and not as so many say, postage stamps. Besides long series of *A. grossulariata* [The Gooseberry Moth — more usually known as The Magpie or Currant Moth] in store-boxes there were especially two drawers containing some 170 specimens, which sold for nearly £200.

[Tutt, J. W. 1907. Fifty years ago. Gooseberries at Stevens'. (From *The Entomologist's Record* of 1907). *The Entomologist's Record and Journal of Variation* **69**: 76].

The Revd Gilbert H. Raynor's collection 'was exceedingly rich in varieties of *Abraxas grossulariata* and a few other species'; several individual aberrations of *A. grossulariata* fetched £6 10s. each. Some of the prices realized at the distribution of the sale in October and November 1907 were reported that year by Richard South in *The Entomologist* and by the Revd C. R. N. Burrows in *The Entomologist's Record*.

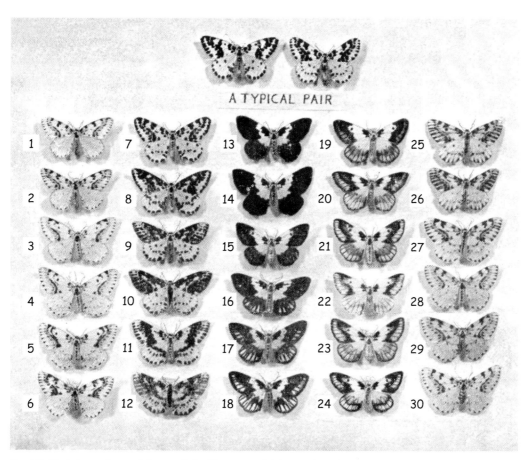

Fig. 137. Varieties and named forms of The Magpie moth (*A. grossulariata*) bred by the Revd Gilbert Raynor (from The Butterfly Farm Ltd's Winter Price List 1963–64). L. Hugh Newman sought to assure potential clients that the market would never be 'flooded' with these rare forms: a clause in the gentleman's will stipulated that a good percentage of his collection of these moths were to be burnt — a task dutifully carried out by his daughter.

THE MODERN ENTOMOLOGIST

Mark Isaak, Sunnyvale, California. (1987)
(with apologies to Gilbert & Sullivan)

I am the very model of a modern entomologist.
I've information useful to a tropical biologist.
I've studied which antennal parts of silverfish are muscular
And know quite well exactly which mosquitoes are crepuscular.
I scan the forest canopy in search of lepidoptera
And burrow beneath rotting logs for certain coleoptera.
I've mapped the complex passageways that termites always scurry in
And studied insect evolution back to the Silurian.
I know the economic consequences of herbivory
And all the different methods used for pesticide delivery.
In short, in matters vital to a tropical biologist,
I am the very model of a modern entomologist.

I watch as ants patrol the tunnels of their nests incessantly;
Some fireflies I have seen conversing bioluminescently.
I'll tell you gruesome stories of Mantodea ferocity
And quote you the statistics of Neuroptera velocity.
And then I've catalogued the major vectors of malaria
And listed all the earwigs in the Indonesian area.
I've analyzed the noises of the cricket and the katydid.
(The ones from Costa Rica made a sound like those from Haiti did.)
I've checked how mayfly populations vary with humidity
And double-checked all E. O. Wilson's theories for validity.
In short, in matters vital to a tropical biologist,
I am the very model of a modern entomologist.

In fact, when I know dragonflies from abdomen to mandible;
When I find aphids, fleas, and lice completely understandable;
When I have skill with killing jars and nets and other gimmickry;
And when I know minutiae of camouflage and mimicry;
When I have very detailed observations of a myriad
Of locusts reproducing in a seventeen year period;
When I know how cockroaches grow from instar to maturity—
My papers (when I write them) won't be destined for obscurity.
Although I've studied insects, and in all their great diversity,
I've yet to get my tenure at a major university,
But still, in matters vital to a tropical biologist,
I am the very model of a modern entomologist.

[Isaak, M. 1987. The Modern Entomologist. www.home.earthlink.net/~misaak/modent.html].

A SOCIETY FOR THE PROTECTION OF BUTTERFLIES?

Brig.-Gen. J. B. G.Tulloch, Hyères, France. (1928)

There are societies for the protection of birds, other animals and plants, and it seems as if we will soon have to have one for the protection of butterflies. I refer to the enormous destruction which must be going on in the manufacture of the articles ornamented with butterflies' wings which are to be seen in increasing numbers in jewellers' and fancy article shops. When this trade first began it was confined to small articles of jewellery, such as brooches, ornamented with pieces from the wings of Morphos. Now quite large articles are covered with the wings, such as plaques, saucers and pin-trays. And the articles are being turned out in large numbers, and the ornamentation is no longer confined to wings from tropical butterflies. I have now seen European species used. One saucer was overlaid with *Gonepteryx* and *Parnassius'* wings, and another had a pattern composed of peacock and tortoiseshell butterfly wings. I counted ten right-hand upper wings of *Parnassius apollo* [Apollo] used as part ornamentation of one article. Many things contain enough wings to supply a good cabinet series of any special butterfly. In other words many tens of thousands of butterflies must be used up in the wholesale manufacture of the articles which must now be going on, and one can easily imagine an area which is being worked by collectors for manufacturers being completely denuded of all butterflies but the most soberly coloured ones. One knows what indiscriminate destruction can do on the Continent by the fact that small bird life has almost totally disappeared in many places. Fancy the Alps, say, as destitute of butterfly life as the South of France is of singing birds! Here, it seems to me, is an opportunity for entomological societies to do good work.

The Entomological Society of London might circularize other societies and also bring the matter forward at International Entomological meetings, with a view to getting entomologists and their friends to abstain from buying the articles in question. The sale of the articles must be increasing and be very big, as I have noticed them in so many places. One window here is full of things which can only last but a short time, and the insects sacrificed in this display would suffice for a cabinet full of series of first-rate insects which would last a lifetime and more, and be of some scientific value.

[Tulloch, J. B. G. 1928. A society for the protection of butterflies? *The Entomologist* **61**: 164–165].

Brigadier-General Tulloch had clearly anticipated the formation of the British Butterfly Conservation Society (now Butterfly Conservation), although a further forty years had to pass before its foundation in 1968.

Fig. 138. The future of butterfly collecting is in the hands of the next generation.

APPENDIX

An index of those specific names for European Lepidoptera mentioned in this book, listed alphabetically alongside their modern equivalents in *The Lepidoptera of Europe* (Karsholt, O. & Razowski, J. (1996). Stenstrup, Apollo Books).

The English names mostly follow those in: *The Moths and Butterflies of Great Britain and Ireland* Volume 7, Part I (Emmet, A. M. & Heath. J. (Eds) (1989). Colchester, Harley Books); *Butterflies of Britain and Europe* (Tolman, T. (1997). London, HarperCollins); and *Colour Identification Guide to Moths of the British Isles* (Skinner, B. (1998). London, Viking).

(In this list Denis & Schiffermüller is abbreviated as D. & S.)

Old Latin Names	Modern Latin Names	English Names
achilleae	*Zygaena loti* (D. & S., 1775)	Slender Scotch Burnet
achine	*Lopinga achine* (Scopoli, 1763)	Woodland Brown
acis	*Polyommatus semiargus* (Rottemburg, 1775)	Mazarine Blue
actæon	*Thymelicus acteon* (Rottemburg, 1775)	Lulworth Skipper
adippe	*Argynnis adippe* (D. & S., 1775)	High Brown Fritillary
admetus	*Agrodiaetus admetus* (Esper, 1783)	Anomalous Blue
adonis	*Meleageria bellargus* (Rottemburg, 1775)	Adonis Blue
adusta	*Mniotype adusta* (Esper, 1790)	Dark Brocade
aegeria	*Pararge aegeria* (Linnaeus, 1758)	Speckled Wood
aegon	*Plebeius argus* (Linnaeus, 1758)	Silver-studded Blue
aëllo	*Oeneis glacialis* (Moll, 1783)	Alpine Grayling
aethiopellus	*Erebia aethiopella* (Hoffmannsegg, 1806)	False Mnestra's Ringlet
aethiops	*Erebia aethiops* (Esper, 1777)	Scotch Argus
agestis	*Aricia agestis* (D. & S., 1775)	Brown Argus
agestis artaxerxes	*Aricia artaxerxes* (Fabricius, 1793)	Northern Brown Argus
aglaia	*Argynnis aglaja* (Linnaeus, 1758)	Dark Green Fritillary
aglaja	*Argynnis aglaja* (Linnaeus, 1758)	Dark Green Fritillary
albicillata	*Mesoleuca albicillata* (Linnaeus, 1758)	Beautiful Carpet
albulata	*Perizoma albulata* (D. & S., 1775)	Grass Rivulet
alchymista	*Catephia alchymista* (D. & S., 1775)	The Alchymist
alciphron	*Lycaena alciphron* (Rottemburg, 1775)	Purple-shot Copper
alcyone	*Hipparchia alcyone* (D. & S., 1775)	Rock Grayling
alexanor	*Papilio alexanor* Esper, 1800	Southern Swallowtail
alexis	*Polyommatus icarus* (Rottemburg, 1775)	Common Blue
alfacariensis	*Colias alfacariensis* Ribbe, 1905	Berger's Clouded Yellow
alsus	*Cupido minimus* (Fuessly, 1775)	Small Blue
alveolus	*Pyrgus malvae* (Linnaeus, 1758)	Grizzled Skipper
anomala	*Stilbia anomala* (Haworth, 1812)	The Anomalous
anteros	*Aricia anteros* (Freyer, 1838)	Blue Argus
anthyllidis	*Zygaena anthyllidis* Boisduval, 1828	Pyrenean Burnet
antiopa	*Nymphalis antiopa* (Linnaeus, 1758)	Camberwell Beauty

antiqua	*Orgyia antiqua* (Linnaeus, 1758)	Vapourer Moth
apiciaria	*Epione repandaria* (Hufnagel, 1767)	Bordered Beauty
apollo	*Parnassius apollo* (Linnaeus, 1758)	Apollo
aragonensis	*Polyommatus albicans* (Herrich-Schäffer, 1851)	Spanish Chalk-hill Blue
arcanius	*Coenonympha arcania* (Linnaeus, 1761)	Pearly Heath
archippus	*Danaus plexippus* (Linnaeus, 1758)	The Monarch
areola	*Xylocampa areola* (Esper, 1789)	Early Grey
argentula	*Deltote bankiana* (Fabricius, 1775)	Silver Barred
argiades	*Everes argiades* (Pallas, 1771)	Short-tailed Blue
argiolus	*Celastrina argiolus* (Linnaeus, 1758)	Holly Blue
argus	*Plebeius argus* (Linnaeus, 1758)	Silver-studded Blue
arion	*Maculinea arion* (Linnaeus, 1758)	Large Blue
artaxerxes	*Aricia artaxerxes* (Fabricius, 1793)	Northern Brown Argus
artemis	*Euphydryas aurinia* (Rottemburg, 1775)	Marsh Fritillary
artenus	*Euphydryas aurinia* (Rottemburg, 1775)	Marsh Fritillary
arundinis	*Phragmataecia castaneae* (Hübner, 1790)	Reed Leopard
astrarche	*Aricia agestis* (D. & S., 1775)	Brown Argus
astrarche ab. *salmacis*	*Aricia artaxerxes salmacis* (Stephens, 1831)	Castle Eden Argus
atalanta	*Vanessa atalanta* (Linnaeus, 1758)	Red Admiral
athalia	*Melitaea athalia* (Rottemburg, 1775)	Heath Fritillary
atrata	*Odezia atrata* (Linnaeus, 1758)	Chimney Sweeper
atropos	*Acherontia atropos* (Linnaeus, 1758)	Death's-head Hawk-moth
aurago	*Xanthia aurago* (D. & S., 1775)	Barred Sallow
aurelia	*Melitaea aurelia* Nickerl, 1850	Nickerl's Fritillary
aurinia	*Euphydryas aurinia* (Rottemburg, 1775)	Marsh Fritillary
aurorina	*Colias aurorina heldreichii* Staudinger, 1862	Greek Clouded Yellow
ausonia	*Euchloe simplonia* (Boisduval, 1828)	Mountain Dappled White
australis	*Colias alfacariensis* Ribbe, 1905	Berger's Clouded Yellow
autumnaria	*Ennomos autumnaria* (Werneburg, 1859)	Large Thorn
avis	*Callophrys avis* Chapman, 1909	Chapman's Hairstreak
ballus	*Tomares ballus* (Fabricius, 1787)	Provence Hairstreak
bankiana	*Deltote bankiana* (Fabricius, 1775)	Silver Barred
barrettii	*Hadena luteago barrettii* (Doubleday, 1864)	Barrett's Marbled Coronet
baton var. *panoptes*	*Pseudophilotes baton panoptes* (Hübner, 1813)	Panoptes Blue
bavius	*Pseudophilotes bavius* (Eversmann, 1832)	Bavius Blue
belemia	*Euchloe belemia* (Esper, 1800)	Green-striped White
belia	*Anthocharis belia* (Linnaeus, 1767)	Moroccan Orange Tip
bellargus	*Polyommatus bellargus* (Rottemburg, 1775)	Adonis Blue
bellidice	*Pontia daplidice* (Linnaeus, 1758)	Bath White
betulae	*Thecla betulae* (Linnaeus, 1758)	Brown Hairstreak
bicoloria	*Leucodonta bicoloria* (D. & S., 1775)	White Prominent
blandina	*Erebia aethiops* (Esper, 1777)	Scotch Argus
boeticus	*Lampides boeticus* (Linnaeus, 1767)	Long-tailed Blue
bractea	*Autographa bractea* (D. & S., 1775)	Gold Spangle

brassicae	*Pieris brassicae* (Linnaeus, 1758)	Large White
brevilinea	*Chortodes brevilinea* (Fenn, 1864)	Fenn's Wainscot
brumata	*Operophtera brumata* (Linnaeus, 1758)	Winter Moth
büttneri	*Sedina buettneri* (E. Hering, 1858)	Blair's Wainscot
caelestissima	*Polyommatus caelestissima* Verity, 1921	Azure Chalk-hill Blue
caenosa	*Laelia coenosa* (Hübner, 1808)	Reed Tussock
caja	*Arctia caja* (Linnaeus, 1758)	Garden Tiger
c-album	*Polygonia c-album* (Linnaeus, 1758)	Comma
callidice	*Pontia callidice* (Hübner, 1800)	Peak White
camilla	*Limenitis camilla* (Linnaeus, 1764)	White Admiral
captiuncula	*Photedes captiuncula* (Treitschke, 1825)	Least Minor
cardamines	*Anthocharis cardamines* (Linnaeus, 1758)	Orange-tip
cardui	*Vanessa cardui* (Linnaeus, 1758)	Painted Lady
carswelli	*Cupido carswelli* Stempffer, 1927	Carswell's Little Blue
cassiope	*Erebia epiphron* (Knoch, 1783)	Small Mountain Ringlet
castaneae	*Phragmataecia castaneae* (Hübner, 1790)	Reed Leopard
celerio	*Hippotion celerio* (Linnaeus, 1758)	Silver-striped Hawk-moth
ceto	*Erebia alberganus* (Prunner, 1798)	Almond-eyed Ringlet
chryseis	*Lycaena hippothoe* (Linnaeus, 1761)	Purple-edged Copper
chrysorrhoea	*Euproctis chrysorrhoea* (Linnaeus, 1758)	Brown-tail
chrysotheme	*Colias chrysotheme* (Esper, 1781)	Lesser Clouded Yellow
cinxia	*Melitaea cinxia* (Linnaeus, 1758)	Glanville Fritillary
cleopatra	*Gonepteryx cleopatra* (Linnaeus, 1767)	Cleopatra
c-nigrum	*Xestia c-nigrum* (Linnaeus, 1758)	Setaceous Hebrew Character
coenosa	*Laelia coenosa* (Hübner, 1808)	Reed Tussock
comma	*Hesperia comma* (Linnaeus, 1758)	Silver-spotted Skipper
comma	*Polygonia c-album* (Linnaeus, 1758)	Comma
compta	*Hadena compta* (D. & S., 1775)	Varied Coronet
conigera	*Mythimna conigera* (D. & S., 1775)	Brown-line Bright-eye
conspersa	*Hadena confusa* (Hufnagel, 1766)	Marbled Coronet
conspicillaris	*Egira conspicillaris* (Linnaeus, 1758)	Silver Cloud
convolvuli	*Agrius convolvuli* (Linnaeus, 1758)	Convolvulus Hawk-moth
coridon	*Polyommatus coridon* (Poda, 1761)	Chalk Hill Blue
corydon	*Polyommatus coridon* (Poda, 1761)	Chalk Hill Blue
craccæ	*Lygephila craccae* (D. & S., 1775)	Scarce Blackneck
crataegi	*Aporia crataegi* (Linnaeus, 1758)	Black-veined White
crataegi	*Trichiura crataegi* (Linnaeus, 1758)	Pale Eggar
crenata	*Gluphisia crenata* (Esper, 1785)	Dusky Marbled Brown
croceus	*Colias croceus* (Fourcroy, 1785)	Clouded Yellow
cydippe	*Agynnis adippe* (D. & S., 1775)	High Brown Fritillary
cynthia	*Euphydryas cynthia* (D. & S., 1775)	Cynthia's Fritillary
damone	*Anthocharis damone* Boisduval, 1836	Eastern Orange Tip
daphne	*Brenthis daphne* (D. & S., 1775)	Marbled Fritillary
daplidicæ	*Pontia daplidice* (Linnaeus, 1758)	Bath White

daplidice	*Pontia daplidice* (Linnaeus, 1758)	Bath White
davus	*Coenonympha tullia* (Müller, 1764)	Large Heath
decimalis	*Tholera decimalis* (Poda, 1761)	Feathered Gothic
dejone	*Melitaea deione* (Geyer, 1832)	Provençal Fritillary
delphinii	*Periphanes delphinii* (Linnaeus, 1758)	Pease Blossom
dentina	*Hada plebeja* (Linnaeus, 1761)	The Shears
desfontainii	*Euphydryas desfontainii* (Godart, 1819)	Spanish Fritillary
dia	*Boloria dia* (Linnaeus, 1767)	Weaver's Fritillary
dictynna	*Melitaea diamina* (Lang, 1789)	False Heath Fritillary
didyma	*Melitaea didyma* (Esper, 1778)	Spotted Fritillary
didymata	*Perizoma didymata* (Linnaeus, 1758)	Twin-spot Carpet
dipsacea	*Heliothis viriplaca* (Hufnagel, 1766)	Marbled Clover
dispar	*Lycaena dispar* (Haworth, 1802)	Large Copper
dispar	*Lymantria dispar* (Linnaeus, 1758)	Gypsy Moth
divisella	*Monochroa divisella* (Douglas, 1850)	(a gelechiid moth)
dorylas	*Polyommatus dorylas* (D. & S., 1775)	Turquoise Blue
duponcheli	*Leptidea duponcheli* (Staudinger, 1871)	Eastern Wood White
edusa	*Colias croceus* (Fourcroy, 1785)	Clouded Yellow
egea	*Polygonia egea* (Cramer, 1775)	Southern Comma
egeria	*Pararge aegeria* (Linnaeus, 1758)	Speckled Wood
electra	*Colias croceus* (Fourcroy, 1785)	Clouded Yellow
elymi	*Chortodes elymi* (Treitschke, 1825)	Lyme Grass
emarginata	*Idaea emarginata* (Linnaeus, 1758)	Small Scallop
empyrea	*Trigonophora flammea* (Esper, 1785)	Flame Brocade
epiphron	*Erebia epiphron* (Knoch, 1783)	Small Mountain Ringlet
ergane	*Pieris ergane* (Geyer, 1828)	Mountain Small White
eros	*Polyommatus eros* (Ochsenheimer, 1808)	Eros Blue
escheri	*Polyommatus escheri* (Hübner, 1823)	Escher's Blue
eupheme	*Zegris eupheme* (Esper, 1804)	Sooty Orange Tip
euphenoides	*Anthocharis euphenoides* Staudinger, 1869	Moroccan Orange Tip
euphorbiæ	*Hyles euphorbiae* (Linnaeus, 1758)	Spurge Hawk-moth
euphrosyne	*Boloria euphrosyne* (Linnaeus, 1758)	Pearl-bordered Fritillary
europome	*Colias palaeno* (Linnaeus, 1761)	Moorland Clouded Yellow
euryale	*Erebia euryale* (Esper, 1805)	Large Ringlet
expolita	*Photedes captiuncula* (Treitschke, 1825)	Least Minor
exsoleta	*Xylena exsoleta* (Linnaeus, 1758)	Sword-grass
exulis	*Apamea zeta* (Treitschke, 1825)	The Exile
fagi	*Stauropus fagi* (Linnaeus, 1758)	Lobster Moth
favicolor	*Mythimna favicolor* (Barrett, 1896)	Mathew's Wainscot
ferruginea	*Agrochola circellaris* (Hufnagel, 1766)	The Brick
fidia	*Hipparchia fidia* (Linnaeus, 1767)	Striped Grayling
filipendulae	*Zygaena filipendulae* (Linnaeus, 1758)	Six-spot Burnet
flammea	*Mythimna flammea* (Curtis, 1828)	Flame Wainscot
flavicornis	*Achyla flavicornis* (Linnaeus, 1758)	Yellow Horned

fluxa	*Chortodes fluxa* (Hübner, 1809)	Mere Wainscot
fraxini	*Catocala fraxini* (Linnaeus, 1758)	Clifden Nonpareil
fulva	*Chortodes pygmina* (Haworth, 1809)	Small Wainscot
furcata	*Hydriomena furcata* (Thunberg, 1784)	July Highflyer
furcatellus	*Catoptria furcatellus* (Zetterstedt, 1839)	(a crambid moth)
fusconebulosa	*Pharmacis fusconebulosa* (DeGeer, 1778)	Map-winged Swift
galatea	*Melanargia galathea* (Linnaeus, 1758)	Marbled White
galathea	*Melanargia galathea* (Linnaeus, 1758)	Marbled White
galii	*Hyles galii* (Rottemburg, 1775)	Bedstraw Hawk-moth
gamma	*Autographa gamma* (Linnaeus, 1758)	Silver-Y
gemina	*Apamea remissa* (Hübner, 1809)	Dusky Brocade
glacialis	*Oeneis glacialis* (Moll, 1783)	Alpine Grayling
glyphica	*Euclidia glyphica* (Linnaeus, 1758)	Burnet Companion
gorge	*Erebia gorge* (Hübner, 1804)	Silky Ringlet
gorgone	*Erebia gorgone* Boisduval, 1833	Gavarnie Ringlet
gorgophone	*Erebia mnestra* (Hübner, 1804)	Mnestra's Ringlet
graeca	*Pseudochazara graeca* (Staudinger, 1870)	Grecian Grayling
griseata	*Lithostege griseata* (D. & S., 1775)	Grey Carpet
grossulariata	*Abraxas grossulariata* (Linnaeus, 1758)	The Magpie
gruneri	*Anthocharis gruneri* Herrich-Schäffer, 1851	Gruner's Orange Tip
heldreichi	*Colias aurorina* Herrich-Schäffer, 1850	Greek Clouded Yellow
helena	*Polyommatus semiargus* (Rottemburg, 1775)	Mazarine Blue
hellmanni	*Chortodes fluxa* (Hübner, 1809)	Mere Wainscot
helvola	*Eilema depressa* (Esper, 1787)	Buff Footman
hera	*Euplagia quadripunctaria* (Poda, 1761)	Jersey Tiger
hermione	*Hipparchia fagi* (Scopoli, 1763)	Woodland Grayling
hero	*Coenonympha hero* (Linnaeus, 1761)	Scarce Heath
hippolyte	*Pseudochazara hippolyte* (Esper, 1784)	Nevada Grayling
hippothoë	*Lycaena hippothoe* (Linnaeus, 1761)	Purple-edged Copper
humuli	*Hepialus humuli* (Linnaeus, 1758)	Ghost Moth
huntera	*Vanessa virginiensis* (Drury, 1773)	American Painted Lady
hyale	*Colias hyale* (Linnaeus, 1758)	Pale Clouded Yellow
hyperanthes	*Aphantopus hyperantus* (Linnaeus, 1758)	Ringlet
hyperanthus	*Aphantopus hyperantus* (Linnaeus, 1758)	Ringlet
ianira	*Maniola jurtina* (Linnaeus, 1758)	Meadow Brown
icarius	*Polyommatus amandus* (Schneider, 1792)	Amanda's Blue
icarus	*Polyommatus icarus* (Rottemburg, 1775)	Common Blue
ichneumoniformis	*Bembecia ichneumoniformis* (D. & S., 1775)	Six-belted Clearwing
ida	*Pyronia cecilia* (Vallantin, 1894)	Southern Gatekeeper
idas	*Plebeius idas* (Linnaeus, 1761)	Idas Blue
ilia	*Apatura ilia* (D. & S., 1775)	Lesser Purple Emperor
ilicis	*Satyrium ilicis* (Esper, 1779)	Ilex Hairstreak
impura	*Mythimna impura* (Hübner, 1808)	Smoky Wainscot
incerta	*Orthosia incerta* (Hufnagel, 1766)	Clouded Drab

ino	*Brenthis ino* (Rottemburg, 1775)	Lesser Marbled Fritillary
interjecta	*Noctua interjecta* Hübner, 1803	Least Yellow Underwing
io	*Inachis io* (Linnaeus, 1758)	Peacock
iris	*Apatura iris* (Linnaeus, 1758)	Purple Emperor
irregularis	*Hadena irregularis* (Hufnagel, 1766)	Viper's Bugloss
janira	*Maniola jurtina* (Linnaeus, 1758)	Meadow Brown
jurtina	*Maniola jurtina* (Linnaeus, 1758)	Meadow Brown
krueperi	*Pieris krueperi* Staudinger, 1860	Krueper's Small White
krüperi	*Pieris krueperi* Staudinger, 1860	Krueper's Small White
lachesis	*Melanargia lachesis* (Hübner, 1790)	Iberian Marbled White
l-album	*Mythimna l-album* (Linnaeus, 1767)	L-album Wainscot
lambda	*Lithophane lamda* (Fabricius, 1787)	The Nonconformist
larissa	*Melanargia larissa* (Geyer, 1828)	Balkan Marbled White
lathonia	*Issoria lathonia* (Linnaeus, 1758)	Queen of Spain Fritillary
latona	*Issoria lathonia* (Linnaeus, 1758)	Queen of Spain Fritillary
lefebvrei	*Erebia lefebvrei* (Boisduval, 1828)	Lefèbvre's Ringlet
leucographa	*Cerastis leucographa* (D. & S., 1775)	White-marked
leucophaea	*Pachetra sagittigera* (Hufnagel, 1766)	Feathered Ear
leucostigma	*Celaena leucostigma* (Hübner, 1808)	The Crescent
levana	*Araschnia levana* (Linnaeus, 1758)	Map Butterfly
ligea	*Erebia ligea* (Linnaeus, 1758)	Arran Brown
ligniperda	*Cossus cossus* (Linnaeus, 1758)	Goat Moth
ligustri	*Craniophora ligustri* (D. & S., 1775)	The Coronet
ligustri	*Sphinx ligustri* Linnaeus, 1758	Privet Hawk-moth
limbaria	*Isturgia limbaria* (Fabricius, 1775)	Frosted Yellow
linea	*Thymelicus sylvestris* (Poda, 1761)	Small Skipper
lineata	*Hyles livornica* (Esper, 1779)	Striped Hawk-moth
lineola	*Thymelicus lineola* (Ochsenheimer, 1808)	Essex Skipper
lithargyria	*Mythimna ferrago* (Fabricius, 1787)	The Clay
littoralis	*Mythimna litoralis* (Curtis, 1827)	Shore Wainscot
lonicerae	*Zygaena lonicerae* (Scheven, 1777)	Narrow-bordered Five-spot Burnet
lota	*Agrochola lota* (Clerck, 1759)	Red-line Quaker
lubricipeda	*Spilosoma lubricipeda* (Linnaeus, 1758)	White Ermine
lucina	*Hamearis lucina* (Linnaeus, 1758)	Duke of Burgundy Fritillary
luctuosa	*Tyta luctuosa* (D. & S., 1775)	The Four-spotted
lunaris	*Minucia lunaris* (D. & S., 1775)	Lunar Double-stripe
lunigera	*Agrotis trux* (Hübner, 1824)	Crescent Dart
lutosa	*Rhizedra lutosa* (Hübner, 1803)	Large Wainscot
machaon	*Papilio machaon* Linnaeus, 1758	Swallowtail
macularia	*Pseudopanthera macularia* (Linnaeus, 1758)	Speckled Yellow
maera	*Lasiommata maera* (Linnaeus, 1758)	Large Wall Brown
malvae	*Pyrgus malvae* (Linnaeus, 1758)	Grizzled Skipper
manto	*Erebia manto* (D. & S., 1775)	Yellow-spotted Ringlet
maritima	*Chilodes maritima* (Tauscher, 1806)	Silky Wainscot

maturna	*Euphydryas maturna* (Linnaeus, 1758)	Scarce Fritillary
maura	*Mormo maura* (Linnaeus, 1758)	Old Lady
medon	*Aricia agestis* (D. & S., 1775)	Brown Argus
medusa	*Erebia medusa* (D. & S., 1775)	Woodland Ringlet
megaera	*Lasiommata megera* (Linnaeus, 1767)	Wall
megera	*Lasiommata megera* (Linnaeus, 1767)	Wall
melanops	*Glaucopsyche melanops* (Boisduval, 1828)	Black-eyed Blue
meleager	*Polyommatus daphnis* (D. & S., 1775)	Meleager's Blue
mensuraria	*Scotopteryx chenopodiata* (Linnaeus, 1758)	Shaded Broad-bar
menthastri	*Spilosoma lubricipeda* (Linnaeus, 1758)	White Ermine
mi	*Callistege mi* (Clerck, 1759)	Mother Shipton
minima	*Cupido minimus* (Fuessly, 1775)	Small Blue
minimus	*Cupido minimus* (Fuessly, 1775)	Small Blue
mnemosyne	*Parnassius mnemosyne* (Linnaeus, 1758)	Clouded Apollo
mnestra	*Erebia mnestra* (Hübner, 1804)	Mnestra's Ringlet
monoglypha	*Apamea monoglypha* (Hufnagel, 1766)	Dark Arches
montanata	*Xanthorhoe montanata* (D. & S., 1775)	Silver-ground Carpet
mundana	*Nudaria mundana* (Linnaeus, 1761)	Muslin Footman
munitata	*Xanthorhoe decoloraria* (Esper, 1806)	Red Carpet
muricata	*Idaea muricata* (Hufnagel, 1767)	Purple-bordered Gold
myrtilli	*Anarta myrtilli* (Linnaeus, 1761)	Beautiful Yellow Underwing
napi	*Pieris napi* (Linnaeus, 1758)	Green-veined White
neoridas	*Erebia neoridas* (Boisduval, 1828)	Autumn Ringlet
neurica	*Archanara neurica* (Hübner, 1808)	White-mantled Wainscot
neustria	*Malacosoma neustria* (Linnaeus, 1758)	Lackey
niobe	*Argynnis niobe* (Linnaeus, 1758)	Niobe Fritillary
nitens	*Polia bombycina* (Hufnagel, 1766)	Pale Shining Brown
nubeculosa	*Brachionycha nubeculosa* (Esper, 1785)	Rannoch Sprawler
nupta	*Catocala nupta* (Linnaeus, 1767)	Red Underwing
nymphaealis	*Elophila nymphaeata* (Linnaeus, 1758)	Beautiful China Mark
obscuraria	*Charissa obscurata* (D. & S., 1775)	The Annulet
obscuratus	*Charissa obscurata* (D. & S., 1775)	The Annulet
ocellaris	*Xanthia ocellaris* (Borkhausen, 1792)	Pale-lemon Sallow
ochrata	*Idaea ochrata* (Scopoli, 1763)	Bright Wave
ochroleuca	*Eremobia ochroleuca* (D. & S., 1775)	Dusky Sallow
oculea	*Amphipoea oculea* (Linnaeus, 1761)	Ear Moth
oo	*Dicycla oo* (Linnaeus, 1758)	Heart Moth
orichalcea	*Thysanoplusia orichalcea* (Fabricius, 1775)	Slender Burnished Brass
orientalis	*Carcharodus orientalis* Reverdin, 1913	Oriental Marbled Skipper
ottomanus	*Lycaena ottomanus* (Lefèbvre, 1830)	Grecian Copper
palaemon	*Carterocephalus palaemon* (Pallas, 1771)	Chequered Skipper
palæno	*Colias palaeno* (Linnaeus, 1761)	Moorland Clouded Yellow
pallens	*Mythimna pallens* (Linnaeus, 1758)	Common Wainscot
palustris	*Athetis pallustris* (Hübner, 1808)	Marsh Moth

pamphilus	*Coenonympha pamphilus* (Linnaeus, 1758)	Small Heath
pandrose	*Erebia pandrose* (Borkhausen, 1788)	Dewy Ringlet
paniscus	*Carterocephalus palaemon* (Pallas, 1771)	Chequered Skipper
paphia	*Argynnis paphia* (Linnaeus, 1758)	Silver-washed Fritillary
papilionaria	*Geometra papilionaria* (Linnaeus, 1758)	Large Emerald
parallellaria	*Epione vespertaria* (Linnaeus, 1767)	Dark Bordered Beauty
parthenie	*Melitaea parthenoides* Keferstein, 1851	Meadow Fritillary
pasiphaë	*Pyronia bathseba* (Fabricius, 1793)	Spanish Gatekeeper
pastinum	*Lygephila pastinum* (Treitschke, 1826)	Blackneck
pavonia	*Saturnia pavonia* (Linnaeus, 1758)	Emperor Moth
peltigera	*Heliothis peltigera* (D. & S., 1775)	Bordered Straw
perspicillaris	*Actinotia polyodon* (Clerck, 1759)	Purple Cloud
petiverella	*Dichrorampha petiverella* (Linnaeus, 1758)	(a tortrix moth)
phaedra	*Minois dryas* (Scopoli, 1763)	Dryad
phicomone	*Colias phicomone* (Esper, 1780)	Mountain Clouded Yellow
phlaeas	*Lycaena phlaeas* (Linnaeus, 1761)	Small Copper
phloeas	*Lycaena phlaeas* (Linnaeus, 1761)	Small Copper
phlomidis	*Spialia phlomidis* (Herrich-Schäffer, 1845)	Persian Skipper
phoebe	*Melitaea phoebe* (D. & S., 1775)	Knapweed Fritillary
pictaria	*Aleucis distinctata* (Herrich-Schäffer, 1839)	Sloe Carpet
piniaria	*Bupalus piniaria* (Linnaeus, 1758)	Bordered White
pistacina	*Agrochola lychnidis* (D. & S., 1775)	Beaded Chestnut
pityocampa	*Thaumetopoea pityocampa* (D. & S., 1775)	Pine Processionary
plantaginis	*Parasemia plantaginis* (Linnaeus, 1758)	Wood Tiger
platyptera	*Calophasia platyptera* (Esper, 1788)	Antirrhinum Brocade
plexippus	*Danaus plexippus* (Linnaeus, 1758)	The Monarch
plumigera	*Ptilophora plumigera* (D. & S., 1775)	Plumed Prominent
podalirius	*Iphiclides podalirius* (Linnaeus, 1758)	Scarce Swallowtail
polychloros	*Nymphalis polychloros* (Linnaeus, 1758)	Large Tortoiseshell
polydactyla	*Alucita hexadactyla* Linnaeus, 1758	Twenty-plume Moth
polygrammata	*Trichopteryx polycommata* (D. & S., 1775)	The Many-lined
polyodon	*Actinotia polyodon* (Clerck, 1759)	Purple Cloud
polyodon	*Apamea monoglypha* (Hufnagel, 1766)	Dark Arches
polyxena	*Zerynthia polyxena* (D. & S., 1775)	Southern Festoon
popularis	*Tholera decimalis* (Poda, 1761)	Feathered Gothic
populi	*Laothoe populi* (Linnaeus, 1758)	Poplar Hawk-moth
populi	*Limenitis populi* (Linnaeus, 1758)	Poplar Admiral
populi	*Poecilocampa populi* (Linnaeus, 1758)	December Moth
potatoria	*Euthrix potatoria* (Linnaeus, 1758)	Drinker, The
prasinana	*Bena bicolorana* (Fuessly, 1775)	Scarce Silver-lines
prieuri	*Chazara prieuri* (Pierret, 1837)	Southern Hermit
primulae	*Diarsia mendica* (Fabricius, 1775)	Ingrailed Clay
procellaria	*Melanthia procellata* (D. & S., 1775)	Pretty Chalk Carpet
pronuba	*Noctua pronuba* Linnaeus, 1758	Large Yellow Underwing

pruni	*Satyrium pruni* (Linnaeus, 1758)	Black Hairstreak
pulchella	*Utetheisa pulchella* (Linnaeus, 1758)	Crimson Speckled
purpuralis	*Zygaena purpuralis* (Brünnich, 1763)	Transparent Burnet
putrescens	*Mythimna putrescens* (Hübner, 1824)	Devonshire Wainscot
pygmæola	*Eilema pygmaeola* (Doubleday, 1847)	Pigmy Footman
pyrenaica	*Erebia epiphron* (Knoch, 1783)	Small Mountain Ringlet
pyri	*Saturnia pyri* (D. & S., 1775)	Great Peacock Moth
quadripunctaria	*Euplagia quadripunctaria* (Poda, 1761)	Jersey Tiger
quercana	*Bena bicolorana* (Fuessly, 1775)	Scarce Silver-lines
quercus	*Lasiocampa quercus* (Linnaeus, 1758)	Oak Eggar
quercus	*Neozephyrus quercus* (Linnaeus, 1758)	Purple Hairstreak
rapae	*Pieris rapae* (Linnaeus, 1758)	Small White
repandata	*Alcis repandata* (Linnaeus, 1758)	Mottled Beauty
rhamni	*Gonepteryx rhamni* (Linnaeus, 1758)	Brimstone
rivata	*Epirrhoe rivata* (Hübner, 1813)	Wood Carpet
roboris	*Laeosopis roboris* (Esper, 1793)	Spanish Purple Hairstreak
rubi	*Callophrys rubi* (Linnaeus, 1758)	Green Hairstreak
rubi	*Macrothylacia rubi* (Linnaeus, 1758)	Fox Moth
rubiginata	*Scopula rubiginata* (Hufnagel, 1767)	Tawny Wave
rubiginea	*Conistra rubiginea* (D. & S., 1775)	Dotted Chestnut
rufa	*Coenobia rufa* (Haworth, 1809)	Small Rufous
rumina	*Zerynthia rumina* (Linnaeus, 1758)	Spanish Festoon
salicis	*Leucoma salicis* (Linnaeus, 1758)	White Satin Moth
saponariæ	*Heliophobus reticulata* (Goeze, 1781)	Bordered Gothic
satellitia	*Eupsilia transversa* (Hufnagel, 1766)	The Satellite
satura	*Blepharita satura* (D. & S., 1775)	Beautiful Arches
sebrus	*Cupido osiris* (Meigen, 1829)	Osiris Blue
selene	*Boloria selene* (D. & S., 1775)	Small Pearl-bordered Fritillary
semele	*Hipparchia semele* (Linnaeus, 1758)	Grayling
semiargus	*Polyommatus semiargus* (Rottemburg, 1775)	Mazarine Blue
semibrunnea	*Lithophane semibrunnea* (Haworth, 1809)	Tawny Pinion
sephirus	*Plebeius pylaon* (Fischer & Waldheim, 1832)	Zephyr Blue
sibylla	*Limenitis camilla* (Linnaeus, 1764)	White Admiral
simplonia	*Euchloe simplonia* (Boisduval, 1828)	Mountain Dappled White
sinapis	*Leptidea sinapis* (Linnaeus, 1758)	Wood White
spini	*Satyrium spini* (D. & S., 1775)	Blue-spot Hairstreak
stabilis	*Orthosia cerasi* (Fabricius, 1775)	Common Quaker
stellatarum	*Macroglossum stellatarum* (Linnaeus, 1758)	Humming-bird Hawk-moth
strigilis	*Oligia strigilis* (Linnaeus, 1758)	Marbled Minor
strigosa	*Acronicta strigosa* (D. & S., 1775)	Marsh Dagger
strigula	*Lycophotia porphyrea* (D. & S., 1775)	True Lover's Knot
stygne	*Erebia meolans* (Prunner, 1798)	Piedmont Ringlet
subrosea	*Coenophila subrosea* (Stephens, 1829)	Rosy Marsh Moth
sulphuralis	*Emmelia trabealis* (Scopoli, 1763)	Spotted Sulphur

sylvanus	*Ochlodes venata* (Bremer & Grey, 1853)	Large Skipper
sylvata	*Calospilos sylvata* (Scopoli, 1763)	Clouded Magpie
sylvius	*Carterocephalus silvicola* (Meigen, 1829)	Northern Chequered Skipper
taeniata	*Perizoma taeniata* (Stephens, 1831)	Barred Carpet
tages	*Erynnis tages* (Linnaeus, 1758)	Dingy Skipper
tagis	*Euchloe tagis* (Hübner, 1804)	Portuguese Dappled White
telicanus	*Leptotes pirithous* (Linnaeus, 1767)	Lang's Short-tailed Blue
temeraria	*Lomographa temerata* (D. & S., 1775)	Clouded Silver
templi	*Dasypolia templi* (Thunberg, 1792)	Brindled Ochre
testata	*Eulithis testata* (Linnaeus, 1761)	The Chevron
theophrastus	*Tarucus theophrastus* (Fabricius, 1793)	Common Tiger Blue
thersites	*Polyommatus thersites* (Cantener, 1835)	Chapman's Blue
thetis	*Lycaena thetis* Klug, 1834	Fiery Copper
thetis	*Polyommatus bellargus* (Rottemburg, 1775)	Adonis Blue
tiphon	*Coenonympha tullia* (Müller, 1764)	Large Heath
tithonus	*Pyronia tithonus* (Linnaeus, 1767)	Gatekeeper
trabealis	*Emmelia trabealis* (Scopoli, 1763)	Spotted Sulphur
trifolii	*Zygaena trifolii* (Esper, 1783)	Five-spot Burnet
tristata	*Epirrhoe tristata* (Linnaeus, 1758)	Small Argent & Sable
tritici	*Euxoa tritici* (Linnaeus, 1761)	White-line Dart
tritophus	*Notodonta tritophus* (D. & S., 1775)	Three-humped Prominent
trivia	*Melitaea trivia* (D. & S., 1775)	Lesser Spotted Fritillary
tullia	*Coenonympha tullia* (Müller, 1764)	Large Heath
tyndarus	*Erebia tyndarus* (Esper, 1781)	Swiss Brassy Ringlet
typhon	*Coenonympha tullia* (Müller, 1764)	Large Heath
ulmata	*Calospilos sylvata* (Scopoli, 1763)	Clouded Magpie
umbrosa	*Xestia sexstrigata* (Haworth, 1809)	Six-striped Rustic
unanimis	*Apamea unanimis* (Hübner, 1813)	Small Clouded Brindle
uncula	*Deltote uncula* (Clerck, 1759)	Silver Hook
urticae	*Aglais urticae* (Linnaeus, 1758)	Small Tortoiseshell
vaccinii	*Conistra vaccinii* (Linnaeus, 1761)	The Chestnut
valligera	*Agrotis vestigialis* (Hufnagel, 1766)	Archer's Dart
venosa	*Simyra albovenosa* (Goeze, 1781)	Reed Dagger
vernaria	*Chlorissa viridata* (Linnaeus, 1758)	Small Grass Emerald
versicolora	*Endromis versicolora* (Linnaeus, 1758)	Kentish Glory
vetusta	*Xylena vetusta* (Hübner, 1813)	Red Sword-grass
vicrama	*Pseudophilotes vicrama* (Moore, 1865)	Eastern Baton Blue
vinula	*Cerura vinula* (Linnaeus, 1758)	Puss Moth
virens	*Calamia tridens occidentalis* Cockayne, 1954	Burren Green
virgaureæ	*Lycaena virgaureae* (Linnaeus, 1758)	Scarce Copper
w-album	*Satyrium w-album* (Knoch, 1782)	White-letter Hairstreak
xerampelina	*Atethmia centrago* (Haworth, 1809)	Centre-barred Sallow
zapateri	*Erebia zapateri* Oberthür, 1875	Zapater's Ringlet
zollikoferi	*Luperina zollikoferi* (Freyer, 1836)	Scarce Arches

Adkin, R. (1911). Unrecorded occurrences of *Euvanessa antiopa. Entomologist* **44**: 112.

Adkin, R. (1932). One summer hour. *Entomologist* **65**: 52.

Albin, E. (1720). *The natural history of English insects.* London, Innys.

Allan, P. B. M. (1937; revd edn 1947). *A moth-hunter's gossip.* London, Watkins & Doncaster.

Allan, P. B. M. (1938). *See* 'Old Moth-Hunter, An'.

Allan, P. B. M. (1943). *Talking of moths.* Newtown, Montgomery, privately published.

Allan, P. B. M. (1946). On becoming 1000. *Entomologist* **79**: 195–208.

Allan, P. B. M. (1953). Collecting in the Nineties. *Entomologist's Rec. J. Var.* **65**: 205–209.

Allan, P. B. M. (1954). *See* 'Old Moth-Hunter, An'.

Allan, P. B. M. (1954). Larva-hunting in spring. *Entomologist's Rec. J. Var.* **66**: 146–148.

Allan, P. B. M. (1957). 'The Trade' in the 'Nineties. *Entomologist's Rec. J. Var.* **69**: 274–277.

Allan, P. B. M. (1965). *See* 'Old Moth-Hunter, An'.

Allan, P. B. M. (1965). 'Will-o'-the-Wisp.' *Entomologist's Rec. J. Var.* **77**: 252–259; 273–280.

Allan, P. B. M. (1974). O. M. H. *Entomologist's Rec. J. Var.* **86**: 171.

Allan, P. B. M. (1980). *Leaves from a moth-hunter's notebook.* Faringdon, Classey.

Allen, D. E. (1965). The origin of sugaring. *Entomologist's Rec. J. Var.* **77**: 117–121.

Allen, D. E. (1969). *The Victorian fern craze: a history of pteridomania.* London, Hutchinson.

Allen, D. E. (1976). *The naturalist in Britain.* Harmondsworth, Allen Lane.

Allison, H. (1987). Wicken Fen: a living laboratory. The National Trust Magazine, summer 1987.

Anderson, J. jun. (1879). Extraordinary abundance of *Plusia gamma. Entomologist* **12**: 222–223.

Anon. (1856). The President's collation. *Entomologist's Wkly Intell.* **1**: 102–103.

Anon. (1856). Singular coincidence. *Entomologist's Wkly Intell.* **1**: 103.

Anon. (1856). The sportsman and the entomologist. *Substitute* No. 6: 58–60.

Anon. (1858). From an American newspaper, (1858). [A Humbug]. *Entomologist's Wkly Intell.* **4**: 72.

Anon. (1861). The peril of pursuing entomological studies at night. *Entomologist's Wkly Intell.* **10**: 38–39.

Anon. (1874). An entomologist's visit to Dalmatia in 1873. *Entomologist's Annual,* pp.164–170.

Anon. (1888). Obituary. John Scott. *Entomologist's mon. Mag.* **25**: 114–116.

Anon. (1918). Current notes and short notices. *Entomologist's Rec. J. Var.* **30**: 54.

Bacot, A. (1913). *Gnophos obscuraria* and rabbit-burrows. *Entomologist's Rec. J. Var.* **25**: 282.

Baines, J. M. (1939). Analysis of Lepidoptera eaten by bats. *Entomologist* **73**: 139–140.

Barrett, C. G. (1856). *Edusa* at Forest Hill. *Entomologist's Wkly Intell.* **1**: 165.

Barrett, C. G. (1884). Effect of cyanide upon colour. *Entomologist's mon. Mag.* **21**: 23.

Barrett, J. M. (1904). *Vanessa cardui* in great numbers near Hunstanton. *Entomologist's mon. Mag.* **40**: 61–62.

Barrington, R. (1999). The influence of childhood on an entomologist – and a very rare fritillary.
  Entomologist's Rec. J. Var. **111**: 261–265.

Bartlett, J. P. (1845). Captures of moths with sugar. *Zoologist* **3**: 1087–1088.

Bayford, E. G. (1931). A moth chased by sparrows. *Entomologist* **67**: 252.

Beadnell, C. M. (1939). Warning sound emitted by the Peacock butterfly. *Entomologist* **72**: 45.

Beirne, B. P. (1933). The large thorn moth in Co. Wexford: an addition to the Irish list. *Ir. Nat. J.* **4**: 137.

Beirne, B. P. (1952). *British pyralid and plume moths.* London, Warne.

Beirne, B. P. (1952). *The origin and history of the British fauna.* London, Methuen.

Beirne, B. P. (1952). It happened at . . . Collecting in the Burren district. *Entomologist's Gaz.* **3**: 2.

Beirne, B. P. (1952). It happened at . . . *Entomologist's Gaz.* **3**: 42.

Beirne, B. P. (1953). It happened at . . . *Entomologist's Gaz.* **4**: 34–35.

Beirne, B. P. (1953). It happened at . . . *Entomologist's Gaz.* **4**: 35–36.

Bell, S. J. (1905). Sugaring prohibited in the New Forest. *Entomologist's Rec. J. Var.* **17**: 261–262.

Berger, L. A. (1948). A *Colias* new to Britain (Lep. Pieridae), *Entomologist* **81**: 129–131.

Berger, L. A. & Fontaine, M. (1947–48). Une espèce méconnue de genre *Colias* F. *Lambillionea* **47**: 91–98, **48**: 12–15, 21–24, 90–110.

Bethune-Baker, G. T. (1892). *Polyommatus dispar* var. *rutilus* in England. *Entomologist's mon. Mag.* **28**: 190.

Bethune-Baker, G. T. (1912). A fortnight at Gavarnie. Hautes Pyrenées. *Entomologist's Rec. J. Var.* **24**: 150–152; 157–162.

Bethune-Baker, G. T. (1914). July in the Eastern Pyrenees. *Entomologist's Rec. J. Var.* **26**: 8–15.

Birchall, E. (1866). Catalogue of the Lepidoptera of Ireland. *Proc. nat. Hist. Soc. Dublin* **5**: 57–85.

Blair, K. G. (1922). Presidential Address. *Proc. Trans. S. Lond. ent. nat. Hist. Soc.* **1921–1922**: 9–29.

Blows, W. T. (1998). Conversations with a naturalist: the life and geological work of Richard Ford 1913–1996. *Geol. Curator* **6**(9): 323–331.

Bold, T. J. (1869). Great abundance of *Pieris rapae*. *Entomologist's mon. Mag.* **6**: 171.

Boyd, B. & Pyle, R. M. (Eds.), (2000). *Nabokov's butterflies*. London, Allen Lane.

Bree, W. T. 1834. A profile of the human face is observable upon the upper side of the primary wings of *Còlias Edusa*, female. A profile of Chancellor Brougham is observable on the reverse of *Hippárchia Janìra. Mag. nat. Hist.* **7**: 262–263.

Bree, W. T. (1834). Extreme cold does not destroy the life in the eggs, etc., of insects; with some facts on *Lycænìa díspar. Mag. nat. Hist.* **7**: 522–523.

Bright, P. M. (1925). Over-collecting. *Entomologist* **58**: 273–275.

Bright, P. M. & Leeds, H. A. (1938). *A monograph of the British aberrations of the Chalk-Hill Blue butterfly.* Bournemouth, Richmond Hill.

Broad, W. & Wade, N. (1982). *Betrayers of the truth: fraud and deceit in the halls of science.* New York, Simon & Schuster.

Buckler, W. (1886–1901). *The larvae of the British butterflies and moths.* London, Ray Society.

Burrows, C. R. N. (1907). Sale of the "Raynor" collection of Lepidoptera. *Entomologist's Rec. J. Var.* **19**: 293–297.

C. A. B. [Charles A. Briggs] (1908). Obituary: John Thomas Carrington. *Entomologist* **41**: 73–74.

Campbell-Taylor, J. E. (1922). The relative attractiveness of various types of electric light for moths. *Entomologist* **55**: 165–166.

Campbell-Taylor, J. E. (1946). Long-tailed field mouse (*Apodemus sylvaticus* L.) eating *Nymphalis io* L. (Lep., Nymphalidae). *Entomologist's mon. Mag.* **82**: 65.

Cardew, P. A. (1938). Entomology and crime. *Entomologist* **71**: 67.

Carrington, J. T. (1879). Localities for beginners, No. III — Darenth. *Entomologist* **12**: 209–214.

Carrington, J. T. (1879). Profusion of *Plusia gamma*. *Entomologist* **12**: 223.

Carrington, J. T. (1880). Localities for beginners, No. VIII — Wicken. *Entomologist* **13**: 169–177.

Carrington, J. T. (1881). Extraordinary abundance of *Triphæna pronuba*. *Entomologist* **14**: 180.

Carrington, J. T. (1886). Spurious varieties of Lepidoptera. *Entomologist* **19**: 273–276.

Castle Russell, S. G. (1952). The New Forest in the Nineties and after. *Entomologist's Rec. J. Var.* **64**: 138–144.

Castle Russell, S. G. (1955). Phenomenal numbers of Rhopalocera larvae and imagines. *Entomologist's Rec. J. Var.* **67**: 111–113.

Cater, W. F. (Ed.) (1980). *Love among the butterflies: travels and adventures of a Victorian lady, Margaret Fountaine.* London, Collins.

Cater, W. F. (Ed.) (1986). *Butterflies and late loves: the further travels and adventures of a Victorian lady, Margaret Fountaine.* London, Collins.

Chalmers-Hunt, J. M. (1966). Early photograph taken at Wicken Fen, Cambridgeshire, with notes on its associations. *Entomologist's Rec. J. Var.* **78**: 298.

Chalmers-Hunt, J. M. (1977). The 1976 invasion of the Camberwell Beauty. *Entomologist's Rec. J. Var.* **99**: 89–105.

Chaney, W. C. (1857). *Colias hyale. Entomologist's Wkly Intell.* **2**: 171–172.

Chapman, T. A. (1904). Note on drowning in lepidopterous larvae. *Entomologist's mon. Mag.* **40**: 81–82.

Chapman, T. A. (1911). Obituary. James William Tutt. *Entomologist* **44**: 77–80.

Chapman, T. A. (1914). The mystery of *Lycaena arion. Entomologist's Rec. J. Var.* **26**: 245–246.

Chatfield, J. (1987). *F. W. Frohawk: his life and work.* Ramsbury, Crowood Press.

Christy, M. (1888). The origin of 'sugaring': to whom does the credit rightly belong? *Essex Nat.* **2**: 69–70.

Clarke, A. H. (1906). Lepidopterological reminiscences. *Entomologist's Rec. J. Var.* **18**: 24.

Classey, E. W. (1950). The mysterious case of Parson Greene's silver trowel. *Entomologist's Gaz.* **1**: 32–36.

Classey, E. W. (1951). *See* Lisney, A. A., Classey, E. W., & Robinson, H. S.

Cockayne, E. A. (1950). It happened at . . . "Fen fun". *Entomologist's Gaz.* **1**: 157–158.

Cockayne, E. A. (1952). *Colias croceus* Fourcroy ab. *duplex* Cockerell. The story of a fraud. *Entomologist's Rec. J. Var.* **64**: 193–194.

Cockayne, E. A. (1954). Current literature. *Entomologist's Rec. J. Var.* **66**: 89.

Cockayne, E. A., Hawkins, C. N., Lees, F. H., Whitehouse, B. & Williams, H. B. (1937). *Catocala fraxini* L.: a new British record of capture and breeding. *Entomologist* **70**: 240–246.

Coleman, W. S. (1859). *Our woodlands, heaths, and hedges.* London, Routledge.

Coleman, W. S. (1860). *British butterflies.* London, Routledge.

Collier, A. E. (1959). Obituary. John Christopher Beadnell Craske. *Entomologist's Rec. J. Var.* **71**: 59–60.

Colthrup, C. W. (1913). Protective resemblance. *Entomologist's Rec. J. Var.* **25**: 179–182; 245–250.

Colthrup, C. W. (1913). *Gnophos obscuraria* and rabbit-burrows. *Entomologist's Rec. J. Var.* **25**: 282–283.

Cooke, B. H. (1928). An entomological motor tour in Spain in 1927. *Entomologist* **61**: 154–159; 176–182; 197–202.

Cordeaux, J. (1884). Report on the migration of birds, 1884. London.

Cowan, C. F. (1965). Suspended animation in a moth. *Entomologist's Rec. J. Var.* **77**: 113.

Cox, G. L. (1904). A week on the Norfolk Broads. *Entomologist* **37**: 325–327.

Cox, G. L. & Brooke, J. (1906). Noctuæ in Huntingdonshire, 1905, and a sequel in the High Court of Chancery. *Entomologist* **39**: 127–132.

Cox, H. R. (1875). Collecting as it was, and as it now is. *Entomologist* **8**: 103–104.

Cox, H. R. (1875). A few remarks on some collectors. *Entomologist* **8**: 179–180.

Crotch, W. D. (1856). "A rare old plant is the ivy green." *Substitute* No. 9: 100–101.

Crotch, W. D. (1859). Pinning and setting Lepidoptera. *Entomologist's Wkly Intell.* **6**: 30–31.

Curtis, W. P. (1903). Kestrel destroying butterflies. *Entomologist* **36**: 68.

Curtis, W. P. (1934; 1947). A list of the Lepidoptera of Dorset. *Trans. Soc. Br. Ent.* Pt. 1 (1934) vol. 1, 185–286; Pt. 2 (1947) vol. 9, 1–134.

D'Abrera, B. (1997). On preparation of the butterflies of the world series. *Metamorphosis* Supplement **3**: 116–119.

Dale, C. W. (1890). *The history of our British butterflies.* London, John Kempster.

Dale, J. C. (1833). Observations on the influence of locality, time of appearance, &c on species and varieties of butterflies. *Ent. Mag.* **1**: 357.

Dale, J. C. (1833). Moths attracted by sugar. *Ent. Mag.* **1**: 514.

Dale, W. C. (1879). Insect hunting in Abbot's Wood. *Entomologist* **12**: 155–157.

Dannat, W. (1909). Entomology in Cornwall and Devon in July, 1908. *Entomologist* **42**: 67–71.

Darwin, C. (1839). *A naturalist's voyage round the world. Journal of researches into the natural history and geology of the countries visited during the voyage round the world of H.M.S. 'Beagle' under command of Captain Fitz Roy, R.N.* London, John Murray.

Day, A. (1990). *Wicken: a fen village in old photographs.* Shropshire, S. B. Publications.

Dell, D. S. (1859). The Post Office. *Entomologist's Wkly Intell.* **6**: 167–168.

Demuth, R. P. (1956). An unusual pairing. *Entomologist's Rec. J. Var.* **68**: 191–192.

Demuth, R. P. (1984–1985). Reminiscences of an elderly entomologist. *Entomologist's Rec. J. Var.* **96**: 189–195; 264–272; **97**: 13–19; 46–50; 97–105.

Dickens, C. (1838). *Memoirs of Joseph Grimaldi,* edited by 'Boz'. London.

Dicksee, A., Uvarov, B. P. & Burr, M. (1923). The distress of Russian entomologists. *Entomologist* **56**: 99.

Dobrée, N. F. (1887). A new method of sugaring. *Entomologist* **20**: 164–165.

Dobson, H. T., jun. (1878). Intoxicated insects. *Entomologist* **11**: 117–118.

Donovan, C. (1936). *A Catalogue of the Macrolepidoptera of Ireland.* Published privately.

Donovan, E. (1792–1813). *The natural history of British insects, &c.* London, Rivington.

Doubleday, E. (1833). Singular mode of capturing Noctuae. *Ent. Mag.* **1**: 310.

Doubleday, E. (1840). Remarks on the Lepidoptera of North America . . . *Mag. Nat. Hist. N. S.* **4**: 213–219; 268–280.

Doubleday, H. (1841). Captures of moths on the blossoms of sallows, in Epping Forest. *Entomologist.* **1**: 102–103.

Doubleday, H. (1842). *Polia occulta. Entomologist.* **1**: 407.

Doubleday, H. (1843). Note on the capture of Noctuae with sugar, in the autumn of 1842, at Epping. *Zoologist* **1**: 201.

Doubleday, H. (1873). *Argynnis niobe* (Linn.) in Kent. *Entomologist* **6**: 483.

Douglas, J. W. (1842). Notes on captures. *Entomologist* **1**: 358–359.

Douglas, J. W. (1858). The Birch Wood dinner. *Entomologist's Wkly Intell.* **4**: 135–136.

Douglas, J. W. (1859). Seasonable notes. Gamekeepers. *Entomologist's Wkly Intell.* **6**: 62–63.

Dows, A. (1881). Vitality of *Acherontia atropos. Entomologist* **14**: 114–115.

D. T. B. (1856). Two days hunting of butterflies and moths in Suffolk. *Substitute* No. 13: 151–154.

Duffey, E. (1957). Woodwalton Fen National Nature Reserve. *Entomologist's Gaz.* **8**: 143–150.

Duncan, J. (1836). *The naturalist's library,* Vol.IV. British moths, sphinxes, etc. Edinburgh, Lizars.

Durant, E. W. W. (1946). A mixed pairing. *Entomologist* **79**: 194.

E. A. C. [E. A. Cockayne]. (1954). Current literature. *Entomologist's Rec. J. Var.* **66**: 89.

Editor. (1833). Rather extraordinary. *Ent. Mag.* **1**: 317–318.

Editor. (1836). Reply. *Ent. Mag.* **4**: 84.

Editor. (1856). Entomological Society notes. *Petasia nubeculosa. Entomologist's Wkly Intell.* **1**: 45–46.

Editor. (1858). Parcel postage. *Entomologist's Wkly Intell.* **4**: 152.

Editor. (1867). Hammerschmidt redivivus. *Entomologist's mon. Mag.* **4**: 43.

Editors. (1872–1873). Butterflies at sea. *Entomologist's mon. Mag.* **9**: 246.

Editor. (1878). An exhibition of insects. *Entomologist's mon. Mag.* **14**: 211.

Editor. (1878). An exhibition of insects. *Entomologist's mon. Mag.* **14**: 260–261.

Editor. (1886). Newspaper entomology. *Entomologist* **19**: 140.

Editor. (1892). Electricity for entomologists. *Entomologist* **25**: 214–215.

Editor. (1896). A sign of the times. The over-collecting of British butterflies. *Entomologist's Rec. J. Var.* **8**: 81–83.

Editor. (1915). *Colias hyale* near firing line. *Entomologist* **48**: 289.

Editor. (1915). Butterflies in the trenches. *Entomologist* **48**: 289–290.

Editor. (1921). Some news of the Russian entomologists. *Entomologist's mon. Mag.* **57**: 155–156.

Editors. (1922). The Ghost Swift moth and the 'Will-o'-the-Wisp.' *Entomologist's mon. Mag.* **58**: 252.

Edmunds, A. jun. (1835). Two pupæ of *Saturnia* in one cocoon. *Ent. Mag.* **3**: 206–207.

Edwards, P. J. (1993). Izaak Walton — entomologist, not just fisherman. *Bull. amat. Ent. Soc.* **52**: 281–282.

Edwards, P. J. (1996). Dangers of collecting at night. Unpublished diary.

Edwards, T. W. (1856). The sugar bait. *Substitute* No. 12: 135.

Embry, B. (1951). It happened at . . . The match box mystery. *Entomologist's Gaz.* **2**: 201.

Emmet, A. M. (1972). Wicken Fen, with special reference to its Microlepidoptera. *Proc. Trans. Br. ent. nat. Hist. Soc.* **5**: 46–74.

Emmet, A. M. (1979). *A field guide to the smaller British Lepidoptera.* London, British Entomological & Natural History Society.

Emmet, A. M. (1981). *The smaller moths of Essex.* The Essex Naturalist New Series No. 6. London.

Emmet, A. M. (1991). *The scientific names of the British Lepidoptera — their history and meaning.* Colchester, Harley Books.

Emmet, A. M. & Heath, J. (Eds) (1989). *The moths and butterflies of Great Britain and Ireland.* Vol. 7, Part 1. Hesperiidae–Nymphalidae. Colchester, Harley Books.

English, J. (1882). The first night's 'sugaring' in England — a reminiscence of Epping Forest in 1843. *Trans. Epping Forest Nat. Field Club.* **2**: 32–35.

Entomological Society of London. (1929). *Report of the Committee for the Protection of British Lepidoptera* **4**: 53–68.

Evans, C. E. (1949). The Chequered Skipper *C. palaemon* in West Inverness. *Scott. Nat.* **61**: 176.

Farren, W. S. (1926). Memories of Wicken. In: *The natural history of Wicken Fen*, ed. by J. S. Gardiner, pp. 173–189. Cambridge, Bowes & Bowes.

Fleming, W. A. (1975). *Butterflies of West Malaysia and Singapore.* Kuala Lumpur, Longman Malaysia.

Ford, H. D. (1928). The hibernation of *Melitaea aurinia. Entomologist* **61**: 188–189.

Ford, R. L. E. (1952). *The observer's book of the larger British moths.* London, Warne.

Ford, R. L. E. (1963). *Practical entomology.* London, Warne.

Ford, R. L. E. (1979). Entomological cabinets. *Entomologist's Rec. J. Var.* **91**: 308–310.

Fountaine, M. E. (1902). Butterfly hunting in Greece, in the year 1900. *Entomologist's Rec. J. Var.* **14**: 29–35; 64–67.

Freer, W. L. (1938). Wholesale slaughter. *Entomologist* **71**: 66–67.

Frohawk, F. W. (1903). A new butterfly net. *Entomologist* **36**: 191.

Frohawk, F. W. (1922). Killing with cyanide. *Entomologist* **55**: 280.

Frohawk, F. W. (1922). Destruction of *Papilio machaon* larvæ by cuckoos. *Entomologist* **55**: 280–281.

Frohawk, F. W. (1924). *Natural history of British butterflies.* London, Hutchinson.

Frohawk, F. W. (1933). *Danaus plexippus* in Dorset and Devon. *Entomologist* **66**: 250.

Frohawk, F. W. (1934). *The complete book of British butterflies.* London, Ward Lock.

Frohawk, F. W. (1938). *Varieties of British butterflies.* London, Ward Lock.

Frohawk, F. W. (1938). Unrecorded occurrence of *Pontia daplidice* in numbers. *Entomologist* **71**: 66.

Gardiner, B. O. C. (1993). Father and son: the Newmans and their Kent butterfly farm. *Entomologist's Rec. J. Var.* **105**: 105–114.

Gardiner, B. O. C. (2003). Reminiscences of an elderly entomologist. Unpublished.

Gascoyne, G. (1858). Heavy postage rates on entomological parcels. *Entomologist's Wkly Intell.* **4**: 68–69.

Gillett, F. (1923). *Porthesia chrysorrhoea. Entomologist* **56**: 89–90.

Goodson, A. L. (1950). It happened at . . . *Entomologist's Gaz.* **1**: 162.

Goss, H. (1892). Reported occurrence of *Papilio podalirius* in Sussex. *Entomologist's mon. Mag.* **28**: 190.

Graves, P. P. (1925). Over-collecting. *Entomologist* **58**: 297–298.

Graves, P. P. (1952). "The Claddagh". *Entomologist's Gaz.* **3**: 74.

Greene, J. (1863). *The insect hunter's companion, being instructions for collecting and preserving butterflies and moths, and comprising an essay on pupa digging.* London, Van Voorst.

Greene, J. (1878). "Butterfly pictures." *Entomologist's mon. Mag.* **14**: 261–262.

Greene, J. (1896). On the value of rare British Lepidoptera. *Entomologist's Rec. J. Var.* **8**: 33–34.

Gregson, C. S. (1844). Note on capturing moths with sugar. *Zoologist* **2**: 800.

Grensted, L. W. (1957). Entomology rampant. *Entomologist's mon. Mag.* **94**: 13.

Hall, C. G. (1883). Peculiar odour emitted by *Acherontia atropos*. *Entomologist* **16**: 14–15.

Harbottle, A. H. H. (1950). *See* Vallins, F. T., Dewick, A. J. & Harbottle, A. H. H.

Harbottle, A. H. H. (1950). The occurrence of *Pontia daplidice* Linn. in North Cornwall in 1945. *Entomologist's Gaz.* **1**: 49–50.

Harbottle, A. H. H. (2003). Personal communication (The Bath White in North Cornwall).

Harding, H. J. *See* 'Octogenarian, An'.

Harmer, A. S. (1980). Entomological cabinets. *Entomologist's Rec. J. Var.* **92**: 258.

Harper, E. E. (1960). An entomologist's wife. *Entomologist's Rec. J. Var.* **72**: 169–171.

Harris, M. (1776). *The Aurelian or natural history of insects; namely, moths and butterflies. Together with the plants on which they feed.* London, printed for the author.

Harrison, J. W. Heslop (1939). *Argynnis aglaia* and *Pieris napi* flying out to sea. *Entomologist* **72**: 59.

Harwood, W. H. (1859). An entire parish turned entomologists. *Entomologist's Wkly Intell.* **6**: 29.

Hawker, W. H. (1859). *Pieris daplidice. Entomologist's Wkly Intell.* **6**: 186.

Hawkins, C. N. (1937). *See* Cockayne, E. A., Hawkins, C. N., Lees, F. H., Whitehouse, B. & Williams, H. B.

Haworth, A. H. (1803–1828). *Lepidoptera Britannica.* London, John Murray.

Haynes, R. F. (1958). Was the Large Copper ever an Irish insect? *Entomologist's Rec. J. Var.* **70**: 150–151.

H. C. & Co. (1858). Two or three days in the Isle of Thanet. *Entomologist's Wkly Intell.* **4**: 116–117.

Healy, C. (1858). A pugnacious *Quercus. Entomologist's Wkly Intell.* **4**: 20.

Hellins, J. (1870). A fact! *Entomologist's mon. Mag.* **7**: 162.

Hellins, J. (1886). *Danais Archippus* at Exmouth. *Entomologist's mon. Mag.* **22**: 211.

Hellins, J. (1886). Superstition regarding *Acherontia atropos. Entomologist's mon. Mag.* **22**: 212.

Heseltine, G. (1888). *Apatura iris* in Hampshire. *Entomologist* **21**: 209–210.

Heslop, I. R. P. (1955). The Mazarine Blue. *Entomologist's Rec. J. Var.* **67**: 178–179.

Heslop, I. R. P. (1967). How I came to start collecting. *Entomologist's Rec. J. Var.* **79**: 225–229.

Hewett, G. M. A. (1894). A ditty. *Entomologist's Rec. J. Var.* **6**: 22.

Hewett, G. M. A. (1895). *Iris. Entomologist's Rec. J. Var.* **6**: 145–147.

Hewett, G. M. A. (1895). On the prowl. *Entomologist's Rec. J. Var.* **6**: 168.

Hollier, J. A. (1989). Sherlock Holmes, entomologist. *Bull. amat. Ent. Soc.* **48**: 107–109.

Hopley, E. (1865). Incredible masses of larvae. *Entomologist's mon. Mag.* **1**: 243–244.

Hopley, E. (1867). A curious visitor at sugar. *Entomologist's mon. Mag.* **4**: 89.

Howarth, T. G. (1949). Prison camp entomology in the Far East, 1941/45. *Proc. Trans. S. Lond. ent. nat. Hist. Soc.* **1949–50**: 94–110.

Howarth, T. G. (1952). Collecting Lepidoptera in the South of France in 1950 and 1951. *Proc. Trans. S. Lond. ent. nat. Hist. Soc.* **1951–52**: 55–65.

Howarth, T. G. (1973). *South's British butterflies.* London, Warne.

Howarth, T. G. (2004). Variation in *Euphydryas cynthia* (D. & S.) in the Alpes Maritime, southern France. *Br. J. Ent. Nat. Hist.* **17**: 101–102.

Howe, T. L. (1901). The vitality of *Hybernia rupicapraria. Entomologist* **34**: 131.

Humphreys, H. N. & Westwood, J. O. (1841). *British butterflies and their transformations.* London, Smith.

Humphreys, H. N. & Westwood, J. O. (1843–45). *British moths and their transformations.* London, Smith.

Humphreys, H. N. & Westwood, J. O. (1849). *British butterflies and their transformations.* London, Wm. S. Orr & Co.

'Inquisitor'. (1837). Note on butterflies questionably British. *Ent. Mag.* **4**: 177–179.

Isaak, M. (1987). The modern entomologist. www.home.earthlink.net/~misaak/modent.html

Jacobs, J. J. (1910). A street blocked by a moth. *Entomologist's mon. Mag.* **21**: 162–163.

James, R. E. (1904). Lepidoptera at Witherslack and Ambleside. *Entomologist's Rec. J. Var.* **16**: 297–300.

James, R. E. (1915). Lepidopterological notes for 1914. *Entomologist's Rec. J. Var.* **27**: 1–7.

Jardine, Sir W. (1837). An address to the members of the Berwickshire Naturalists' Club. *Hist. Berwicks. Nat. Club* **1**: 101–106.

Jenkins, E. C. F. (1859). A lament for the Large Copper. *Entomologist's Wkly Intell.* **7**: 79–80.

Joicey, J. J., & Noakes, A. (1907). Lepidoptera in Glenshian, Inverness-shire, in July 1907. *Entomologist's mon. Mag.* **43**: 255–256.

Karsholt, O. & Razowski, J. (1996). *The Lepidoptera of Europe, a distributional checklist.* Stenstrup, Apollo Books.

Kershaw, S. H. (1955). The Mazarine Blue in England. *Entomologist's Rec. J. Var.* **67**: 100.

Kershaw, S. H. (1956). Luck and coincidence. *Entomologist's Rec. J. Var.* **68**: 21–23.

Kershaw, S. H. (1956). Some recollections of Albert Brydges Farn. *Entomologist's Rec. J. Var.* **68**: 150–155.

Kershaw, S. H. (1958). Some memories of S. G. Castle Russell. *Entomologist's Rec. J. Var.* **70**: 1–4; 37–41; 94–100; 156–160.

Kettlewell, H. B. D. (1945). *Pontia daplidice, Everes argiades* and *Colias hyale* in South Cornwall. *Entomologist* **78**: 123–124.

Kettlewell, H. B. D. (1946). Further observations on the season 1945, with special reference to *Pontia daplidice, etc. Entomologist* **79**: 111–115.

Kirby, W. & Spence, W. (1815–1826). *An introduction to entomology: or elements of the natural history of insects &c.* London, Longman, Rees, Hurst, Orme, & Brown.

Kirkaldy, G. W. (1900). The flavour of caterpillars. *Entomologist* **33**: 87.

Knaggs, H. G. (1869). *The lepidopterist's guide.* London, Van Voorst.

Knaggs, H. G. (1869). Note on the odour of *Sphinx convolvuli. Entomologist's mon. Mag.* **6**: 166.

Knaggs, H. G. (1893). Suggestions for decoying butterflies. *Entomologist* **26**: 154–157; 180–182; 207–210.

Lanktree, P. A. D. (1960). Some old records of Lepidoptera, and "the last Apollo seen in England" — an allegation referring to 95 years ago. *Entomologist's Rec. J. Var.* **72**: 120–125.

Lawrance, A. J. (1903). The New Forest in July. *Entomologist* **36**: 247–248.

Layard, E. L. (1892). A reminiscence. *Entomologist* **25**: 196.

Lewin, W. (1795). *The papilios of Great Britain* [originally published in same year under the title: *The insects of Great Britain*]. London, J. Johnson.

Lewis, W. A. (1875). Some remarks on collecting and collectors. *Entomologist* **8**: 127–130.

Lipscomb, G. C. (1966). An entomologist at war. *Entomologist's Rec. J. Var.* **78**: 121–124.

Lisney, A. A. (1951). It happened at . . . *Entomologist's Gaz.* **2**: 105–106.

Lisney, A. A., Classey, E. W., & Robinson, H. S. (1951). Irish Lepidoptera — a brief introduction. *Entomologist's Gaz.* **2**: 85–99.

Littlewood, F. (1922). Attractiveness of electric light for moths. *Entomologist* **55**: 90.

Littlewood, F. (1922). Killing with cyanide. *Entomologist* **55**: 260. **56**: 90–92.

Longstaff, G. B. (1905). Notes on the butterflies observed in a tour through India and Ceylon, 1903–4. *Trans. ent. Soc. Lond.* Pt.1. (May): 61–144.

Longstaff, G. B. (1912). *Butterfly-hunting in many lands: notes of a field naturalist.* London, Longmans, Green.

Lovett, E. (1881). Stridulation in *Arctia caja. Entomologist* **14**: 178.

Lowe, F. (1902). Collecting Lepidoptera in 1902. *Entomologist's Rec. J. Var.* **14**: 330–334.

Mackett, W. H. (1892). *Deiopeia pulchella. Entomologist* **25**: 166.

Mackworth-Praed, C. W. (1942). *Carterocephalus palaemon* in Western Inverness-shire. *Entomologist* **75**: 216.

Mackworth-Praed, C. W. & Grant, C. H. B. (1952–1973). *The African handbook of birds.* London, Longmans.

Marcon, J. N. (1975). Reminiscences of a butterfly hunter. *Entomologist's Rec. J. Var.* **87**: 7–10.

Marcon, J. N. (1976). The hazards of the chase. *Entomologist's Rec. J. Var.* **88**: 213–217.

Marcon, J. N. (1978). Further memoirs of a butterfly hunter. *Entomologist's Rec. J. Var.* **90**: 167–169.

Marcon, J. N. (1980). Further reminiscences of a butterfly hunter. *Entomologist's Rec. J. Var.* **92**: 34–37.

Marcon, J. N. (1980). *Argynnis paphia* L. and *Limenitis camilla* L. in the New Forest in 1941/42. *Entomologist's Rec. J. Var.* **92**: 277–279.

Marren, P. (1995). *The new naturalists.* London, Harper Collins.

Marshall, T. (1836). Correspondence. *Ent. Mag.* **3**: 511–512.

Mathew, G. F. (1877). Notes on *Lycaena arion. Entomologist* **10**: 35–40; 70–73.

McLachlan, R. (1893). Obituary. Professor John Obadiah Westwood. *Entomologist's mon. Mag.* **29**: 49–51.

McRae, W. (1885). *Deiopeia pulchella* in Hampshire. *Entomologist* **18**: 298–299.

Meldola, R. (1911). What has become of the British Satyridae? *Entomologist* **44**: 146–148.

Melvill, J. C. (1883). Cannibalism in *Pieris crataegi. Entomologist* **16**: 15–16.

Michael, P. (1951). Death of a butterfly. *Bull. amat. Ent. Soc.* **10**: 84.

Mitchell, J. (1993). Lepidopterists before the bench. *Entomologist's Rec. J. Var.* **105**: 42.

Moon, J. F. (1858). *Toxocampa pastinum* in a railway carriage. *Entomologist's Wkly Intell.* **4**: 117.

Moore, T. (1859). *British ferns and their allies.* London. Routledge, Warne, and Routledge.

Morley, C. (1903–1914). *Ichneumologia Britannica. The ichneumons of Great Britain.* Plymouth, J. H. Keys.

Morley, C. (1911). By the way. *Entomologist* **44**: 272; 297–298.

Morley, C. (1918). Awkward incidents in an entomological career. *Entomologist* **51**: 163–164.

Morris, F. O. (1853). *A history of British butterflies.* London, Groombridge.

Morris, F. O. (1871). *A history of British moths.* London, Knox.

Mosley, C. (1926). Pierids eaten by a cat. *Entomologist* **59**: 254.

Muggleton, J. (1966). Will-o'-the-wisp — a reply. *Entomologist's Rec. J. Var.* **78**: 83–84.

Müller, A. (1873). Perception of *Gonepteryx rhamni* at fault. *Entomologist's mon. Mag.* **10**: 20.

Naish, A. (1856). Search the gas-lights. *Entomologist's Wkly Intell.* **1**: 163–164.

Naish, A. (1856). How the Post-office breaks our boxes. *Entomologist's Wkly Intell.* **1**: 165.

Nash, W. G. (1922). Attractiveness of electric light for moths. *Entomologist* **55**: 89–90.

Neal, E. (1994). *The badger man — memoirs of a biologist.* Cambridge, Providence Press.

Nelson, C. 1858. *Vanessa antiopa. Entomologist's Wkly Intell.* **4**: 187.

Newman, E. (1844). Note on capturing moths with sugar. *Zoologist* **2**: 688.

Newman, E. (1871). *The illustrated natural history of British butterflies.* London, W. H. Allen & Co.

Newman, L. H. (1946). A mixed pairing — *Papilio machaon* x *Smerinthus populi. Entomologist* **79**: 244.

Newman, L. H. (1967). *Living with butterflies.* London, John Baker.

Newman, L. W. & Leeds, H. A. (1913). *The text book of British butterflies and moths.* St. Albans, Gibbs & Bamforth.

Nicholson, C. (1922). Non-attractiveness of electric light. *Entomologist* **55**: 90–91.

Norcombe, E. S. (1856). Parchment labels for posting boxes. *Entomologist's Wkly Intell.* **1**: 149.

Oates, M. (1996). The demise of butterflies in the New Forest. *British Wildlife* **7**: 205–216.

'Octogenarian, An' [H. J. Harding] (1883). Entomological reminiscences. *Entomologist* **16**: 127–132.

'Old Moth-Hunter, An' [P. B. M. Allan] (1938). Heresy most foul. *Entomologist's Rec. J. Var.* **50**: 157–159.

'Old Moth-Hunter, An' [P. B. M. Allan] (1953). West Country tour. *Entomologist's Rec. J. Var.* **65**: 355–357.

'Old Moth-Hunter, An' [P. B. M. Allan] (1954). Larva-hunting in spring. *Entomologist's Rec. J. Var.* **66**: 146–148.

'Old Moth-Hunter, An' [P. B. M. Allan] (1954). Accidentals. *Entomologist's Rec. J. Var.* **66**: 183–184.

'Old Moth-Hunter, An' [P. B. M. Allan] (1960). Adjuncts to sugaring. *Entomologist's Rec. J. Var.* **72**: 216–218.

'Old Moth-Hunter, An' [P. B. M. Allan] (1965). The bog at the back of beyond. *Entomologist's Rec. J. Var.* **77**: 33–36.

Oliver, G. B. (1954). Discovery of the larva of *Maculinea arion* Linn. *Entomologist's Rec. J. Var.* **66**: 153.

'Omega'. (1857). The sugarer. *Entomologist's Wkly Intell.* **2**: 79–80.

Partridge, C. E. (1892). *Deiopeia pulchella* at Shorncliffe. *Entomologist's mon. Mag.* **28**: 191.

Perkins, V. R. (1881). Abundance of *Orgyia antiqua* in London. *Entomologist* **14**: 178–179.

Petiver, J. (1702–06). *Gazophylacii naturae & artis: decas prima-decas decima.* London, printed for the author.

Pickard-Cambridge, O. (1893). Some reminiscences of the late Prof. Westwood. *Entomologist* **26**: 74–75.

Pickard-Cambridge, O. (1896). Brockenhurst revisited. *Entomologist* **29**: 146–149.

Pratt, C.; Craske, P. C. B.; Carter, D. & Barrington, R. (2001). Obituary. Robert Mervyn Craske. *Br. J. Ent. Nat. Hist.* **14**: 248–254.

Purefoy, E. B. (1953). An unpublished account of the experiments carried out at East Farleigh, Kent, in 1915 and subsequent years on the life history of *Maculinea arion*, the Large Blue butterfly. *Proc. R. ent. Soc. Lond.* (A) **28**: 160–162.

Purefoy, J. B. (1948). Aberrations of *Colias croceus* and *Argynnis euphrosyne*. *Entomologist* **81**: 270.

Raby, P. (2001). *Alfred Russel Wallace. A life.* London, Pimlico.

Rendall, P. (1886). Enemies to the entomologist. *Entomologist* **19**: 234.

R. F. (1948). Lament of a treacler. *Entomologist* **81**: 270.

Roberts, C. (1858). *Vanessa antiopa. Entomologist's Wkly Intell.* **4**: 186–187.

Robertson, R. B. (1918). Shooting larvæ. *Entomologist* **51**: 162.

Robinson, W. (1873). Locusts on a balloon. *Entomologist* **6**: 525.

Rossell, H. G. (1957). A Cornish postscript. *Entomologist's Rec. J. Var.* **69**: 119–120.

Rothschild, M. (1979). *Nathaniel Charles Rothschild 1877-1923.* Cambridge, University Press.

Rothschild, M. (1983). *Dear Lord Rothschild. Birds, butterflies and history.* London, Hutchinson.

Rothschild, M. (1995). Presidential Address 1994: Man and Monarchs. *Antenna* **16** (2): 53–59.

Rothschild, M. & Marren, P. (1997). *Rothschild's reserves. Time and fragile nature.* Colchester, Balaban & Harley Books.

Rowland-Brown, H. (1887). Moths settling on water. *Entomologist* **20**: 283.

Rowland-Brown, H. (1908). Entomological Society of London — Conversazione. *Entomologist* **41**: 154–156.

Rowland-Brown, H. (1911). Unrecorded occurrences of *Euvanessa antiopa*. *Entomologist* **44**: 68–69.

Rowland-Brown, H. (1911). *Chrysophanus dispar* — a memory. *Entomologist* **44**: 226–227.

Rowland-Brown, H. (1917). Obituary. Octavius Pickard-Cambridge. *Entomologist* **50**: 96.

Rowland-Brown, H. (1917). *Chrysophanus dispar* and other butterflies at St Quentin. *Entomologist* **50**: 97–99.

Rowland-Brown, H. (1919). The Cotteswold *arion*. *Entomologist* **52**: 174–178.

Rowley, G. D. (1939). Stridulation in *Nymphalis io*. *Entomologist* **72**: 116.

R. S. [R. Saundby] (1951). There was a young fellow named Harris . . . *Entomologist's Gaz.* **2**: 108.

R. S. [R. Saundby] (1952). A Wigan collector called Caley . . . *Entomologist's Gaz.* **3**: 2.

R. S. [R. Saundby] (1952). A chap who had scores of *arion* . . . *Entomologist's Gaz.* **3**: 39.

Russell, A. (1857). *Vanessa antiopa. Substitute* No. 17: 196–197.

Sabine, E. (1882). *Argynnis lathonia* at Dover. *Entomologist* **15**: 258–259.

Sadler, E. A. (1968). Death of a moth. *Entomologist's Rec. J. Var.* **80**: 283.

Salisbury, E. J. (1940). 'Stridulation' in *Nymphalis io* L. (Lep.). *Entomologist's mon. Mag.* **76**: 117.

Salmon, M. A. (2000). *The Aurelian legacy: British butterflies and their collectors.* Colchester, Harley Books.

Saunders, H. St. G. (1949). *The Middlesex Hospital. 1745–1948.* London, Parrish.

Scott, J. (1856). *Chrysophanus dispar* in Staffordshire. *Entomologist's Wkly Intell.* **1**: 51.

Scott, P. (1955). *Parnassius apollo* L. at Folkestone. *Entomologist's Rec. J. Var.* **67**: 273.

Selby, P. J. (1837). *Hist. Berwicks. Nat. Club* **1**: 139; 160.

Selby, P. J. (1839). The fauna of Twizell. *Ann. Nat. Hist.* **3**: 361–375.

Selby, P. J. (1848). Observations and notes made during the year 1846 . . . *Hist. Berwicks. Nat. Club* **2**: 205–210.

Sheldon, W. G. (1909). The Large "Copper," its habits and one of its haunts. *Entomologist* **42**: 219–221.

Sheldon, W. G. (1935). Obituary. Robert Adkin. *Entomologist* **68**: 145–147.

Shepheard-Walwyn, H. W. (1898). Captures at street-lamps. *Entomologist* **31**: 294.

Sich, A. (1911). The worm and the butterfly. *Entomologist's Rec. J. Var.* **23**: 274.

Skinner, B. & Wilson, D. (1998). *Colour identification guide to moths of the British Isles.* London, Viking.

Slater, J. W. (1879). A cloud of butterflies. *Entomologist* **12**: 180.

South, R. (1881). Collecting in North Devon. *Entomologist* **14**: 202–205.

South, R. (1906). *The butterflies of the British Isles.* London, Warne.

South, R. (1906–1907). *The moths of the British Isles.* London, Warne.

South, R. (1907). The Raynor collection of British Lepidoptera. *Entomologist* **40**: 294–295.

Stainton, H. T. (1855–1873). *The natural history of the Tineina.* London, Van Voorst.

Stainton, H. T. (1856). The Entomological Society. *Entomologist's Wkly Intell.* **1**: 134–135.

Stainton, H. T. (1856). *Colias Edusa. Entomologist's Wkly Intell.* **1**: 165.

Stainton, H. T. (1857–59). *A manual of British butterflies and moths.* London, Van Voorst.

Stainton, H. T. (1857). Portrait-painting. *Entomologist's Wkly Intell.* **2**: 113–114.

Stephens, J. F. (1828). *Illustrations of British entomology* (Haustellata). London, Baldwin & Cradock.

Stephens, J. F. (1835). Mode of killing insects. *Ent. Mag.* **2**: 436–437.

Stevens, S. (1843). Capture of *Catocala fraxini* at Hammersmith. *Zoologist* **1**: 30.

Stone, F. (1916). The naturalist at the front. *Entomologist* **49**: 64–65.

Straubenzee, C. H. C. van, (1932). Three months' butterfly collecting in Greece. *Entomologist* **65**: 154–159.

Tarbat, J. E. (1922). Non-attractiveness of electric light: a query. *Entomologist* **55**: 64–65.

Taylor, H. S. (1837). Notice of the capture of *Vanessa antiopa* in the neighbourhood of London. *Ent. Mag.* **4**: 253.

Thomas, E. (1914). *In pursuit of spring.* London, Nelson & Sons.

Thomas, J. & Webb, N. (1984). *Butterflies of Dorset.* Dorchester, Dorset Natural History & Archaeological Society, Dorset County Museum.

Thompson, B. B. (1894). Sound produced by *Neuronia popularis. Entomologist's Rec. J. Var.* **5**: 148–149.

Thomson, G. (1980). *The butterflies of Scotland.* London, Croon Helm.

Tolman, T. and Lewington, R. (1997). *Collins field guide: butterflies of Britain & Europe.* London, HarperCollins.

Trimen, R. (1857). *Colias hyale. Entomologist's Wkly Intell.* **2**: 172.

Trimen, R. (1858). A day's collecting near Dorking. *Entomologist's Wkly Intell.* **3**: 174–175; 181–184.

Tubbs, R. (1978). A new aberration of *Melanargia galathea* (L.) (Lep.: Satyridae) [ab. *craskei*] from Sussex. *Proc. Trans. Br. ent. nat. Hist. Soc.* **11**: 87–88, pls. VI, VII.

Tulloch, J. B. G. (1928). A society for the protection of butterflies? *Entomologist* **61**: 164–165.

Tulloch, J. B. G. (1940). Mass movement of *Pieris brassicae* and *P. rapae. Entomologist* **74**: 32–35.

Turner, H. J. (1944). Obituary. W. G. Sheldon. *Entomologist's Rec. J. Var.* **56**: 128–129.

Tutt, J. H. (1908). Something for Christmas. *Entomologist's Rec. J. Var.* **20**: 310–311.

Tutt, J. W. (1891-2). *The British Noctuæ and their varieties.* London, Swan, Sonnenschein & Co.

Tutt, J. W. (1892). *Stray notes on the Noctuæ.* Published by the author, London.

Tutt, J. W. (1894). *Random recollections of woodland, fen and hill.* London, Swan, Sonnenschein & Co.

Tutt, J. W. (1894). Butterfly-catching in the neighbourhood of Mont Blanc. *Entomologist's Rec. J. Var.* **5**: 233–235.

Tutt, J. W. (1896). *British butterflies*. London, George Gill & Sons.

Tutt, J. W. (1896). Notes on collecting, etc. The Exchange Club. *Entomologist's Rec. J. Var.* **7**: 61–62.

Tutt, J. W. (1896). The Large Copper butterfly (*Chrysophanus dispar*). *Entomologist's Rec. J. Var.* **8**: 57–65.

Tutt, J. W. (1896). The gradual decadence of *Lycaena arion*. *Entomologist's Rec. J. Var.* **8**: 121–125.

Tutt, J. W. (1899–1914). *The natural history of the British Lepidoptera*. London, Swan, Sonnenschein & Co.

Tutt, J. W. (1905). Lepidoptera of the Val d'Herens — Arolla. *Entomologist's Rec. J. Var.* **17**: 1–6.

Tutt, J. W. (1907). Fifty years ago. Gooseberries at Stevens'. (From *The Entomologist's Record* of 1907). *Entomologist's Rec. J. Var.* **69**: 76.

Two Old Hands. (1856). Hints to young collectors. *Entomologist's Wkly Intell.* **1**: 150.

Vallins, F. T., Dewick, A. J. & Harbottle, A. H. H. (1950). The name and identification of the New Clouded Yellow butterfly. *Entomologist's Gaz.* **1**: (part 3), 120–125.

'V. W.' (1858). An entomologist's dream. *Entomologist's Wkly Intell.* **4**: 78.

Walker, J. S. (1873). Insects at sea. *Entomologist* **6**: 457.

Walton, J. (1835). Capture of nocturnal Lepidoptera on yew trees in Norbury Park. *Ent. Mag.* **2**: 205–212.

Weaver, R. (1856). *Chrysophanus dispar* in Staffordshire. *Entomologist's Wkly Intell.* **1**: 18; 67.

Webb, S. (1895). *Chœrocampa celerio* in a book-case. *Entomologist's Rec. J. Var.* **7**: 62–63.

Wells, H. G. (1895). The moth. *Pall Mall Gazette*.

White, F. Buchanan (1872). Extraordinary migration of *Pyrameis cardui*. *Entomologist's mon. Mag.* **9**: 149.

Wilkinson, R. S. (1976). Prideaux J. Selby, the Doubledays and the modern method of "sugaring". *Entomologist's Rec. J. Var.* **88**: 23–25.

Wilkinson, R. S. (1977). The great Cornhill fire and the demise of the first Aurelian Society. *Entomologist's Rec. J. Var.* **89**: 250–251.

Wilkinson, R. S. (1979). On being "stared and grinned at by the vulgar". *Entomologist's Rec. J. Var.* **91**: 289–293.

Williams, C. B. (1930). *The migration of butterflies*. Edinburgh, Oliver & Boyd.

Williams, C. B. (1958). *Insect migration*. The New Naturalist. No. 36. London, Collins.

Williams, J. T. (1892). *Deiopeia pulchella*. *Entomologist* **25**: 167.

Williams, K. F. (1998). Unusual mating of *Pyronia tithonus* L. with *Maniola jurtina* L. (Lep.: Nymphalidae). *Entomologist's Rec. J. Var.* **110**: 20.

Winter, W. (1858). *Chrysophanus dispar*. *Entomologist's Wkly Intell.* **4**: 131.

Wood, J. G. (1870). *The common moths of England*. London, Routledge.

Woodforde, F. C. (1903). Taking *Apatura iris* L. by hand. *Entomologist's Rec. J. Var.* **66**: 88.

Worms, C. G. M. de, (1939). An entomological trip to Shetland, July, 1938. *Entomologist* **72**: 60–65.

Worms, C. G. M. de, (1975). Obituary. Cyril Wynthrop Mackworth-Praed. *Entomologist* **87**: 29–30.

Worthington-Smith, B. (1951). *Collecting and breeding butterflies and moths*. Wayside and Woodland Books. London, Warne.

INDEX

Page references in bold type indicate biographical details. Figure and plate references are in bold type. Page numbers in *italic* refer to illustrations. Synonyms are indicated by a cross-reference e.g. *acis, Papilio* (= *Polyommatus*).